FOUNDATIONS OF MODERN PHYSICS

PAUL A. TIPLER

Oakland University, Rochester, Michigan

FOUNDATIONS OF MODERN PHYSICS

WORTH PUBLISHERS, INC.

Copyright © 1969 by Worth Publishers, Inc.
All rights reserved
Library of Congress Catalog Card Number 69-17676
Printed in the United States of America
Designed by Wladislaw Finne
Third printing June 1971

WORTH PUBLISHERS, INC.
70 Fifth Avenue
New York, New York 10011

PREFACE

This book is a result of my experience in teaching a one-semester course taken by physics, chemistry, mathematics, and engineering majors in their sophomore or junior year at Oakland University. These students have had two semesters of elementary physics and two or more semesters of calculus. I am convinced that they are best served by a careful presentation, based upon mathematical and physical reasoning, of the foundations of modern physics: special relativity, quantum mechanics, and atomic physics — together with an introduction to topics in molecular, solid-state, low-temperature, and nuclear physics. In this book, I have attempted to treat these subjects in an elementary but realistic and interesting way.

The student faces many difficulties in the study of modern physics. The concepts of special relativity and quantum mechanics are difficult; his intuition and common sense are not as helpful here as in classical physics. The magnitudes of microscopic quantities are unfamiliar, resulting in a lack of confidence in calculations. Then there are the usual difficulties with mathematics. And too often, despite the efforts of the instructor, the student views physics as a collection of facts and formulas — dull and impersonal.

In this book I have tried to aid the student in overcoming these difficulties. In addition to receiving a solid introduction to modern physics, the student is encouraged to take an interest in the cultural heritage of physics and actually to do physics — make order-of-magnitude estimates of unknown quantities, analyze phenomena in terms of simple models, and compare theory with experiment.

FEATURES The first chapter begins with a statement of Einstein's postulates of special relativity. The student is thus immediately confronted with something new and interesting. The implications of these postulates are discussed carefully, with emphasis placed on the physical content of the theory. For example, time dilation, length contraction, and the lack of clock synchronization are developed directly from the postulates before the Lorentz transformation is mentioned.

The subject of kinetic theory introduces the student in Chapter 2 to microscopic physics and to the use of distribution functions. In my experience, students find the concept of distribution functions difficult, but by taking it up prior to the discussion of quantum mechanics, the difficulty is reduced.

The ideas of quantization, the nuclear atom, and wave properties of matter are introduced in Chapters 3, 4, and 5, with close attention paid to important experiments. I believe that the historical approach is still the best way to introduce quantum mechanics to undergraduates. Throughout the book, direct quotations from original papers are used to bring to life the history of physics and to encourage the student to read some of these papers. Real experimental data are used in graphs and tables whenever possible rather than the barren, dataless curves so often seen. Many photographs of people, apparatus, diffraction patterns, spectra, particle tracks, etc., are included.

After the introduction of the electron-volt energy unit and its multiples in Chapter 1 and Planck's constant in Chapter 3, the student is shown how to use the combinations hc, $\hbar c$, and $e^2/4\pi\epsilon_0$ in eV-angstroms or MeV-fermis along with masses in MeV/c^2 and the fine-structure constant to simplify numerical calculations. Throughout the remainder of the book, sample calculations are done using this system. Students are quick to recognize its usefulness. Eliminating the need for manipulating numbers like 10^{-34} far outweighs their initial unfamiliarity with the system. They are much less reluctant to make order-of-magnitude calculations when they have confidence in their ability to get the right power of 10 in the result.

Much of the qualitative content of quantum mechanics is introduced in the discussion of wave functions, wave packets, probability distributions, and the uncertainty principle in Chapter 5. This discussion is adequate for the understanding of most of the material in Chapters 8, 9, and 10 on atomic, molecular, solid state, and nuclear physics. In addition, an elementary introduction to the use of the Schroedinger equation is given in Chapters 6 and 7. I have found that most students profit by an early introduction to the mathematics of quantum mechanics. Though some of the mathematics here is beyond the experience of most students, I believe it is preferable to show the steps in the solutions of important problems rather than merely to give the results. In many cases topics are first discussed qualitatively and then the more difficult steps are presented in sections set off from the main text by the use of a second color. This technique is also used in earlier chapters for passages that are more difficult and that can be skipped without loss of continuity. Many of the figure captions in these and other chapters are self-contained. If the student is completely turned off by the mathematics, he can look at the pictures and follow much of the argument in the captions.

Much use is made of qualitative quantum mechanics and simple models. For example, the uncertainty principle is used to estimate the order of magnitude of atomic and nuclear energies. These magnitudes are again estimated using the one-dimensional square well. The square well is also used in one dimension to introduce the concept of fermi energy, to show how the space symmetric wave function is concentrated between two protons leading to the bonding of the hydrogen molecule, and even to estimate the vibration energies of diatomic molecules.

Each chapter contains two sets of problems. The problems in set A are quite easy. All students should be able to do any of these after reading the chapter. I have included several plug-in problems in set A in order to give the student practice in the calculation of microscopic quantities. The guarantee of easiness, even if it is only the word of the author, encourages many students to work more problems than they ordinarily would and thus gain some degree of confidence before they tackle the more difficult set. Answers are given for nearly all the problems in set A. The problems in set B are either more difficult or require longer calculations. Occasionally the student is asked to use "reasonable" values to estimate an order of magnitude — a task often asked of physicists but, for reasons unknown to me, rarely of students. Other problems in set B help the student to derive results that extend the text material. The purpose of the problems in both sets is to provide the student with more information and a better understanding of the subject rather than to test his ingenuity or manipulative skills. I suggest that the student read all the problems, even those he is not required to work.

USE   Although this book was written for a one-semester course, there is, for the sake of greater flexibility, much more material than can be covered in a semester. With the exception of Section 9·5, which depends on Sections 9·3 and 9·4, the sections in Chapters 9 and 10 are fairly independent of each other and can be included or omitted. If the students have studied kinetic theory, the measurements of e, the photoelectric effect, the Bohr theory, etc., in elementary physics, the early chapters can be skimmed or omitted, leaving more time for the later chapters. On the other hand, if most of the material in the earlier chapters is included, the more mathematical material in Chapters 6 and 7 may be skimmed quickly in order to have more time for the study of atomic physics in Chapter 8 and selected topics in Chapters 9 and 10. If all the material is included, the book could serve for a two-semester course.

ACKNOWLEDGEMENTS   Many people have contributed to this book. I would like to thank all those who reviewed the preliminary edition or the class notes for their many helpful suggestions. I am particularly grateful to Marc Ross for his continual help at all stages of this project. Special thanks go also to Peter Roll, who suggested many of the figures, and to Libor Velinsky, who was always ready to help with ideas, photographs, and figure sketches. I owe much to the support of the Oakland University physics department and the many students there who offered valuable suggestions and criticisms as they suffered through various preliminary versions. The excellent typing by Dorothy Hubert and Sue Nast and the diligence of Jerry Griggs greatly aided in the preparation of the preliminary edition and the final manuscript. I am also grateful to the many people who contributed photographs and to Bill Prokos, who did the final artwork. Finally, I should like to thank my wife Sue and my daughters Rebecca and Ruth for their patience during the many evenings and weekends they spent without me.

PAUL A. TIPLER
December 1968

CONTENTS

FOUNDATIONS
OF MODERN
PHYSICS

ONE
SPECIAL
RELATIVITY

1·1

THE EINSTEIN POSTULATES

In 1905, Albert Einstein published a paper, "On the Electrodynamics of Moving Bodies,"[1] in which he proposed what is now called the *Special Theory of Relativity*. The postulates of this theory can be simply stated:

I. Absolute, uniform motion cannot be detected.

II. The speed of light is independent of the motion of the source.

It is interesting to read Einstein's original statement of these postulates.[2]

"It is known that Maxwell's electrodynamics — as usually understood at the present time — when applied to moving bodies, leads to asymmetries which do not appear to be inherent in the phenom-

---

[1]*Annalen der Physik*, **17** (1905). In the same volume were two other papers by Einstein, one concerning Brownian motion and the other, the photoelectric effect. It was the latter for which Einstein received the Nobel prize in 1921.

[2]Taken from the beginning of Einstein's first paper on relativity, "Zur Electrodynamik bewegter Körper," *Annalen der Physik*, **17,** 891 (1905), translated by W. Perrett and G. B. Jeffery in *The Principle of Relativity* by Einstein, Lorentz, Minkowski, and Weyl, published by Dover Publications, Inc., New York, and reprinted through permission of the publisher. A brief discussion of the interaction of a magnet and a conductor has been omitted in this quotation.

figure 1–1

*Albert Einstein in 1905
at the time of his greatest productivity.
(Courtesy of Lotte Jacobi.)*

ena. Take, for example, the reciprocal electrodynamic action of a magnet and a conductor. The observable phenomenon here depends only on the relative motion of the conductor and the magnet, whereas the customary view draws a sharp distinction between the two cases in which either the one or the other of these bodies is in motion. . . .

"Examples of this sort, together with the unsuccessful attempts to discover any motion of the earth relatively to the "light medium," suggest that the phenomena of electrodynamics, as well as of mechanics, possess no properties corresponding to the idea of absolute rest. They suggest rather that, as has already been shown to the first order of small quantities, the same laws of electrodynamics and optics will be valid for all frames of reference for which the equations of mechanics hold good. We will raise this conjecture (the purport of which will hereafter be called the "Principle of Relativity") to the status of a postulate, and also introduce another postulate, which is only apparently irreconcilable with the former, namely, that light is always propagated in empty space with a definite velocity c which is independent of the state of motion of the emitting body. These two postulates suffice for the attainment of a simple and consistent theory of the electrodynamics of moving bodies based on Maxwell's theory for stationary bodies."

Although each of the above postulates seems quite reasonable, many of the implications resulting from the two together are quite surprising and contradict what is often called common sense. An example is shown in Figure 1–2. Although observer A is at rest

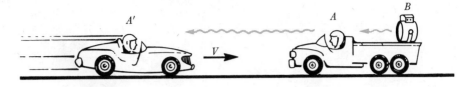

figure 1-2 (a) *Observer A is at rest relative to the light source B and measures the speed of light to be c.* (b) *According to postulate I, observer A' can be considered to be at rest, with A and B moving at speed V. Since the speed of light is independent of the source speed (postulate II), A' also measures c for the speed of light from source B.*

relative to the light source and observer A' is moving toward the source with speed V, the Einstein postulates imply that both observers measure the same number (about 3×10^8 m/sec) for the speed of light. This contradicts the commonsense result that if A measures the speed of light to be c, the speed measured by A' should be $c + V$. In fact, we can immediately see that these postulates imply that every observer measures the same speed for light. Before we examine other implications of Einstein's postulates, let us look briefly at the scientific problems that prompted him to make such bold postulates that contradicted common sense and revolutionized man's ideas of space and time.[3]

In 1860, James Clerk Maxwell published his theory of electromagnetism, which not only summarized all known experimental facts of electricity and magnetism in concise mathematical equations but also predicted the existence of electromagnetic waves which would be propagated through space with speed 3×10^8 m/sec. Maxwell noted that this speed was the same as the measured speed of light and suggested that light might be such a wave. All the laws of classical optics (reflection, refraction, polarization, etc.) can be derived from Maxwell's equations. It is impossible, however, to produce light waves in the laboratory with macroscopic circuits because of the extremely high frequency of light (5×10^{14} cycles/sec for light of wavelength 6,000 Å). Electromagnetic waves of much lower frequency were first produced in 1896 by Hertz.

---

[3]Excellent discussions giving more details concerning the scientific problems leading to the special theory of relativity can be found in Refs. 9 and 10 of this chapter.

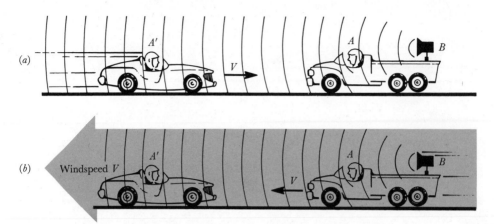

figure 1–3   *The same situation as in Figure 1–2 except B is now a sound source at rest relative to still air. If we consider A' to be at rest, we must add wind of speed V as in Figure 1–3b. If the speed of sound is c relative to still air, it is c + V relative to A'.*

For all other known wave phenomena, a medium supports the vibrations. For example, water is the medium for water waves; air, for sound waves; and the string, for waves on a string. The medium once supposed to support light and other electromagnetic waves was called *ether*. The properties of the ether seemed quite amazing. It had to have great rigidity to support waves of such high velocity (recall that the speed of waves on a string is proportional to the square root of the tension), yet it apparently had no effect on the motion of the planets, for their orbits could be predicted quite accurately from Newton's laws using the attraction of the sun and other planets without any ether drag. The ether was also needed to give a reference frame in which the speed of light was c. In any frame moving relative to the ether, the speed of light would be greater or less than this according to the usual method of adding velocities. (The role of ether in the classical theory of light is exactly the same as that of air in the theory of sound. The speed of sound at standard conditions is about 332 m/sec, not relative to the source or observer but relative to still air. Figure 1–3 is identical to Figure 1–2 except that B is now a sound source. If A and B are at rest relative to the air, A will measure the speed of sound as 332 m/sec. For this case, a wind speed of V must be added to Figure 1–2b; thus A' measures the speed of sound as $V + 332$ m/sec.)

1·2
THE MICHELSON-MORLEY EXPERIMENT

It was of considerable interest to determine the velocity of the earth relative to the ether. Maxwell pointed out that in terrestrial measurements of the speed of light (such as Fizeau's toothed-wheel method, illustrated in Figure 1–4), the earth's speed, V, relative to the ether appeared as a second-order term, V^2/c^2, which was too small to

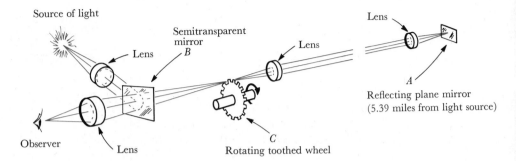

Source of light

Lens

Semitransparent mirror
B

Lens

Lens

A

Reflecting plane mirror
(5.39 miles from light source)

Observer

Lens

C
Rotating toothed wheel

figure 1–4   *Fizeau's method of measuring the speed of light. Light from the source is reflected by mirror B and transmitted through a gap in the toothed wheel to mirror A. The speed of light is determined by measuring the angular speed of the wheel such that the reflected light is transmitted by the next gap in the toothed wheel and an image of the source is observed.* (*From Jaffe,* Michelson and the Speed of Light, *Doubleday Company, Inc., Garden City, N.Y., 1960.*)

determine. In these measurements, the time for a light pulse to travel to and from a mirror is determined. Figure 1–5 shows a light source and mirror a distance L apart. If we assume that both are moving with speed V through the ether, classical theory predicts that the light will travel toward the mirror with speed $c - V$ relative to the mirror and will travel away from the mirror with speed $c + V$. Thus the total time for the trip will be

$$T_1 = \frac{L}{c - V} + \frac{L}{c + V} = \frac{2cL}{c^2 - V^2} = \frac{2L}{c}\left(1 - \frac{V^2}{c^2}\right)^{-1} \quad (1\text{–}1)$$

For V much less than c, we can expand this result using the binomial expansion

figure 1–5   *Determination of c relative to the "ether." If the source and mirror are moving with speed V through the ether as shown, classical theory predicts that the speed of light relative to the source and mirror will be c − V toward the mirror and c + V away from the mirror.*

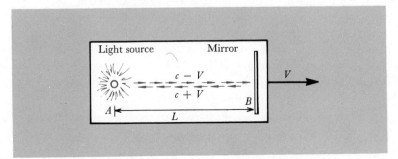

Light source   Mirror

$c - V$

$c + V$

V

A L B

$$(1 + x)^n \approx 1 + nx + \cdots \qquad \text{for } x \ll 1$$

Thus

$$T_1 \approx \frac{2L}{c}\left(1 + \frac{V^2}{c^2} + \cdots\right) \tag{1-2}$$

If we take the orbital speed of the earth about the sun for an estimate of V, we have $V \approx 3 \times 10^4$ m/sec $= 10^{-4}c$ and $V^2/c^2 = 10^{-8}$. Thus the correction for the earth's motion is indeed small. Albert A. Michelson realized that though this effect is too small to be measured directly, it should be possible to determine V^2/c^2 by a difference measurement. Figure 1–6 is a diagram of his apparatus, called a *Michelson interferometer*. Light from the source is partially reflected and partially transmitted by mirror A. The transmitted beam travels to mirror B and is reflected back to A. The reflected beam travels to mirror C and is reflected back to A. The two beams recombine and form an interference pattern, which is viewed by an observer at O. We have just calculated the round-trip time, T_1, for the transmitted beam. Since the reflected beam travels (relative to the earth) perpendicular to the earth's velocity, the velocity of this beam relative to earth is the vector difference $\mathbf{u} = \mathbf{c} - \mathbf{V}$.

The magnitude of $\mathbf{u}$ is $(c^2 - V^2)^{1/2}$; thus the round-trip time for this beam is

$$T_2 = \frac{2L}{(c^2 - V^2)^{1/2}} = \frac{2L}{c}\left(1 - \frac{V^2}{c^2}\right)^{-1/2}$$

$$\approx \frac{2L}{c}\left(1 + \frac{1}{2}\frac{V^2}{c^2} + \cdots\right) \tag{1-3}$$

where again the binomial expansion has been used. There is thus a time difference

$$\Delta T = T_1 - T_2 \approx \frac{2L}{c}\left(1 + \frac{V^2}{c^2}\right) - \frac{2L}{c}\left(1 + \frac{1}{2}\frac{V^2}{c^2}\right)$$

$$= \frac{LV^2}{c^3} \tag{1-4}$$

The time difference is detected by observing the interference of the two beams of light. Because of the difficulty of making the two paths of equal length to the precision required, the interference pattern of the two beams is observed and then the whole apparatus is rotated 90°. The rotation produces a time difference given by Equation (1–4) for each beam. This time difference of $2\,\Delta T$ is equivalent to a path difference of $2c\,\Delta T$. The fringes observed in the first orientation should thus shift by

$$\Delta N = \frac{2c\,\Delta T}{\lambda} = \frac{2L}{\lambda}\frac{V^2}{c^2} \tag{1-5}$$

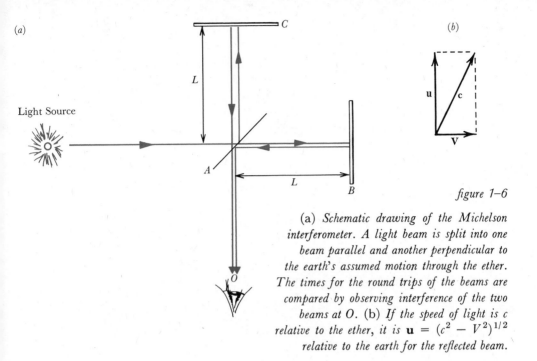

Light Source

figure 1–6

(a) *Schematic drawing of the Michelson interferometer. A light beam is split into one beam parallel and another perpendicular to the earth's assumed motion through the ether. The times for the round trips of the beams are compared by observing interference of the two beams at O.* (b) *If the speed of light is c relative to the ether, it is* $\mathbf{u} = (c^2 - V^2)^{1/2}$ *relative to the earth for the reflected beam.*

where λ is the wavelength of the light. In Michelson's first attempt, in 1881, L was about 1.2 meters and λ was 5.9×10^{-7} meter. Using $V^2/c^2 = 10^{-8}$, ΔN was expected to be 0.04 fringe. The experimental uncertainties were estimated to be about this same magnitude. However, when no shift was observed, Michelson reported this as evidence that the earth did not move relative to the ether. In 1887, he repeated the experiment with Edward W. Morley, using an improved system for rotating the apparatus without introducing a fringe shift because of mechanical strains and increasing the effective path length L to about 11 meters by a series of multiple reflections. Figure 1–8 shows the configuration of the Michelson-Morley apparatus. For this attempt, N was expected to be about

figure 1–7

A student-type Michelson interferometer. The fringes are produced on a ground-glass screen by light from a laser. (Courtesy of Dr. L. Velinsky.)

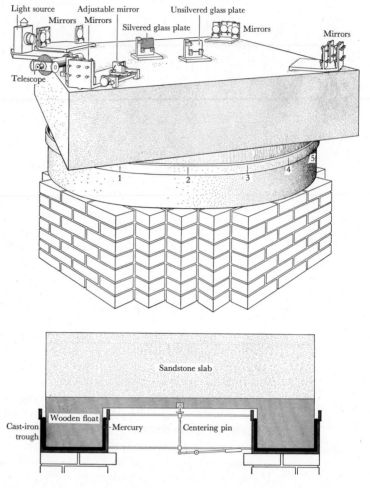

figure 1–8　*Drawing of Michelson-Morley apparatus used in their experiment in 1887. The optical parts were mounted on a sandstone slab 5 ft square which was floated in mercury, thereby reducing the strains and vibrations that had so affected the earlier experiments. Observations could be made in all directions by rotating the apparatus in the horizontal plane. ("The Michelson-Morley Experiment," R. S. Shankland. Copyright © November 1964 by Scientific American, Inc. All rights reserved.)*

0.4 fringe, about 20 to 40 times the minimum possible to observe. Once again, no shift was observed. The experiment has since been repeated under various conditions by a number of people, and no shift has been found.

The explanation that the earth drags the ether with it just as it does the atmosphere is ruled out by observations of the phenomenon known as the *aberration of light* from distant stars. Consider Fig-

figure 1–9   Albert A. Michelson at Irvine, California in 1930 with some of his instruments used to measure the speed of light with a mile-long vacuum chamber. (Courtesy of Wide World Photos.)

ure 1–10. If the light comes straight down while the telescope is moving with speed V, the telescope must be inclined at the very small angle $\theta \approx \tan \theta = V/c$ so that the light will not hit the sides of the telescope. If the ether is dragged with the telescope, the telescope should be pointed vertically. Experiment shows that the telescope must be inclined at this small angle.

figure 1–10   Stellar aberration. In order to see a star directly overhead, the telescope must be inclined at a small angle because of the earth's motion. During one year, the apparent position of the star traces out a circular path.

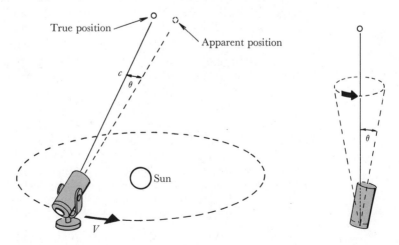

Another explanation, offered by Lorentz and Fitzgerald (Ref. 6), was that a body contracts in the direction of motion by just the amount needed to give the null result of the Michelson-Morley experiment. Though this explanation cannot be arbitrarily ruled out, it is not very satisfying to have a theory to explain just one experiment.

The Einstein explanation is contained in postulate I given at the beginning of this chapter[4] — there is no absolute ether frame, i.e., absolute motion cannot be detected. Thus one might as well take the earth to be at rest, and the null result of the Michelson-Morley experiment follows. The general acceptance today of Einstein's special relativity theory is based on the perfect agreement of this theory with a vast number of experiments, particularly in atomic and nuclear physics. In many of these experiments, the results differ from those predicted by nonrelativistic calculations by factors of 100 or more. In the next section we shall apply postulates I and II directly to derive some kinematical results of special relativity.

1·3 KINEMATICAL CONSEQUENCES OF EINSTEIN'S POSTULATES

In this section we shall derive the well-known relativistic effects of time dilation and length contraction directly from Einstein's postulates. We shall also examine some problems connected with the concepts of simultaneity and clock synchronization. The results obtained can easily be derived from the Lorentz transformation, as will be shown in the next section. It is instructive, however, to consider some special cases first to gain a physical feeling for these somewhat strange results. Throughout this chapter we shall be comparing measurements made by observers who are moving with respect to each other. We shall consider a rectangular coordinate system x, y, z with origin O, called the S reference frame, and another coordinate system x', y', z' with origin O', called the S' reference frame, moving to the right along the x (or x') direction with speed V relative to S as in Figure 1–11. It will be convenient to refer to S as the stationary frame and S' as the moving frame, although it should be kept in mind that by postulate I either could be considered to be at rest. In each reference frame there are as many observers as are needed, equipped with clocks and meter sticks that are identical when compared at rest. We shall assume that all clocks are set to read zero when the origins of S and S' coincide.

---

[4]It is not clear how much influence the Michelson-Morley experiment had on Einstein's first paper. He did not refer to it directly, and in his later years he was not sure he had even been aware of the experiment before 1905. See "Conversations with Einstein," by R. S. Shankland, *American Journal of Physics*, **31,** 47 (1963).

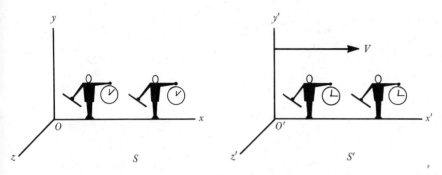

figure 1–11   *Coordinate reference frames S and S' moving with relative speed V. In each frame are observers with meter sticks and clocks.*

TIME DILATION   Consider observer A' at rest in S' a distance D from a mirror, as shown in Figure 1–12a. He explodes a flash gun and measures the time interval $\Delta t'$ for the light to hit the mirror and return. A "clock" to measure such a time interval might be a photocell that sends a voltage pulse, giving a vertical deflection of the trace on an oscilloscope, as in Figure 1–13. The phosphorescent material on the face of the oscilloscope tube gives a persistent light that can be observed visually or photographed. The time is determined by measuring the distance between pulses and knowing the sweep speed of the scope. Such a clock, which can be easily calibrated and compared with other types of clocks, is often used in nuclear-physics experiments. The time interval $\Delta t'$ measured by A' is, of course, $\Delta t' = 2D/c$.

figure 1–12   *(a) A' and mirror are at rest in S'. The time measured by A' between sending a light pulse and receiving the reflected light from the mirror is $2D/c$. (b) These events as seen in reference frame S. A' is at x_1 when the pulse is sent and at x_2 when it is received. Since the light path is longer in S, the time measured in S between the sending and receiving of the pulse is greater than $2D/c$ if the speed of light is the same.*

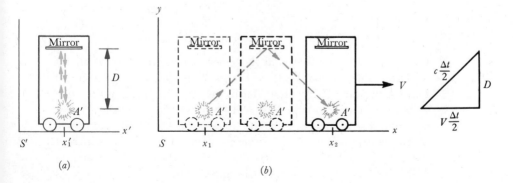

(a)   (b)

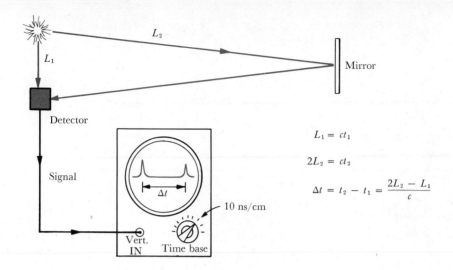

$$L_1 = ct_1$$

$$2L_2 = ct_2$$

$$\Delta t = t_2 - t_1 = \frac{2L_2 - L_1}{c}$$

figure 1–13   *Time intervals can be conveniently determined by reading distance between pulses with an oscilloscope clock after calibrating the sweep speed.*

Now consider these same two events, the original flash of light and the returning light, as observed in S. The events happen at two different places in S, for during the time Δt between the events as measured in S, A' has moved from x_1 to x_2, a distance of $V \Delta t$, as shown in Figure 1–12b. Since the path of the light beam is longer in S than in S', the time interval Δt is larger than $\Delta t'$, for by Einstein's postulates, the speed of light is the same in both reference frames. We can easily calculate Δt. From the triangle in Figure 1–12b, we have

$$\left(\frac{c\,\Delta t}{2}\right)^2 = D^2 + \left(\frac{V\,\Delta t}{2}\right)^2 \tag{1–6}$$

or

$$\Delta t = \frac{2D}{\sqrt{c^2 - V^2}}$$

Using $\Delta t' = 2D/c$, we have

$$\Delta t = \frac{\Delta t'}{\sqrt{1 - V^2/c^2}} \tag{1–7}$$

Observers in S would say that A''s clock runs slowly since he claims a shorter time interval for these events. Note that we have assumed that the distance D perpendicular to the relative motion is the same in both reference frames. This will be proved later. It should also be noted that A' can measure the times of the light flash and return on the same clock, while in S these events happen at two different places. We have thus assumed that there are clocks at x_1 and x_2 which have previously been synchronized. The time between events that happen at the *same place* in a reference frame (as with A' in S' in this case) is called *proper time*. We shall see that the time interval measured in any other reference frame is always longer than the proper time.

LENGTH
CONTRACTION The phenomenon of length contraction can be thought of as a corollary of time dilation. Suppose that x_1 and x_2 in the example above are at the ends of a measuring rod of length $L_0 = x_2 - x_1$, fixed in S, as shown in Figure 1–14. Since A' is moving with speed V for a time Δt in S, evidently $L_0 = V \Delta t$. What is the length of the rod measured in S'? A' sees the rod moving past him with speed V, for a time $\Delta t'$. Thus the length in S' is $L' = V \Delta t'$, or

$$L' = L_0\sqrt{1 - V^2/c^2} \tag{1–8}$$

(We have assumed that they both measure the same relative velocity. Otherwise there would be a lack of symmetry and postulate I would be violated; i.e., we could choose the frame with the smaller or greater relative velocity to be a preferred frame.) Thus the length of the rod is smaller when measured in a frame in which it is moving. Since this contraction is just the amount proposed by Lorentz and

figure 1–14 *Measuring rod between x_1 and x_2*
has length $x_2 - x_1 = V \Delta t$ measured in S.
Its length measured in S' is
$V \Delta t' = (1 - V^2/c^2)^{1/2}(x_2 - x_1)$
because it takes only
$\Delta t' = (1 - V^2/c^2)^{1/2} \Delta t$
to pass A' moving
with speed V.

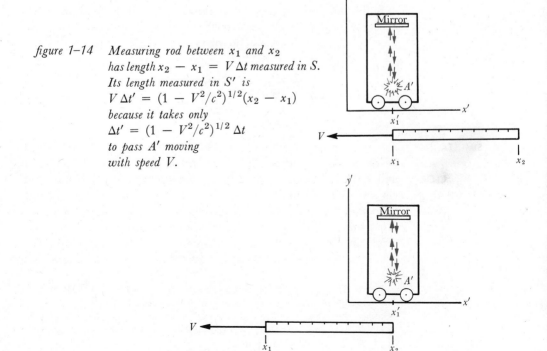

Fitzgerald to explain the Michelson-Morley experiment, it is often called the *Lorentz-Fitzgerald contraction.*

An interesting example of the observation of these phenomena is afforded by the appearance of muons as secondary radiation from cosmic rays. Muons decay according to the statistical law of radioactivity

$$N(t) = N_0 e^{-t/T} \qquad (1-9)$$

where N_0 is the number at time $t = 0$, $N(t)$ is the number at time t, and T is the mean lifetime, which is about 2×10^{-6} sec for muons at rest. Since they are created (from the decay of π-mesons) high in the atmosphere, usually several thousand meters above sea level, few muons should reach sea level. A typical muon moving with speed of $0.998c$ would travel only about 600 meters in 2×10^{-6} sec. However, the lifetime of the muon measured in the earth's reference frame is increased by the factor $1/\sqrt{1 - V^2/c^2}$, which is 15 for this particular speed. The mean lifetime measure in the earth's reference frame is therefore 30×10^{-6} sec, and a muon of this speed travels about 9,000 meters in this time. From the muon's point of view, it lives only 2×10^{-6} sec but the atmosphere is rushing past it with a speed of $0.998c$. The distance of 9,000 meters in the earth's frame is thus contracted[5] to only 600 meters, as indicated in Figure 1–15.

Both muons and π-mesons of various speeds have been produced in the laboratory using nuclear accelerators. Their observed mean lifetimes are always consistent with the relativistic expression

$$T_{\text{lab}} = \frac{T_{\text{rest}}}{\sqrt{1 - V^2/c^2}} \qquad (1-10)$$

SIMULTANEITY AND CLOCK SYNCHRONIZATION

A better understanding of time dilation and length contraction can be gained by examining the concept of simultaneity. Suppose A and B are at rest in S a distance L apart. They each have identical clocks and would like to synchronize them. One way would be for A to look at B's clock and set his so that he sees both clocks read the same time. This has the obvious disadvantage that any other observer in S would observe the clocks reading different times. For example, B would see A's clock reading a time $2L/c$ later than his

[5]See D. H. Frisch and J. H. Smith, *American Journal of Physics,* **31,** 342 (1963). The experiment described in this article is also described in a film, "Time Dilation—An Experiment with μ-mesons," by D. H. Frisch and J. H. Smith, available from Educational Services Incorporated, 47 Galen Street, Watertown, Mass.

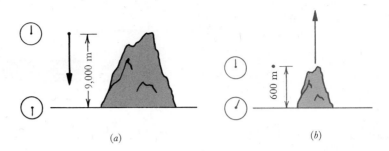

(a)   (b)

figure 1–15   *Although muons are created high above the earth and their mean lifetime is only about 2 μsec when at rest, many appear at the earth's surface. (a) In the earth's reference frame, a typical muon moving with nearly the speed of light travels about 9,000 meters in its lifetime of 30 μsec. (b) In the muon's reference frame, the distance is only 600 meters and its lifetime is 2 μsec.*

own. If other observers corrected for the time for light to reach them from the clocks, they would calculate different readings for the two clocks.

A better method would be for A to set his clock a time L/c ahead of what he sees on B's clock. Then, although different observers in S would see different times on the two clocks depending on their position, after correction for the time for the light to reach them, all observers would agree that the clocks were synchronized. An equivalent method would be for a third observer C, situated midway between A and B, to send a light signal and for A and B to set their clocks to zero (or any convenient prearranged time) when they receive the signal. We can easily extend either of the last two methods to other observers in S such that all their clocks are synchronized as determined by all observers in S.

We now examine the question of simultaneity. Suppose A and B agree to explode bombs at t_0 (having previously synchronized their clocks). Observer C will see the light from the two explosions at the same time, and since he is equidistant from A and B, he will conclude that the explosions were simultaneous. Other observers in S will see the light from A or B first, depending on their location. However, after correcting for the time the light takes to reach them, they also will conclude that the explosions were simultaneous. *We shall thus define two events in a reference frame to be simultaneous if the light signals from the events reach an observer halfway between the events at the same time.*

We shall now show that events that are simultaneous in S are not simultaneous in other frames moving relative to S. Consider a spaceship fixed in S' which is moving with speed V relative to S. For convenience, let us suppose that the front of the ship coincides with B and the back with A at the time t_0 (measured in S) when A and B

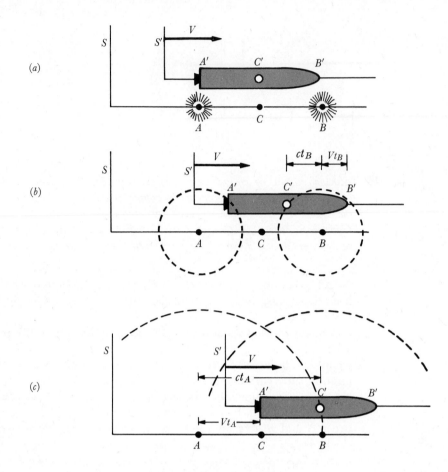

figure 1–16   If the light flashes at the front and back of the ship are simultaneous in S, they are not simultaneous in S'. The drawings above show successive positions of the ship fixed in S' as seen in S. (a) Bombs explode at A and B, which are coincident with back of ship A' and front of ship B', respectively. (b) Light from front explosion has reached observer C' (fixed in middle of ship) after time t_B, given by $ct_B = \frac{1}{2}L - Vt_B$, where L is the (contracted) length of ship measured in S. (c) Light from back explosion has reached observer C' after time t_A, given by $ct_A = \frac{1}{2}L + Vt_A$. The time between arrival of light pulses at C' is $t_A - t_B$, given by Eq. (1–11). Drawings opposite show successive positions of A and B fixed in S as seen in S'. The length of the ship in S' is greater than in the upper drawings, and the distance $\overline{AB}$ is contracted. (d) B' and B are coincident when explosion occurs at front of ship. (e) A' and A are coincident when explosion occurs at back of ship. Light from front explosion has not yet reached observer C, who is midway between A and B. (f) Light from back explosion reaches C at same time as that from front explosion.

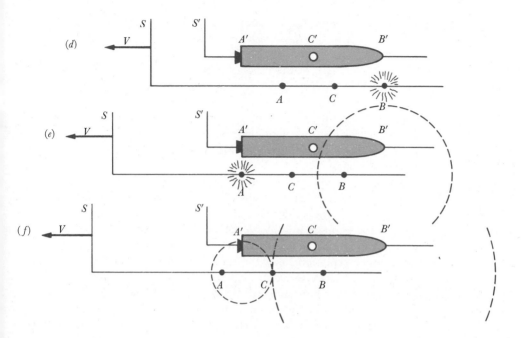

explode their bombs as shown in Figure 1–16. The explosions burn the ship at the front and back but do not affect its motion. The distance between A and B is the length of the ship as measured in S. (This method of measuring length is equivalent to measuring the time Δt for the ship to pass and calculating the length $L = V\,\Delta t$, as was done in our first example.)

Now consider an observer C' in S' at the midpoint of the ship. By the time the light from the front explosion reaches him, he will have moved closer to B, and he will see the light from the explosion at B before that from A. Since he is midway between the events (the burning of the ends of the spaceship in his reference frame), he must conclude that these events were not simultaneous. The front was burned before the back. As we have seen in the above discussion, all observers in S' will agree with C' when they correct for the different times it takes light to reach them from the front or back of the ship.

It is worth the student's time to think through this example carefully in order to convince himself that C' is correct in saying that the explosions were not simultaneous by our definition of simultaneity, just as C is correct in saying that they were simultaneous. Simultaneity is *not* an absolute relation. Events that *are* simultaneous in one frame are *not* simultaneous in another. (Note that we have refrained from phrases like "seem simultaneous" or "appear simultaneous," for events that *are* simultaneous in S do not seem or appear simultaneous to any observers in S except those equidistant from the events.)

Since the length of the moving ship was measured in S to be L, we know that the proper length, L_0, measured in S' (in which the ship is at rest) is $L_0 = L/\sqrt{1 - V^2/c^2}$ because the ship's length is contracted when measured in S. It is not difficult for C' to understand why the measurement made in S gives a result smaller than L_0. The position of the front of the ship was measured before the position of the back.

Suppose an observer B' in the front of the ship records on his clock the time t_B' when the bomb exploded at the front (at this time, B and B' are coincident, so either could read the time on B''s clock), and suppose an observer A' at the back of the ship records the time t_A' when the explosion occurs at the back. Since the light from either explosion takes the same time to reach C', $t_A' - t_B'$ is the time interval between the arrival of the signals at C' as measured in S'. This is the time interval between the explosions in S' which are simultaneous in S. According to observers in S, the clocks in S' are out of synchronization by this amount. It is easiest to calculate this time interval by first calculating in S the time between arrival of the signals at C'. From Figure 1–16 we see that this time interval in S is

$$\Delta t = t_A - t_B = \frac{\frac{1}{2}L}{c - V} - \frac{\frac{1}{2}L}{c + V} = \frac{LV}{c^2 - V^2} \qquad (1\text{--}11)$$

where L is the length of the ship measured in S. These signals are received by C' at different places in S. In S', C' is of course at rest; thus the time interval between reception of the signals measured by C' is proper time and is shorter by the factor $\sqrt{1 - V^2/c^2}$. Thus

$$t_A' - t_B' = \Delta t \sqrt{1 - \frac{V^2}{c^2}} = \frac{V}{c^2} \frac{L}{\sqrt{1 - V^2/c^2}}$$

or

$$t_A' - t_B' = \frac{V}{c} \frac{L_0}{c} \qquad (1\text{--}12)$$

where we have written L_0 for the proper length $L/\sqrt{1 - V^2/c^2}$. This result is worth remembering: *two clocks separated by a proper distance L_0 and synchronized in their rest frame are unsynchronized in a reference frame in which they are moving with speed V; the chasing clock is ahead by VL_0/c^2.*

Consider the same example except that A and B are along the y axis while S' is still moving along the x axis. C is halfway between A and B and sees the signals from them simultaneously. Consider C'

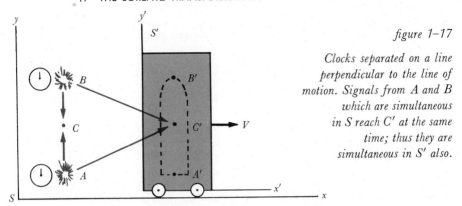

figure 1–17

*Clocks separated on a line
perpendicular to the line of
motion. Signals from A and B
which are simultaneous
in S reach C' at the same
time; thus they are
simultaneous in S' also.*

at the midpoint of his spaceship, which is now moving sideways,
i.e., its ends coincide with A and B when the bombs explode.
Figure 1–17 shows the situation as seen in S. For this case, C' is
always equidistant from A and B, and he will also receive the signals
simultaneously. C' will thus agree that clocks in S are synchronized.
We can now see why the assumption was made earlier that perpendicular lengths were the same measured in either system. If
observers in S determine the positions of the ends of the spaceship
simultaneously, the determination is also simultaneous in S'; thus
observers in both reference frames must agree on the results.

1·4

**THE LORENTZ
TRANSFORMATION**

We have seen how the Einstein postulates of special relativity lead
to the phenomena of time dilation, length contraction, and lack of
synchronization of moving clocks. We shall now derive the general
relation between the coordinates x, y, z and time t of an event in S
and the coordinates x', y', z' and the time t' of the same event in S'.
The set of equations giving x', y', z', and t' in terms of x, y, z, and t
is called a *transformation of coordinates*. We want to find a transformation that is consistent with Einstein's postulates. For simplicity, we
shall continue to consider only the special case in which S' is coincident with S at $t = 0$ and moves to the right along the x axis with
speed V. The nonrelativistic transformation (known as the *galilean
transformation*), which is in accord with "common sense," is

$$x' = x - Vt$$
$$y' = y$$
$$z' = z \qquad (1\text{–}13)$$
$$t' = t$$

and the inverse transformation is

$$x = x' + Vt'$$
$$y = y'$$
$$z = z' \qquad (1\text{–}14)$$
$$t = t'$$

If the velocity u_x, u_y, u_z is measured in S, the velocity measured in S' is

$$u'_x = u_x - V$$
$$u'_y = u_y \qquad\qquad\qquad (1\text{-}15)$$
$$u'_z = u_z$$

as can be seen by taking the time derivative of Eqs. (1-13). Similarly, an acceleration a_x, a_y, a_z in S is found in S' to be

$$a'_x = a_x$$
$$a'_y = a_y \qquad\qquad\qquad (1\text{-}16)$$
$$a'_z = a_z$$

The acceleration is the same in both frames. Thus, if Newton's laws hold in one frame (such a reference frame is called an *inertial frame*), they also hold in any other reference frame moving with constant velocity relative to it. This result is sometimes called *newtonian relativity*. The galilean transformation is in agreement with experience for low velocities; however, it is obviously inconsistent with Einstein's postulates. If light is traveling along the x axis with speed c in S, this transformation gives $c - V$ for the speed in S'.

In addition to satisfying the Einstein postulates, the relativistic transformation equations must be linear and must reduce to Eqs. (1-13) at low velocities. (If the transformation were not linear, a length $x_2 - x_1$ would depend on the location of the origin, or a time interval $t_2 - t_1$ would depend on when t was chosen to be zero.) We can simplify our derivation by using our knowledge that transverse lengths are the same in both reference frames. It is thus reasonable to assume that the equations for y and z are the same as for the galilean transformation: $y = y'$ and $z = z'$. We thus need only to find x and t as functions of x' and t'. The most general linear transformation $x = f(x', t')$ can be written

$$x = \gamma x' + \alpha t' = \gamma \left(x' + \frac{\alpha}{\gamma} t' \right)$$

where γ and α are independent of x' and t'. If this is to reduce to Eqs. (1-13) for low velocities, γ must approach 1 as V/c approaches zero and α/γ must equal V. The transformation can thus be written

$$x = \gamma(x' + Vt') \qquad\qquad\qquad (1\text{-}17)$$

The inverse transformation must look the same except for the sign of the relative motion. Thus

$$x' = \gamma(x - Vt) \qquad\qquad\qquad (1\text{-}18)$$

Suppose a light pulse begins at the origin at $t = 0$ and travels along the x axis. Since the speed of light is c, the x coordinate of the pulse will be given by

$$x = ct \tag{1-19}$$

To be consistent with Einstein's postulates, the speed of the pulse measured in S' must also be c; thus the x' coordinate of the pulse will be given by

$$x' = ct' \tag{1-20}$$

Substituting Eqs. (1–19) and (1–20) into (1–17) and (1–18) gives

$$ct = \gamma(ct' + Vt') = \gamma(c + V)t'$$

and

$$ct' = \gamma(ct - Vt) = \gamma(c - V)t$$

Eliminating t from these two equations gives

$$ct' = \gamma(c - V)\frac{1}{c}\gamma(c + V)t' \tag{1-21}$$

Equation (1–21) can be satisfied only if

$$\gamma^2 = \frac{c^2}{c^2 - V^2} = \frac{1}{1 - V^2/c^2}$$

or

$$\gamma = \frac{1}{\sqrt{1 - V^2/c^2}} \tag{1-22}$$

We can obtain the transformation equation for t from Eq. (1–18) using Eq. (1–17) for x:

$$x' = \gamma[\gamma(x' + Vt') - Vt]$$

or

$$t = \gamma t' + \left(\gamma - \frac{1}{\gamma}\right)\frac{x'}{V}$$

$$= \gamma\left(t' + \frac{Vx'}{c^2}\right) \tag{1-23}$$

where we have used $1 - 1/\gamma^2 = V^2/c^2$ from Eq. (1–22).
    The complete relativistic transformation is thus

$$x = \gamma(x' + Vt')$$

$$y = y'$$

$$z = z' \tag{1-24}$$

$$t = \gamma\left(t' + \frac{Vx'}{c^2}\right)$$

with $\gamma = 1/\sqrt{1 - V^2/c^2}$. The inverse transformation is

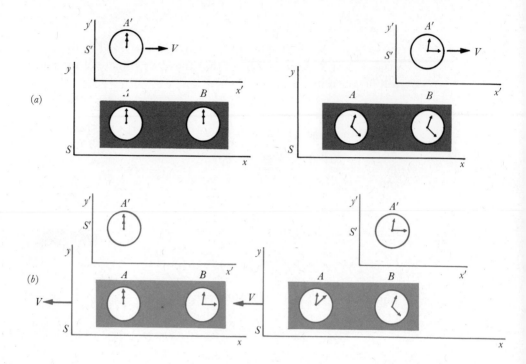

figure 1-18   *Illustration of time dilation. (a) As seen in S, the clock at A' is moving and the clocks at A and B are synchronized. (b) As seen in S', the clocks at A and B are moving and are not synchronized. Note that in both (a) and (b), the interval measured by clock A' is less than that calculated from the readings of clocks A and B and that in each case, the time elapsed on a moving clock is less than that on a stationary clock.*

$$x' = \gamma(x - Vt)$$
$$y' = y$$
$$z' = z$$
$$t' = \gamma\left(t - \frac{Vx}{c^2}\right)$$

(1-25)

Equations (1-24) and (1-25) are called the *Lorentz transformation.*

It is instructive to derive expressions for time dilation, length contraction, and lack of clock synchronization directly from the Lorentz transformation.

TIME DILATION   Let $\Delta t' = t'_2 - t'_1$ be the proper time interval measured by a clock fixed at x'_0 in S'. The interval $\Delta t = t_2 - t_1$ can be obtained from the fourth of Eqs. (1–24):

$$t_2 = \gamma\left(t_2' + \frac{x_2'V}{c^2}\right) = \gamma\left(t_2' + \frac{x_0'V}{c^2}\right)$$

$$t_1 = \gamma\left(t_1' + \frac{x_1'V}{c^2}\right) = \gamma\left(t_1' + \frac{x_0'V}{c^2}\right)$$

$$\Delta t = t_2 - t_1 = \gamma(t_2' - t_1') = \frac{1}{\sqrt{1 - V^2/c^2}}\,\Delta t'$$

Thus clocks in S read a time longer than the proper time as we have previously seen. Note that Eqs. (1–25) are not as convenient for this calculation because $x_2 \neq x_1$.

LENGTH CONTRACTION   Consider a measuring rod with ends at x_2' and x_1', as indicated in Figure 1–19. Its proper length is $L_0 = x_2' - x_1'$. Viewed in S, its length is $L = x_2 - x_1$, where x_2 and x_1 are the positions of the ends *at the same time* t_0 in S. Here we use Eqs. (1–25):

$$x_2' = \gamma(x_2 - Vt_2) = \gamma(x_2 - Vt_0)$$

$$x_1' = \gamma(x_1 - Vt_1) = \gamma(x_1 - Vt_0)$$

$$x_2 - x_1 = \frac{x_2' - x_1'}{\gamma}$$

or

$$L = L_0\sqrt{1 - V^2/c^2}$$

Note that Eqs. (1–24) are not as convenient, because $t_2' \neq t_1'$.

CLOCK SYNCHRONIZATION   Consider two clocks synchronized in S', clock B' at x_2' and clock A' at x_1'. What times do they read at time t_0 in S? From Eqs. (1–25) we have

$$t_B' = \gamma\left(t_0 - \frac{x_2 V}{c^2}\right)$$

$$t_A' = \gamma\left(t_0 - \frac{x_1 V}{c^2}\right)$$

$$t_A' - t_B' = \gamma(x_2 - x_1)\frac{V}{c^2} = \frac{L_0 V}{c^2}$$

where $L_0 = \gamma(x_2 - x_1) = x_2' - x_1'$ is the proper distance between the clocks. We thus see that the Lorentz transformation easily reproduces all the results we had previously obtained directly from the Einstein postulates.

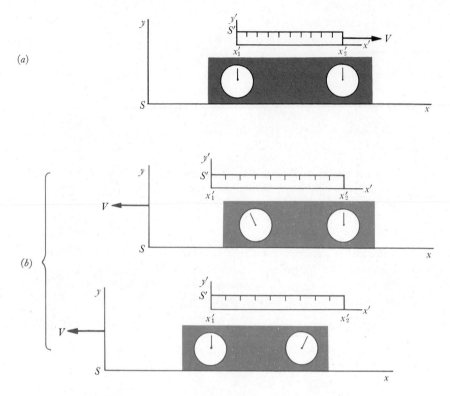

figure 1–19   *The length of a moving rod is less than its proper length. (a) As seen in S. Positions of ends are measured simultaneously. (b) As seen in S'. Position of front end of the rod was measured before position of back end.*

1·5
THE VELOCITY
TRANSFORMATION

The transformation of velocities is obtained by differentiation of Eqs. (1–24) and (1–25). Let a velocity u'_x, u'_y, u'_z be measured in S'. What is the velocity u_x, u_y, u_z in S? We have

$$dx = \gamma(dx' + V\,dt')$$
$$dy = dy'$$
$$dz = dz'$$
$$dt = \gamma\left(dt' + \frac{V\,dx'}{c^2}\right)$$
$$u_x = \frac{dx}{dt} = \frac{\gamma(dx' + V\,dt')}{\gamma[dt' + (V/c^2)\,dx']} = \frac{dx'/dt' + V}{1 + (V/c^2)\,dx'/dt'}$$

or

$$u_x = \frac{u'_x + V}{1 + Vu'_x/c^2} \tag{1–26a}$$

Similarly,

$$u_y = \frac{dy}{dt} = \frac{u_y'}{\gamma(1 + Vu_x'/c^2)} \tag{1-26b}$$

$$u_z = \frac{dz}{dt} = \frac{u_z'}{\gamma(1 + Vu_x'/c^2)} \tag{1-26c}$$

As V/c approaches 0, these approach the galilean equations $u_x = u_x' + V$, $u_y = u_y'$, and $u_z = u_z'$. Let us examine some special cases.

Example 1-1 Light pulse in the x' direction;

$$u_x' = c \qquad u_y' = 0 \qquad u_z' = 0$$

Then $u_x = (c + V)/(1 + cV/c^2) = c$ and $u_y = u_z = 0$. Thus the light moves in the x direction with speed c in S as required by the Einstein postulates.

*

Example 1-2 Light pulse in the y' direction;

$$u_x' = 0 \qquad u_y' = c \qquad u_z' = 0$$

Then $u_x = V$, $u_y = c/\gamma$, $u_z = 0$. Thus in S the light travels at an angle θ to the y axis, where $\tan \theta = u_x/u_y = \gamma V/c$. This is the effect called the *aberration of light*. The magnitude of the speed in S is u:

$$u = (u_x^2 + u_y^2 + u_z^2)^{1/2} = \left[V^2 + \left(\frac{c}{\gamma} \right)^2 \right]^{1/2} = c$$

Note that $\tan \theta$ differs from the classical calculation by the factor γ. For the earth's orbital velocity $V \approx 10^{-4} c$, $\gamma \approx 1$ and this difference cannot be observed.

*

Example 1-3 Rocket A moves to the right, and rocket B moves to the left. Each moves with speed $0.8c$ relative to the earth. What is the speed of one rocket as measured by the other? Let the earth be at rest in S', which moves with speed $V = 0.8c$ relative to rocket B, which is fixed in S. The velocity of A in S' is

$$u_x' = 0.8c$$

The velocity of A relative to B is then

$$u_x = \frac{u_x' + V}{1 + u_x'V/c^2} = \frac{0.8c + 0.8c}{1 + (0.8)^2} = \frac{1.6}{1.64}c = 0.976c$$

This is quite different from the result of $1.6c$ predicted by the galilean velocity transformation. Note that if the rocket speeds are small, the denominator in Eq. (1–26a) differs very little from 1. (See Problem 1–3.)

*

Example 1–4
Fizeau's experiment

Our next example of the application of the velocity transformation is the calculation of the amount light is "dragged" by a moving medium. The speed of light through still water is c/n, where n is the index of refraction, which is about 1.333 for water. It was proposed by Fizeau that moving water would somehow drag the light with it. The speed of light in water moving with speed V was expressed as $u = (c/n) + \alpha V$. The dragging coefficient, α, was measured by Fizeau in 1881 and by Michelson and Morley with greater accuracy in 1886. Both experiments yielded the same result, $\alpha = 0.434$.

Let the water be at rest in S'. The speed of light in S' is $u'_x = c/n$, and in S it is

$$u_x = \frac{(c/n) + V}{1 + (c/n)V/c^2} = \left(\frac{c}{n} + V\right)\left(1 + \frac{V}{nc}\right)^{-1}$$

For small speeds V, we can use the approximation

$$\left(1 + \frac{V}{nc}\right)^{-1} \approx 1 - \frac{V}{nc}$$

and neglecting terms of order V/c, we obtain

$$u_x \approx \frac{c}{n} + V\left[1 - \left(\frac{1}{n}\right)^2\right]$$

Thus

$$\alpha = 1 - \left(\frac{1}{n}\right)^2 = 1 - \left(\frac{1}{1.333}\right)^2 = 0.437$$

in good agreement with the experiment.

*

The change in frequency when a sound source and listener are in relative motion is a familiar phenomenon. This effect, called the *Doppler effect* is characteristic of all wave motion. We shall give the relativistic calculation for the frequency shift in the case of light and compare it with the classical result.

For a source of natural frequency f_0, moving with speed V, the classical result for the frequency observed by a stationary observer is

$$f = \frac{f_0}{1 \pm V/c} \qquad \text{classical, moving source} \qquad (1\text{–}27)$$

If the source is at rest and the observer is moving, the observed frequency is

$$f = \left(1 \pm \frac{V}{c}\right)f_0 \qquad \text{classical, moving observer} \qquad (1\text{-}28)$$

The + or − sign is to be used depending on whether the source and observer are approaching or receding. The observed frequency is higher if they are approaching each other and lower if they are receding. We see that the classical result distinguishes between moving source and moving observer [but only in terms of order V^2/c^2 (see Problem 1–19)]. This distinction is contrary to postulate I of special relativity. We shall now derive the relativistic expression for the observed frequency.

Let a source of frequency f_0 be fixed in S', which (as usual) is moving relative to S with speed V. In time $\Delta t'$, the source emits N waves, where $N = f_0 \Delta t'$.

The situation in S is shown in Figure 1–20. The N waves are emitted in time Δt, which, because of time dilation, is larger than the proper time $\Delta t'$ by

$$\Delta t = \frac{\Delta t'}{\sqrt{1 - V^2/c^2}}$$

During the time interval Δt, the source has moved a distance $V \Delta t$ and the first wave has traveled a distance $c \Delta t$. Since there are N

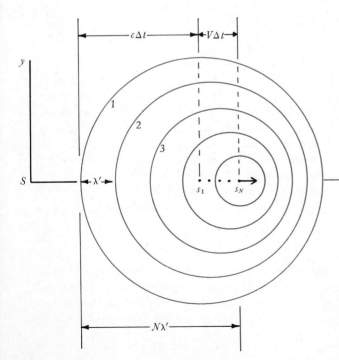

figure 1–20

Doppler effect. If the source moves away from the listener, the wavelength behind the source is greater than for a stationary source, and thus the observed frequency is lower. The relativistic Doppler calculation differs from the classical one because of time dilation.

waves in the space $(c \pm V) \Delta t$ (the minus sign is for the case of an approaching source not shown), the wavelength in S is

$$\lambda = \frac{(c \pm V) \Delta t}{N} = \frac{(c \pm V)}{f_0} \frac{\Delta t}{\Delta t'}$$

The frequency observed in S is $f = c/\lambda$, or

$$f = \frac{f_0}{1 \pm V/c} \frac{\Delta t'}{\Delta t} = \frac{f_0 \sqrt{1 - V^2/c^2}}{1 \pm V/c} \qquad (1\text{--}29)$$

We see that this result differs from the classical one only in the time-dilation factor. It is left as a problem to do the relativistic calculation, assuming the source to be in the stationary frame and the observer moving, and to show that the result is the same as Eq. (1–29). See Problem 1–18 on page 54. If the relative motion is perpendicular to the line joining the source and observer, there is no classical Doppler effect. However, time dilation still occurs, and thus there is a transverse relativistic Doppler effect

$$f = \sqrt{1 - V^2/c^2} f_0$$

It is not difficult to generalize to the case where the relative motion makes an angle θ with the line joining the source and observer. The observed frequency is then

$$f = \frac{\sqrt{1 - V^2/c^2}}{1 \pm (V/c) \cos \theta} f_0 \qquad (1\text{--}30)$$

Spectral lines emitted from atoms in other galaxies are observed to be shifted toward longer wavelengths (this is called *the red shift*) or lower frequencies than the corresponding lines from atoms on earth. Assuming this shift to be due to the Doppler effect, the velocities of the receding galaxies can be calculated. In many cases, this velocity is small enough for the relativistic time-dilation effect to be neglected. For some cases, however, this is a significant correction to the nonrelativistic result. See Problem 1–4.

Before we proceed to the study of relativistic dynamics, we shall study in some detail a famous paradox called the twin or clock paradox.

1·7

THE TWIN PARADOX

Suppose Tom and Homer are identical twins. Tom travels at a high speed to a distant planet (beyond the solar system) and returns, while Homer remains at home. When they are together again, which twin is older, or are they the same age? The correct answer

Laboratory reference spectrum

Star approaching

Star receding

Laboratory reference spectrum

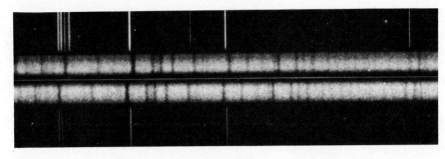

figure 1–21   *Two spectrograms (taken at different times) of the binary star α^1 Geminorum showing the Doppler shift. Only one of the two stars emits enough light to be detected. When the star is approaching the earth, the spectrum is shifted toward higher frequencies and when the star is receding, the spectrum is shifted toward lower frequencies, relative to the Laboratory reference spectrum. (Courtesy of Lick Observatory.)*

is that Homer, the twin that remains at home, is older. This problem, with variations, has been the subject of spirited debate for decades, though there are very few who disagree with the answer. A collection of some of the more important papers concerning this paradox can be found in *Special Relativity Theory, Selected Reprints*, published for the American Association of Physics Teachers by the American Institute of Physics, 1963. The problem is called a paradox because of the seemingly symmetric roles played by the twins with the asymmetric result in their aging. The paradox is resolved when the asymmetry of the twins' roles is noted. The relativistic result conflicts with our common sense based on our strong but incorrect belief in absolute simultaneity. We shall consider a particular case with numerical magnitudes which, though impractical, make the calculations easy.

Let Homer on earth and planet P be fixed in reference frame S a distance L_0 apart, as in Figure 1–22. (We shall neglect the small motion of the earth.) Reference frames S' and S'' are moving with speed V toward and away from the planet, respectively. Tom quickly accelerates to speed V, then coasts in S' until he reaches the planet, at which time he stops (being momentarily at rest in S). He then quickly accelerates to speed V toward earth and coasts in S'' until he reaches earth, where he stops. We can assume that the acceleration times are negligible compared with the coasting times. (Given the time needed to reach the speed V, we can formulate the problem with L_0 large enough to meet this condition.) We use the following values for illustration: $L_0 = 8$ light-years, $V = 0.8c$; then $\sqrt{1 - V^2/c^2} = \frac{3}{5}$.

It is easy to analyze the problem from Homer's point of view.

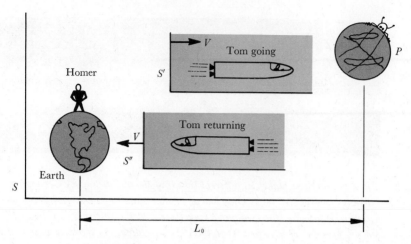

figure 1–22   *Twin paradox. Earth and planet P are fixed in reference frame S. Tom coasts in S' to planet, then coasts in S'' back to earth. His twin Homer stays on earth. When Tom arrives home, he is younger than his twin. The twins do not play symmetric roles. Homer remains in an inertial reference frame, whereas Tom must accelerate if he is to return home.*

According to his clock, Tom coasts in S' for a time $L_0/V = 10$ years and in S'' for an equal time. Thus Homer is 20 years older when Tom returns. The time interval in S' between leaving earth and arriving at the planet is shorter because this is proper time; thus the time to reach the planet by Tom's clock is

$$\Delta t' = \sqrt{1 - \frac{V^2}{c^2}}\, \frac{L_0}{V} = \tfrac{3}{5} \times 10 = 6 \text{ years}$$

The same time will be required for the return trip. Thus Tom will have recorded 12 years for the round trip and will be 8 years younger than his twin, Homer.

From Tom's point of view, the calculation of his trip time is also not difficult. The distance from earth to planet is contracted and is only

$$L_0\sqrt{1 - \frac{V^2}{c^2}} = \tfrac{3}{5} \times 8 \text{ light-years}$$

At $V = 0.8c$, it takes only 6 years each way. The real difficulty in this problem is for Tom to understand why his twin ages 20 years during this trip. If we consider Tom at rest and Homer moving away, is it not true that the time interval measured on Homer's clock is proper time? When Tom measures 6 years, Homer should measure only $(\tfrac{3}{5})6 = 3.6$ years. Then why should not Homer age only 7.2 years during the round trip? This, of course, is the paradox. The difficulty with the analysis from the point of view of Tom is that he does not remain in an inertial frame. What happens while Tom is stopping and starting? To investigate this problem in detail, we would need to learn how to treat accelerated reference frames, a subject dealt with in the study of general relativity but beyond the scope of this book. However, we can get some insight into the problem by considering the lack of synchronization of moving clocks.

Suppose there is a clock at the planet P synchronized in S with Homer's clock at earth. In S', these clocks are unsynchronized by the amount L_0V/c^2. For our example, this is 6.4 years. Consider Tom coasting in S' near the planet. The clock at the planet leads that at earth by 6.4 years. After Tom stops, and is in S, he must observe that these two clocks agree, for all observers in S agree on clock synchronization. Thus somehow, in the negligible time (according to Tom) it takes Tom to stop, his twin ages 6.4 years. Added to the 3.6 years that Homer aged during the coasting, this makes Homer 10 years older by the time Tom is stopped in S. When Tom is in S'' coasting home, the clock at earth leads that at P by 6.4 years, and it will run another 3.6 years until Tom arrives home. We need not know the detailed behavior of the clocks during the acceleration in order to know the cumulative effect; we need only the special relativity theory to know that if the clocks at earth and the planet are synchronized in S, the clock at earth lags that at P by $L_0V/c^2 = 6.4$ years when viewed in S' and the clock on earth leads that at P by this amount when viewed in S''.

The difficulty in understanding the analysis of Tom lies in the difficulty of giving up the idea of absolute simultaneity. Suppose Tom sends a signal calculated to arrive at earth just as Tom arrives at P. If the arrival of this signal and the arrival of Tom at the planet are simultaneous in S', they are not simultaneous in S; in fact, the signal arrives at earth 6.4 years before Tom arrives at the planet, according to observers in S. We see thus that the roles of the twins are not symmetric. Tom does not remain in an inertial reference frame but must accelerate.

It is instructive to have each twin send regular signals to each other so that each can record the age of the other continuously. Suppose they arrange for each to send a signal once a year. The age of the other can then be determined merely by counting the signals received. The frequency of the arrival of the signals will not be one per year because of the Doppler shift. The frequency observed will be given by Eq. (1–29), which for our example is $\frac{1}{3}$ per year or 3 per year, depending on whether the source is approaching or receding.

Let us first consider the situation from the point of view of Tom. During the 6 years it takes him to reach the planet (remember that the distance is contracted in his frame), he receives signals at the rate of $\frac{1}{3}$ per year; thus he receives 2 signals. As soon as he turns around and starts back to earth, he receives 3 signals per year; thus in the 6 years it takes him to return he receives 18 signals, giving a total of 20 for the trip. He accordingly expects his twin to have aged 20 years.

We now consider the situation from Homer's point of view. He receives signals at the rate of $\frac{1}{3}$ per year not only for the 10 years it takes Tom to reach the planet but also for the 8 years it takes for the last signal sent by Tom from S' to get back to earth. (He cannot know that Tom turned around until the signals reach him.) During the first 18 years, Homer thus receives only 6 signals. In the final 2 years before Tom arrives, Homer receives 6 signals, or 3 per year. (The first signal sent after Tom turns around takes 8 years to reach earth, whereas Tom, traveling at $0.8c$, takes 10 years to return and therefore arrives just 2 years after Homer begins to receive signals at the faster rate.) Thus Homer expects Tom to have aged 12 years. In this analysis, the asymmetry of the twins' roles is apparent. We see that both twins agree that the one who is accelerated will be younger, when they are together again, than the one who stayed home.

In order to test experimentally the prediction of the special theory of relativity concerning the twin paradox, experiments must be done with small particles which can be accelerated to large speeds so that γ is appreciably greater than 1. Unstable particles can be accelerated and trapped in circular orbits in a magnetic field, for example, and their lifetimes compared with those of identical particles at rest. In such cases, the accelerated particles live longer on the average than those at rest, as predicted. For a discussion of experimental tests of the twin paradox, see C. W. Sherwin, "Some Recent Experimental Tests of the Clock Paradox," *Physical Review*, **120**, 17 (1960).

1·8

RELATIVISTIC MOMENTUM

If a particle has acceleration a'_x in S', according to the galilean transformation its acceleration in S is $a_x = a'_x$. Thus, assuming that the force is the same in both frames, Newton's second law $\mathbf{F} = m\mathbf{a}$ holds in S' if it holds in S. However, such is not the case for the Lorentz transformation, for if a particle has acceleration a'_x and velocity u'_x in S', the acceleration obtained in S by computing du_x/dt from Eqs. (1–26) is

$$a_x = \frac{a'_x}{\gamma^3(1 + u'_x V/c^2)^3} \tag{1–31}$$

Thus either the force changes by

$$F_x = \frac{F'_x}{\gamma^3(1 + u'_x V/c^2)^3}$$

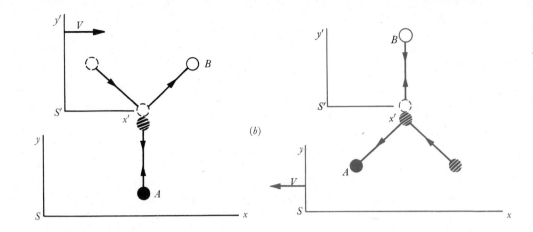

figure 1–23 (a) *Elastic collision of two balls as seen in S. The vertical component of the velocity of ball B is u_0/γ in S if it is u_0 in S'. (b) The same collision as seen in S'.*

or $\mathbf{F} = m\mathbf{a}$ does not hold. It is reasonable to expect that $\mathbf{F} = m\mathbf{a}$ does not hold at high speeds, for this equation implies that a constant force will accelerate a particle to unlimited velocity if it acts for a long time. However, if a particle's velocity were greater than c in some reference frame S', we could not transform from S' to the rest frame of the particle because γ becomes imaginary when $V > c$. We can see from the velocity transformation that if a particle's velocity is less than c in some frame S, it is less than c in all frames moving relative to S with $V < c$. Thus it seems reasonable to conclude that particles never have speeds greater than c.

Let us avoid the problem of how to transform forces by considering a problem in which the total force is zero, namely, a collision of two masses. In classical mechanics, the total momentum is conserved. We can see by a simple example that the quantity $m\mathbf{u}$ is not conserved relativistically. Consider an observer in S with a ball A and one in S' with a ball B. The balls each have mass m and are identical when compared at rest. Each observer throws his ball with speed u_0 along his y or y' axis so that the balls collide. Assuming the collision to be perfectly elastic, each observer will see his ball rebound with its original speed u_0. Figure 1–23 shows the collision as seen from S and S'. It is easy to see that if the total momentum is to be conserved, the y component must be zero for this problem, because for each ball this component is reversed by the collision. If the total y component of momentum were P_y before the collision, it would be $-P_y$ afterwards, and $-P_y = +P_y$ only for $P_y = 0$. We shall now show that the quantity mu_y is not the same for each ball as seen in S.

For ball A we have $u_{xA} = 0$, $u_{yA} = u_0$, and $u_{zA} = 0$. For ball

B, we have in S', $u'_{xB} = 0$, $u'_{yB} = -u_0$, and $u'_{zB} = 0$. Using the velocity transformation (Eqs. 1–26), the velocity of ball B in S is

$$u_{xB} = V$$

$$u_{yB} = \frac{(-)u_0}{\gamma}$$

$$u_{zB} = 0$$

Thus

$$mu_{yA} = +mu_0 \qquad\qquad (1\text{--}32)$$

while $mu_{yB} = (-)mu_0/\gamma = (-)mu_0\sqrt{1 - V^2/c^2}$, and the total y component of momentum is not zero in S. Since the velocities are reversed in an elastic collision, momentum as defined by $\mathbf{P} = m\mathbf{u}$ is not conserved in S. It should be clear that the analysis of this problem in S' leads to the same conclusion. In the classical limit, $V \ll c$, momentum is conserved, of course, because $\gamma \approx 1$.

We recall that the reason for defining momentum to be $m\mathbf{u}$ in classical mechanics is that this quantity is conserved when there are no external forces such as in collisions. We see now that this quantity is conserved only in the approximation $V \ll c$. We shall define *relativistic momentum*, $\mathbf{P}$, to have the following properties:

1. $\mathbf{P}$ is conserved in collisions.
2. $\mathbf{P}$ approaches $m\mathbf{u}$ as u/c approaches zero.

Let us see if we can find an expression that meets these requirements. Consider the special case of a glancing collision for which u_0 is very small. For this case, the speed of B in S is approximately V, and

$$\gamma = \frac{1}{\sqrt{1 - V^2/c^2}} \approx \frac{1}{\sqrt{1 - u_B^2/c^2}}$$

We can see from Eq. (1–32) that for this case, "momentum" would be conserved if we replace the mass m by the quantity

$$\frac{m}{\sqrt{1 - u^2/c^2}}$$

where u is the speed. For ball B, we have

$$\frac{mu_{yB}}{\sqrt{1 - u_B^2/c^2}} = (-)\frac{mu_0\sqrt{1 - V^2/c^2}}{\sqrt{1 - u_B^2/c^2}} \approx (-)mu_0$$

for $V \approx u_B$, while for ball A, we have

$$\frac{mu_{yA}}{\sqrt{1 - u_A^2/c^2}} = (+)\frac{mu_0}{\sqrt{1 - u_0^2/c^2}} \approx (+)mu_0$$

for $u_0 \ll c$. Thus for the special case of a glancing collision, the expression for relativistic momentum

$$\mathbf{P} = \frac{m\mathbf{u}}{\sqrt{1 - u^2/c^2}} \qquad (1\text{-}33)$$

meets both requirements 1 and 2 above. We shall now show that this quantity is conserved in our example for arbitrary u_0. Thus we shall take Eq. (1-33) as the definition of relativistic momentum. The speed of ball A in S is u_0; thus the y component of relativistic momentum is

$$P_{yA} = \frac{mu_0}{\sqrt{1 - u_0{}^2/c^2}}$$

The speed of ball B in S is more complicated. We have

$$u_B{}^2 = u_{xB}{}^2 + u_{yB}{}^2$$

$$= V^2 + \left(u_0\sqrt{1 - \frac{V^2}{c^2}}\right)^2 = V^2 + u_0{}^2 - \frac{u_0{}^2 V^2}{c^2}$$

Thus

$$1 - \frac{u_B{}^2}{c^2} = 1 - \frac{V^2}{c^2} - \frac{u_0{}^2}{c^2} + \frac{u_0{}^2 V^2}{c^4} = \left(1 - \frac{V^2}{c^2}\right)\left(1 - \frac{u_0{}^2}{c^2}\right)$$

The y component of relativistic momentum of B in S is therefore

$$P_{yB} = \frac{mu_{yB}}{\sqrt{1 - u_B{}^2/c^2}} = \frac{(-)mu_0\sqrt{1 - V^2/c^2}}{\sqrt{(1 - V^2/c^2)(1 - u_0{}^2/c^2)}}$$

$$= \frac{(-)mu_0}{\sqrt{1 - u_0{}^2/c^2}}$$

Since this has the same magnitude as P_{yA}, the definition of relativistic momentum by Eq. (1-33) meets our requirements. Because of the similarity of the factor $1/\sqrt{1 - u^2/c^2}$ and γ in the Lorentz transformation, Eq. (1-33) is often written

$$\mathbf{P} = \gamma m\mathbf{u} \qquad (1\text{-}34)$$

with $\gamma = 1/\sqrt{1 - u^2/c^2}$.

This use of the symbol γ for two different quantities can cause some confusion. The notation is standard, however, and it simplifies many of the equations. We shall use the notation except when considering transformations between reference frames. Then, to avoid confusion, we shall write out the factor $\sqrt{1 - u^2/c^2}$ and reserve γ for $1/\sqrt{1 - V^2/c^2}$, where V is the relative speed of the frames.

One interpretation of Eq. (1-33) is that the mass of an object increases with speed. The quantity

$$\frac{m}{\sqrt{1 - u^2/c^2}} = \gamma m$$

is sometimes called the *relativistic mass* and written $m(u)$. The mass of the body in its rest frame is written m_0 and called the *rest mass*. Though this makes the expression for relativistic momentum, $m(u)u$, similar to the nonrelativistic expression, the use of relativistic mass often leads to mistakes. For example, the expression $\frac{1}{2}m(u)u^2$ is *not* the correct relativistic expression for kinetic energy. (See Problem 1–27.) The measurement of relativistic mass involves measuring the force needed to produce a given change in momentum. The experimental evidence often cited as verification that mass depends on velocity can also be interpreted merely as evidence of the validity of the assumption that the force equals the time rate of change of relativistic momentum. (See Figure on page 46.) We shall avoid the use of a symbol for relativistic mass. The symbol m in this book always refers to the rest mass.

1·9
RELATIVISTIC ENERGY

We have seen that the quantity $m\mathbf{u}$ is not conserved in collisions but that $m\gamma\mathbf{u}$ is, with $\gamma = (1 - u^2/c^2)^{-1/2}$. Evidently Newton's law in the form $\mathbf{F} = m\mathbf{a}$ cannot be correct relativistically, for it leads to the conservation of $m\mathbf{u}$. We can get a hint as to the correct form of Newton's second law by writing it $\mathbf{F} = d\mathbf{P}/dt$ (as did Newton). Let us assume that this equation is correct if relativistic momentum $\mathbf{P}$ is used. The validity of this assumption can be determined only by examining its consequences, since an unbalanced force on a high-speed particle is measured by its effect on momentum and energy. We are essentially defining force by the equation $\mathbf{F} = d\mathbf{P}/dt$. As in classical mechanics, we shall define kinetic energy as the work done by an unbalanced force, i.e.,

$$T = \int_{u=0}^{u} F \, ds = \int_{0}^{u} \frac{d(\gamma mu)}{dt} \, ds = \int_{0}^{u} u \, d(\gamma mu) \qquad (1\text{–}35)$$

using $u = ds/dt$ and confining ourselves to one dimension for simplicity. We now use a little algebra in order to do the integration in Eq. (1–35):

$$d(\gamma mu) = m\gamma \, du + mu \, d\gamma$$

$$d\gamma = d\left(1 - \frac{u^2}{c^2}\right)^{-1/2} = \frac{u}{c^2}\left(1 - \frac{u^2}{c^2}\right)^{-3/2} du$$

thus

$$d(\gamma mu) = m\left[\left(1 - \frac{u^2}{c^2}\right)^{-1/2} du + \frac{u^2}{c^2}\left(1 - \frac{u^2}{c^2}\right)^{-3/2} du\right]$$

$$= m\left(1 - \frac{u^2}{c^2}\right)^{-3/2} du$$

and

$$T = \int_0^u u\, d(\gamma mu) = \int_0^u m\left(1 - \frac{u^2}{c^2}\right)^{-3/2} u\, du$$

$$= mc^2\left[\left(1 - \frac{u^2}{c^2}\right)^{-1/2} - 1\right]$$

or

$$T = \gamma mc^2 - mc^2 \tag{1-36}$$

We can check this expression for low speeds by noting that for $u/c \ll 1$,

$$\gamma = \left(1 - \frac{u^2}{c^2}\right)^{-1/2} \approx 1 + \frac{1}{2}\frac{u^2}{c^2} + \cdots$$

thus

$$T \approx mc^2\left(1 + \frac{1}{2}\frac{u^2}{c^2} + \cdots - 1\right) = \tfrac{1}{2}mu^2$$

agreeing with the classical expression. The quantity mc^2, which is independent of the speed of the particle, is called the *rest energy*, E_0. We define the *total energy* E to be the sum of the kinetic energy and the rest energy:

$$E = T + mc^2 = \gamma mc^2 = \gamma E_0 \tag{1-37}$$

where $E_0 = mc^2$.

There is a useful relation between total energy, rest energy, and relativistic momentum which follows from Eqs. (1–33) and (1–37). We have

$$E^2 = \gamma^2 E_0^2$$

and

$$P^2 = \gamma^2 m^2 u^2 = \gamma^2 E_0^2 u^2/c^4$$

Thus

$$E^2 - P^2 c^2 = \gamma^2 E_0^2 (1 - u^2/c^2)$$

or

$$E^2 = P^2 c^2 + E_0^2 \tag{1-38}$$

using $\gamma^2 = 1/(1 - u^2/c^2)$.

The work done by an unbalanced force can be thought of as increasing the energy from the rest energy mc^2 to γmc^2 (or as increasing the mass from m to γm). Identifying the term mc^2 as rest energy is not merely a convenience, for as is well known, it is possible to convert rest energy into kinetic energy. The following example should make the relation of mass and energy more clear.

We shall now show that the rest mass of a system must change in an inelastic collision if conservation of momentum is to hold in all inertial reference frames. Consider two particles moving toward each other each with speed u measured in reference frame S. (See Figure 1–24.) Between the particles is a massless spring, which is compressed and locks shut. (The spring is just an artificial device used to visualize the storing of energy.) Let m_1 be the (rest) mass of each particle before the collision and M_2 be the total rest mass of the system after the collision. Momentum conservation implies that both particles are at rest in S after the collision. (We are assuming a perfectly inelastic collision.) We now wish to view the collision from a reference frame S' moving to the right with speed $V = u$ relative to S. In this frame, one of the particles is initially at rest and the other has speed

$$u' = \frac{u + V}{1 + uV/c^2} = \frac{2u}{1 + u^2/c^2} \tag{1–39}$$

After the collision, the particles move together with speed u (since they are at rest in S). The original momentum in S' is

$$P_1' = \frac{m_1 u'}{\sqrt{1 - u'^2/c^2}} \qquad \text{to the left}$$

The final momentum is

$$P_2' = \frac{M_2 u}{\sqrt{1 - u^2/c^2}} \qquad \text{to the left}$$

Using Eq. (1–39) for u' and doing some algebra, we have

$$1 - \frac{u'^2}{c^2} = 1 - \frac{4u^2/c^2}{(1 + u^2/c^2)^2} = \frac{(1 - u^2/c^2)^2}{(1 + u^2/c^2)^2}$$

thus

$$P_1' = \frac{m_1[2u/(1 + u^2/c^2)]}{(1 - u^2/c^2)/(1 + u^2/c^2)} = \frac{2m_1 u}{1 - u^2/c^2}$$

If momentum is to be conserved in S', $P_1' = P_2'$, or

$$\frac{2m_1 u}{1 - u^2/c^2} = \frac{M_2 u}{\sqrt{1 - u^2/c^2}}$$

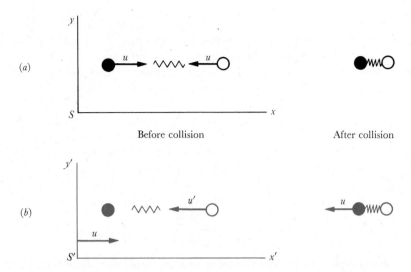

figure 1–24   *Inelastic collision of identical balls. (a) In reference frame S, the total momentum is zero. After the collision, the spring locks shut and the final velocity is zero. (b) In reference frame S′ moving with speed u relative to S, one of the balls is originally at rest. After the collision, the spring locks shut and both balls move to the left with speed u. If momentum is to be conserved in both reference frames, the total rest mass must be greater after the collision than before.*

which holds only if

$$M_2 = \frac{2m_1}{\sqrt{1 - u^2/c^2}}$$

We see that conservation of momentum holds in both S and $S′$ if the rest mass increases by the amount

$$\Delta m = M_2 - 2m_1 = 2m_1\left[\left(1 - \frac{u^2}{c^2}\right)^{-1/2} - 1\right]$$

$$= 2m_1(\gamma - 1) \tag{1–40}$$

The original kinetic energy in S,

$$T = 2m_1c^2(\gamma - 1) = c^2\,\Delta m \tag{1–41}$$

has been changed into rest energy. It is left as an exercise to show that the loss of kinetic energy is the same in both S and $S′$. If we add the rest energy to the kinetic energy, we see that the total energy is conserved in this problem. The original kinetic energy in S is changed into potential energy, which appears as an increase in rest energy. This is an example of a positive potential energy between the masses corresponding to repulsion. If the spring is released, the two particles will fly apart with kinetic energy equal to the total decrease in rest energy. This inverse problem in which rest energy is converted into kinetic energy occurs frequently in radioactivity and in bombs.

If the potential energy is negative corresponding to attraction between the masses, the rest mass of the combined system is less than that of the separate masses. The difference in the rest energy for this case is called the *binding energy* of the system. In order to separate the masses, energy equal to the binding energy must be supplied. We shall give some examples of the calculation of binding energy in the next section.

1·10

MASS AND BINDING ENERGY

In this section we give some numerical examples from atomic and nuclear physics to illustrate changes in rest mass and rest energy. There are two units convenient for discussing atomic and nuclear masses and energies. One is the unified mass unit u, defined as one-twelfth of the mass of the neutral atom consisting of the C^{12} nucleus and six electrons. (This unit replaces the older atomic mass unit based on the oxygen atom.) Since 1 mole of carbon[6] contains Avogadro's number of atoms and has a mass of 12 grams, the relation between the unified mass unit and the gram is

$$1u = \frac{1 \text{ gram}}{6.02252 \times 10^{23}} = 1.66043 \times 10^{-24} \text{ gram}$$

$$= 1.66043 \times 10^{-27} \text{ kg} \qquad (1\text{-}42)$$

For purposes of rough calculations, we can write $1u \approx 1.66 \times 10^{-24}$ gram $= 1.66 \times 10^{-27}$ kg. The other convenient unit is an energy unit, the electron volt, written eV, and defined as the energy acquired by a particle of one electronic charge e, accelerated through a potential difference of 1 volt. Since one electron charge is 1.602×10^{-19} coul, we have

$$1 \text{ eV} = 1.602 \times 10^{-19} \text{ coul-volt} = 1.602 \times 10^{-19} \text{ joule}$$
$$(1\text{-}43)$$

or approximately

$$1 \text{ eV} \approx 1.60 \times 10^{-19} \text{ joule}$$

Commonly used multiples of the eV are

---

[6]A mole is defined as the amount of substance containing the same number of atoms as 12 grams of the pure carbon isotope ^{12}C. This number $N_A \approx 6.02 \times 10^{23}$ is called *Avogadro's number.*

$$1 \text{ keV} = 10^3 \text{ eV}$$
$$1 \text{ MeV} = 10^6 \text{ eV}$$
$$1 \text{ GeV} = 10^9 \text{ eV}$$

(Note: The expression BeV is also used for 10^9 eV.)

The rest energy of 1 gram is

$$1 \text{ gram} \times c^2 = (10^{-3} \text{ kg})(3 \times 10^8 \text{ m/sec})^2$$
$$= 9 \times 10^{13} \text{ joules} = 5.61 \times 10^{32} \text{ eV} \qquad (1\text{--}44)$$

Similarly, using Eq. (1–42), the energy in a unified mass unit is

$$1\text{u} \times c^2 = 931.5 \text{ MeV} \qquad (1\text{--}45)$$

The rest masses and rest energies of some elementary particles and some light nuclei are given in Table 1–1.

table 1–1
Rest energies of some elementary particles and light nuclei.

particle	symbol	rest energy in MeV
electron	e	0.511006
muon	μ	105.7
pi meson	π^0	135.
pi meson	$\pi^{\pm}$	139.6
proton	p	938.256
neutron	n	939.550
deuteron	H^2	1875.580
triton	H^3	2808.873
alpha	He^4	3727.315

From this table we can see that the mass of a nucleus is not the same as the sum of the masses of its parts.

Example 1–5   The simplest example is that of the deuteron H^2, consisting of a neutron and a proton bound together. Its rest energy is 1875.58 MeV. Adding the rest energies of the proton and neutron 938.26 + 939.55 = 1877.81 MeV.

Since this is greater than the rest energy of the deuteron, the deuteron cannot spontaneously break up into a neutron and a proton. The binding energy of the deuteron is 1877.81 − 1875.58 = 2.23 MeV. In order to break up the deuteron into a proton and a neutron, at least 2.23 MeV must be added. This can be done by bombarding deuterons with energetic particles or with electromagnetic radiation.

If a deuteron is formed by combination of a neutron and proton, energy must be released. When neutrons from a reactor are incident on protons, some neutrons are captured. The nuclear reaction is $n + p \rightarrow d + \gamma$. (The γ stands for a gamma ray, electromagnetic radiation from nuclear reactions.) Most of these reactions occur for the low-energy neutrons (kinetic energy less than 1 eV). The energy of the γ plus the kinetic energy of the deuteron is 2.23 MeV.

*

Example 1–6 A free neutron decays into a proton plus an electron plus an antineutrino (the rest energy of the antineutrino is zero):

$$n \rightarrow p + e + \bar{\nu}$$

What is the kinetic energy of the decay products? Here rest energy is converted into kinetic energy. Before decay, $(mc^2)_n = 939.55$ MeV. After decay, $(mc^2)_p + (mc^2)_e + (mc^2)_{\bar{\nu}}, = 938.26 + 0.511 + 0 = 938.77$ MeV. Thus rest energy of $939.55 - 938.77 = 0.78$ MeV has been converted into kinetic energy of the decay products.

*

Example 1–7 The binding energy of the hydrogen atom (energy to remove the electron from the atom) is 13.6 eV. How much mass is lost when an electron and a proton form a hydrogen atom? The mass of a proton plus that of an electron must be greater than that of the hydrogen atom by

$$\frac{13.6 \text{ eV}}{931.5 \text{ MeV/u}} = 1.46 \times 10^{-8} \text{ u}$$

This mass difference is very small and is usually neglected.

*

Example 1–8 How much energy is needed to remove one proton from a He^4 nucleus? From Table 1–1, the rest energy of H^3 plus that of a proton is $2808.87 + 938.26 = 3747.13$ MeV. This is about 19.8 MeV greater than the rest energy of He^4.

*

We see from these examples that because atomic binding energies are so small (of the order of 1 eV to 1 keV), the mass changes are negligible in atomic (or chemical) reactions, but the nuclear binding energies are quite large and involve appreciable changes in mass.

1·11
SOME USEFUL
APPROXIMATIONS

Since the classical or nonrelativistic expressions are usually easier to use than the relativistic ones, it is important to know when the nonrelativistic expressions are accurate enough. As $\gamma \rightarrow 1$, all the relativistic expressions approach the classical ones. In most situations, the kinetic energy, or total energy, is given; thus the most convenient expressions for calculating γ are from Eq. 1–37.

$$\gamma = \frac{E}{mc^2} = 1 + \frac{T}{mc^2} \tag{1-46}$$

Thus when $T \ll mc^2$, the relativistic and nonrelativistic expressions differ very little. We can get an indication of the error made in using the classical expression for kinetic energy,

$$T = \tfrac{1}{2}mu^2$$

rather than the relativistic expression,

$$T = (\gamma - 1)mc^2$$

by expanding γ, using the binomial expansion as was done in Section 1–9, and examining the first term that is neglected in the classical approximation. We have

$$\gamma = \left(1 - \frac{u^2}{c^2}\right)^{-1/2} \approx 1 + \frac{1}{2}\frac{u^2}{c^2} + \frac{3}{8}\frac{u^4}{c^4} + \cdots$$

Then

$$T = (\gamma - 1)mc^2 \approx \tfrac{1}{2}mu^2 + \frac{3}{2}\frac{(\tfrac{1}{2}mu^2)^2}{mc^2} \tag{1-47}$$

The error made in keeping only the first term is approximately equal to the first neglected term (assuming that this term is small). We see, then, that the classical expression is accurate to about 1 percent or better if $\tfrac{3}{2}T^2/E_0 \lesssim 1\% \, T$ or $T \lesssim \tfrac{2}{3}\% \, E_0 = E_0/150$. For example, the rest energy of a proton or neutron is about 940 MeV. The classical expression for kinetic energy can be used for kinetic energies of these particles up to about 6 MeV. If 5 percent accuracy is sufficient, the classical expression can be used for kinetic energies up to about 30 MeV.

For kinetic energies large in comparison with the rest energy, we can use Eq. (1–38) to obtain a useful approximation. We have

$$E = (p^2c^2 + E_0{}^2)^{1/2} = pc\left(1 + \frac{E_0{}^2}{p^2c^2}\right)^{1/2}$$

$$\approx pc\left(1 + \frac{1}{2}\frac{E_0{}^2}{p^2c^2} + \cdots\right) \tag{1-48}$$

for $pc \gg E_0$. Thus for high energies, we can use the approximation

$$E \approx pc \tag{1-49}$$

The first neglected term is

$$\frac{1}{2}\frac{E_0^{\,2}}{pc} \approx \frac{1}{2}\frac{E_0^{\,2}}{E}$$

The error using this approximation will be about 1 percent or less when $\frac{1}{2}E_0^{\,2}/E < 1\%\ E$ or $E > E_0\sqrt{50} \approx 7E_0$.

We shall now give numerical examples.

Example 1-9 An electron and a proton are each accelerated through a potential of 10 million volts. Find the momentum and speed of each.

(a) The rest energy of the electron is 0.51 MeV, about one-twentieth of 10 MeV. We cannot use the classical approximation, for

$$\gamma = 1 + \frac{T}{E_0} = 1 + \frac{10}{0.51} = 20.6 \neq 1$$

Using the extreme relativistic approximation, we have

$$P = \frac{E}{c} = \frac{E_0 + T}{c} = 10.51 \text{ MeV}/c$$

The unit MeV/c is a convenient unit for momentum. The speed can be obtained from

$$P = \gamma mu = \frac{\gamma(mc^2)u}{c^2}$$

$$\frac{u}{c} = \frac{Pc}{\gamma mc^2} = \frac{10.51 \text{ MeV}}{(20.6)(0.51) \text{ MeV}} = 0.999$$

(b) The rest energy of the proton is about 938 MeV, which is considerably greater than 10 MeV. We have

$$\gamma = 1 + \tfrac{10}{938} = 1.01 \approx 1$$

We thus expect the classical expressions to be quite good:

$$\tfrac{1}{2}mu^2 = 10 \text{ MeV}$$

$$\left(\frac{u}{c}\right)^2 = \frac{2(10) \text{ MeV}}{mc^2} = \frac{20}{938} = 2.13 \times 10^{-2}$$

$$u \approx 0.146c$$

The momentum can be calculated from either

$$P = \gamma mu = \frac{(1.01)mc^2u}{c^2} = (1.01)(938)(0.146) \text{ MeV}/c$$

$$\approx 138 \text{ MeV}/c$$

or from the classical expression

$$T = \frac{P^2}{2m} = \frac{P^2 c^2}{2mc^2}$$

$$Pc = (2mc^2 T)^{1/2} = (2 \times 938 \times 10)^{1/2} \text{ MeV}$$

$$P = 137 \text{ MeV}/c$$

To three significant figures these expressions are nearly the same. Note that for this case $P \neq E/c$.

*

1·12

CHARGED PARTICLE IN A MAGNETIC FIELD

The assumption that the force equals the rate of change of relativistic momentum can be checked by observing the path of a charged particle in a magnetic field. A charged particle with velocity **u** in an electric field $\mathcal{E}$ and magnetic field **B** experiences a force

$$\mathbf{F} = q(\mathcal{E} + \mathbf{u} \times \mathbf{B}) \tag{1–50}$$

Setting this equal to the rate of change of momentum, we have

$$q(\mathcal{E} + \mathbf{u} \times \mathbf{B}) = \frac{d\mathbf{P}}{dt} = m\frac{d(\gamma\mathbf{u})}{dt} \tag{1–51}$$

We shall consider the special case $\mathcal{E} = 0$. The magnetic force is always perpendicular to the velocity and therefore does no work on the particle. Thus the energy is constant, and from Eq. (1–38) we can see that the magnitude of the momentum, and thus γ and u, are also constant. Since the speed is constant, the acceleration must be perpendicular to the velocity, and for the case $\mathbf{u} \perp \mathbf{B}$, the particle moves in a circle with centripetal acceleration u^2/R. (If **u** is not perpendicular to **B**, the path is a helix. Since the component of **u** parallel to **B** is unaffected, we shall consider only motion in a plane.) We have then

$$quB = m\gamma \left|\frac{d\mathbf{u}}{dt}\right| = m\gamma \left(\frac{u^2}{R}\right)$$

or

$$BqR = m\gamma u = P \tag{1–52}$$

Equation (1–52) is the same as the nonrelativistic expression except for the γ. This equation can be tested by measuring the speed of a particle and then finding the magnetic field necessary to bend it in a circle of radius R. The speed can easily be measured by passing the beam of particles through crossed electric and magnetic fields so that the electric force $q\mathcal{E}$ just cancels the magnetic force $q\mathbf{u} \times \mathbf{B}$ for particles of speed $u = (\mathcal{E}/B)$. These particles pass through a collimator, whereas particles of other speeds are deflected away. Figure 1–25 shows a plot of BqR/mu versus u/c.

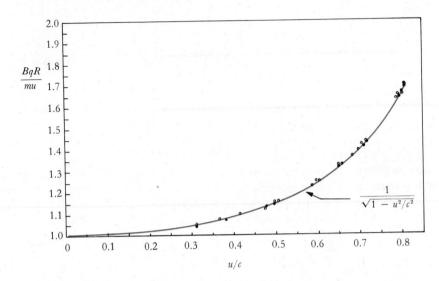

figure 1–25   *A plot of BqR/mu versus u/c for particles of charge q and mass m moving in circular orbits of radius R in a magnetic field B. The agreement of the data with the curve predicted by relativity theory supports the assumption that the force equals the time rate of change of relativistic momentum. (Adapted from Kaplan, Nuclear Physics, 2d ed., Addison-Wesley Publishing Company, Inc., Reading, Mass., 1962; by permission.)*

The solid curve is the function $\gamma = (1 - u^2/c^2)^{-1/2}$, predicted by Eq. (1–52). As discussed in Section 1–8, these data can also be interpreted as showing that the (relativistic) mass depends on speed.

1·13
TRANSFORMATION
OF MOMENTUM
AND ENERGY[7]

In Section 1·8 we needed to find the momentum of a particle in S' when we knew it in S. We did this using the velocity transformation. Because it is often necessary to transform momentum and energy from one frame to another, it is worth deriving general transformation laws. We shall see below that the transformation laws for momentum and energy are easy to remember because they are similar to those for position and time.

Consider a particle of mass m with velocity u'_x, u'_y, u'_z in S' which is moving with speed V along the x axis of S. The momentum and energy of the particle in S' are

$$\mathbf{P}' = \frac{m\mathbf{u}'}{(1 - u'^2/c^2)^{1/2}}$$

$$E' = \frac{mc^2}{(1 - u'^2/c^2)^{1/2}}$$

[7]Textual matter printed in brown may be skipped without loss of continuity.

We wish to find the momentum and energy in S given by

$$\mathbf{P} = \frac{m\mathbf{u}}{(1 - u^2/c^2)^{1/2}}$$

$$E = \frac{mc^2}{(1 - u^2/c^2)^{1/2}}$$

The velocity u in S is related to u' in S' by the velocity transformation Eqs. (1–26). We need to compute the quantity $1 - u^2/c^2$ in terms of u'_x, u'_y, u'_z, and V. We have

$$1 - \frac{u^2}{c^2} = 1 - \frac{1}{c^2}\left[\frac{\gamma^2(u'_x + V)^2 + u'^2_y + u'^2_z}{\gamma^2(1 + Vu'_x/c^2)^2}\right]$$

$$= \frac{(1 - V^2/c^2)(1 - u'^2/c^2)}{(1 + Vu'^2_x/c^2)^2}$$

where $u'^2 = u'^2_x + u'^2_y + u'^2_z$, and several algebraic manipulations have been omitted. Then

$$\left(1 - \frac{u^2}{c^2}\right)^{-1/2} = \frac{1 + Vu'^2_x/c^2}{(1 - V^2/c^2)^{1/2}(1 - u'^2/c^2)^{1/2}}$$

$$= \frac{\gamma(1 + Vu'_x/c^2)}{(1 - u'^2/c^2)^{1/2}}$$

The momentum and energy in S are:

$$P_x = \frac{mu_x}{(1 - u^2/c^2)^{1/2}} = \frac{m(u'_x + V)}{(1 + Vu'_x/c^2)} \frac{\gamma(1 + Vu'_x/c^2)}{(1 - u'^2/c^2)^{1/2}}$$

$$= \frac{\gamma m(u'_x + V)}{(1 - u'^2/c^2)^{1/2}}$$

$$P_y = \frac{mu_y}{(1 - u^2/c^2)^{1/2}} = \frac{mu'_y}{(1 - u'^2/c^2)^{1/2}}$$

$$P_z = \frac{mu_z}{(1 - u^2/c^2)^{1/2}} = \frac{mu'_z}{(1 - u'^2/c^2)^{1/2}}$$

$$E = \frac{mc^2}{(1 - u^2/c^2)^{1/2}} = \frac{\gamma mc^2(1 + Vu'_x/c^2)}{(1 - u'^2/c^2)^{1/2}}$$

Using the expressions for momentum and energy in S', these can be written

$$P_x = \gamma\left(P'_x + \frac{VE'}{c^2}\right)$$

$$P_y = P'_y \tag{1-53}$$

$$P_z = P'_z$$

$$E = \gamma(E' + VP'_x)$$

Comparing these equations with the Lorentz transformation for coordinates, Eqs. (1–24), we see that P_x transforms like x, and E like c^2t.

Example 1–10   As an example of the use of these equations, consider the following problem. A proton-antiproton pair is to be created by bombarding protons at rest with protons of kinetic energy T_{lab}. The reaction is $p + p \rightarrow p + p + p + \bar{p}$, where $\bar{p}$ stands for an antiproton which has the same rest mass as the proton but is negatively charged. What is the minimum energy, T_{lab}, needed?

The rest energy on the right side of the reaction is greater than that on the left by $2mc^2 = 1{,}876$ MeV. Evidently this amount of kinetic energy must be converted to rest energy; thus 1,876 MeV would be the amount needed if there were no kinetic energy remaining, i.e., if the four particles on the right side of the reaction were at rest. However, the total momentum before the reaction is not zero. Conservation of momentum thus implies that the four particles cannot be at rest. This problem is most easily solved in a reference frame S' in which the total momentum is zero before and after the reaction. This frame is called the *center of mass* (or *center of momentum) frame*. Before the reaction, the two protons are approaching each other with speed V in S'. The kinetic energy of

figure 1–26   (a) *A proton moving with speed u strikes another proton at rest, and a proton-antiproton pair is created. At the minimum energy needed for this reaction, all the particles move with the same velocity after the reaction.* (b) *In the center of momentum reference frame S', the particles are at rest after the reaction. The minimum kinetic energy required in this reference frame is just the increase in rest energy $2mc^2$. In the laboratory reference frame S, the minimum kinetic energy is $6mc^2$.*

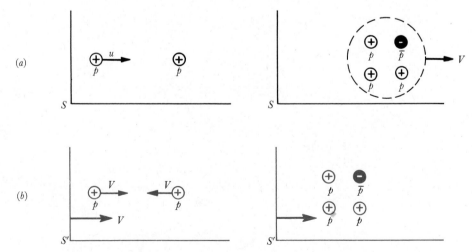

figure 1–27   *"Bevatron" at University of California Lawrence Radiation Laboratory, Berkeley, with which the antiproton was discovered. Protons are injected from a linear accelerator (shown at lower right) and accelerated to 6.2 GeV ($1\ GeV = 10^9\ eV$ was formerly called 1 BeV). (Courtesy of Lawrence Radiation Laboratory.)*

each is equal to its rest energy mc^2. After the reaction, the four particles are at rest in S with no kinetic energy, the excess kinetic energy $2mc^2$ going into the rest energy of the two extra particles. Figure 1–26 shows this reaction as seen in S and S'. For each proton before the reaction, $E' = 2mc^2 = \gamma mc^2$; therefore, $\gamma = 2 = (1 - V^2/c^2)^{-1/2}$ and $V/c = \frac{1}{2}\sqrt{3}$. We can now use the energy-transformation equations (1–53) to find the energy of the bombarding proton in the lab frame S. Since one of the original protons

figure 1–28

Bubble-chamber tracks showing creation of a proton-antiproton pair in the collision of an incident 25 GeV proton from the Brookhaven Alternating Gradient Synchrotron with a liquid hydrogen nucleus (stationary proton).
The nuclear reaction is
$p + p \rightarrow p + p + p + \bar{p}.$
(Courtesy of Dr. Robert Ehrlich.)

is at rest in S, S' moves to the right with speed V relative to S. Thus $E = \gamma(E' + VP'_x)$, with $\gamma = 2$, $V = \frac{1}{2}\sqrt{3}\,c$, $P'_x = \gamma mV = 2m(\frac{1}{2}\sqrt{3}\,c) = mc\sqrt{3}$, and $E' = 2mc^2$. Using these values, we obtain

$$E = 2[2mc^2 + (\tfrac{1}{2}\sqrt{3}\,c)(mc\sqrt{3})] = 7mc^2$$

and

$$T_{\text{lab}} = E - mc^2 = 6mc^2 = 6(938) = 5{,}628 \text{ MeV}$$

The 6,200 MeV = 6.2 GeV Bevatron was built at the University of California in Berkeley to produce this reaction, and in 1955 the discovery of the antiproton was announced by scientists working with this machine. (See *Scientific American*, June, 1956.)

*

SUMMARY   Because of the relative nature of simultaneity implied by the Einstein postulates, time and length intervals between events are not the same in all reference frames. The classical transformation between inertial frames must be replaced by the Lorentz transformation.

When the classical expressions for momentum and energy are replaced by the relativistic expressions, the laws of conservation of momentum and energy hold in all inertial frames. We shall list for future reference some of the more important equations developed in this chapter.

Time Dilation

Proper time is the time between two events that occur at the same space point; thus it can be measured on a single clock. If $\Delta t'_0$ is the proper time interval measured on a clock that moves with speed V in frame S, the time interval measured in S is longer:

$$\Delta t = \gamma \, \Delta t'_0 \qquad \text{with } \gamma = \left(1 - \frac{V^2}{c^2}\right)^{-1/2}$$

Length Contraction

The proper length of a rod is the length measured in the rest frame of the rod. If a rod of proper length L'_0 moves with speed V in S, its length measured in S is

$$L = \frac{L'_0}{\gamma}$$

Clock Synchronization

Two clocks separated by a proper distance, L_0, and synchronized in their rest frame will be unsynchronized in a frame in which they are moving parallel to their separation. If the clocks are moving with speed V in S, with clock b chasing clock a, the time difference at some instant in S will be

$$t_b - t_a = \frac{L_0 V}{c^2}$$

Lorentz Transformation

$$x' = \gamma(x - Vt)$$
$$y' = y$$
$$z' = z$$
$$t' = \gamma\left(t - \frac{xV}{c^2}\right)$$

The inverse transformation is obtained by changing V to $-V$ and switching primes.

Velocity Transformation

$$u_x' = \frac{u_x - V}{1 - u_x V/c^2}$$

$$u_y' = \frac{u_y}{\gamma(1 - u_x V/c^2)}$$

$$u_z' = \frac{u_z}{\gamma(1 - u_x V/c^2)}$$

Momentum

$$\mathbf{P} = \frac{m\mathbf{u}}{\sqrt{1 - u^2/c^2}} = \gamma m \mathbf{u}$$

Energy

$$E = \frac{mc^2}{\sqrt{1 - u^2/c^2}} = \gamma mc^2$$
$$E^2 = P^2 c^2 + (mc^2)^2$$

Kinetic Energy

$$T = E - mc^2 = (\gamma - 1)mc^2$$

For $u/c \ll 1$, $T \approx \frac{1}{2}mu^2$; for $u/c \approx 1$, $T \approx pc - mc^2$.

Momentum and Energy Transformations

$$P_x' = \gamma\left(P_x - \frac{VE}{c^2}\right)$$
$$P_y' = P_y$$
$$P_z' = P_z$$
$$E' = \gamma(E - VP_x)$$

REFERENCES

1. T. M. Helliwell, *Introduction to Special Relativity*, Allyn and Bacon, Inc., Boston, 1966.
2. C. Kacser, *Introduction to Special Theory of Relativity*, Prentice-Hall, Inc., Englewood Cliffs, N. J., 1967.
3. E. P. Ney, *Electromagnetism and Relativity*, Harper & Row, Publishers, Inc., New York, 1962.
4. R. Resnick, *Introduction to Special Relativity*, John Wiley & Sons, Inc., New York, 1968.
5. E. F. Taylor and J. A. Wheeler, *Spacetime Physics*, W. H. Freeman and Company, San Francisco, 1966.
   Each of the above references is a short book written for students.
6. A. Einstein et al., *The Principle of Relativity*, Dover Publications, Inc., New York, 1923. A collection of original papers pertaining to special and general relativity.
7. "Resource Letter SRT-1 on Special Relativity Theory," *American Journal of Physics*, **30,** 462 (1962). This article is a list of references.
8. *Special Relativity Theory*, selected reprints published for the American Association of Physics Teachers by the American Institute of Physics. This booklet is a collection of some of the papers listed in "Resource Letter SRT-1."
9. A. P. French, *Relativity (An Introduction to the Special Theory) A Part of Physics; A New Introductory Course*. Revised preliminary edition published by the Science Teaching Center at the Massachusetts Institute of Technology, 1966. This is an excellent text with a particularly good discussion of the historical basis of special relativity.
10. F. K. Richtmyer, E. H. Kennard, and T. Lauritsen, *Introduction to Modern Physics*, McGraw-Hill Book Company, New York, 1955. This is the fifth edition of an excellent text originally published in 1928 and intended for a survey course for graduate students. This is a standard source for reference material pertaining to modern physics.
11. George Gamow, *Mr. Tompkins in Paper Back*, Cambridge University Press, New York, 1965. This delightful book contains "Mr. Tompkins in Wonderland," "Mr. Tompkins Explores the Atom," and other stories. In one of the stories, Mr. Tompkins visits a dream world in which the speed of light is 10 miles per hour and relativistic effects are quite noticeable.

SET A

PROBLEMS

1–1. An airplane flies from point A to point B and returns. Compare the time required for the round trip when the wind blows from A to B with speed V, with that when the wind blows perpendicularly to the line AB with speed V.

1–2. A meter stick moves with speed $u = 0.8c$ relative to you. Find the length of the stick measured by you. How long does it take for the meter stick to pass you?

1–3. Two rocket ships are approaching each other.
   (a) If the speed of each is $0.9c$ relative to the earth, what is the speed of one relative to the other?
   (b) If the speed of each relative to the earth is 30,000 m/sec, what is the speed of one relative to the other? (30,000 m/sec is about 100 times the speed of sound.)
   (c) For case (b), about what error is made in calculating the relative speed neglecting relativity?

1–4. The 3C-9 quasar is receding from the earth at speed V. The ultraviolet Lyman-α line from hydrogen at $\lambda_0 = 1{,}216$ Å is shifted toward a longer wavelength (this is known as the red shift). The line is observed to be at $\lambda' = 3{,}663$ Å. Assuming this shift to be due to the Doppler effect, calculate V.

1–5. In the ground state of the hydrogen atom, the electron has kinetic energy of 13.6 eV. Show that its speed is about $\frac{1}{137}$ of c.

1–6. An experiment was done at MIT to measure the kinetic energy T of electrons as a function of their speed u. (See *American Journal of Physics*, July, 1964, p. 551.) Sketch the expected result of T in MeV versus u in m/sec.

1–7. Calculate the momentum in units of MeV/c of
   (a) A 30-MeV electron
   (b) A 30-MeV proton

1–8. The energy required to remove a neutron from He^4 nucleus is 21.6 MeV. What percent error is made taking the mass of He^4 to be the sum of the masses of He^3 and the neutron?

1–9. What field in gauss (10^4 gauss $= 1$ weber/m^2) is needed to bend a 20-MeV electron in an arc of radius 2 meters?

1–10. The mass of the Na^{24} nucleus is 23.98493 u and that of the Mg^{24} nucleus is 23.97846 u. Na^{24} is radioactive and decays by $Na^{24} \rightarrow Mg^{24} + e^- + \bar{\nu}$. The $\bar{\nu}$ is massless. Most of the kinetic energy is shared by the e^- and $\bar{\nu}$. (Why?) How much energy is this in MeV?

1–11. A K^0-meson at rest decays into $2\pi^0$-mesons. $K^0 \rightarrow \pi^0 + \pi^0$. The masses are $M_{K^0} = 498$ MeV/c^2 and $M_{\pi^0} = 135$ MeV/c^2.
   (a) What is the kinetic energy of each π^0?
   (b) What is the velocity of each π^0?
   (c) What is the magnitude of the momentum of each π^0?

1–12. If the rest energy of 1 gram were completely converted to heat, how much water could be heated from 0°C to 100°C. (1 calorie ≈ 4.2 joules.)

SET B

1–13. The following quotations are taken from Einstein's first relativity paper (Ref. 6):

"If at the points A and B of K there are stationary clocks which, viewed in the stationary system, are synchronous; and if the clock at A is moved with the velocity V along the line AB to B, then on its arrival at B the two clocks no longer synchronize, but the clock moved from A to B lags behind the other which has remained at B by $\frac{1}{2}tV^2/c^2$ (up to magnitudes of fourth and higher order), t being the time occupied in the journey from A to B."

Prove the above statement.

"Hence we conclude that a balance-clock at the equator must go more slowly, by a very small amount than a precisely similar clock situated at one of the poles under otherwise identical conditions."

Calculate the time difference of these two clocks after one century.

1–14. There are two ways of measuring the length of a moving rod. One is to determine the positions of the ends x_1 and x_2 simultaneously in your reference frame, $L = x_2(t) - x_1(t)$; the other is to measure the time Δt for the rod to pass one point and use $L = V \Delta t$. Show that these are equivalent.

1–15. Observers in S and S' synchronize their clocks to read 0 at their origins when they coincide. The observer in S reads the clock in S' through a telescope. What time does he see when *his* clock reads 20 minutes if $V^2 = \frac{8}{9}c^2$?

1–16. By differentiating Eq. (1–26a) for the velocity transformation, derive Eq. (1–31).

1–17. An observer A' at rest in S' (which moves along the x axis of S with speed V) is a distance D along the y' axis from a mirror (see Figure 1–12). A' is coincident with A in S at the time of occurrence of a light flash and is coincident with B as A' receives the reflected signal. Show that, even though the time interval measured in S is $\Delta t = \gamma \Delta t'$, the clock at B appears to A' to be running slowly. (Hint: Remember that Δt is a time difference between clocks at A and B which to A' are unsynchronized.)

1–18. Assuming a stationary source emitting frequency f_0, derive the expression

$$f' = \frac{f_0(1 + V/c)}{\sqrt{1 - V^2/c^2}}$$

for an observer moving toward the source with speed V. Show that this expression is identical to

$$f' = \frac{f_0\sqrt{1 - V^2/c^2}}{1 - V/c}$$

as derived in the text for a moving source.

1-19. Show that the classical expressions for the Doppler effect for moving sources and moving observers are identical to each other and to the relativistic expressions to first order in V/c.

1-20. A light source of frequency f_0 moves toward an observer with speed V and then away with the same speed. Show that the average of the observed frequencies is higher than f_0.

1-21. The equation for a spherical pulse of light starting from the origin at $t = t' = 0$ is $x^2 + y^2 + z^2 = c^2t^2$. Using the Lorentz transformations, calculate x'^2, y'^2, z'^2, and t'^2 and show that $x'^2 + y'^2 + z'^2 = c^2t'^2$ and thus the pulse is spherical in S' also.

1-22. A man in the back of a rocket shoots a high-speed bullet. The bullet speed measured by the man is $0.6c$. The rocket ship is 60 meters long measured by the man. The ship moves with speed $0.8c$ relative to the earth. Find
(a) The velocity of the bullet relative to earth
(b) The time that the bullet is in the air as measured by observers on the rocket
(c) The time that the bullet is in the air as measured by observers on the earth

1-23. (a) Find the energies of an electron and a proton for which the approximation $T \approx \frac{1}{2}mu^2$ is accurate to about 5 percent.
(b) Do the same for the approximation $E \approx Pc$.

1-24. Show that for $pc \ll E_0$, the kinetic energy T is $T \approx p^2/2m - \frac{1}{8}p^4c^4/E_0{}^3 \approx p^2/2m - T^2/2E_0$. For what value of T/E_0 is $T = P^2/2m$ accurate to 1 percent?

1-25. Show that the velocity of a particle is given by $\mathbf{u} = \mathbf{p}c^2/E$.

1-26. Show that the speed of a particle is given by $u = dE/dp$.

1-27. A common student mistake is to use $\frac{1}{2}\gamma mu^2$ for the relativistic kinetic energy instead of the correct $T = (\gamma - 1)mc^2$. Compare these expressions by using the binomial expansion for γ, and show that the incorrect expression does not even give the lowest order relativistic correction to $T = \frac{1}{2}mu^2$.

1-28. A spaceman with 50 years to live wants to visit the Large Magellanic Cloud, which is 160,000 light-years away. If his rest mass is M, what kinetic energy does he need assuming he travels at constant speed V? What is his speed?

TWO
THE KINETIC
THEORY OF
MATTER

In this chapter we shall study some aspects of kinetic theory, the first successful microscopic model of matter. We shall see how the first estimates and measurements were made of the size and number of molecules. The introduction to the statistical methods of distribution functions and averages in this chapter should prove valuable in Chapter 6, where the same methods are used in quantum mechanics.

The idea that all matter is composed of tiny particles, or atoms, dates back to the speculations of the Greek philosopher Democrites and his teacher Leucippus about 450 B.C. There was little attempt to correlate such speculations with observations of the physical world, however, until the seventeenth and eighteenth centuries. Pierre Gassendi, in the middle of the seventeenth century, and somewhat later Robert Hooke (now well known for his experiments with springs), attempted to explain the states of matter and transitions between them with a model of tiny indestructible solid objects flying in all directions.

In 1662, Robert Boyle published results of his experiments that showed that the product of the pressure and volume of a gas remains constant at constant temperature. Isaac Newton in his *Principia* (1687) showed that Boyle's law could be derived by assuming the gas to consist of hard *static* particles which repel each other with a force varying inversely with their separation. The first mathematical derivation of Boyle's law using a *kinetic* model was done by D. Bernoulli in 1738. Little more was done along these lines for nearly a century.

The nineteenth century saw a rapid development of the kinetic theory of matter by many people, notably Herapath, Waterston, Joule, Clausius, Maxwell, and Boltzmann. A parallel development of the theory of atoms took place in the beginning of the nineteenth century from attempts to understand the laws of chemistry. John Dalton in 1808 assumed that an element consisted of identical indestructible atoms to explain the law of definite proportions postulated by J. L. Proust (1754–1826); elements that make up a chemical compound always combine in the same definite proportions by weight. In the same year (1808), Joseph L. Gay-Lussac announced the law of combining volumes; when two gases combine to form a third, the ratios of the volumes are ratios of integers. He showed, for example, that when hydrogen combined with oxygen to form water vapor, the ratio of the volume of hydrogen to that of oxygen was 2 to 1 within 0.1 percent accuracy. (It is interesting to note that Dalton did not believe Gay-Lussac's law because it did not agree with his static atomic model, a model which he thought had been proved by Newton's derivation of Boyle's law. Dalton also had data less accurate than Gay-Lussac's; it showed deviations from ratios of integers.) In 1811 an Italian physicist, Amedeo Avogadro, proposed a remarkable hypothesis which, though not accepted for some time, eventually paved the way for the understanding of the atomic theory of chemistry. Avogadro assumed that:

1. Particles of a gas were small compared with the distances between them.
2. The particles of elements sometimes consisted of two or more atoms stuck together. These particles he called molecules to distinguish them from atoms.
3. Equal volumes of gases at constant temperature and pressure contained equal numbers of molecules.

Using these hypotheses along with the work of Gay-Lussac, Dalton, Proust, and others, Avogadro could work out the composition of molecules, and in particular he found that it was necessary to assume that the molecules of a gas such as hydrogen and oxygen contained two atoms. At first, few scientists believed these hypotheses, mainly because of the difficulty of understanding why, if two oxygen atoms attracted each other to form the molecule O_2, three or four atoms did not bind together. (This was not completely understood until the development of quantum mechanics.)

Avogadro's hypotheses were not really accepted until the latter half of the nineteenth century. It is interesting to note that he had no knowledge of the magnitude of the number of molecules in a given volume of gas, only that the number was very large. The first calculation of this number was done by Loschmidt in 1865 from the kinetic theory of gases.[1] We do not have the space in this brief introduction to go into more detail concerning the fascinating history of the discovery of the atomic theory of chemistry. The interested reader is referred to the excellent discussion in Ref. 1, on which much of this introduction is based. We shall investigate some of the important ideas of the kinetic theory developed in the latter part of the nineteenth century. Before we undertake this study, we need to understand the use of distribution functions.

2·1

DISTRIBUTION FUNCTIONS

Suppose a teacher gave a 25-point quiz to a large number, N, of students. In order to describe the results of the quiz, he might give the average score or the median score, but this would not be a complete description. For example, if all N students received 12.5, this is a quite different result than if $N/2$ students received 25 and $N/2$ received 0, though both results have the same average. A complete description would be to give the number n_i who received the score s_i for all scores s_i between 0 and 25. An alternative would be to divide n_i by the total number of students, N, to give the fraction of the students, $f_i = n_i/N$, receiving the score s_i. Either of the two functions of s_i, n_i or f_i, is called a *distribution function*. The fractional distribution, f_i, is slightly more convenient to use. The probability that one of the N students selected at random received the score s_i equals the number of students that received that score, $n_i = Nf_i$, divided by the total number N; thus this probability equals the distribution function f_i. Note that

$$\sum_{i=1}^{N} f_i = \sum_i \frac{n_i}{N} = \frac{1}{N} \sum_i n_i$$

and since

$$\sum_i n_i = N$$

we have

$$\sum_i f_i = 1 \qquad\qquad (2\text{--}1)$$

[1]This number is often called *Loschmidt's number*, particularly in Europe.

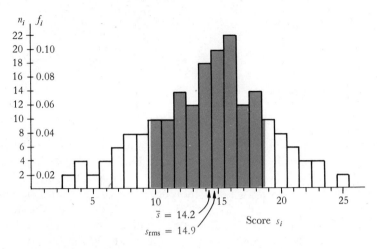

figure 2–1   Grade distribution for a 25-point quiz given to 200 students; n_i is the number and $f_i = n_i/N$ is the fraction of the number of students receiving the score s_i. The average score $\bar{s}$ and root-mean-square score s_{rms} are indicated. The shaded area indicates the scores between $\bar{s} - \sigma$ and $\bar{s} + \sigma$, where σ is the standard deviation, which for this distribution is 4.6.

Equation (2–1) is called the *normalization condition* for fractional-distribution functions. A possible distribution function for a 25-point quiz is shown in Figure 2–1.

To find the average score, all the scores are added and the result is divided by N. Since each score s_i was obtained by $n_i = Nf_i$ students, this procedure is equivalent to

$$\bar{s} = \frac{1}{N} \sum_i s_i n_i = \sum_i s_i f_i \tag{2–2}$$

We shall take Eq. (2–2) for the definition of the average score $\bar{s}$. Similarly, the average of any function $g(s)$ is defined by

$$\overline{g(s)} = \sum_i g(s_i) f_i \tag{2–3}$$

In particular, the average square score is often useful:

$$\overline{s^2} = \sum_i s_i^2 f_i$$

A particularly useful quantity characterizing a distribution is the standard deviation, σ, defined by

$$\sigma = \left[\sum_i (s_i - \bar{s})^2 f_i \right]^{1/2} \tag{2–4}$$

Note that

$$\sum_i (s_i - \bar{s})^2 f_i = \sum_i s_i^2 f_i + \bar{s}^2 \sum_i f_i - 2\bar{s} \sum_i s_i f_i = \overline{s^2} - \bar{s}^2$$

Therefore,

$$\sigma = (\overline{s^2} - \bar{s}^2)^{1/2} \tag{2-5}$$

The standard deviation is an important measure of the spread of the values s_i about the mean. For most distributions there will be few values s_i that differ from $\bar{s}$ by more than one or two multiples of σ. In the case of the normal or gaussian distribution, common in the theory of errors, about two-thirds of the values will lie within $\pm\sigma$ of the mean value. A gaussian distribution is shown in Figure 2–2.

If a student were selected at random from the class and one had to guess his score, the best guess would be the score obtained by the greatest number of students, called the *most probable score*, s_m. For the distribution in Figure 2–1, s_m is 16 and the average score, $\bar{s}$, is 14.2. The root-mean-square score, $s_{rms} = (\overline{s^2})^{1/2}$, is 14.9, and the standard deviation, σ, is 4.6. Note that 66 percent of the scores for this distribution lie within $s \pm \sigma = 14.2 \pm 4.6$. We shall now consider the problem of continuous distributions.

Suppose we wanted to know the distribution of heights of a large number of people. For a finite number N, the number of persons *exactly* 6 ft tall would be zero. If we assume that height can be determined to any desired accuracy, there is an infinite number of possible heights; thus the chance that anybody has a particular height is zero. We therefore divide the heights into intervals Δh (for example, Δh could be 0.1 ft) and ask what fraction of people have heights in any particular interval. This number depends on the size of the interval. We define the distribution function $f(h)$ as the fraction of the number of people with heights in a particular interval divided by the size of the interval. Thus for N people, $Nf(h)\,\Delta h$ is the number of people with height in

figure 2–2

Gaussian or normal-distribution curve. The curve is symmetrical about the mean $\bar{x}$, which is also the most probable value. Sixty-eight percent of the area under the curve is within one standard deviation of the mean. This curve describes the distribution of random errors in many experimental situations.

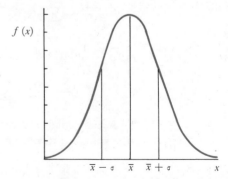

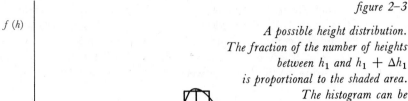

figure 2-3

A possible height distribution. The fraction of the number of heights between h_1 and $h_1 + \Delta h_1$ is proportional to the shaded area. The histogram can be approximated by a continuous curve as shown.

the interval between h and $h + \Delta h$. A possible height-distribution function is plotted in Figure 2–3. The fraction of people with heights in a particular interval is just the area of the rectangle $\Delta h \times f(h)$. The total area represents the sum of all fractions; thus it must equal 1. If N is very large, we can choose Δh very small and still have $f(h)$ vary only slightly between intervals. The histogram $f(h)$ versus h approaches a smooth curve as $N \rightarrow \infty$ and $\Delta h \rightarrow 0$. In most practical cases, the number of objects N is extremely large, and the intervals can be taken as small as measurement allows. The distribution functions $f(h)$ are usually considered to be continuous functions, intervals are written dh, and the sums are replaced by integrals. For example, if $f(h)$ is a continuous function, the average height $\bar{h}$ is[2]

$$\bar{h} = \int hf(h) \, dh \qquad (2\text{-}6)$$

and the normalization condition expressing the fact that the sum of all fractions is 1 is

$$\int f(h) \, dh = 1 \qquad (2\text{-}7)$$

Example 2–1 The distribution function for lifetimes of radioactive nuclei is given by

$$f(t) = Ce^{-\lambda t} \qquad (2\text{-}8)$$

[2]The limits on the integration depend on the range of the variable. For this case, h ranges from 0 to ∞. We shall often omit the explicit indication of the limits when the range of the variable is clear.

where λ, called the *decay constant*, depends on the particular kind of nucleus (and the type of radioactivity). Assuming λ is known, find the constant C and the mean lifetime.

The fraction of lifetimes between t and $t + dt$ is $f(t)\, dt$. The fraction of lifetimes between $t = 0$ and $t = \infty$ must be 1; thus the normalization condition is

$$\int_0^\infty f(t)\, dt = \int_0^\infty C e^{-\lambda t}\, dt = 1 \tag{2-9}$$

The integral $\int_0^\infty e^{-\lambda t}\, dt$ has the value λ^{-1}; thus $C\lambda^{-1} = 1$, or $C = \lambda$. Because the constant C is determined by the normalization condition, it is called the *normalization constant*. The mean lifetime is calculated by

$$\bar{t} = \int_0^\infty t f(t)\, dt = \lambda \int_0^\infty t e^{-\lambda t}\, dt = \lambda^{-1}$$

Thus the mean lifetime is the reciprocal of the decay constant.

*

2·2 PRESSURE OF A GAS

We are now ready to calculate the pressure exerted by a gas on the walls of a container. We make the following assumptions:

1. The gas consists of a large number, N, of molecules that make elastic collisions with each other and with the walls of the container.
2. The molecules are separated by distances large compared with their diameters, and they exert no forces on each other except when they collide.
3. In the absence of external forces (we can neglect gravity), there is no preferred position for a molecule in the container, and there is no preferred direction for the velocity vector.

For the moment, we shall neglect the collisions the molecules make with each other. To simplify the discussion, we shall consider a rectangular box of length L along the x direction and of side area A. Let $f(v_x)$ be the distribution function for the x component of velocity; that is, $N f(v_x)\, dv_x$ is the number of molecules with x component of velocity between v_x and $v_x + dv_x$. To avoid using this rather long phrase over and over, we shall hereafter use the expression "the number in dv_x at v_x" or sometimes merely "the number in dv_x." In a short time interval, dt, these molecules will hit the right end if they are within $\ell = v_x\, dt$ of that end, i.e., if they are in the shaded region of Figure 2–4. These molecules may have any y and z components of velocity. They may hit the top

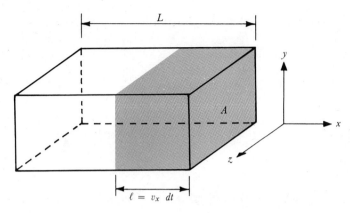

figure 2-4 *Molecules that are within $\ell = v_x \, dt$ of the end of the box will hit the end in time dt.*

or side of the box first, for such a collision, if elastic as assumed, will not affect the motion in the x direction. The number of molecules in the shaded region in Figure 2–4 is

$$N \frac{\ell A}{V} = nAv_x \, dt \tag{2-10}$$

where V is the volume of the container and n is the number density defined by $n = N/V$. Multiplying $nAv_x \, dt$ by the fraction of these molecules with v_x in the interval dv_x gives the number of molecules with this x component of velocity which hit the end in time dt. This number is

$$nAv_x \, dt \, f(v_x) \, dv_x$$

Upon hitting the end, each molecule has its x component of momentum changed from $+mv_x$ to $-mv_x$, a total change of $2mv_x$ to the left. The force exerted by the wall on the molecule is dp/dt, and by Newton's law of action and reaction, each molecule exerts an equal force outward on the wall. The total force exerted by these molecules is thus

$$F_v = n \, Av_x \, dt \, f(v_x) \, dv_x \, \frac{2mv_x}{dt}$$
$$= 2Anmv_x{}^2 f(v_x) \, dv_x$$

The pressure on the right wall of the box exerted by molecules with x components of velocity in the interval dv_x is this force divided by the area. We get the total pressure by summing over all the molecules moving to the right:

$$P = 2nm \int_0^\infty v_x{}^2 f(v_x) \, dv_x \tag{2-11}$$

Though we do not know the distribution function, $f(v_x)$, we do know that $f(-v_x) = f(+v_x)$ by our assumption that there is no preferred direction for velocities. Then

$$\int_0^\infty v_x^2 f(v_x)\, dv_x = \tfrac{1}{2}\int_{-\infty}^{+\infty} v_x^2 f(v_x)\, dv_x = \tfrac{1}{2}\overline{v_x^2}$$

Thus

$$P = nm\overline{v_x^2} \tag{2-12}$$

The assumption of random directions also implies that

$$\overline{v_x^2} = \overline{v_y^2} = \overline{v_z^2} = \tfrac{1}{3}\overline{v^2}$$

where $v^2 = v_x^2 + v_y^2 + v_z^2$. We can thus write Eq. (2–12) as

$$P = \tfrac{1}{3}nm\overline{v^2} \tag{2-13}$$

This equation can be written in several other interesting forms. Noting that the average kinetic energy of translation is

$$\overline{E}_k = \tfrac{1}{2}m\overline{v^2}$$

and $n = N/V$, we can write

$$PV = \tfrac{2}{3}N\overline{E}_k = \tfrac{2}{3}U \tag{2-14}$$

where $U = N\overline{E}_k$ is the total kinetic energy for all N molecules in the box.

Note that Eqs. (2–13) and (2–14) do not depend on the form of the distribution functions $f(v_x)$ or $f(v)$, since only the average values of v_x^2 and v^2 enter the calculation. Any assumed distribution will, of course, give the same result. For example, the assumption is sometimes made that all molecules move with the same speed, u, with one-sixth of them moving to the right along the x axis. This assumption is hardly likely; however, the result is the same. We can see that ignoring molecular collisions is not critical to the argument, for since momentum is conserved, collisions will not affect the total momentum in any given direction.

We can now compare our result with the ideal gas relation

$$PV = \nu RT \tag{2-15}$$

where ν is the number of moles and R is the gas constant, $R = 1.99$ cal/°K-mole $= 8.31$ J/°K-mole.

The total number of molecules, N, is related to the number of moles through Avogadro's number:

$$N = \nu N_A \qquad (2\text{–}16)$$

Comparing Eqs. (2–14) and (2–15), we have

$$\nu RT = \tfrac{2}{3} N \bar{E}_k$$

$$\bar{E}_k = \frac{3}{2} \frac{R}{N_A} T = \frac{3}{2} kT \qquad (2\text{–}17)$$

where $k \equiv R/N_A$ is called *Boltzmann's constant.*

$$k = 1.38 \times 10^{-23} \, \text{J/°K} = 8.63 \times 10^{-5} \, \text{eV/°K}$$

At $T = 300°\text{K}$,

$$kT = 2.59 \times 10^{-2} \, \text{eV} \approx \tfrac{1}{40} \, \text{eV}$$

Thus at room temperature the mean kinetic energy of gas molecules is only a few hundredths of an electron volt. There are two important results we can obtain from this simple calculation:

1. *Speed of a molecule in a gas.* Without knowing $f(v)$ or even $\bar{v}$, we can get an idea of the size of molecular speeds from

$$\overline{v^2} = \frac{2E_k}{m} = \frac{3RT}{N_A m} = \frac{3RT}{\mathfrak{M}} \qquad (2\text{–}18)$$

where $\mathfrak{M} = N_A m$ is the mass of 1 mole. (This is commonly called the *molecular weight*.) Thus the rms speed is

$$v_{\text{rms}} = \left(\frac{3RT}{\mathfrak{M}}\right)^{1/2} \qquad (2\text{–}19)$$

It is not hard to remember the order of magnitude of molecular speeds if we recall that the speed of sound in air is given by

$$v_{\text{sound}} = \left(\frac{\gamma RT}{\mathfrak{M}}\right)^{1/2}$$

where γ is the ratio of the specific heat at constant pressure to the specific heat at constant volume:

$$\gamma = \frac{c_p}{c_v} = 1.4 \text{ for air}$$

Example 2–2 Calculate the root-mean-square speed of nitrogen molecules at $T = 300°K$. We have

$$\mathfrak{M} = 28 \text{ g/mole} = 28 \times 10^{-3} \text{ kg/mole}$$

$$v_{rms} = \left(\frac{3 \times 8.31 \text{ J}°\text{K}^{-1} \text{ mole}^{-1} \times 300°\text{K}}{28 \times 10^{-3} \text{ kg mole}^{-1}} \right)^{1/2} = 517 \text{ m/sec}$$

*

2. *Heat capacities.* The molar heat capacity at constant volume is defined by

$$C_v = \lim_{\Delta T \to 0} \frac{\Delta Q}{\Delta T}$$

where ΔQ is the heat input and ΔT is the temperature rise for 1 mole of a substance. Since no work is done if the volume is constant, the heat input equals the change in internal energy U. Thus

$$C_v = \left(\frac{\partial U}{\partial T} \right)_v \tag{2–20}$$

If we assume that the total internal energy is *translational* kinetic energy, we have from Eq. (2–17) for 1 mole,

$$U = N_A \overline{E}_k = \tfrac{3}{2}RT$$

and

$$C_v = \tfrac{3}{2}R = 2.98 \text{ cal/mole}$$

This result agrees well with experiments for monatomic gases such as argon and helium (see Table 2–2, page 81). For other gases, the measured molar heat capacity is greater than this, indicating that the heat input goes into internal energy, other than translational kinetic energy, such as energy of rotation or vibration.

2·3
THE MAXWELL-BOLTZMANN DISTRIBUTION

The distribution function for molecular velocities was first obtained by Maxwell in 1859. The problem can be stated as follows: Given N molecules of a gas confined to some volume V, let the number with velocity components v_x in dv_x, v_y in dv_y, and v_z in dv_z be $NF(v_x,v_y,v_z) \, dv_x \, dv_y \, dv_z$. What is the form of $F(v_x,v_y,v_z)$ when the gas is in equilibrium at temperature T?

Some insight to this problem can be gained by examining some simple distributions to see if they are possible solutions. Consider the distribution — all molecules moving with the same speed, one-sixth of them in the positive x direction, one-sixth in the negative x direction, one-sixth in the positive y direction, etc. Place the molecules at random positions in the box at time zero. It is obvious that the molecules will collide and that many of the collisions will not be head-on collisions; thus their velocities will change and the original distribution will not persist. If we assume some model such as hard spheres for the molecules, we can calculate (statistically) what collisions will take place knowing the original distribution. The equilibrium distribution is the one that remains unchanged by the collisions determined by the distribution.

Maxwell assumed that the components v_x, v_y, and v_z were independent and that, therefore, the probabilities of a molecule having a certain v_x, v_y, v_z could be factored into the product of the probability of having v_x times the probability of having v_y times the probability of having v_z. He also assumed that the distribution could depend only on the speed, i.e., the velocity components could occur only in the combination $v_x{}^2 + v_y{}^2 + v_z{}^2$. His derivation is given below.[3]

"Prop. IV. To find the average number of particles whose velocities lie between given limits, after a great number of collisions among a great number of particles.

"Let N be the whole number of particles. Let x, y, z be the components of the velocity of each particle in three rectangular directions, and let the number of particles for which x lies between x and $x + dx$, be $Nf(x)\,dx$, where $f(x)$ is a function of x to be determined.

"The number of particles for which y lies between y and $y + dy$ will be $Nf(y)\,dy$, and the number for which z lies between z and $z + dz$ will be $Nf(z)\,dz$ where f always stands for the same function.

"Now the existence of the velocity x does not in any way affect that of the velocities y or z, since these are all at right angles to each other and independent, so that the number of particles whose velocity lies between x and $x + dx$, and also between y and $y + dy$, and also between z and $z + dz$, is

$$Nf(x)f(y)f(z)\,dx\,dy\,dz$$

"If we suppose the N particles to start from the origin at the same instant, then this will be the number in the element of volume (dx,dy,dz) after unit of time, and the number referred to unit volume will be

$$Nf(x)f(y)f(z)$$

[3]Quoted from "Illustrations of the Dynamical Theory of Gases," by J. C. Maxwell, in *Scientific Papers*, edited by W. Niven, Hermann & Cie, Paris, 1927, and Dover Publications, Inc., New York, 1952. Maxwell's use of x, y, and z for the velocity components which we designate by the symbols v_x, v_y, and v_z may cause some confusion.

figure 2–5

James Clerk Maxwell.
(Courtesy of Culver
Pictures, Inc.)

"But the directions of the coordinate are perfectly arbitrary, and therefore this number must depend on the distance from the origin alone, that is,

$$f(x)f(y)f(z) = \phi(x^2 + y^2 + z^2)$$

Solving this functional equation,[4] we find

$$f(x) = Ce^{Ax^2} \qquad \phi(r^2) = C^3 e^{Ar^2}$$

"If we make A positive, the number of particles will increase with the velocity, and we should find the whole number of particles infinite. We therefore make A negative and equal to $-1/a^2$ so that the number between x and $x + dx$ is

$$NCe^{-x^2/a^2}\, dx$$

Integrating from $x = -\infty$ to $x = +\infty$, we find the whole number of particles,

$$NCa\sqrt{\pi} = N$$
$$C = \frac{1}{a\sqrt{\pi}}$$

[4]Solving this functional equation is not trivial, but the result is easy to check. The mathematical details of solution do not add much clarity to this derivation. The interested reader is referred to pages 41 to 48 in Ref. 8 for a more detailed treatment.

$f(x)$ is therefore

$$\frac{1}{a\sqrt{\pi}} e^{-x^2/a^2}$$

whence we may draw the following conclusions. . . ."

We shall use a notation slightly more convenient than that in the quotation above. Let $\lambda = 1/a^2$. The distribution function for v_x is then

$$f(v_x) = Ce^{-\lambda v_x^2} \tag{2-21}$$

The constant C is determined by the normalization condition

$$\int_{-\infty}^{\infty} f(v_x)\, dv_x = \int_{-\infty}^{\infty} Ce^{-\lambda v_x^2}\, dv_x = 1 \tag{2-22}$$

We shall need to evaluate integrals of the form

$$I_n = \int_0^{\infty} x^n e^{-\lambda x^2}\, dx \tag{2-23}$$

several times in this chapter. Table 2–1, derived in Appendix B, lists I_n for values of n from 0 to 5. Using this table to evaluate Eq. (2–18), we find

$$C = \left(\frac{\lambda}{\pi}\right)^{1/2}$$

table 2–1   Values of the integral $I_n = \int_0^{\infty} x^n e^{-\lambda x^2}\, dx$ for $n = 0$ to $n = 5$.

n	I_n
0	$\frac{1}{2}\sqrt{\pi/\lambda}$
1	$1/2\lambda$
2	$\frac{1}{4}\sqrt{\pi/\lambda^3}$
3	$1/2\lambda^2$
4	$\frac{3}{8}\sqrt{\pi/\lambda^5}$
5	$1/\lambda^3$
If n is even,	$\int_{-\infty}^{\infty} x^n e^{-\lambda x^2}\, dx = 2I_n$
If n is odd,	$\int_{-\infty}^{\infty} x^n e^{-\lambda x^2}\, dx = 0$

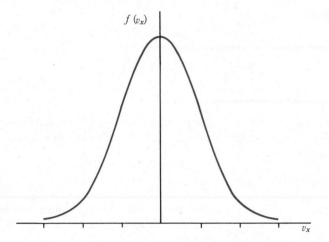

figure 2–6   *The distribution function $f(v_x)$ for the x component of velocity. This is a gaussian curve, given by Eq. (2–25).*

The constant λ can be determined by calculating $\overline{v_x^2}$:

$$\overline{v_x^2} = \int_{-\infty}^{+\infty} v_x^2 f(v_x) \, dv_x = \int_{-\infty}^{+\infty} v_x^2 C e^{-\lambda v_x^2} \, dv_x = 2CI_2$$

$$= 2 \left(\frac{\lambda}{\pi}\right)^{1/2} \frac{1}{4} \left(\frac{\pi}{\lambda^3}\right)^{1/2}$$

Thus $\overline{v_x^2} = \frac{1}{2}\lambda^{-1}$. Comparing with Eq. (2–18),

$$\overline{v_x^2} = \frac{1}{3}\overline{v^2} = \frac{2}{3}\frac{\overline{E_k}}{m} = \frac{kT}{m}$$

We find

$$\lambda = \frac{m}{2kT} \tag{2–24}$$

Thus the complete distribution function $f(v_x)$ is

$$f(v_x) = \left(\frac{m}{2\pi kT}\right)^{1/2} e^{-mv_x^2/2kT} \tag{2–25}$$

Figure 2–6 shows a sketch of $f(v_x)$ versus v_x. Of course, $f(v_x)$ is symmetrical about the origin, $f(v_x) = f(-v_x)$; thus the average of v_x is zero. As can be seen from the figure, the most probable

v_x is also zero. The complete velocity distribution is thus

$$F(v_x,v_y,v_z) = f(v_x)f(v_y)f(v_z) = \left(\frac{m}{2\pi kT}\right)^{3/2} e^{-m(v_x^2+v_y^2+v_z^2)/2kT}$$

$$(2\text{--}26)$$

We can calculate the *speed* distribution from the velocity distribution. Let $g(v)\,dv$ be the fraction of molecules with speeds v in the range dv. The difference between $F(v_x,v_y,v_z)$ and $g(v)$ can be seen most easily by examining what is called *velocity space*. Imagine the velocity vector of each molecule placed with its tail at the origin of the coordinate system v_x, v_y, v_z. (See Figure 2–7). $F(v_x,v_y,v_z)\,dv_x\,dv_y\,dv_z$ is the fraction of these vectors whose tips end in the "volume" element $dv_x\,dv_y\,dv_z$. On the other hand, $g(v)\,dv$ is the fraction whose tips end in the "volume" element between the sphere of radius v and one of radius $v + dv$. We could also represent each molecular velocity by a point at the tip of the vector in the velocity space shown in Figure 2–7. Then $F(v_x,v_y,v_z)$ is the density of points in this space. Since this density depends only on the "distance" $v = (v_x^2 + v_y^2 + v_z^2)^{1/2}$, the number of points between v and $v + dv$ is just the density times the "volume" of the spherical shell of thickness dv, or

$$g(v)\,dv = 4\pi v^2\,dv\,F(v_x,v_y,v_z) = 4\pi\left(\frac{m}{2\pi kT}\right)^{3/2} v^2 e^{-mv^2/2kT}\,dv$$

$$(2\text{--}27)$$

figure 2–7 *Velocity vectors in velocity space. Each molecular velocity can be represented by a point in velocity space at the tip of the velocity vector. The velocity distribution function $NF(v_x,v_y,v_z)$ is the number of points per unit volume $dv_x\,dv_y\,dv_z$, where N is the number of molecules.*

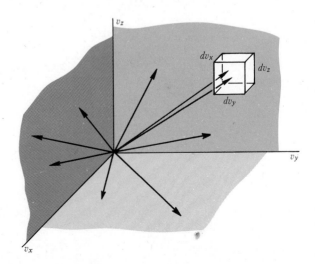

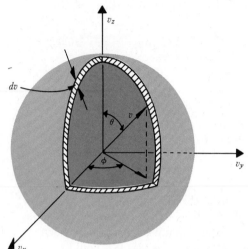

figure 2–8

One octant of a spherical shell in velocity space.
The volume of the entire spherical
shell is $4\pi v^2 \, dv$.
The speed distribution $Ng(v)$
is the number of points per unit length dv
in the spherical shell.

The speed-distribution function $g(v)$ is sketched in Figure 2–9. The mean speed is

$$\bar{v} = \int_0^{\infty} v g(v) \, dv = \left(\frac{8kT}{\pi m}\right)^{1/2} \qquad (2\text{--}28)$$

It is left as an exercise to show that the most probable speed is

$$v_m = \left(\frac{2kT}{m}\right)^{1/2} \qquad (2\text{--}29)$$

The energy-distribution function, $F(E) \, dE$, is the fraction of molecules with energies between E and $E + dE$. We can calculate the energy distribution by noting that

$$F(E) \, dE = g(v) \, dv$$

with $E = \frac{1}{2}mv^2$ and $dE = mv \, dv$. Thus

$$v^2 \, dv = \frac{v \, dE}{m} = \left(\frac{2E}{m}\right)^{1/2} \frac{dE}{m}$$

The energy distribution is thus

$$F(E) \, dE \propto E^{1/2} e^{-E/kT} \, dE \qquad (2\text{--}30)$$

The proportionality constant can be determined by the normalization condition.

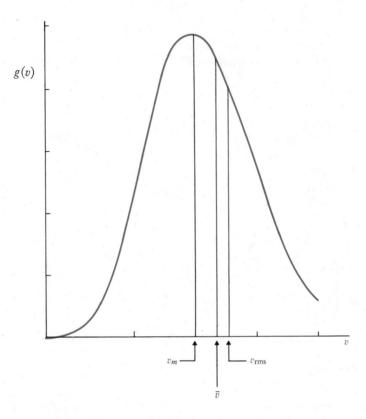

figure 2–9   *Maxwell's speed distribution* $g(v)$. *The most probable speed* v_m, *the mean speed* $\bar{v}$, *and the rms speed* v_{rms} *are indicated.*

The first direct measurement of the speed distribution of molecules was made by O. Stern in 1926. Since then, measurements have been made by Zartman and Ko (1930); I. Estermann, O. C. Simpson, and O. Stern (1946); and Miller and Kusch (1955). These experiments employed various methods of selecting a range of speeds of molecules escaping from a small hole in an oven and determining the number of molecules in this range. Zartman and Ko, for example, allowed the beam to pass through a slit in a rotating cylinder and measured the intensity versus position on the collecting plate. In the more recent experiment of Miller and Kusch, illustrated in Figure 2–10, a collimated beam from the oven is aimed at a fixed detector. Most of the beam is stopped by a rotating cylinder. Small helical slits in the cylinder allow passage of those molecules in a narrow speed range determined by the angular velocity of the cylinder. The Miller and Kusch results are shown in Figure 2–11.

figure 2–10

Schematic sketch of apparatus of Miller and Kusch
for measuring the speed distribution of molecules.
Only one of the 720 helical slits in the cylinder is
shown. For a given angular velocity ω,
only molecules of a certain speed
from the oven pass through
the helical slit to the detector.
[From Miller and Kusch,
Physical Review, **99**,
1314 (1955).]

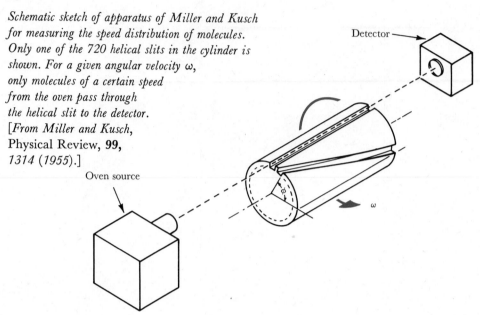

Detector

Oven source

figure 2–11   *Data of Miller and Kusch showing distribution of speeds of thallium atoms*
from an oven. The data have been corrected to give the distribution inside the
oven. The solid curve is that predicted by the Maxwell speed distribution.
[From Miller and Kusch, Physical Review, **99**, *1314 (1955).]*

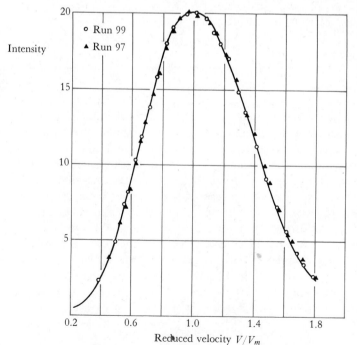

2·4 OTHER DERIVATIONS OF THE MAXWELL-BOLTZMANN DISTRIBUTION

In Maxwell's derivation, no mention is made of molecular collisions. The assumption that the velocity components are independent seems to be correct in that the resulting distribution is correct; however, there is little a priori reason for this assumption to be true. Maxwell and others recognized the flaws in this derivation, and many other derivations have been given, all resulting in the same distribution. This distribution is now called the *Maxwell-Boltzmann distribution*. We shall discuss briefly the two most important derivations.

The most satisfying derivation from the standpoint of dynamics is due to the German physicist Ludwig Boltzmann. It is also the most difficult. A general distribution function $f(x,y,z,v_x,v_y,v_z)$ is assumed, and the effects of molecular collisions are calculated in detail using conservation of energy and momentum. The equilibrium distribution is the one that remains unchanged by the collisions it predicts. Boltzmann was able to show that, given any initial velocity distribution, a gas tends quickly toward the equilibrium Maxwell distribution. This derivation is greatly superior to that of Maxwell because molecular collisions are explicitly involved and also because nonequilibrium situations can be treated.

Another derivation due to the American physicist and chemist J. W. Gibbs and others is based on statistics. The six-dimensional space x, y, z, P_x, P_y, P_z (where P_x, P_y, and P_z are components of momentum) is divided into a number of cells r. This space is called *phase space*. The probabilities of various arrangements of N molecules in the r cells are calculated. It is assumed that:

1. The equilibrium distribution is the most probable distribution consistent with a constant number of particles and constant energy.
2. The particles are identical but distinguishable.
3. There is no restriction on the number of particles in any cell.

The most probable distribution of N objects in r cells with no other restrictions is just N/r in each cell. The condition of conservation of energy places a severe restriction on the number of arrangements possible. If the total energy is E, the number of particles in the ith cell for the most probable distribution is proportional to $e^{-\beta E_i}$, where E_i is the characteristic energy of the ith cell. (For example, the kinetic-energy characteristic of cells far from the origin in phase space is large because the magnitude of the momentum far from the origin is large.) The constant, β, can be determined to be $1/kT$ by applying this result to the case of an ideal gas. This derivation is given in Appendix C.

Because the Maxwell-Boltzmann distribution is applicable to a wide variety of systems other than gases (for example, atoms in a solid), it will be stated in a more general form here.

Given a system of particles for which the energy E can be a function of the coordinates x, y, z and momentum P_x, P_y, P_z, the probability of a particle being in the cell[5]

$$d\tau = dx\ dy\ dz\ dP_x\ dP_y\ dP_z$$

is

$$f(x,y,z,P_x,P_y,P_z)\ d\tau = Ce^{-E/kT}\ d\tau \qquad (2\text{--}31)$$

where the constant C is determined by the normalization condition.

$$\int Ce^{-E/kT}\ d\tau = 1 \qquad (2\text{--}32)$$

If we apply this to the case of an ideal gas for which the energy is given by

$$E = \frac{P^2}{2m} = \frac{1}{2m}(P_x^2 + P_y^2 + P_z^2)$$

we have

$$f(x,y,z,P_x,P_y,P_z)\ d\tau = Ce^{-(P_x^2+P_y^2+P_z^2)/2mkT}\ d\tau$$

We can compare this with Eq. (2–26) if we integrate over the position coordinates. If we designate the momentum distribution by $F(P_x,P_y,P_z)$, we have

$$F(P_x,P_y,P_z)\ dP_x\ dP_y\ dP_z = \int_x \int_y \int_z f(x,y,z,P_x,P_y,P_z)\ d\tau$$
$$= CVe^{-(P_x^2+P_y^2+P_z^2)/2mkT}$$
$$\times dP_x\ dP_y\ dP_z \qquad (2\text{--}33)$$

where V is the volume of the container.

Equation (2–33) is essentially the same as Eq. (2–26) except that momentum is used instead of velocity and therefore the normalization constant is slightly different.

We shall see in the next chapters that, in general, the energy of a system is not a continuous variable but takes on only a discrete set of values. (The energy often appears to be continuous because these discrete energies are often very close together.) It is useful therefore to have a statement of the Maxwell-Boltzmann distribution for the case of discrete energy states.

[5]This distribution also holds if we interpret P to be angular momentum and the coordinates to be the corresponding angles. For example, P_z can be the z component of angular momentum, in which case z is the angle of rotation ϕ.

Given a system of particles for which the energy has a discrete set of values, the probability of a particle having the energy E_i is

$$f_i = Cg_ie^{-E_i/kT} \qquad (2\text{-}34)$$

where the constant C is determined by the normalization condition and g_i is the statistical weight. The statistical weight is the number of quantum states having the same energy. In our study of quantum mechanics in Chapters 6 and 7, we shall see how to determine g_i for various systems.

Example 2–3 The first excited state of the hydrogen atom is 10.2 eV above the ground state. What is the ratio of the number of atoms in the first excited state to the number in the ground state at $T = 300°K$? We shall see in Chapter 7 that the statistical weights for these states are $g_0 = 2$ and $g_1 = 8$. The ratio is f_1/f_0, given by Eq. (2–34).

$$\frac{f_1}{f_0} = \frac{g_1e^{-E_1/kT}}{g_0e^{-E_0/kT}} = \frac{g_1}{g_0}e^{-(E_1-E_0)/kT} = 4e^{-(10.2/0.026)}$$
$$= 4e^{-393} \approx 10^{-171}$$

We see that because of the great energy difference compared with kT, very few atoms are in the first excited state.

*

We can generalize Eq. (2–34) to the case of continuous energy by replacing f_i by $f(E)\,dE$, the fraction of particles with energy in dE, and replacing g_i by $g(E)\,dE$, the number of energy states in dE which is proportional to the volume of phase space in dE. Then,

$$f(E)\,dE = Cg(E)e^{-E/kT}\,dE \qquad (2\text{-}35)$$

Example 2–4 Use Eq. (2–35) to find the energy distribution for an ideal gas for which the energy is given by

$$E = \frac{1}{2m}(P_x{}^2 + P_y{}^2 + P_z{}^2) = \frac{P^2}{2m} \qquad (2\text{-}36)$$

We need to find the function $g(E)\,dE$. Since the energy does not depend on coordinates, we need only consider the momentum part of phase space. Differentiating Eq. (2–36) gives

$$dE = P\frac{dP}{m}$$

The volume in phase space between P and $P + dP$ is the volume of the spherical shell in momentum space, analogous to Figure 2–8.

This volume is

$$4\pi P^2 \, dP = 4\pi P \, P \, dP = 4\pi(2mE)^{1/2} \, m \, dE$$

We thus see that $g(E) \, dE$ is proportional to $E^{1/2} \, dE$. We can lump the proportionality constants in with the normalization constant and write

$$f(E) \, dE = C'E^{1/2}e^{-E/kT} \, dE$$

We see that this result is the same as Eq. (2–30).

*

2·5
EQUIPARTITION THEOREM AND HEAT CAPACITIES OF GASES AND SOLIDS

A simple but important theorem can be derived from the Maxwell-Boltzmann distribution. Consider a system in which the energy of a particle is continuous and given by

$$E = c_1 u^2 + c_2 w^2$$

where c_1 and c_2 are constants and u and w are any type of position or momentum coordinates. The average energy is

$$\bar{E} = \iint Ef(u,w) \, du \, dw$$

Using Eq. (2–31) for $f(u,w)$, we have

$$\bar{E} = \iint (c_1 u^2 + c_2 w^2)Ce^{-(c_1 u^2 + c_2 w^2)/kT} \, du \, dw$$

with $\iint Ce^{-(c_1 u^2 + c_2 w^2)/kT} \, du \, dw = 1$. Using Table 2–1, these integrals are easily found. The result is $\bar{E} = \frac{1}{2}kT + \frac{1}{2}kT = kT$.

This is an example of the equipartition theorem:

An average energy of $\frac{1}{2}kT$ is associated with each coordinate or momentum component appearing in the energy as a squared term.

We have already seen an example of the application of this theorem. The energy of an ideal-gas molecule contains the terms P_x^2, P_y^2, and P_z^2. The equipartition theorem thus predicts the average energy to be $\frac{3}{2}kT$. The total energy of a mole of gas is then

$$U = N_A \bar{E}_k = \frac{3}{2}N_A kT = \frac{3}{2}RT$$

and the molar heat capacity is

$$C_v = \frac{dU}{dT} = \frac{3}{2}R \approx 3 \text{ cal/°K-mole}$$

We have already remarked that though this agrees with the measured values for monatomic gas, the molar heat capacity is greater than $1.5R$ for other gases. For example, $C_v \approx 2.49R$ for nitrogen. Clausius correctly surmised, in about 1880, that the extra internal energy of nitrogen and other gases for which $C_v \approx 2.5R$ is due to rotation. He concluded that these gases consist of diatomic molecules. A diatomic molecule has a large moment of inertia about each of the two axes perpendicular to the line joining the atoms and a small one about this line. Let us call the line joining the atoms the z axis. If the atoms are assumed to be points, the moment of inertia about the z axis is zero, and the rotational energy is

$$E_{rot} = \tfrac{1}{2}I\omega_x{}^2 + \tfrac{1}{2}I\omega_y{}^2 = \frac{L_x{}^2}{2I} + \frac{L_y{}^2}{2I}$$

where we have written $L_x = I\omega_x$ and $L_y = I\omega_y$ for the x and y components of angular momentum.

Since for this model, the energy has five squared terms, three for translation and two for rotation, the equipartition theorem predicts the average energy to be $\tfrac{5}{2}kT$ and the molar heat capacity to be $2.5R$.

If a diatomic molecule is not rigid, the atoms can vibrate along the line of separation. Then, in addition to the translational energy of the center of mass, and rotational energy, there can be vibrational energy. The vibration adds two more squared terms to the energy, one for the potential energy, which is proportional to $(r - r_0)^2$, and one for kinetic energy proportional to $(dr/dt)^2$, where r is the

figure 2–12   *Models of a diatomic molecule.* (a) *Rigid-dumbbell model can rotate and translate but not vibrate.* (b) *Compressible-spring model can vibrate as well as rotate and translate.*

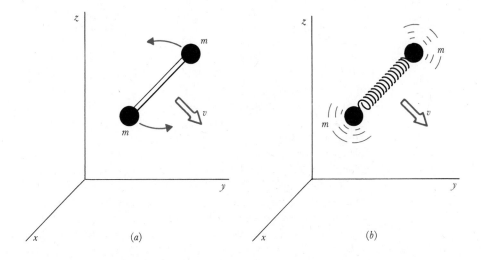

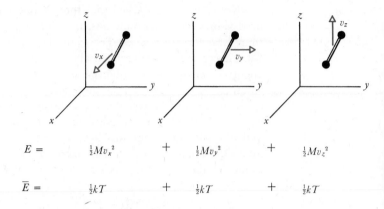

$$E = \quad \tfrac{1}{2}Mv_x{}^2 \quad + \quad \tfrac{1}{2}Mv_y{}^2 \quad + \quad \tfrac{1}{2}Mv_z{}^2$$

$$\overline{E} = \quad \tfrac{1}{2}kT \quad + \quad \tfrac{1}{2}kT \quad + \quad \tfrac{1}{2}kT$$

figure 2–13   *Energy modes of a diatomic molecule. With each of the seven possible motions, there is associated an average energy of $\tfrac{1}{2}kT$. If the atoms are not assumed to be points, there is an eighth mode — rotation about the line joining the atoms — which is not shown.*

separation of the atoms which has the value r_0 at equilibrium. Thus, for a diatomic molecule that is translating, rotating, and vibrating, the equipartition theorem predicts a molar heat capacity of $(3 + 2 + 2)\tfrac{1}{2}R$, or $3.5R$.

Table 2–2 lists experimental values of C_v for several gases. For all the diatomic molecules except Cl_2, these data are consistent with the equipartition-theorem prediction, assuming a rigid non-vibrating molecule. The value for Cl_2 is about halfway between that predicted for a rigid molecule and that predicted for a vibrating molecule. The situation for molecules with three or more atoms is slightly more complicated and will not be examined in detail here. [In general, the number of squared terms in the energy is found by adding twice the number of normal modes of vibration to the three translational and three rotational (for nonlinear molecules) terms. A nonlinear molecule with n atoms has $3n - 6$ normal modes (for $n > 2$); thus the equipartition theorem predicts C_v to be $\{3 + 3 + 2(3n - 6)\} R/2$, or $3(n - 1)R$, assuming translation, rotation, and vibration.]

It is difficult to understand why the equipartition theorem in conjunction with the point-atom, rigid-dumbbell model is so successful in predicting the molar heat capacity for most diatomic molecules but not for all of them. Why should not diatomic gas molecules vibrate? If the atoms are not points, the moment of inertia about the line joining the atoms is not zero, and there are three terms for rotational energy rather than two. Assuming no vibration, C_v should be $\tfrac{6}{2}R$. This agrees with the measured value for Cl_2 but not for the other diatomic gases. Furthermore, mona-

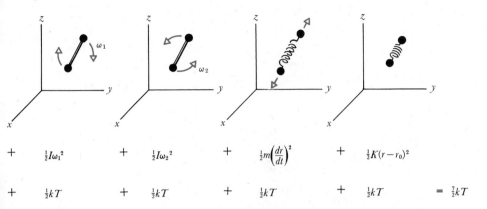

$$+ \quad \tfrac{1}{2}I\omega_1{}^2 \qquad + \quad \tfrac{1}{2}I\omega_2{}^2 \qquad + \quad \tfrac{1}{2}m\!\left(\frac{dr}{dt}\right)^{\!2} \qquad + \quad \tfrac{1}{2}K(r-r_0)^2$$

$$+ \quad \tfrac{1}{2}kT \qquad\quad + \quad \tfrac{1}{2}kT \qquad\quad + \quad \tfrac{1}{2}kT \qquad\qquad + \quad \tfrac{1}{2}kT \qquad = \tfrac{7}{2}kT$$

tomic molecules would have three terms for rotational energy if the atoms were not points, and C_v should be $\tfrac{6}{2}R$ for these atoms also. Since the average energy is calculated by *counting* terms, it does not matter how small the atoms are as long as they are not merely points.

In addition to the difficulties discussed above, the molar heat capacity is found to depend on temperature, contrary to the predictions from the equipartition theorem. The most spectacular case is that of H_2, as shown in Figure 2–14. Apparently, at very low temperatures, H_2 behaves like a monatomic molecule and does not rotate. At very high temperatures H_2 begins to vibrate, but the molecule dissociates before C_v reaches $3.5R$. Other diatomic gases show similar behavior, except that at low temperatures they liquefy before C_v reaches $1.5R$.

table 2–2   *Molar heat capacities of some gases at 15°C and 1 atm. (Data are from J. R. Partington and W. G. Shilling,* The Specific Heats of Gases, *Ernest Benn, Ltd., London, 1924, p. 201.)*

Gas	C_v (cal/mole-deg)	C_v/R
Ar	2.98	1.50
He	2.98	1.50
CO	4.94	2.49
H_2	4.87	2.45
HCl	5.11	2.57
N_2	4.93	2.49
NO	5.00	2.51
O_2	5.04	2.54
Cl_2	5.93	2.98
CO_2	6.75	3.40
CS_2	9.77	4.92
H_2S	6.08	3.06
N_2O	6.81	3.42
SO_2	7.49	3.86

$$R = 1.987 \text{ cal/mole-deg}$$

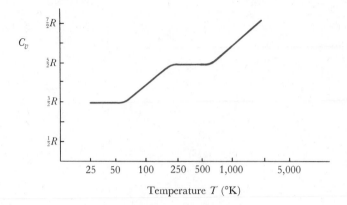

figure 2–14   *Temperature dependence of molar heat capacity of H_2. Between about 250°K and 1000°K, C_v is $\frac{5}{2}R$, as predicted by the model of a rigid dumbbell, which can rotate but not vibrate. At low temperatures, C_v is only $\frac{3}{2}R$, as would be predicted for a nonrotating molecule. At high temperature, C_v seems to be approaching $\frac{7}{2}R$, as predicted for a rotating and vibrating molecule, but the molecule dissociates before this plateau is reached.*

The equipartition theorem is also useful in understanding the heat capacity of solids. In 1819, Dulong and Petit pointed out that the molar heat capacity of most solids was very nearly equal to 6 cal/°K-mole $\approx 3R$. This result was used by them to obtain unknown molecular weights from the experimentally determined heat capacities. The Dulong-Petit law is easily derived from the equipartition theorem by assuming that the internal energy of a solid consists of the vibrational energy of the molecules. If the force constants in the x, y, and z directions are K_1, K_2, and K_3, the vibrational energy of each molecule is

$$E = \frac{1}{2m}(P_x{}^2 + P_y{}^2 + P_z{}^2) + \tfrac{1}{2}(K_1x^2 + K_2y^2 + K_3z^2)$$

figure 2–15   *Simple model of atoms in a solid. Each atom can vibrate in three dimensions as if it were connected to its neighbors by springs.*

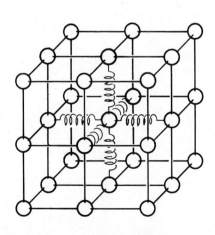

Since there are six squared terms, the average energy per molecule is $6(\frac{1}{2}kT)$, and the total energy of 1 mole is $3N_AkT = 3RT$; thus C_v is $3R$.

At high temperature, the Dulong-Petit law is obeyed for all solids. For temperatures below some critical temperature, C_v drops appreciably below the value of $3R$ and approaches zero as T approaches zero. The critical temperature is characteristic of the solid. It is lower for soft solids such as lead than for hard solids such as diamond. The general temperature dependence of C_v for solids is shown in Figure 2–16. The fact that C_v for metals is not appreciably different from that for insulators is somewhat puzzling. A model of a metal, which is moderately successful in describing conduction, proposes that approximately one electron per atom is free to roam about the metal, making collisions with the atoms much as molecules do in a gas. According to the equipartition theorem, this "electron gas" should have an average energy of $\frac{3}{2}kT$ per electron; thus the molar heat capacity should be about $\frac{3}{2}R$ greater for a metal than for an insulator. Although the molar heat capacity for metals is slightly greater than $3R$ at very high temperatures, the difference is much less than the $1.5R$ predicted for the contribution from the electron gas.

The failure of the kinetic theory in predicting heat capacities of gases and solids is not a failure of the model but rather a failure of classical mechanics. The search for an understanding of specific heats was instrumental in the discovery of energy quantization in the beginning of the twentieth century. We shall see in the next chapter how energy quantization provides a basis for the complete understanding of the problems discussed in this section.

figure 2–16   *Temperature dependence of molar heat capacity of solids. At high temperatures, C_v is $3R$, as predicted by the equipartition theorem. At low temperatures, however, C_v approaches zero. The critical temperature at which C_v becomes nearly $3R$ is different for different solids. (See Figure 3–21.)*

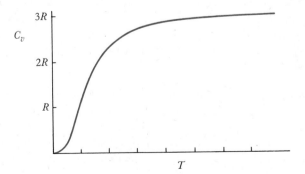

2·6 TRANSPORT PHENOMENA

In the calculation of the pressure exerted by a gas on its container, the size of the molecules was not involved. We shall now consider viscosity, heat conduction, and diffusion in gases. These phenomena depend directly on the size of the gas molecules. The success of the application of kinetic theory to these phenomena provided one of the first convincing demonstrations of the essential validity of this theory, and thus of the existence of molecules.

In the kinetic theory, viscosity involves the transport of momentum, heat conduction involves the transport of kinetic energy, and diffusion involves the transport of the density of the molecules. Molecular collisions play an important role in the transport of these quantities, and the frequency of collisions depends directly on the size of the molecules and the number of molecules per unit volume. The comparison of the predictions of kinetic theory with macroscopic measurements of viscosity and heat conduction provided one of the first estimates of molecular sizes and of Avogadro's number. We shall consider only the most elementary treatment of the kinetic theory of transport phenomena.

An important quantity characterizing molecular collisions is the average distance a molecule travels between collisions. This distance is called the *mean free path*, ℓ. We should expect ℓ to depend inversely on the molecular size and the density of the gas. We can relate ℓ to the number density n and the diameter d as follows.

Consider one molecule moving with speed v through a region of stationary molecules of number density n. It will collide with another molecule if the centers are a distance $2r$, or d, apart. In time t, the molecule moves a distance vt and collides with every molecule in the cylindrical volume $\pi d^2 vt$. The number of molecules in this volume is $nvt\pi d^2$. (After each collision, the direction of the molecule changes; thus the path is really a zigzag one.) The total path length divided by the number of collisions is the mean free path[6]:

$$\ell \simeq \frac{vt}{nvt\pi d^2} = \frac{1}{n\pi d^2} \qquad (2\text{-}37)$$

The quantity πd^2 is the effective area presented by one molecule of diameter d to another of the same size. This area is called the *collision cross section*, σ. If the molecules are of different size, the collision cross section would be $\sigma = \pi(r_1 + r_2)^2$, where r_1 and r_2 are the radii. In terms of the collision cross section,

$$\ell = \frac{1}{n\sigma} \qquad (2\text{-}38)$$

---

[6]Of course, all the molecules but one are not stationary. If we assume a Maxwell-Boltzmann distribution of velocities, the calculation is considerably more involved, with the result $\ell = 0.707/n\pi d^2$ (see Ref. 9, p. 78). For our purposes, we need not worry about this and other corrections.

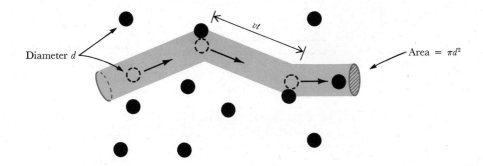

figure 2–17   *Model of a molecule moving in a gas. In time t, a molecule with diameter d will collide with any similar molecule whose center is in a cylinder of volume $\pi\, d^2 vt$, where v is the speed of the molecule. In this picture, all the molecules but one are assumed to be at rest.*

Let us now examine the phenomenon of viscosity. Consider a gas between two plates; the upper plate is pulled to the right with a speed V_0, while the bottom plate is held stationary. It is found that the gas has a net flow to the right, the speed varying with height z from the bottom plate. Essentially, the gas near the top tends to follow the upper plate with speed V_0, while that near the bottom tends to remain at rest. The flow velocity $V(z)$ is superimposed on the random, or thermal, velocity of the molecules. A force is necessary to keep the upper plate moving with constant speed and to hold the bottom plate at rest. Evidently there is a drag force exerted by the gas; this force is called a *viscous force*. The coefficient of viscosity is defined as follows.

Consider a hypothetical plane surface of area A parallel to the plates at a height z_1 above the lower plate, as in Figure 2–18. The gas above this surface exerts a force to the right on the gas below, and of course the gas below exerts an equal but opposite force to the left on the gas above. This force is tangential to the plane and proportional to the area A and to the velocity gradient dV/dz. The force per unit area is called the *viscous stress, S.*

$$S = \eta \frac{dV}{dz} \tag{2–39}$$

This equation defines the coefficient of viscosity, η. We shall consider the force on the gas below z_1 (shaded region in Figure 2–18). Molecules crossing the plane from above bring in x momentum mV_1, while those crossing from below carry away x momentum mV_2. Since the x component of momentum of those crossing from above is larger on the average than that of those from below, there is a net transfer of momentum. The transfer of momentum across the plane per second per unit area equals the stress exerted on the lower gas. We can get an order-of-magnitude estimate of this stress as follows.

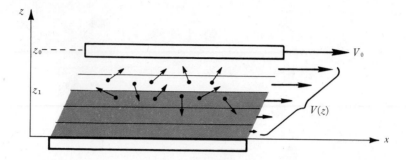

figure 2–18   *Because of the relative motion of the plates, the gas between them has a flow velocity which varies from nearly 0 at the bottom plate to nearly V_0 at the top plate. For simplicity, only two layers of the gas are pictured here. Molecules crossing the z_1 plane from the upper layer have a greater momentum in the x direction, on the average, than those crossing from the lower layer. Thus momentum is transported across this plane, resulting in a viscous force exerted by each layer of gas on the other.*

Let n be the number density. The number of molecules that hit A from above in time Δt is roughly of the order of the number in the volume $\bar{v} \, \Delta t \, A$ when $\bar{v}$ is the mean speed. This number is $n\bar{v} \, \Delta t A$. Since the molecules are not all moving straight down with speed $\bar{v}$, this is an overestimate, but we shall neglect this detail for the moment. (If molecules moved only parallel to the x, y, or z axis, only one-sixth of this number would be moving down; however, there would then be no x component of momentum carried in by these molecules.) We shall assume that the flow velocity of a molecule is that of the gas at the point z where the molecule made its last collision. If Δz is the average height above z_1 of the molecule's last collision, the molecule will carry in x component of momentum $mV(z_1 + \Delta z)$. The total transfer of x component of momentum from above in time Δt is then roughly

$$n\bar{v} \, \Delta t \, AmV(z_1 + \Delta z)$$

Similarly, that carried out from below is

$$n\bar{v} \, \Delta t AmV(z_1 - \Delta z)$$

Using the approximations

$$V(z_1 + \Delta z) \approx V(z_1) + \frac{dV}{dz} \Delta z$$

$$V(z_1 - \Delta z) \approx V(z_1) - \frac{dV}{dz} \Delta z$$

the net momentum carried in is roughly

$$n\bar{v}\,\Delta t\,Am[V(z_1 + \Delta z) - V(z_1 - \Delta z)] \approx 2n\bar{v}m\,\frac{dV}{dz}\,\Delta z\,A\,\Delta t$$

The average height of the molecule's last collision, Δz, is of the order of the mean free path ℓ. Replacing Δz by ℓ and dividing by the time Δt and area A, we obtain for an estimate of the stress

$$S \approx 2n\bar{v}m\ell\,\frac{dV}{dz}$$

This expression is an overestimate because we have neglected to take into account the various directions of the velocities of the molecules. (All the molecules in the cylinder in Figure 2–19 are not moving down with speed $\bar{v}$.) A more detailed calculation taking this into account introduces a factor of $\frac{1}{6}$, giving

$$S = \tfrac{1}{3}n\bar{v}m\ell\,\frac{dV}{dz} \tag{2–40}$$

figure 2–19 *Simplified picture for calculating viscosity. In time Δt, the number of molecules crossing z_1 from above is of the order of the number in the cylinder on the left, which has a volume $\bar{v}\,\Delta tA$. The average x component of momentum transported by these molecules is $n\bar{v}\,\Delta tAmV(z_1 + \Delta z)$, where n is the number per unit volume. The cylinder on the right is used to calculate the average x component of momentum transported from below, which is less than that from above because the flow velocity is less below the plane. This calculation overestimates the momentum transport (by a factor of 6) because the average component of velocity toward the plane is less than $\bar{v}$.*

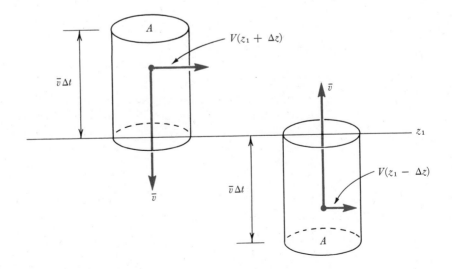

Using this expression, the coefficient of viscosity is

$$\eta = \tfrac{1}{3}n\bar{v}\ell m \tag{2-41}$$

Equation (2-41) was obtained by Maxwell in 1860. Using Eq. (2-37) for the mean free path, we obtain

$$\eta = \frac{m\bar{v}}{3\pi d^2} \tag{2-42}$$

Note that this expression is independent of density. This surprising result was first pointed out by Maxwell and verified by him experimentally over a wide range of densities. (At extremely low densities, this theory breaks down because the mean free path becomes of the order of the size of the container.) Equation (2-42) also implies that η depends on temperature only through $\bar{v}$, which increases as $T^{1/2}$. The experimental results, so easily understood by a simple kinetic theory model, that the viscosity of gas is independent of density (and therefore independent of pressure at constant T) and increases with temperature (rather than decreasing, as is the case for liquids), were an important factor in the general acceptance of the kinetic theory in the nineteenth century.

The first reliable estimate of Avogadro's number was made by Loschmidt in 1865 using measurements of the viscosities of gases. If we write the mass of a molecule in terms of the molecular weight $\mathfrak{M}$ and Avogadro's number N_A, $m = \mathfrak{M}/N_A$, Eq. (2-42) can be written

$$\eta = \frac{\mathfrak{M}\bar{v}}{3\pi N_A d^2}$$

or

$$N_A d^2 = \frac{\mathfrak{M}}{3\pi\eta}\left(\frac{8RT}{\pi\mathfrak{M}}\right)^{1/2} \tag{2-43}$$

using the Maxwell result for $\bar{v}$.

All the quantities on the right side of Eq. (2-43) are directly measurable macroscopic properties of a gas. We can get another relation between N_A and the molecular diameter d from the density of solids. If we assume each molecule to occupy a cube of side d, the volume of 1 mole of a solid is $N_A d^3$; thus the density is

$$\rho = \frac{\mathfrak{M}}{N_A d^3} \tag{2-44}$$

Using Eqs. (2-43) and (2-44), both N_A and d can be determined from macroscopic measurements. Loschmidt estimated d to be

gas	$\eta(15°C)$ (newton-sec/m)	$\ell(15°C, 1\ atm)$ (Å)	r (Å)
He	1.94×10^{-6}	1860	1.09
Ne	31.0	1320	1.30
A	22.0	666	1.82
H_2	8.71	1180	1.37
N_2	17.3	628	1.88
O_2	20.0	679	1.80
CO_2	14.5	419	2.30
NH_3	9.7	451	2.22
CH_4	10.8	516	2.07

table 2–3 *Some values of the molecular radius computed from viscosity measurements. (From Lee, Sears, and Turcotte, Statistical Thermodynamics, Addison-Wesley Publishing Company, Inc., Reading, Mass., 1963.)*

about 10^{-8} cm and N_A to be 10×10^{23}. This is reasonably close to the modern value of 6.023×10^{23}.

If we use the modern value of N_A, we can compute the molecular radius[7] from viscosity measurements using Eq. (2–43) and the mean free path using Eq. (2–37). Table 2–3 lists the results for several gases. From this table we see that molecular radii are about 1 or 2 Å ($1Å = 10^{-10}$ meter), and at normal densities the mean free paths are several hundred times this.

The treatment of heat conduction is similar to that of viscosity except that we consider the transport of molecular energy rather than of momentum. Consider the plates shown in Figure 2–18 to be at rest and at different temperatures. If ΔQ is the heat conducted across area A in time Δt, it is found that ΔQ is proportional to A, Δt, and the temperature gradient dT/dz. The coefficient of heat conduction, K, is defined by

$$\frac{\Delta Q}{A\,\Delta t} = K\,\frac{dT}{dz} \qquad (2\text{--}45)$$

We can use the same analysis that we used for viscosity if we replace the momentum mV by the average energy per molecule $\bar{E}$. Molecules crossing the plane from above transport more energy than those from below if the upper plate is at a higher temperature. Equa-

[7]It should be pointed out that we are not implying that molecules are spherical. It is the collision cross section that is determined from Eq. (2–43). By radius, we mean the quantity related to the collision cross section by $\sigma = 4\pi r^2$.

tion (2–40) then becomes for the case of heat conduction

$$\frac{\Delta Q}{A \, \Delta t} = \tfrac{1}{3} n \bar{v} \ell \frac{d\bar{E}}{dz} \tag{2-46}$$

If we multiply the average energy per molecule by N_A, we obtain the energy per mole. Thus $\bar{E} N_A = C_v T$ and

$$\frac{\Delta Q}{A \, \Delta t} = \frac{1}{3} \frac{n \bar{v} \ell C_v}{N_A} \frac{dT}{dz} \tag{2-47}$$

Thus

$$K = \frac{1}{3} \frac{n \bar{v} \ell C_v}{N_A} \tag{2-48}$$

Comparing with Eq. (2–41) for η, we have

$$\frac{K}{\eta} = \frac{C_v}{N_A m} = \frac{C_v}{\mathfrak{M}}$$

or

$$\frac{K \mathfrak{M}}{\eta C_v} = 1 \tag{2-49}$$

The experimental determination of this ratio yields numbers between about 1.5 and 2.5 for most gases. The agreement within a factor of 3 of theory and experiment is another success of the kinetic model, for there is little reason from the macroscopic point of view to suspect heat conduction and viscosity to be so simply related. The discrepancy is due to the oversimplification of the theory.

The coefficient of self-diffusion[8] is defined by

$$\frac{\Delta n}{A \, \Delta t} = D \frac{dn}{dz} \tag{2-50}$$

where Δn is the number of molecules crossing the plane of area A in time Δt. In this case it is the number of molecules that varies, leading to the transport of molecules. The simple theory gives

$$D = \tfrac{1}{3} \ell \bar{v} \tag{2-51}$$

It should be pointed out that we have given only the most elementary treatment of transport phenomena. Thus we should expect

[8]Self-diffusion is the diffusion of molecules into others of the same kind because of a density difference. Restricting the problem to like molecules simplifies the calculations because all the collision cross sections are the same. Experimentally, self-diffusion can be observed by using radioactive tracer methods to tag certain molecules without changing their collision cross sections.

only qualitative results at best. We certainly should not take the factor $\frac{1}{3}$ in Eqs. (2–41), (2–48), and (2–51) seriously. In the case of mutual diffusion, or diffusion of large objects through a gas or liquid, this simple, mean-free-path treatment is not even a good starting point.

2·7 BROWNIAN MOTION AND THE RANDOM-WALK PROBLEM

In 1828 a botanist, Robert Brown, observed an irregular zigzag motion of pollen grains suspended in water. After much experimentation, he concluded that the cause of the motion was not organic, for he observed it in a wide variety of materials. This motion, now called *Brownian motion*, went unexplained for nearly half a century, until the kinetic theory was developed. (Many thought that the motion was due to convection currents or vibrations transmitted through the liquid.) The true cause of Brownian motion, the irregular bombardment of the grains by the molecules of the suspending fluid, was finally understood at the beginning of the twentieth century. The first complete theory was given by Einstein in 1905. In 1908, Jean Perrin made exhaustive quantitative observations of the paths of many suspended particles of different sizes. From these observations, which were in good agreement with Einstein's theory, Perrin calculated Avogadro's number. Perrin's monumental work finally laid aside all doubts as to the validity of the kinetic theory of matter.

The Brownian motion of suspended particles is similar to the diffusion of molecules, except that the particles are much larger than the molecules. We can get some insight into a number of statistical processes, such as diffusion, Brownian motion, and the combination of errors, by considering a simple statistical problem called the *random-walk problem*. In the one-dimensional version of this problem, a man flips a coin and takes one step forward if the result is heads or one step backward if the result is tails. We are interested in determining how far the man gets from the starting point on the average. Suppose the man takes N steps each of size unity. After N steps, the man is a distance x_N from the origin. Since the probabilities of a forward step and a backward step are equal, the average distance $\bar{x}_N$ will be zero. What is the root-mean-square distance?

$$(x_N)_{\text{rms}} = \sqrt{(x_N{}^2)_{\text{ave}}}$$

We can relate $(x_{N+1}^2)_{\text{ave}}$ to $(x_N{}^2)_{\text{ave}}$. We have

$$x_{N+1} = x_N \pm 1$$
$$x_{N+1}^2 = x_N{}^2 + 1 \pm 2x_N \tag{2-52}$$
$$(x_{N+1}^2)_{\text{ave}} = (x_N{}^2)_{\text{ave}} + 1$$

where we have used the fact that $(x_N)_{\text{ave}}$ is zero. For $N = 1$, $x_1 = \pm 1$. Thus

$$(x_1{}^2)_{\text{ave}} = 1$$

Equation (2–52) implies, then, that

$$(x_2{}^2)_{\text{ave}} = 1 + 1 = 2$$

and

$$(x_N{}^2)_{\text{ave}} = N \tag{2–53}$$

If the step size is ℓ, the above argument gives

$$(x_N{}^2)_{\text{ave}} = N\ell^2 \tag{2–54}$$

and

$$x_{\text{rms}} = N^{1/2}\ell \tag{2–55}$$

This result can be applied to error theory. The probable resulting error due to the combination of a large number, N, of small random errors of size ℓ is given by Eq. (2–55). We can also relate this to the problem of self-diffusion by taking N to be the number of collisions made and ℓ to be the mean free path. If the mean speed of the molecules is $\bar{v}$, the number of collisions made in time t is $N = \bar{v}t/\ell$; so

$$(x^2)_{\text{ave}} = \bar{v}\ell t$$

Thus the mean square distance is proportional to the time.

Since Brownian motion of a suspended particle is the result of many small irregular movements due to random molecular bombardment, the mean square distance for this motion is also proportional to the number of collisions made by the particle and therefore to the time. We shall give the Langevin derivation of the Einstein equation for Brownian motion. This derivation is somewhat artificial but is easier to follow than Einstein's with the same result.

Consider a particle moving under the influence of a fluctuating external force F_0 and a viscous drag force proportional to the velocity. Newton's law of motion is then

$$F_0 - b\,\frac{dx}{dt} = m\,\frac{d^2x}{dt^2} \tag{2–56}$$

where b is related to the viscosity. For a sphere of radius a in a fluid which has a coefficient of viscosity η, the viscous force is given by Stokes' law as $F = 6\pi\eta a(dx/dt)$. Thus

$$b = 6\pi\eta a \tag{2-57}$$

We are interested in obtaining an equation for $(x^2)_{ave}$ as a function of time. Note that

$$\frac{d(x^2)}{dt} = 2x \frac{dx}{dt} \tag{2-58}$$

and

$$\frac{d^2}{dt^2} x^2 = 2x \frac{d^2x}{dt^2} + 2\left(\frac{dx}{dt}\right)^2 \tag{2-59}$$

This suggests that we multiply Eq. (2–56) by x:

$$xF_0 - bx \frac{dx}{dt} = mx \frac{d^2x}{dt^2}$$

or, using Eqs. (2–58) and (2–59)

$$xF_0 - \tfrac{1}{2}b \frac{d}{dt} x^2 = \tfrac{1}{2}m \frac{d^2}{dt^2} x^2 - m\left(\frac{dx}{dt}\right)^2 \tag{2-60}$$

We now average over a large number of particles. Since the position x is unrelated to the random force F_0, the average of xF_0 will be zero. The equipartition theorem implies that the average value of $m(dx/dt)^2$ is kT. Equation (2–60) thus becomes

$$\tfrac{1}{2}m \frac{d^2}{dt^2} (x^2)_{ave} + \tfrac{1}{2}b \frac{d}{dt} (x^2)_{ave} = kT \tag{2-61}$$

where we have used the fact that time differentiation and averaging over the particles are independent and can be interchanged. If we let $f = (d/dt)(x^2)_{ave}$, Eq. (2–61) is

$$\tfrac{1}{2}m \frac{df}{dt} + \tfrac{1}{2}bf = kT$$

The solution of this equation is

$$f = \frac{2kT}{b} + Ce^{-bt/m} \tag{2-62}$$

For the very small masses that must be used in order to observe Brownian motion, the quantity bt/m is very large except for a very short time, so we can neglect the second term in Eq. (2–62). We have then

$$\frac{d}{dt} (x^2)_{\text{ave}} = \frac{2kT}{b}$$
$$(x^2)_{\text{ave}} = \frac{2kT}{b} t \tag{2–63}$$

where we have chosen $(x^2)_{\text{ave}}$ to be zero for $t = 0$. Using Stokes' law for b [Eq. (2–57)], we have

$$(x^2)_{\text{ave}} = \frac{kT}{3\pi\eta a} t$$

or

$$(x^2)_{\text{ave}} = \frac{RT}{3\pi\eta a N_A} t \tag{2–64}$$

Equation (2–64) is the same as that obtained by Einstein in 1905.[9] He pointed out that it could be used to obtain Avogadro's number.

In 1908 Jean Perrin made a series of remarkable measurements of Avogadro's number. In order to use Eq. (2–64), he needed a large number of small but visible particles of equal radius a. He found that he could make emulsions of gamboge (prepared from a dried vegetable latex) and mastic which, after several months of separation by centrifuging, contained grains of nearly equal size.[10] In one series of measurements, he watched individual particles as they moved about and recorded their positions at equal time intervals. He verified that the mean square displacement was proportional to the time and determined N_A. Figure 2–20 is a diagram of the horizontal projections of the positions of a grain of radius 0.53×10^{-6} meter observed at intervals of 30 sec. The following quotation is taken from Perrin's Nobel Prize address in 1926.[11]

"These theories can be judged by experiment if we know how to *prepare spherules of a measurable radius.* I was, therefore, in a position to attempt this check as soon as I knew, thanks to Langevin, of the work of Einstein.

[9]Reference 5 contains a collection of Einstein's papers on the theory of Brownian motion.

[10]An interesting account of Perrin's experiments can be found in *Atoms*, by Jean Perrin, D. Van Nostrand Company, Inc., Princeton, N.J., 1923.

[11]From *Nobel Prize Lectures: Physics*, Elsevier Publishing Company, Amsterdam, New York, © Nobel Foundation, 1964.

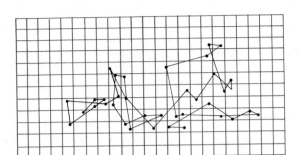

figure 2–20 *Brownian motion. Points indicate successive positions of a particle observed in 30-sec intervals. The lines between the points are added to indicate the sequence of positions; the particle does not move in straight lines between observations, for it is struck by millions of molecules each second. (From J. Perrin, Atoms, D. Van Nostrand Company, Inc., Princeton, N.J., 1923.)*

"I must say that, right at the beginning, Einstein and Smoluchovski had pointed out that the order of magnitude of the Brownian movement seemed to correspond to their predictions. And this approximate agreement gave already much force to the kinetic theory of the phenomenon, at least in broad outline.

"It was impossible to say anything more precise so long as spherules of known size had not been prepared. Having such grains, I was able to check Einstein's formulae by seeing whether they led always to the same value for Avogadro's number and whether it was appreciably equal to the value already found.

"This is obtained for the displacements by noting on the camera lucida (magnification known) the horizontal projections of the same grain at the beginning and at the end of an interval of time equal to the duration chosen, in such a manner as to measure a large number of displacements, for example, in one minute.

"In several series of measurements I varied, with the aid of several collaborators, the size of the grains (in the ratio of 1 to 70,000) as well as the nature of the liquid (water, solutions of sugar or urea, glycerol) and its viscosity (in the ratio of 1 to 125). They gave values between 55×10^{22} and 72×10^{22}, with differences which could be explained by experimental errors. The agreement is such that it is impossible to doubt the correctness of the kinetic theory of the translational Brownian movement."

In another series of measurements, Perrin determined N_A by measuring the density of particles suspended in an emulsion at different heights. If a fluid is in a uniform gravitational field in the

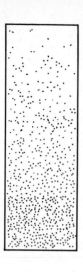

figure 2–21

Equilibrium height distribution of particles in a gravitational field. The distribution is the same as that for air molecules $n(z) = n(0)e^{-mgz/kT}$.

negative z direction, the pressure is given by the law of atmospheres (see Problem 2–19):

$$p(z) = p(0)e^{-\mathfrak{M}gz/RT} \tag{2-65}$$

where $p(0)$ is the pressure at $z = 0$ and $\mathfrak{M}$ is the molecular weight of the fluid. Assuming that the density is proportional to the pressure, the number density varies with z in a similar manner:

$$n(z) = n(0)e^{-\mathfrak{M}gz/RT} \tag{2-66}$$

If a visible particle is suspended in the fluid, its tendency to sink because of gravity is counteracted by a tendency to rise because it is struck by more molecules from below than from above (due to the greater density below as shown by Eq. (2–66). The equilibrium distribution of the visible particles is given by Eq. (2–66) with $\mathfrak{M} = N_A m$, where m is the mass of the particle. Thus N_A can be determined by measuring the mass of the particles and the number versus height.

Perrin also measured the rotation of particles in a fluid due to bombardment by molecules, and he calculated N_A from the theory of rotational Brownian motion given by Einstein.

figure 2–22

Jean Baptiste Perrin. (Courtesy of Wide World Photos.)

SUMMARY   The probability of occurrence of a value x in the range dx is given by $f(x)\, dx$, where $f(x)$ is the distribution function. This function obeys the normalization condition

$$\int f(x)\, dx = 1$$

The average value of x is defined by

$$\bar{x} = \int x f(x)\, dx$$

A simple model assuming that the pressure of a gas is due to molecules bouncing off the walls of a container implies that the mean kinetic energy of the molecules is proportional to the temperature. The Maxwell velocity distribution is

$$F(v_x, v_y, v_z) = \left(\frac{m}{2\pi kT}\right)^{3/2} e^{-m(v_x{}^2 + v_y{}^2 + v_z{}^2)/2kT}$$

and the speed distribution is

$$f(v)\, dv = 4\pi v^2 \left(\frac{m}{2\pi kT}\right)^{3/2} e^{-mv^2/2kT}\, dv$$

The Maxwell-Boltzmann distribution function for discrete energy states is

$$f_i = C g_i e^{-E_i/kT}$$

where C is a normalization constant and g_i is the number of states having the energy E_i.

The mean translational kinetic energy of gas molecules is $\frac{1}{2}m(v_x{}^2 + v_y{}^2 + v_z{}^2) = \frac{3}{2}kT$ independent of any characteristics (such as mass or size) of the molecules. This is an example of the equipartition theorem; the mean energy associated with each squared coordinate or momentum in the energy is $\frac{1}{2}kT$. Molecular speeds are of the order of magnitude of the speed of sound.

An elementary theory of transport yields similar expressions for the coefficients of viscosity, heat conduction, and diffusion in terms of the molecular density, mean speed, and mean free path between collisions. The mean free path varies inversely with density and inversely with the square of the molecular diameter. In particular, this theory predicts that the coefficient of viscosity is independent of density and is proportional to the square root of the temperature in agreement with experiment. From this theory and macroscopic measurements of the viscosity, the first estimates of molecular size and Avogadro's number were made.

In the random-walk problem, the root-mean-square distance is proportional to the square root of the number of steps. This problem is useful in visualizing the processes of diffusion and Brownian motion. Since the number of molecular collisions made is proportional to the time, the rms distance for diffusion or Brownian motion is proportional to the square root of the time. Detailed observations of the positions of particles in colloidal suspension allowed Perrin to make the first accurate measurements of Avogadro's number and to verify directly and quantitatively the predictions of the kinetic theory.

REFERENCES

1. G. Holton, *Introduction to Concepts and Theories in Physical Science*, Addison-Wesley Publishing Company, Inc., Reading, Mass., 1952.
2. H. Boorse and L. Motz (eds.), *The World of the Atom*, Basic Books, Inc., Publishers, New York, 1966. This two-volume, 1,873-page work is a collection of original papers translated and edited. Much of the work referred to in this chapter and throughout this text can be found in this work. Of particular interest for this chapter are the papers by Boyle, Hooke, Bernoulli, Dalton, Gay-Lussac, Avogadro, Herapath, Brown, Waterston, Joule, and Maxwell.
3. W. Niven (ed.), *Scientific Papers of James Clerk Maxwell*, Dover Publications, Inc., New York, 1965.
4. J. Perrin, *Atoms*, D. Van Nostrand Company, Inc., Princeton, N. J., 1923. In this short book, Perrin describes in detail his experiments with suspended particles.
5. Albert Einstein, edited by R. Fürth, *Investigations on the Theory of Brownian Movement*, Dover Publications, Inc., New York, 1965. This book contains five papers on Brownian motion by Einstein, translated with notes by the editor.
6. L. Whyte, *Essay on Atomism from Democritus to 1960*, Harper & Row, Publishers, Inc., New York. This book, TB 565 in the Harper Torchbooks series, contains a chronological table with comments on the development of atomistic ideas.
7. F. Friedman and L. Sartori, *The Classical Atom*, Addison-Wesley Publishing Company, Inc., Reading, Mass., 1965. A concise, sophisticated (but using elementary mathematics) treatment of the topics discussed in this and the next two chapters.
8. J. F. Lee, F. W. Sears, and D. L. Turcotte, *Statistical Thermodynamics*, Addison-Wesley Publishing Company, Inc., Reading, Mass., 1963.
9. R. Present, *Kinetic Theory of Gases*, McGraw-Hill Book Company, New York, 1958.
10. E. Kennard, *Kinetic Theory of Gases*, McGraw-Hill Book Company, New York, 1938.

References 8 and 9 are intermediate-level textbooks; Ref. 10 is at a somewhat higher level.

11. Harold Daw, *Kinetic Theory* (six film loops), Ealing Film-loops, Cambridge, Mass. In these films, molecules are simulated by pucks floating on an air table. The films include "Maxwell Speed Distribution" (80–291), "Random Walk and Brownian Motion" (80–292), "Equipartition of Energy" (80–293), "Gravitational Distribution" (80–294), "Diffusion" (80–295), and "Properties of Gas" (80–296).

PROBLEMS

SET A

2–1. The speed of sound is measured in an elementary laboratory by students A and B. Each takes nine readings. The data are:

A: 345, 350, 338, 340, 335, 334, 346, 342, 330 m/sec
B: 340, 350, 345, 330, 325, 360, 320, 355, 335 m/sec

Compute the mean value and the standard deviation for each set.

2–2. A class of 50 students was given a 10-point quiz. The grade distribution was:

Score, s_i: 10 9 8 7 6 5 4 3 2 1 0
Number, n_i: 1 4 8 7 6 15 6 0 3 0 0

Find the mean grade and the standard deviation. Indicate these on a histogram plot of this distribution.

2–3. The distribution function for some positive quantity x is

$$f(x) = Ax \quad \text{for } x < X_0$$
$$f(x) = 0 \quad \text{for } x > X_0$$

Find A, $\bar{x}$, x_{rms}, and σ. Indicate $\bar{x}$, x_{rms}, and σ on a sketch of $f(x)$.

2–4. Compute the mean speed of an H_2 molecule at $T = 300°K$. At what temperature would $\bar{v}$ equal the escape velocity at the earth's surface? (The escape velocity is about 1.12×10^4 m/sec = 7 mi/sec.)

2–5. Show that the most probable speed in a Maxwell-Boltzmann distribution is $v_m = (2kT/m)^{1/2}$.

2–6. Calculate the mean value of the reciprocal speed, $(\overline{1/v})$, for the Maxwell speed distribution.

2–7. Calculate the most probable energy E_m from the energy distribution (Eq. 2–30) for an ideal gas. Sketch the distribution function $f(E)$ versus E and indicate the most probable energy and the mean energy on your sketch.

2–8. From the absorption spectrum it is determined that about one out of 10^6 hydrogen atoms in a certain star is in the first excited state, 10.2 eV above the ground state (other excited states can be neglected). What is the temperature of the star? (Take the ratio of statistical weights to be 4, as in Example 2–3.)

2–9. The first rotational energy state of the H_2 molecule ($g_1 = 3$) is about 4×10^{-3} eV above the lowest energy state ($g_0 = 1$). What is the ratio of the numbers of molecules in these two states at room temperature of 300°K?

2–10. Using order-of-magnitude estimates for the number density at standard conditions, the mean speed $\bar{v}$, and the molecular diameter d, estimate:

(a) The number of collisions made by a molecule in one second

(b) The mean free path of a molecule

2–11. Using order-of-magnitude estimates for $\bar{v}$ and λ, estimate the time for molecules to diffuse across the room. Is this result in accord with your experience?

SET B

2–12. Given the distribution function

$$f(x) = A \cos^2 (\pi x / L) \qquad \text{for } -L \leq x \leq L$$
$$= 0 \qquad \text{for } |x| > L$$

find A, $\bar{x}$, and x_{rms}.

2–13. Calculate the average value of $|v_x|$ from the Maxwell-Boltzmann distribution.

2–14. The average deviation of the mean, a.d. $\equiv \dfrac{1}{N} \Sigma |\bar{x} - x_i|$, is sometimes used because it is easier to calculate than σ (however, it is not as significant in error theory). For a normal (gaussian) distribution, a.d. $= \sqrt{2/\pi}\,\sigma$. Show this for the special case $\bar{x} = 0$ by comparing your result for the average value of $|v_x|$ from Problem 2–13 with $v_{x,\text{rms}}$.

2–15. Calculate the *order of magnitude* of the fractional Doppler shift, due to thermal motion, by assuming the light source is an oxygen atom moving relative to the observer with speed $\bar{v}$. Do you need to use the relativistic formula for the Doppler effect for this calculation?

2–16. A gas consists of N point particles in an infinite space. Each particle is attracted to the origin by a force proportional to the distance from the origin, $\mathbf{F} = -C\mathbf{r}$; thus in addition to its translational kinetic energy, each particle has potential energy $U = \frac{1}{2}Cr^2 = \frac{1}{2}C(x^2 + y^2 + z^2)$.

(a) What is the Maxwell-Boltzmann distribution function $f(x,y,z,v_x,v_y,v_z)$?

(b) Show that the probability of finding a particle in dr at a distance r is $Ar^2e^{-Cr^2/2kT}\, dr$, and evaluate the constant A.

(c) Find the average values of x, x^2, r, and r^2. (Hint: The equipartition theorem can be used to find the average values of x^2 and r^2.)

(d) What is the average energy per particle?

(e) What is the molar heat capacity C_v for this gas?

2-17. Consider the problem of a two-dimensional gas confined to a rectangle of area A. Derive the expression $P = \frac{1}{2}nmv^2$, where the "pressure" P is the force per unit length.

2-18. Assuming that the velocity distribution for the gas of Problem 2-17 is $f(v_x,v_y) = Ae^{-m(v_x{}^2+v_y{}^2)/2kT}$, find A, the speed distribution, and $\bar{v}$.

2-19. Consider a layer of air of thickness dz and area A. Show that for equilibrium in the earth's gravitational field, the pressure difference must be $-dP = \rho g\, dz = (N/V)mg\, dz$, where N/V is the number of molecules per unit volume and m is the mass of each molecule.

Using the ideal gas law and assuming constant temperature, derive the law of atmospheres $P = P_0 e^{-mgz/kT}$.

2-20. The speed distribution of molecules in a container is the Maxwell distribution $f(v) \propto v^2 e^{-mv^2/2kT}$. The number with speed v that hit the wall in a given time is proportional to the speed v and to $f(v)$. Thus, if there is a very small hole in the wall (too small to have much effect on the distribution inside), the speed distribution of those that escape is $F(v) \propto vf(v) \propto v^3 e^{-mv^2/2kT}$. Show that the mean energy of those that escape is $2kT$.

2-21. The following is a viscosity analog. There are three very long coal trains on three parallel tracks. Train A is kept at rest, while train C, a distance z_0 away, maintains a constant speed V_0. The middle train, B, is free to move. Trains A and C each have a man shoveling R lumps of coal per second into train B, while on train B, one man shovels R lumps/sec into A and another shovels R lumps/sec into C. Each lump of coal has mass m.

(a) If train B is moving with speed V, what is the net drag force on it?

(b) For what speed is the net force on B zero? At this speed, what are the forces B exerts on A and C?

(c) Consider adding two more trains, one between B and A and one between B and C, so that there are five trains equally spaced. Plot the speed $V(z)$ of the trains, where $z = 0$ at the fixed train A and $z = z_0$ at train C moving with speed V_0.

(d) Generalize this problem to a large number of trains N. Show that the force on one train due to the next train is $F = mR\ell(dU/dz)$, where ℓ is the distance between adjacent trains.

2–22. Let N be the number of molecules that go a distance x without making a collision. This number is decreased in the interval dx by the number of collisions made in dx. Assuming this number is proportional to N and to dx, we can write $-dN = \alpha N(x)\, dx$ where α is a constant.

(a) Solve this equation for $N(x)$ assuming N_0 molecules at $x = 0$.

(b) The distribution function for free paths, $f(x)\, dx$, is equal to the fraction that make their first collision in dx, which is $-dN/N_0$. Show that $f(x) = \alpha e^{-\alpha x}$.

(c) Show that the mean free path is $1/\alpha$.

(d) What is the most probable free path?

THREE
THE QUANTIZATION
OF ELECTRICITY,
LIGHT, AND
ENERGY

The great success of Avogadro's hypothesis in interpreting chemical reactions and of the kinetic theory at the end of the nineteenth century and beginning of the twentieth century led to general (though not unanimous) acceptance of the molecular theory of matter. Apparently matter is not continuous, as it appears to us in bulk, but is quantized on the microscopic scale. It is because of the enormous size of Avogadro's number that the discreteness of matter is not readily observable. In this chapter we shall study how three great discoveries were made. We shall study the first evidences of the quantization, or discreteness, of (1) electric charge, (2) light energy, and (3) energy states of mechanical systems. The quantization of electric charge was not particularly surprising to scientists in 1900; it was quite analogous to the quantization of mass as implied by Dalton, Avogadro, and others. However, the quantization of light energy and mechanical energy were revolutionary ideas.

The first estimates of the order of magnitude of the electric charges found in atoms were obtained from Faraday's law. The same quantity of electricity, F, called the faraday and equal to about 96,500 coul, always decomposes 1 gram-ionic weight of monovalent ions. For example, if 96,500 coul pass through a solution of NaCl, 23 grams of Na appear at the cathode and 35.5 grams of Cl at the anode. For ions of valence 2, such as Cu or SO_4, it takes 2 faradays to decompose 1 gram-ionic weight. Since a gram-ionic weight is just Avogadro's number of ions, it is reasonable to assume that each monovalent ion contains the same charge, e, and

$$F = N_A e \tag{3-1}$$

Since the faraday could be measured quite accurately, N_A or e could be determined if the other were known. Faraday was aware of this but could not determine either quantity. In 1874, G. J. Stoney estimated e to be about 1×10^{-20} coul using estimates of N_A from kinetic theory. Helmholtz pointed out in 1880 that it is apparently impossible to obtain a subunit of this charge. The first direct measurement of this smallest unit of charge was made by Townsend in 1897 by an ingenious method which was the forerunner of the famous Millikan oil-drop experiment.

Townsend used electrolysis to produce charged gaseous ions, which formed a cloud when bubbled through water. He measured the mass of the cloud by passing it through drying tubes and determining the increased weight of these tubes. He measured the total charge with an electrometer and determined the average radius of the individual water droplets in the cloud by observing the rate of fall of the cloud due to gravity. The equation of motion for a drop falling in a medium with a retarding force proportional to the velocity is

$$mg - bv = m\frac{dv}{dt} \tag{3-2}$$

The drop quickly reaches its terminal velocity, which we can find from Eq. (3–2) by setting $dv/dt = 0$:

$$v_t = \frac{mg}{b} \tag{3-3}$$

Using Stokes' law for the viscous force on a sphere of radius a [see Eq. (2–57)],

$$b = 6\pi\eta a \tag{3-4}$$

and writing the mass in terms of the density, ρ,

$$m = \tfrac{4}{3}\pi a^3 \rho$$

we obtain for the terminal velocity

$$v_t = \tfrac{2}{9}ga^2\frac{\rho}{\eta} \tag{3-5}$$

where η is the coefficient of viscosity of air in this case. Equation (3-5) was used to determine a. Knowing the average size of the drops and the total mass, Townsend could compute the number of drops in the cloud. Dividing the total charge of the cloud by the number of drops (he assumed each ion formed one waterdrop), he estimated the charge on each ion to be about 1×10^{-19} coul, the same order of magnitude as determined from Faraday's laws of electrolysis and kinetic-theory estimates of N_A. Variations on this technique were made by J. J. Thomson and H. A. Wilson, with little change in accuracy. Wilson produced clouds between the plates of a capacitor and observed their fall due to gravity alone and due to the combination of gravity and an electric field produced between the plates. Table 3-1, giving final results of 11 different trials, illustrates the accuracy obtained.

Difficulties with evaporation of the cloud and the assumption that each drop contained a single charge prohibited any further increase in the accuracy of this method. Millikan tried to eliminate the evaporation problem by using a field strong enough to hold the top surface of the cloud stationary so that he could observe the rate of evaporation and correct for it. The results of this attempt are best described in his paper "A New Modification of the Cloud Method of Determining the Elementary Charge and the Most Probable Value of That Charge," which appeared in the *Philosophical Magazine*, February, 1909, page 209. The following quotation is taken from this paper (pages 216 and 217):

table 3-1

Results of Wilson's determination of e.
[*From* Philosophical Magazine, (6) **5,** *439 (1903).*]

e *(coul)*
0.77×10^{-19}
0.87×10^{-19}
$1.5 \ \times 10^{-19}$
0.90×10^{-19}
$1.1 \ \times 10^{-19}$
$1.3 \ \times 10^{-19}$
$1.3 \ \times 10^{-19}$
$1.0 \ \times 10^{-19}$
$1.2 \ \times 10^{-19}$
0.67×10^{-19}
0.77×10^{-19}

Mean value: 1.03×10^{-19} coul

"The Balancing of Individual Charged Drops by an Electrostatic Field

"My original plan for eliminating the evaporation error was to obtain, if possible, an electric field strong enough exactly to balance the force of gravity upon the cloud and then by means of a sliding contact to vary the strength of this field so as to hold the cloud balance throughout its entire life. In this way it was thought that the whole evaporation history of the cloud might be recorded, and that suitable allowances might then be made in the observations on the rate of fall to eliminate entirely the error due to evaporation. It was not found possible to balance the cloud as had been originally planned, but it was found possible to do something much better: namely, to hold individual charged drops suspended by the field for periods varying from 30 to 60 seconds. I have never actually timed drops which lasted more than 45 seconds, although I have several times observed drops which in my judgment lasted considerably longer than this. The drops which it was found possible to balance by an electric field always carried multiple charges, and the difficulty experienced in balancing such drops was less than had been anticipated.

"The procedure is simply to form a cloud and throw on the field immediately thereafter. The drops which have charges of the same sign rapidly fall, while those which are charged with too many multiples of the sign opposite to that of the upper plate are jerked up against gravity to this plate. The result is that after a lapse of seven or eight seconds the field of view has become quite clear save for a relatively small number of drops, which have just the right ratio of charge to mass to be suspended by the electric field. These appear as perfectly distinct bright points. I have on several occasions obtained but one single such "star" in the whole field and held it there for nearly a minute. For the most part, however, the observations recorded below were made with a considerable number of such points in view. Thin, flocculent clouds, the production of which seemed to be facilitated by keeping the water jackets . . . a degree or two above the temperature of the room, were found to be particularly favorable to observations of this kind.

"Furthermore, it was found possible so to vary the mass of a drop by varying the ionization, that drops carrying in some cases two, in some three, in some four, in some five, and in some six, multiples could be held suspended by nearly the same field. The means of gradually varying the field which had been planned were therefore found to be unnecessary. If a given field would not hold any drops suspended it was varied by steps of 100 or 200 volts until drops were held stationary, or nearly stationary. When the P.D. was thrown off, it was often possible to see different drops move down under gravity with greatly different speeds, thus showing that these drops had different masses and correspondingly different charges."

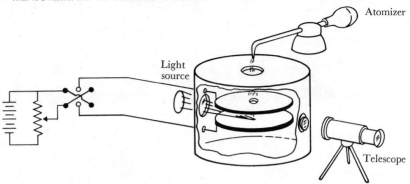

figure 3–1   *Millikan oil-drop apparatus. The drops are sprayed from the atomizer and pick up a static charge. Their fall due to gravity and their rise due to the electric field between the capacitor plates can be observed with the telescope. From measurements of the rise and fall times, the electric charge on a drop can be calculated.*

During this experiment, he noticed that balanced drops sometimes suddenly moved upward or downward, evidently because they had picked up a positive or negative ion. This led to the possibility of observing charges due to single ions. In 1909, Millikan began a series of experiments which not only showed that charges occurred in multiples of an elementary unit, e, but measured the value of e to about 1 part in 1,000. To eliminate evaporation, he used oil drops sprayed into dry air between the plates of a capacitor. These drops were already charged by the friction of the spraying process, and during the course of observation, they picked up or lost additional charges. By switching the field between the plates, a drop could be moved up or down and observed for several hours. When the charge on a drop changed, the velocity of the drop changed. Assuming only that the terminal velocity of the drop was proportional to the force acting on it (this "assumption" was carefully checked experimentally), Millikan's experiment gave conclusive evidence that charges always occur in multiples of a fundamental unit, e. Let us examine this experiment in some detail. Figure 3–1 shows a sketch of Millikan's apparatus. With no field, the downward force is mg and the upward force is bv, where b is given by Stokes' law [Eq. (3–4)]. The equation of motion is Eq. (3–2), and the terminal velocity for falling is

$$v_f = \frac{mg}{b} \qquad\qquad (3\text{–}6)$$

During the upward motion with an electric field ε, the equation of motion for a charge q_n is

$$q_n \varepsilon - mg - bv = m \frac{dv}{dt}$$

figure 3–2 *Millikan's original oil drop apparatus for determining the fundamental unit of electric charge e.* (From R. A. Millikan, Electrons (+ and −), Protons, Photons, Neutrons, Mesotrons, and Cosmic Rays, *University of Chicago Press, 1947. Reproduced with permission of the publishers. Copyright 1947 by University of Chicago. All rights reserved.*)

Thus the terminal velocity for rising is

$$v_r = \frac{q_n \mathcal{E} - mg}{b} \tag{3-7}$$

In this experiment, the terminal speeds were reached almost immediately, and the drops drifted a distance L up or down. Solving Eqs. (3–6) and (3–7) for q_n, we have

$$q_n = \frac{mg}{\mathcal{E} v_f} (v_f + v_r) \tag{3-8}$$

If an additional charge is picked up, the terminal velocity becomes v_r', which is related to the new charge q_n' by

$$v_r' = \frac{q_n' \mathcal{E} - mg}{b} \tag{3-9}$$

The amount of charge picked up is

$$q_n' - q_n = \frac{mg}{\mathcal{E} v_f} (v_r' - v_r) \tag{3-10}$$

The velocities, v_f, v_r, and v_r', are determined by measuring the time taken to fall or rise the distance L between the capacitor plates. Table 3–2, taken from Millikan's book, is typical of his early data

table 3–2
Rise and fall times of a single oil drop
with calculated number of elementary charges on drop.
(*From R. A. Millikan*, Electrons (+ and −), Protons,
Photons, Neutrons, Mesotrons, and Cosmic Rays,
The University of Chicago Press, Chicago, 1947, p. 75.
Copyright 1947 by University of Chicago. All rights reserved.)
The value of 4.991 × 10^{-10} *esu equals*
1.664 × 10^{-19} *coulombs.*

1	2	3	4	5	6	7	8
T_f	T_r	$\dfrac{1}{T'_r} - \dfrac{1}{T_r}$	n'	$\dfrac{1}{n'}\left(\dfrac{1}{T'_r} - \dfrac{1}{T_r}\right)$	$\dfrac{1}{T_f} + \dfrac{1}{T_r}$	n	$\dfrac{1}{n}\left(\dfrac{1}{T_r} + \dfrac{1}{T_f}\right)$
11.848	80.708				0.09655	18	0.005366
11.890	22.366	0.03234	6	0.005390			
11.908	22.390				0.12887	24	0.005371
11.904	22.368	0.03751	7	0.005358			
11.882	140.566				0.09138	17	0.005375
11.906	79.600	0.005348	1	0.005348	0.09673	18	0.005374
11.838	34.748	0.01616	3	0.005387			
11.816	34.762				0.11289	21	0.005376
11.776	34.846						
11.840	29.286				0.11833	22	0.005379
11.904	29.236	0.026872	5	0.005375			
11.870	137.308	0.021572	4	0.005393	0.09146	17	0.005380
11.952	34.638				0.11303	21	0.005382
11.860		0.01623	3	0.005410			
11.846	22.104				0.12926	24	0.005386
11.912	22.268	0.04307	8	0.005384			
11.910	500.1				0.08616	16	0.005387
11.918	19.704	0.04879	9	0.005421			
11.870	19.666				0.13498	25	0.005399
11.888	77.630	0.03794	7	0.005420	0.09704	18	0.005390
11.894	77.806				0.10783	20	0.005392
11.878	42.302	0.01079	2	0.005395			
11.880		Means		0.005386	Means		0.005384

Duration of exp.	45 min	Pressure	75.62 cm
Plate distance	16 mm	Oil viscosity	0.9199
Fall distance	10.21 mm	Air viscosity	1.824 × 10^{-7}
Initial volts	5,088.8	Radius (a)	0.000276 cm
Final volts	5,081.2	Speed of fall	0.08584 cm/sec
Temperature	22.82°C		

$$e = 4.991 \times 10^{-10}$$

on a single drop. The first column gives the time of fall with no field; the second gives the time of rise with a given field. The sixth column is proportional to $v_f + v_r$ and thus to q_n. The number in column 7 is the assumed number of elementary charges in q_n. Dividing column 6 by this integer gives a number in column 8 proportional to e. All the numbers in column 8 are the same within experimental uncertainty. This oil drop began with a charge of $18e$. When the rise velocity changes suddenly, it is assumed that the drop gained or lost charge. Since the second value of rise time in column 2 is smaller than the first, indicating a greater speed of rise, the drop must have gained charge. Column 3 is proportional to $|v_r' - v_r|$ and thus to the charge gained or lost. Dividing the number in column 3 by the integer in column 4, representing the number of charges gained or lost, gives a number in column 5. All the numbers in columns 5 and 8 are thus the same within experimental accuracy. For this trial, the drop began with a charge of $18e$, then picked up $6e$, then lost $7e$, etc.

Millikan did experiments like these with thousands of drops,

figure 3–3   *Albert A. Michelson, Albert Einstein, and Robert A. Millikan at a meeting in Pasadena, California in 1931. (Courtesy of Wide World Photos.)*

some of nonconducting oil, some of semiconductors like glycerine, and some of conductors like mercury (see Ref. 1). In no case was a fractional charge found.

To obtain a value of e from these data, the mass of the drop (or radius, since the density is known) must be found. The radius was obtained using Eq. (3–5) from Stokes' law. (For high precision, the ρ in this equation is replaced by $\rho - \delta$, where δ is the density of air, to account for the buoyant force. In the course of these experiments, Millikan found that Stokes' law did not hold for the smallest of his drops, those for which the inhomogeneities of the medium became comparable with the size of the drops. He found, by successive approximations, an experimental correction to Stokes' law.)

The value of e found by Millikan, 1.591×10^{-19} coul, was accepted for about 20 years until it was discovered that x-ray diffraction measurements of N_A gave values of e that differed from Millikan's by about 0.4 percent. The discrepancy was traced to the value of the coefficient of viscosity η used by Millikan, which was too low. Improved measurements of η gave a value about 0.5 percent higher, thus changing the value of e from the oil-drop experiments to 1.601×10^{-19} coul, in good agreement with the x-ray diffraction data. For the modern determination of the "best" value of e and other atomic constants, the reader is referred to *Fundamental Atomic Constants*, by J. Sanders, Oxford University Press, London, 1961.

**3·2
MEASUREMENTS
OF e/m**

The first information concerning the value of the ratio of charge to mass for atomic particles was obtained by Zeeman in 1896 by looking at the spectra of atoms placed in a strong magnetic field. Faraday in 1862 looked for the effect of a magnetic field on a sodium-flame light source, but he was unable to observe any. A simple analysis of the Zeeman effect is given here. Classical electromagnetic theory shows that a charge oscillating with simple harmonic motion of angular frequency ω ($\omega = 2\pi f$) will emit electromagnetic radiation with the same frequency. When placed in a magnetic field, there will be an additional force on the charge which, to first approximation, merely changes the frequency of oscillation. Depending on the orientation of the atom relative to the magnetic field, the frequency of oscillation increases by a small amount, decreases by a small amount, or remains unchanged. A spectral line of a given frequency will thus be split into three lines: one of slightly higher frequency, one of slightly lower frequency, and one of the original frequency.

Consider oscillation about the origin along the x axis. This motion can be thought of as the sum of two circular motions in a

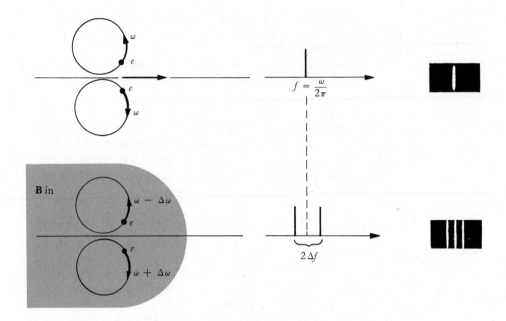

figure 3–4   *Classical model of the Zeeman effect. The simple harmonic motion of a charged particle can be thought of as the sum of two circular motions of the same frequency. In a magnetic field perpendicular to the plane of motion, one of the circular frequencies is slightly increased and one is slightly decreased, leading to a change in the spectral lines, as indicated. Since motion in the plane of the magnetic field is unaffected, the original line is also seen. The change in frequency of the spectral line is proportional to the charge-to-mass ratio, q/m. The photograph at the right shows the Zeeman splitting for a line in the spectrum of zinc. (From* Introduction to Atomic Spectra, *by* H. E. White. *Copyright 1934, McGraw-Hill Book Company. Used by permission of the publishers.)*

plane containing the x axis, one clockwise and one counterclockwise, both of radius R equal to one-half the amplitude of oscillation and in phase, as in Figure 3–4. For the circular motion, $v = R\omega$ and

$$\frac{mv^2}{R} = mR\omega^2 = F_0 \tag{3–11}$$

where F_0 is the force. A magnetic field B perpendicular to the plane of the circle gives an additional force, $qvB = qR\omega B$, which causes ω in one circle to increase and in the other to decrease. Since the changes are small for even the largest B field produced in the laboratory, we can assume that the radius does not change and we can approximate as follows:

$$\Delta F = \Delta(mR\omega^2) \approx 2mR\omega\,\Delta\omega$$

Using $\Delta F = qvB = qR\omega B$, we have

$$qR\omega B \approx 2mR\omega\,\Delta\omega$$

or

$$\Delta\omega \approx \frac{1}{2}\frac{q}{m}B \qquad\qquad (3\text{–}12)$$

Since the frequency of the electromagnetic radiation equals the frequency of motion (according to classical theory), Eq. (3–12) gives the change in frequency of the spectral line. Since the wavelength is related to the frequency by $\lambda = c/f = 2\pi c/\omega$, Eq. (3–12) implies a change in λ which can be observed. The measurement of $\Delta\lambda$ will thus determine q/m for the charge that is oscillating and radiating. Zeeman's first measurement gave q/m to be of the order of 10^{11} coul/kg; later he measured 1.6×10^{11} coul/kg, which compares quite favorably with the presently accepted value of 1.76×10^{11}. From the polarization of the spectral lines, he concluded that the oscillating particles were negatively charged.

A more direct method of measuring e/m, due principally to J. J. Thomson, evolved from the study of electrical discharge in gases. Many studies of this phenomenon were done in the late nineteenth century, and interest was greatly increased by the discovery of x rays, which ionized the gases, thus permitting the control of the conductivity of the gases. It was found that ions responsible for the gaseous conduction carried the same charge as did those in electrolysis. The cathode-ray tube used by Thomson (Figure 3–5) is typical of those used. At sufficiently low pressure, the space near the cathode becomes dark, and as the pressure is lowered, this dark

figure 3–5 *J. J. Thomson's tube for measuring e/m. Electrons from the cathode C pass through the slits at A and B and strike a phosphorescent screen. The beam can be deflected by an electric field between the plates D and E or by a magnetic field (not shown). From measurements of the deflections, e/m can be determined. [From J. J. Thomson,* Philosophical Magazine, (5) **44** (*1897*).]

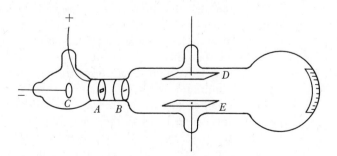

space extends across the tube until finally it reaches the glass, which then glows. When apertures are placed at A and B, the glow becomes a spot on the glass that can be deflected by electrostatic fields or magnetic fields. These "cathode rays" were caught on an electrometer and were shown by Perrin in 1895 to have negative charge. In 1897, J. J. Thomson measured the ratio of the mass to charge of these rays. Figure 3–5, taken from his paper on cathode rays, *Philosophical Magazine*, 5, **44** (1897), shows his apparatus. We quote from this paper:

"The experiments discussed in this paper were undertaken in the hope of gaining some information as to the nature of the Cathode Rays. The most diverse opinions are held as to these rays; according to the almost unanimous opinion of German physicists they are due to some process in the aether to which — inasmuch as in a uniform magnetic field their course is circular and not rectilinear — no phenomenon hitherto observed is analogous: another view of these rays is that, so far from being wholly aetherial, they are in fact wholly material, and that they mark the paths of particles of matter charged with negative electricity. It would seem at first sight that it ought not to be difficult to discriminate between views so different, yet experience shows that this is not the case, as amongst the physicists who have most deeply studied the subject can be found supporters of either theory.

"The electrified-particle theory has for purposes of research a great advantage over the aetherial theory, since it is definite and its consequences can be predicted; with the aetherial theory it is impossible to predict what will happen under any given circumstances, as in this theory we are dealing with hitherto unobserved phenomena in the aether, of whose laws we are ignorant.

"The following experiments were made to test some of the consequences of the electrified-particle theory. . . .

"The rays from the cathode C pass [see Figure 3–5] through a slit in the anode A, which is a metal plug fitting tightly into the tube and connected with the earth; after passing through a second slit in another earth-connected metal plug B, they travel between two parallel aluminum plates about 5 cm long by 2 broad and at a distance of 1.5 cm apart; they then fall on the end of the tube and produce a narrow well-defined phosphorescent patch. A scale pasted on the outside of the tube serves to measure the deflexion of this patch. At high exhaustions the rays were deflected when the two aluminum plates were connected with the terminals of a battery of small storage cells; the rays were depressed when the upper plate was connected with the negative pole of the battery, the lower with the positive, and raised when the upper plate was connected with the positive, the lower with the negative pole. The deflexion was

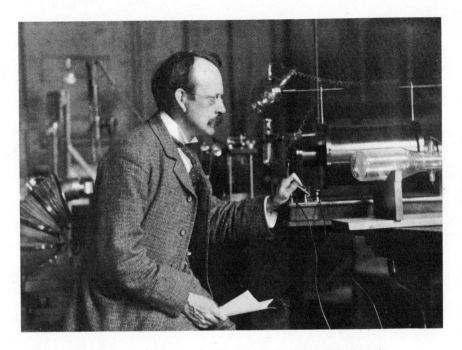

figure 3–6   *Sir J. J. Thomson in his laboratory. (Courtesy of Cavendish Laboratory.)*

proportional to the difference of potential between the plates, and I could detect the deflexion when the potential-difference was as small as 2 volts."

When a magnetic field of strength B is placed perpendicular to the original path, the particles move in a circle of radius given by

$$qvB = \frac{mv^2}{R} \quad \text{or} \quad R = \frac{mv}{qB} \tag{3-13}$$

In his first measurement, Thomson determined the velocity from measurements of the total charge and the temperature change occurring when the beam struck an insulated collector. For N particles, the total charge is $Q = Ne$, while the temperature rise is proportional to the energy loss $W = N\frac{1}{2}mv^2$. Thus measuring R, Q, and W, Thomson obtained

$$\frac{m}{e} = \frac{B^2 R^2 Q}{2W} \tag{3-14}$$

In his second method, which came to be known as the *J. J. Thomson experiment*, he adjusted perpendicular **B** and **ε** fields so that the particles were undeflected. Then $qvB = q\varepsilon$ and $v = \varepsilon/B$. He then turned off the **B** field and measured the deflection of the particles under the constant acceleration $q\mathcal{E}/m$.

$$\delta y = \tfrac{1}{2}at^2 = \frac{1}{2}\frac{e\mathcal{E}}{m}\left(\frac{L}{v}\right)^2 = \frac{1}{2}\frac{e\mathcal{E}}{m}\left(\frac{BL}{\mathcal{E}}\right)^2 \tag{3-15}$$

where L is the distance traveled. It is interesting to note that his original values of e/m from his first method, about 2×10^{11} coul/kg, were closer to the present value, 1.76×10^{11}, than those from his second method, 0.7×10^{11}. Thomson used different gases in the tubes and different metals for cathodes and always obtained the same value of e/m within his experimental accuracy, thus showing that these particles were common to all metals. The agreement of these results with Zeeman's led to the unmistakable conclusion that these particles, called *corpuscles* by Thomson and later called *electrons*, having one unit of negative charge e and mass about 2,000 times less than the lightest known atom, were part of the constituents of all atoms.

**3·3
BLACKBODY
RADIATION**

The question as to the nature of light is one of the oldest in the history of science. The fact that the wavelengths in the visible spectrum are so short precluded the observation of the usual properties of wave motion, namely, diffraction and multislit interference. Newton was unable to believe that light could be a wave motion because diffraction of light was not observed in his time. When Thomas Young demonstrated the diffraction and interference phenomena in his famous two-slit experiment, he was attacked by some for undermining the work of the great Isaac Newton. Eventually the wave theory of light was generally accepted, for (1) it easily explained diffraction and interference, (2) it predicted that light travels more slowly in water than in air, as demonstrated by Foucault in 1850 (the particle theory of Newton predicted the reverse), and (3) Maxwell's electromagnetic theory also predicted waves that propagate at the speed of light.

One of the most puzzling phenomena studied near the end of the nineteenth century was the spectral distribution of blackbody radiation. A blackbody is a system which absorbs all the radiation incident on it; it can be approximated by a cavity with a very small opening. The characteristics of the radiation emitted and absorbed by the walls of the cavity in thermal equilibrium are dependent only on the temperature of the walls. The fraction of the radiant energy of wavelength λ in the interval $d\lambda$ is called the *spectral distribution*, $f(\lambda)\,d\lambda$. The form of the function $f(\lambda)$ can be calculated in a straightforward way. The method involves finding the number of modes of oscillation of the electromagnetic field in the cavity with wave-

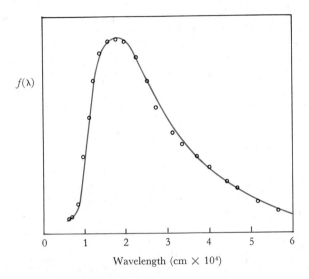

$f(\lambda)$

Wavelength (cm $\times$ 10^4)

figure 3–7   *Spectral distribution of blackbody radiation. The solid curve is the prediction by Planck. Classical theory predicted that $f(\lambda)$ is proportional to λ^{-4}, which agrees with the data for large λ but not for small λ. (Adapted from Richtmyer, Kennard, and Lauritsen,* Introduction to Modern Physics, *5th ed., McGraw-Hill Book Company, New York, 1955; by permission.)*

lengths in the interval $d\lambda$ and multiplying by the average energy per mode. We shall not go into the details of the calculation here. The number of modes of oscillation (per unit volume) is independent of the shape of the cavity and is given by the expression

$$n(\lambda)\,d\lambda = 8\pi\lambda^{-4}\,d\lambda \qquad\qquad (3\text{--}16)$$

According to the classical theory, the average energy per mode of oscillation is kT, the same as for a one-dimensional oscillator. The classical theory thus predicts for the spectral-distribution function

$$f(\lambda)\,d\lambda = 8\pi kT\lambda^{-4}\,d\lambda \qquad\qquad (3\text{--}17)$$

This prediction is called the *Rayleigh-Jeans law*. The function $f(\lambda)$ can be measured experimentally. Figure 3–7 shows a typical result. At large wavelengths, the data agree with the Rayleigh-Jeans law, but as λ approaches zero, this law predicts that $f(\lambda)$ becomes infinite (because the number of modes becomes infinite) whereas the experimentally determined $f(\lambda)$ approaches zero. This result was called the *ultraviolet catastrophe*. In 1900 the German physicist Max Planck announced that by making somewhat strange assumptions about radiation, he could derive a function $f(\lambda)$ which agreed with the experimental data. He first found an empirical function that fitted the data and then searched for a way to modify the usual calculation. He found that he could derive the function if he calculated the average energy per mode of oscillation from

$$\bar{E} = \sum_n E_n e^{-E_n/kT} \tag{3–18}$$

if he did not take the usual step of assuming the energy E to be continuous and replacing the sum by an integral, as is done in deriving the equipartition theorem. He could fit the experimental data if he assumed the energy to be discontinuous and given by

$$E_n = nhf \tag{3–19}$$

where n is an integer, f the frequency, and h a constant of proportionality which is now called *Planck's constant*. The calculation of the sum in Eq. (3–18) is not difficult, but we shall omit the details at this time. (The identical sum occurs in a calculation of heat capacities which we shall do in detail later.) The result obtained by Planck for the average energy per mode of oscillation was

$$\bar{E} = \frac{hf}{e^{hf/kT} - 1} = \frac{hc/\lambda}{e^{hc/\lambda kT} - 1} \tag{3–20}$$

Thus he found the spectral-distribution function to be

$$f(\lambda) = \frac{8\pi hc\lambda^{-5}}{e^{hc/\lambda kT} - 1} \tag{3–21}$$

This function is sketched in Figure 3–7. It is clear from the figure that the result fits the data quite well. For very large λ, we can expand the exponential in Eq. (3–21) using $e^x \approx 1 + x + \cdots$ for $x \ll 1$, where $x = hc/\lambda kT$. Then

$$e^{hc/\lambda kT} - 1 \approx \frac{hc}{\lambda kT}$$

and

$$f(\lambda) \rightarrow 8\pi\lambda^{-4}kT$$

which is the Rayleigh-Jeans formula. For small wavelengths, we can neglect the 1 in the denominator of Eq. (3–21), and we have

$$f(\lambda) \rightarrow 8\pi hc\lambda^{-5}e^{-hc/\lambda kT} \rightarrow 0$$

as $\lambda \rightarrow 0$.

The value of Planck's constant, h, can be determined by fitting the function given by Eq. (3–21) to the experimental data. The presently accepted value is

$$h = 6.626 \times 10^{-34} \text{ joule-sec}$$
$$= 4.136 \times 10^{-15} \text{ eV-sec} \tag{3–22}$$

Planck tried to fit this constant into the framework of classical physics but was unable to do so. The fundamental importance of the quantization assumption implied by Eq. (3–19) was suspected by Planck and others but was not generally appreciated until 1905, when Einstein applied the same ideas to explain the photoelectric effect and suggested that, rather than being merely a mysterious property of blackbody radiation, quantization is a fundamental characteristic of light energy.

3·4

THE PHOTOELECTRIC EFFECT

It is perhaps ironic that in the famous experiment of Hertz in 1887 in which he produced and detected electromagnetic waves in the laboratory (thus confirming Maxwell's theory), the photoelectric effect was discovered. Hertz was using a spark gap in a tuned circuit to generate the waves and another similar circuit to detect them. He noticed accidentally that when the light from the generating gap was shielded from the receiving gap, the receiving gap had to be made shorter to allow the sparks to pass. Light from any spark which fell on the terminals of the gap facilitated the passage of the sparks.

Hertz did not pursue this investigation further, but many others did. It was found that negative particles were emitted from a clean surface when exposed to light. Lenard in 1900 deflected these "rays" in a magnetic field and found that they had a charge-to-mass ratio of the same magnitude as that measured by Thomson for cathode rays. He also found that the photoelectric current was proportional to the intensity of the light. If the cathode was made positive, some current was still observed, indicating that the electrons were emitted with some kinetic energy. By varying the potential of the cathode and measuring the current at the anode for a constant light source, the energy distribution of the electron was determined. (See Figure 3–8.) For $V > V_0$, no current reached the anode, indicating that the electrons had a maximum kinetic energy of

$$\tfrac{1}{2}mv^2 = eV_0 \tag{3–23}$$

Lenard found, much to his surprise, that the so-called "stopping potential," V_0, was independent of the intensity of the light hitting the cathode. The higher the intensity, the more energy per second falls on the cathode; thus it would seem that the electrons ejected would have more energy. In 1905, Einstein offered an explanation in a remarkable paper in *Annalen der Physik*, vol. 17, the same volume that contains his papers on special relativity and Brownian motion.

Einstein assumed that energy quantization used by Planck in the blackbody problem was a universal characteristic of light. Rather than being distributed evenly in the space through which it is propagated, light energy is composed of quanta of energy hf. When these quanta, called *photons*, penetrate the surface of the cathode, their energy is given completely to electrons. If ϕ is the energy necessary to remove an electron from the surface (ϕ is called the *work function* and is characteristic of the metal), the maximum energy of the electrons leaving the surface will be $hf - \phi$. (Some electrons will have less than this amount because of energy loss traversing the metal.) Thus the stopping potential V_0 should be given by

$$eV_0 = \tfrac{1}{2}mv^2 = hf - \phi \tag{3-24}$$

"If the derived formula is correct, then V_0, when represented in cartesian coordinates as a function of the frequency of the incident

figure 3–8   *Schematic sketch of apparatus for observing the photoelectric effect. Light passes through the hole in the anode (disk A) and strikes the cathode C. Electrons from the cathode reach the anode and produce a current in the circuit. Voltage can be applied between anode and cathode to either attract or repel the electrons. The maximum energy of the electrons can be determined from the voltage needed to reduce the current to zero (by stopping the electrons from reaching the anode).*

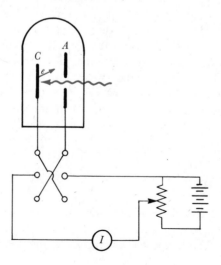

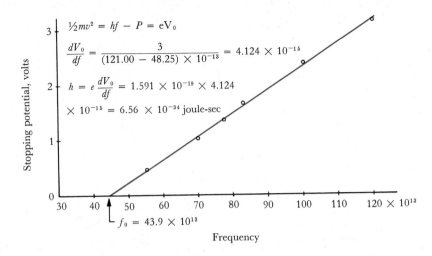

$$\tfrac{1}{2}mv^2 = hf - P = eV_0$$

$$\frac{dV_0}{df} = \frac{3}{(121.00 - 48.25) \times 10^{-13}} = 4.124 \times 10^{-15}$$

$$h = e\frac{dV_0}{df} = 1.591 \times 10^{-19} \times 4.124$$

$$\times\, 10^{-15} = 6.56 \times 10^{-34}\ \text{joule-sec}$$

$f_0 = 43.9 \times 10^{13}$

Frequency

figure 3–9   *Millikan's data for stopping potential versus frequency for the photoelectric effect. The data fall on a straight line which has a slope h/e, as predicted by Einstein a decade before the experiment.* [*From Millikan,* Physical Review, **7**, *362,* (*1916*).]

light, must be a straight line whose slope is independent of the nature of the emitting substance."[1]

As can be seen from Eq. (3–24), called the *Einstein equation,* the slope of V_0 versus f should equal h/e. At the time of this prediction, there was no evidence that Planck's constant had anything to do with the photoelectric effect. Also, there was no evidence for the dependence of stopping potential V_0 on frequency. In fact, this turned out to be a difficult experiment, and as late as 1913[2] it was not clear whether the data could be fitted better by f proportional to V_0 or to $V_0^{1/2}$. Careful experiments by Millikan, reported in 1914 and in more detail in 1916, showed that Eq. (3–24) was correct, and measurements of h from it agreed with the value obtained by Planck. A plot taken from this work is shown in Figure 3–9.

The threshold frequency, labeled f_0 in this plot, and the corresponding threshold wavelength, λ_t, are related to the work function ϕ by

$$\phi = hf_0 = \frac{hc}{\lambda_t} \tag{3–25}$$

Photons of frequency less than f_0 (and therefore having wavelengths greater than λ_t) do not have enough energy to eject an electron

---

[1]From Einstein's original paper, as translated by A. B. Arons and M. B. Peppard in the *American Journal of Physics,* **33**, 367 (1965).

[2]See Ref. 1 for a complete discussion of the difficulties in the experimental verification of the Einstein equation.

from the metal. Work functions for metals are typically a few electron volts. Since wavelengths are usually given in angstroms and energies in electron volts, it is useful to have the value of hc in eV-Å. We have

$$hc = (4.14 \times 10^{-15} \text{ eV-sec})(3 \times 10^8 \text{ m/sec})(10^{10} \text{ Å/m})$$

or

$$hc = 1.24 \times 10^4 \text{ eV-Å} \tag{3-26}$$

Example 3-1 The threshold wavelength for potassium is 5,640 Å. What is the work function for potassium? What is the stopping potential and the maximum speed of the photoelectrons when light of wavelength 4,000 Å is used? Using Eq. (3-26),

$$\phi = \frac{1.24 \times 10^4 \text{ eV-Å}}{5,640 \text{ Å}} = 2.2 \text{ eV}$$

The energy of a photon of wavelength 4,000 Å is

$$E = hf = \frac{hc}{\lambda} = \frac{1.24 \times 10^4 \text{ eV-Å}}{4,000 \text{ Å}} = 3.1 \text{ eV}$$

The maximum energy of the photoelectrons is thus $3.1 - 2.2 = 0.9$ eV.

The speed of these electrons is given by $\frac{1}{2}mv^2 = 0.9$ eV. It is convenient to find v in terms of the speed of light:

$$\frac{1}{2}(mc^2)\left(\frac{v}{c}\right)^2 = 0.9 \text{ eV}$$

$$\frac{v}{c} = \left(\frac{2(0.9) \text{ eV}}{0.51 \times 10^6 \text{ eV}}\right)^{1/2} \approx 1.88 \times 10^{-3}$$

Thus

$$v = (1.88 \times 10^{-3})(3 \times 10^8 \text{ m/sec}) = 5.64 \times 10^5 \text{ m/sec}$$

*

Another interesting feature of the photoelectric effect is the absence of time lag between the turning on of the light source and the appearance of electrons. In the classical theory, given the intensity (energy/sec-area), one can calculate the time necessary for enough energy to fall on the area of an atom to eject an electron, assuming the classical laws of absorption. Using extremely low intensities, for which such a calculation gives time lags of minutes to days, Lawrence and Beams[3] showed that the time lag is less than 1×10^{-9} sec. The photon explanation of this result is that low intensity means very few photons and thus few electrons will be emitted; however, since each photon has enough energy to eject an electron, there is always the chance that one will be absorbed immediately. The classical calculation gives the correct *average* number of photons absorbed per second.

3·5
X RAYS AND THE COMPTON EFFECT

Further evidence of the correctness of the photon concept was furnished by Arthur H. Compton, who measured the scattering of x rays by free electrons. Before we examine Compton scattering in detail, we shall give a very brief description of some of the early work with x rays.

X rays were discovered in 1895 by W. Roentgen when he was working with a cathode-ray tube. He discovered that "rays" originating from the point where cathode rays (electrons) hit the glass tube, or a target within the tube, could pass through materials opaque to light and activate a fluorescent screen or photographic film. He investigated this phenomenon extensively and found that all materials were transparent to these rays to some degree and that the transparency decreased with increasing density. This fact led to the medical use of x rays within months after Roentgen's first paper.[4]

Roentgen was unable to deflect these rays in a magnetic field, nor was he able to observe refraction or interference phenomena associated with waves. He thus gave the rays the somewhat mysterious name of x rays. Since classical electromagnetic theory predicts that charges will radiate electromagnetic waves when accelerated, it is natural to expect that x rays are electromagnetic waves produced by the acceleration of electrons when they are stopped by the target. In 1899 Haga and Wind[5] observed a slight broadening of an x-ray beam after passing through slits a few thousandths of a millimeter wide; assuming that this was due to diffraction, they estimated the wavelength to be of the order of 10^{-10} meters = 1 Å. In 1912 Laue suggested that since the wavelengths of x rays were of the same order of magnitude as the spacing of atoms in a crystal, the regular array of atoms in a crystal might act as a three-dimensional grating for the diffraction of x rays. Upon the suggestion of Laue, Friedrich and Knipping allowed a collimated beam of x rays

[3]*Physical Review*, **29** (1927).

[4]A translation of this paper can be found in the *American Journal of Physics*, **13**, 284 (1945), in Ref. 2 of Chapter 2, and in Ref. 2 of this chapter.

[5]*Annalen der Physik*, **68**, 884 (1899).

THE NEW PHOTOGRAPHIC DISCOVERY.

THANKS TO THE DISCOVERY OF PROFESSOR RÖNTGEN, THE GERMAN EMPEROR WILL NOW BE ABLE TO OBTAIN AN EXACT PHOTOGRAPH OF A "BACKBONE" OF UNSUSPECTED SIZE AND STRENGTH !

figure 3–10   *(left) Early x-ray tube. (Courtesy of Cavendish Laboratory.) (right) This cartoon appeared in the Jan. 25, 1896 issue of* PUNCH, *one month after Roentgen announced his discovery of x rays. (© PUNCH. Reproduced by permission.)*

to pass through a crystal behind which was a photographic plate. In addition to the central beam, they observed a regular array of spots. (See Figure 3–11.) From an analysis of the positions of the spots, they were able to calculate that their x-ray beam contained wavelengths ranging from about 0.1 to 0.5 Å. This experiment confirmed two important assumptions: (1) x rays are a form of electromagnetic radiation and (2) atoms in crystals are arranged in a regular array.

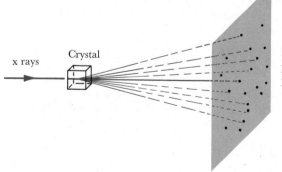

x rays

Crystal

Photographic plate with Laue spots

figure 3–11

Schematic sketch of Laue experiment. The crystal acts as a three-dimensional grating, which diffracts the x-ray beam and produces a regular array of spots, called a Laue *pattern, on a photographic plate.*

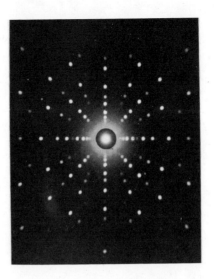

figure 3–12

Modern Laue-type x-ray diffraction pattern using a niobium diboride crystal and 20 kV molybdenum x rays. (Courtesy of General Electric Co.)

A simple and convenient way of analyzing the diffraction of x rays by crystals was proposed by William Lawrence Bragg in 1912. He considered the interference of x rays due to scattering from atoms in various sets of parallel planes, now called *Bragg planes*. Two sets of Bragg planes are illustrated in Figure 3–13 for NaCl, which has a simple crystal structure called *face-centered cubic*. Consider Figure 3–14. Waves scattered from two successive atoms will be in phase and thus interfere constructively, independent of the wavelength, if the scattering angle equals the incident angle. (This condition is the same as for reflection.) Waves scattered at equal angles from atoms in two different planes will be in phase if the path length is an integral number of wavelengths. From

figure 3–13   *A crystal of NaCl showing two sets of Bragg planes.*

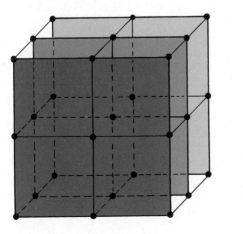
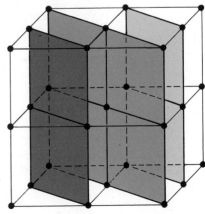

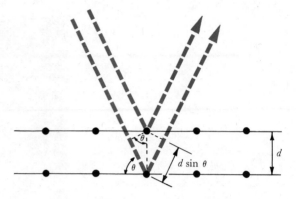

figure 3–14   *Bragg scattering from two successive planes. The waves from the two atoms shown have a path difference of 2d sin θ. They will be in phase if the Bragg condition 2d sin θ = mλ is met.*

Figure 3–14 we see that this condition is satisfied if

$$2d \sin \theta = m\lambda \qquad \text{where } m = \text{an integer} \qquad (3\text{–}27)$$

Equation (3–27) is called the *Bragg condition*. At angles meeting these conditions, waves will be strongly scattered because the waves scattered from many atoms constructively interfere. Figure 3–15 shows the main features of a crystal spectrometer first built by William Henry Bragg, the father of W. L. Bragg. X rays with wavelength satisfying the Bragg condition are scattered at the angle θ equal to the incident angle. Thus a measurement of the scattered intensity versus angle gives the distribution of wavelengths in the incident x-ray beam if the spacing d is known. For a simple crystal such as NaCl, the spacing of Bragg planes can be easily calculated because the distance between the Na^+ and Cl^- ions can be obtained from a measurement of the density and a knowledge of Avogadro's number N_A. (See Problem 3–7.) The scattering of x rays of known wavelength from crystals can be used to obtain information about the structure of crystals. W. H. Bragg and W. L. Bragg were awarded the Nobel Prize in 1915 for their contributions to crystal analysis.

Figure 3–16 shows a typical x-ray spectrum produced by bombarding a molybdenum target by electrons. The spectrum consists of a series of sharp lines, called the *characteristic spectrum*, superimposed on a continuous spectrum. The line spectrum is characteristic of the target material and varies from element to element. The continuous spectrum has a sharp cutoff wavelength, λ_m, which is independent of the target material but depends on the energy

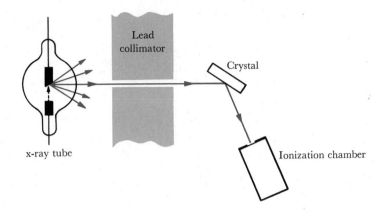

figure 3–15   *Schematic diagram of Bragg crystal spectrometer. A collimated x-ray beam is incident on a crystal and scattered into an ionization chamber. The crystal and ionization chamber can be rotated to keep the angles of incidence and scattering equal as they are varied. By measuring the ionization in the chamber as a function of angle, the spectrum of the x rays can be determined using the Bragg condition 2d sin θ = mλ, where d is the separation of the Bragg planes in the crystal. If the wavelength λ is known, the spacing d can be determined.*

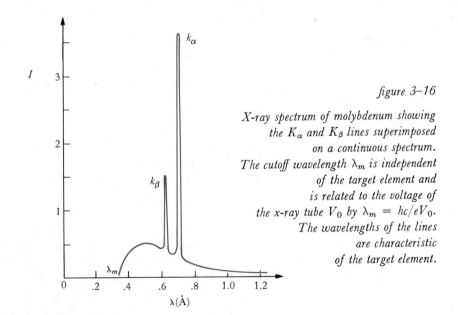

figure 3–16

X-ray spectrum of molybdenum showing the K_α and K_β lines superimposed on a continuous spectrum. The cutoff wavelength λ_m is independent of the target element and is related to the voltage of the x-ray tube V_0 by $\lambda_m = hc/eV_0$. The wavelengths of the lines are characteristic of the target element.

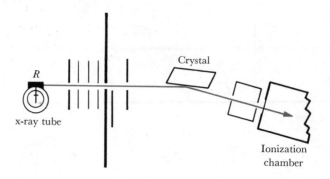

figure 3–17   *Schematic sketch of Compton apparatus. X rays from the tube strike the carbon block R and are scattered into a Bragg-type crystal spectrometer. In this diagram, the scattering angle is 90°.*

of the bombarding electrons. If the voltage of the x-ray tube is V_0 in volts, the cutoff wavelength is given by

$$\lambda_m = \frac{1.24 \times 10^4}{V_0} \text{ Å} \tag{3–28}$$

Equation (3–28) is called the *Duane-Hunt rule*. It is easily explained by the photon theory of x rays. The kinetic energy of each electron accelerated through a potential difference of V_0 is eV_0. (We can neglect the work function and initial kinetic energy of the electrons at the cathode because these are only a few electron volts, whereas V_0 is typically several thousand volts.) If an electron loses all its energy to a single photon, the wavelength of the photon will be given by

$$\frac{hc}{\lambda_m} = eV_0 \tag{3–29}$$

This is the same as Eq. (3–28) since hc is 1.24×10^4 eV-Å. We can see that a measurement of the cutoff wavelength can be used to determine h/e.

Let us now consider the scattering of x rays by electrons. According to the classical theory, when an electromagnetic wave of frequency f_0 is incident on a material containing charges, the charges will oscillate with this frequency f_0 and reradiate electromagnetic waves of the same frequency. Compton pointed out that if the scattering process were considered to be a "collision" between a photon of energy hf_0 and momentum hf_0/c and an electron, the

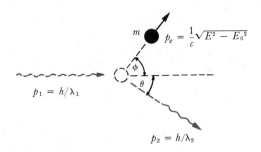

figure 3–18   *The scattering of x rays can be treated as a collision of a photon of initial momentum h/λ_1 and a free electron. Using conservation of momentum and energy, the momentum of the scattered photon h/λ_2 can be related to the initial momentum, the electron mass, and the scattering angle. The resulting Compton equation for the change in the wavelength of the x ray is $\lambda_2 - \lambda_1 = (h/mc)(1 - \cos\theta)$.*

electron would absorb energy due to recoil, and the scattered photon would therefore have less energy and thus a lower frequency. [The fact that electromagnetic radiation of energy E carries momentum E/c was known from classical theory and from experiments of Nichols and Hull in 1903. This relation is also consistent with the relativistic expression $E^2 = p^2c^2 + (mc^2)^2$ for a particle with zero rest mass.] Compton worked out the expected change in wavelength as a function of scattering angle. He verified his result experimentally, using the characteristic x-ray line of wavelength 0.711 Å from molybdenum for the incident monochromatic photons and scattering these photons from graphite. The wavelength of the scattered photons was measured by using a Bragg crystal spectrometer. His experimental arrangement is shown in Figure 3–17.

Figure 3–18 shows the geometry of the collision. If the wavelength of the incident x ray is λ_1 and that of the scattered x ray is λ_2, the corresponding momenta are

$$p_1 = \frac{E_1}{c} = \frac{hf_1}{c} = \frac{h}{\lambda_1} \tag{3–30}$$

and

$$p_2 = \frac{E_2}{c} = \frac{h}{\lambda_2}$$

using $f\lambda = c$. Since the energy of the incident x ray (12,400 eV for $\lambda = 1$ Å) is much greater than the binding energy of the valence electrons in carbon (about 11 eV), the electron can be considered to be essentially free.

Conservation of momentum gives

$$\mathbf{p}_1 = \mathbf{p}_2 + \mathbf{p}_e$$

or

$$p_e{}^2 = p_1{}^2 + p_2{}^2 - 2\mathbf{p}_1 \cdot \mathbf{p}_2 = p_1{}^2 + p_2{}^2 - 2p_1 p_2 \cos \theta \tag{3-31}$$

where $\mathbf{p}_e$ is the momentum of the electron after the collision. The energy of the electron before the collision is just the rest energy $E_0 = mc^2$. After the collision, the energy of the electron is $(E_0{}^2 + p_e{}^2 c^2)^{1/2}$.

Conservation of energy gives

$$p_1 c + E_0 = p_2 c + (E_0{}^2 + p_e{}^2 c^2)^{1/2}$$

Transposing the term $p_2 c$ and squaring, we obtain

$$E_0{}^2 + c^2 (p_1 - p_2)^2 + 2c E_0 (p_1 - p_2) = E_0{}^2 + p_e{}^2 c^2$$

or

$$p_e{}^2 = p_1{}^2 + p_2{}^2 - 2p_1 p_2 + \frac{2E_0 (p_1 - p_2)}{c} \tag{3-32}$$

If we eliminate $p_e{}^2$ from Eqs. (3-31) and (3-32), we obtain

$$\frac{E_0 (p_1 - p_2)}{c} = p_1 p_2 (1 - \cos \theta)$$

Multiplying each term by $hc/p_1 p_2 E_0$ and using $\lambda = h/p$, we obtain Compton's equation:

$$\lambda_2 - \lambda_1 = \frac{hc}{E_0} (1 - \cos \theta)$$

$$= \frac{h}{mc} (1 - \cos \theta) \tag{3-33}$$

The change in wavelength is thus independent of the original wavelength. The quantity $h/mc = hc/E_0$ depends only on the mass of the electron. It has dimensions of length and is called the *Compton wavelength*. The Compton wavelength of the electron is

$$\lambda_c = \frac{hc}{E_0} = \frac{1.24 \times 10^4 \text{ eV-Å}}{0.51 \times 10^6 \text{ eV}} = 0.0243 \text{ Å} \tag{3-34}$$

Because $\lambda_2 - \lambda_1$ is small, it is difficult to observe unless λ_1 is so small that the fractional change $(\lambda_2 - \lambda_1)/\lambda_1$ is appreciable.

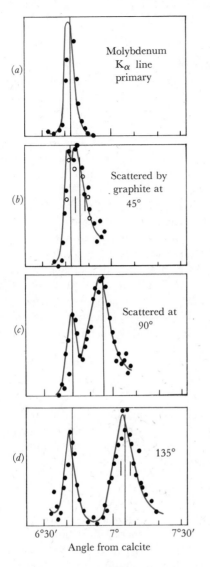

(a) Molybdenum K_α line primary

(b) Scattered by graphite at 45°

(c) Scattered at 90°

(d) 135°

6°30'   7°   7°30'

Angle from calcite

figure 3–19

Intensity versus wavelength for Compton scattering at several angles. The first peak results from photons of the original wavelength due to scattering by bound electrons which have an effective mass equal to that of the atom. The separation in wavelength of the peaks is given by Eq. (3–33). [From Compton, Physical Review, **22**, *411 (1923).]*

Figure 3–19 shows Compton's results. The first peak corresponds to scattering with no shift in the wavelength. This is due to scattering by the inner electrons of carbon. Since these are tightly bound to the atom, the whole atom recoils rather than the individual electron. The expected shift for this case is given by Eq. (3–33), with m being the mass of the atom, which is about 10^4 times that of the electron; thus this shift is negligible. The variation of $\Delta\lambda$ with θ was found to be that predicted by Eq. (3–33). We have seen in this and the preceding two sections that the interaction of electromagnetic radiation with matter is a quantum interaction. It is perhaps curious that after so many years of debate about the nature of light, we now find that we must have both a particle theory to describe in detail the energy exchange between electromagnetic radiation and matter and a wave theory to describe the interference and diffraction of electromagnetic radiation. We shall discuss this so-called "particle-wave duality" in more detail in Chapter 5.

In 1908, Einstein showed that the failure of the equipartition theorem in predicting the specific heats of solids at low temperatures could be understood if the atoms in the solid were allowed to have only certain discrete energies. Einstein's calculation is almost identical to that done by Planck to fit the blackbody-radiation spectrum. We give it in detail here for, from this calculation, we can get an insight into the general problem of why the equipartition theorem sometimes succeeds and sometimes fails to predict correctly the specific heats of gases as well as solids.

Consider 1 mole of a solid consisting of N_A molecules, each free to vibrate in three dimensions about a fixed center. For simplicity, Einstein assumed that all the molecules oscillated with the same frequency f in each direction. The problem is then equivalent to $3N_A$ one-dimensional oscillators, each with frequency f. The energy for each oscillator is

$$E = \tfrac{1}{2}mv^2 + \tfrac{1}{2}Kx^2 = \frac{p^2}{2m} + \tfrac{1}{2}m\omega^2 x^2 \qquad (3\text{-}35)$$

where K is the force constant and $\omega = (K/m)^{1/2} = 2\pi f$ is the angular frequency. The probability of finding an oscillator with position x in dx and momentum p in dp is then the Maxwell-Boltzmann distribution,

$$f(p,x) = C_1 e^{-E/kT} \, dp \, dx$$

where C_1 is determined by $\iint f(p,x) \, dp \, dx = 1$.

Let us change this to an energy distribution. It is convenient first to express the energy in terms of the variables P and Q, related to the momentum p and position x by $P = (1/2m)^{1/2}p$ and $Q = (m/2)^{1/2}\omega x$. In terms of these variables, the energy is

$$E = P^2 + Q^2$$

and

$$dp \, dx = (2/\omega) \, dP \, dQ$$

Thus the distribution in P and Q is

$$f(P,Q) \, dP \, dQ = \frac{2C_1}{\omega} e^{-E/kT} \, dP \, dQ$$

and we can obtain the energy distribution in a way similar to that used to obtain the speed distribution from the velocity distribution. The density of states in the space defined by the axes P and Q is proportional to $e^{-E/kT}$, which depends only on the distance $R = (P^2 + Q^2)^{1/2}$. The number of states in the area between R and $R + dR$ is thus proportional to $e^{-E/kT}$ and to the area

$$2\pi R\, dR = \pi\, dE$$

using $E = R^2$ and $dE = 2R\, dR$. Thus the fraction of oscillators with energies between E and $E + dE$ is

$$f(E)\, dE = \frac{2C_1}{\omega} e^{-E/kT} \pi\, dE = Ce^{-E/kT}\, dE \qquad (3\text{--}36)$$

where we have defined a new normalization constant, C. We can check this result by computing the average energy. If we use Eq. (3–36) to calculate E, we obtain

$$\bar{E} = \int_0^\infty Ef(E)\, dE = kT \qquad (3\text{--}37)$$

This is what we expect since there are two squared terms in the energy expression [Eq. (3–35)]. The total energy for 1 mole consisting of $3N_A$ one-dimensional oscillators is

$$U = 3N_A\bar{E} = 3N_AkT = 3RT$$

and the molar heat capacity is given by the Dulong-Petit law,

$$C_v = \frac{dU}{dT} = 3R$$

Einstein made the same modification that Planck had made. He assumed that the energy was not continuous but could only vary in steps of hf, where h is Planck's constant and f is the frequency of the oscillator. He then set

$$E_n = nhf \qquad (3\text{--}38)$$

and used the Maxwell-Boltzmann distribution law for discrete energies,

$$F_n = Ce^{-E_n/kT} \qquad (3\text{--}39)$$

The normalization condition

$$\sum_{n=0}^\infty F_n = 1$$

gives

$$C = \left(\sum_{n=0}^\infty e^{-E_n/kt} \right)^{-1} \qquad (3\text{--}40)$$

The average energy is given by

$$\bar{E} = \sum_{n=0}^{\infty} E_n F_n = \frac{\sum_{n=0}^{\infty} E_n e^{-E_n/kT}}{\sum_{n=0}^{\infty} e^{-E_n/kT}} = \frac{\sum_{n=0}^{\infty} nhf e^{-n(hf/kT)}}{\sum_{n=0}^{\infty} e^{-n(hf/kT)}} \qquad (3\text{–}41)$$

Equation (3–41) is identical to Eq. (3–18), used by Planck to obtain the average energy per normal mode of oscillation for his calculation of the blackbody-radiation spectrum. We now give the details of this calculation. It is convenient to calculate the denominator first. Let $x = hf/kT$. Then

$$\sum_{n=0}^{\infty} e^{-nhf/kT}$$

$$= \sum_{n=0}^{\infty} e^{-nx} = e^0 + e^{-x} + (e^{-x})^2 + (e^{-x})^3 + \cdots$$

$$= 1 + y + y^2 + \cdots \qquad (3\text{–}42)$$

where $y = e^{-x}$. The right side of Eq. (3–42) is just the series for $(1 - y)^{-1}$, that is

$$(1 - y)^{-1} = 1 + y + y^2 + y^3 + \cdots$$

The numerator of Eq. (3–41) can now be calculated easily if we note that

$$-\frac{d}{dx} \sum e^{-nx} = + \sum ne^{-nx}$$

Thus the numerator is

$$\sum nhf e^{-nhf/kT} = hf \sum ne^{-nx} = -hf \frac{d}{dx}(1 - y)^{-1}$$

$$= +hf(1 - y)^{-2}\left(-\frac{dy}{dx}\right)$$

$$= +hf(1 - y)^{-2}y$$

and

$$\bar{E} = \frac{hfy(1 - y)^{-2}}{(1 - y)^{-1}} = hf \frac{y}{1 - y} = \frac{hfe^{-hf/kT}}{1 - e^{-hf/kT}}$$

$$= \frac{hf}{e^{+hf/kT} - 1} \qquad (3\text{–}43)$$

where the last expression was obtained by multiplying the numerator and denominator of the previous one by $e^{+hf/kT}$.

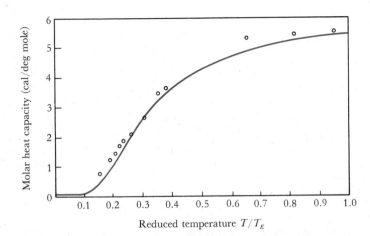

figure 3–20   *Molar heat capacity of diamond versus reduced temperature. The solid curve is that predicted by Einstein. [Taken from Einstein's original paper, Annalen der Physik, **22**, 180 (1907).]*

This result is, of course, the same as Eq. (3–20), obtained for blackbody radiation. At high temperatures, $hf \ll kT$, we can expand the exponential in Eq. (3–43) to obtain $\bar{E} \rightarrow kT$ as $T \rightarrow \infty$, in agreement with the equipartition theorem. For very low temperatures, $hf/kT \gg 1$, $e^{+hf/kT} \gg 1$, and

$$\bar{E} \rightarrow hfe^{-hf/kT} \rightarrow 0 \tag{3–44}$$

The total energy for $3N_A$ oscillators is

$$U = 3N_A\bar{E} = \frac{3N_Ahf}{e^{hf/kT} - 1} \tag{3–45}$$

and the specific heat is

$$C_v = \frac{dU}{dT} = 3N_Ak\left(\frac{hf}{kT}\right)^2 \frac{e^{+hf/kT}}{(e^{+hf/kT} - 1)^2} \tag{3–46}$$

It is left as an exercise to show directly from Eq. (3–46) that $C_v \rightarrow 0$ as $T \rightarrow 0$ and $C_v \rightarrow 3N_Ak = 3R$ as $T \rightarrow \infty$.

Figure 3–20 shows a comparison of this calculation with experiments. As can be seen, the curve fits the experimental points quite well except at very low temperatures, where the data fall slightly above the curve. The lack of detailed agreement of the curve with the data at low T is due to the simplicity of the model. An extension of this model was made by Debye, who gave up the assumption that all the molecules vibrate with the same frequency. He allowed for the possibility that the motion of one molecule could be affected by that of the others; thus he treated the solid as a system of coupled oscillators. The details of calculations with the Debye model are somewhat involved and will not be considered here. The improvement of the Debye model over the Einstein model is shown by Figure 3–21.

By comparing the Einstein calculation of the average energy per molecule with the classical one, we can gain some insight into the problem of when the classical theory will work and when it will fail. Let us define the critical temperature, $T_E = hf/k$, called the *Einstein temperature*. The energy distribution in terms of this temperature is

$$F_n(E) = Ce^{-nT_E/T}$$

For temperatures much higher than T_E, small changes in n have little effect on the exponential in the distribution, that is,

$$F_n \approx F_{n+1}$$

Thus E might as well be treated as a continuous variable and the sum in $\bar{E}$ be replaced by an integral. However, for temperatures much lower than T_E, even the smallest possible change in n, $\delta n = 1$, results in a significant change in $e^{-nT_E/T}$, and one must expect quite different results if E is treated as being continuous. Since we would expect hard metals to have stronger binding forces than soft metals, their frequency of molecular oscillation should be higher; thus T_E should be higher for hard metals than for soft ones. For lead and gold, T_E is of the order of 50° to 100°K; thus ordinary temperatures of around 300°K are "high" for these metals, and they obey the classical Dulong-Petit law at these temperatures. For diamond, T_E is well over 1,000°K; thus 300°K is a "low" temperature, and C_v is much less than the Dulong-Petit value of $3R$ at this temperature.

Let us now see if we can understand the specific heat of diatomic gases on the basis of discrete, or quantized, energies. In Chapter 2 we wrote the energy of a diatomic molecule as the sum of translational, rotational, and vibrational energies. If f is the frequency of vibration and the vibrational energy is quantized $E_{\text{vib}} = nhf$, as we assumed for solids, we know from the previous calculation that for low temperatures the average energy of vibration approaches zero and vibration will not contribute to C_v. We can define a critical temperature for vibration of a diatomic gas molecule by

$$T_v = hf/k \tag{3-47}$$

where f is the frequency of vibration. Apparently $T_v > 15°C$ for all the diatomic gases listed in Table 2–2 except Cl_2. From Fig-

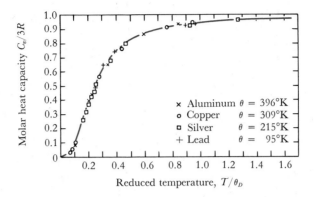

figure 3-21   *Molar heat capacity of several solids versus reduced temperature. The solid curve is that predicted by Debye. The data are taken from Debye's original paper. [From Annalen der Physik, 39, 789 (1912), as adapted by MacDonald, Introductory Statistical Mechanics for Physicists, John Wiley & Sons, Inc., New York, 1963; by permission.]*

ure 2-14 we can see that T_v is of the order of $1,000°$ to $5,000°K$ for H_2.

The rotational energy of a diatomic molecule is

$$E_{\text{rot}} = \tfrac{1}{2}I\omega^2$$

where I is the moment of inertia and ω is the angular velocity of rotation. It is not obvious how the rotational energy is quantized, or if it is; however, let us borrow a result from Bohr's theory of the hydrogen atom, which will be discussed in detail in the next chapter. Bohr found that he could derive the spectrum of the radiation of the hydrogen atom if he assumed that the angular momentum of the atom took on only the values $nh/2\pi$, where n is an integer and h is Planck's constant. If L is the angular momentum of a diatomic molecule, $L = I\omega$, and we can write the energy as

$$E_{\text{rot}} = \frac{L^2}{2I}$$

and using the Bohr quantum condition $L = n(h/2\pi)$,

$$E_{\text{rot}} = n^2 \frac{h^2}{8\pi^2 I} \tag{3-48}$$

The energy distribution will contain the factor

$$e^{-E/kT} = e^{-n^2(h^2/8\pi^2 IkT)}$$

and we can define a critical temperature for rotation

$$T_R = \frac{h^2}{8\pi^2 I k}$$
(3-49)

If this procedure is correct, we expect that for temperatures $T \gg T_R$, the equipartition theorem will hold for rotation and the average energy of rotation will approach $\frac{1}{2}kT$ for each axis of rotation, while for low temperatures, $T \ll T_R$, the average energy of rotation will approach 0. Let us estimate T_R for some cases of interest:

1. H_2, for rotation about the x or y axis, taking the z axis as the line joining the atoms. The moments of inertia I_x and I_y through the center of mass are

$$I_x = I_y = \tfrac{1}{2}MR^2$$

The separation of the atoms is about $R \approx 0.8$ Å. The mass of the H atom is about $M \approx 940 \times 10^6$ eV/c^2. We first calculate kT_R:

$$kT_R = \frac{h^2}{8\pi^2 I} = \frac{(hc)^2}{4\pi^2 M c^2 R^2}$$

$$= \frac{(1.24 \times 10^4 \text{ eV-Å})^2}{4\pi^2 (940 \times 10^6 \text{ eV})(0.8 \text{ Å})^2}$$

$$\approx 6.4 \times 10^{-3} \text{ eV}$$

Using $k \approx 2.6 \times 10^{-2}$ eV/300°K, we obtain

$$T_R = \frac{6.4 \times 10^{-3}}{2.6 \times 10^{-2}} 300°K \approx 74°K$$

As can be seen from Figure 2–14, this is indeed the temperature region below which the rotational energy does not contribute to the heat capacity.

2. O_2. Since the mass of the oxygen atom is 16 times that of the hydrogen atom and the separation is roughly the same, the critical temperature for rotation will be $T_R \approx \frac{74}{16} \approx 4.6°K$. Thus for all temperatures at which O_2 exists as a gas, $T > T_R$.

3. A monatomic gas, or rotation of diatomic gas about the z axis. We shall take the H atom for calculation. The moment of inertia of the atom is due mainly to the electron since the radius of the nucleus is extremely small (about 10^{-15} meter). The distance from the nucleus to the electron is about the same as the separation of atoms in the H_2 molecule; thus since the mass of the

electron is about 2,000 times smaller than that of the atom,

$$I_H \approx \tfrac{1}{2000} I_{H_2}$$

and

$$T_R \approx 2,000 \times 74° \approx 1.5 \times 10^5 \ °K$$

This is always much higher than the dissociation temperature for any gas. Thus $\bar{E}_{rot} \approx 0$ for monatomic gases and rotation of diatomic gases about the line joining the atoms for all attainable temperatures.

We see that energy quantization explains, at least qualitatively, the temperature dependence of the specific heats of gases and solids.

SUMMARY The fundamental electric charge e can be measured directly by the Millikan oil-drop experiment. There is overwhelming evidence that charges always occur in units of e. Avogadro's number, the faraday, and e are related by $F = N_A e$.

J. J. Thomson's measurements with cathode rays showed that the same particles (electrons), with e/m about 2,000 times that of ionized hydrogen, exist in all elements.

The photoelectric effect and Compton effect show that light energy interacts with matter in quantized amounts called *photons*. The photon concept easily explains the experimental results, which are contrary to classical expectation. The Einstein equation for the photoelectric effect is

$$hf = eV_0 + \phi$$

The wavelength shift in the Compton effect is

$$\Delta\lambda = \frac{h}{mc}(1 - \cos\theta)$$

The assumption of discrete energy states for atoms and molecules leads to the temperature dependence of the specific heat, which is in good agreement with experiment. At high temperatures, kT is much greater than the energy-level spacing and the quantum calculation gives the same result as the classical calculation. When the temperature is low enough so that kT is of the same order as the energy-level spacing, the quantum calculation differs from the classical one. Because of the finite energy gap between the lowest and first excited states, the average energy approaches the energy of the lowest state as T approaches zero, and C_v approaches zero.

REFERENCES   1. R. A. Millikan, *Electrons* (+ *and* −), *Protons, Photons, Neutrons, Mesotrons, and Cosmic Rays*, The University of Chicago Press, Chicago, 1947. This book on modern physics by one of the great experimentalists of the times contains fascinating detailed descriptions of Millikan's oil-drop experiment and his verification of the Einstein photoelectric equation. (There is a new edition of this book under the title *The Electron*, but with different page numbers. It is a facsimile of the first edition without the corrections made for the second edition. All page references given in the text refer to the second edition as given above.)

2. M. H. Shamos (ed.), *Great Experiments in Physics*, Holt, Rinehart and Winston, Inc., New York, 1962. This book contains 25 original papers and liberal editorial comment. Those of particular interest for this chapter are by Faraday, Hertz, Roentgen, J. J. Thomson, Einstein (photoelectric effect), Millikan, Planck, and Compton.

3. A. Goble and D. Baker, *Elements of Modern Physics*, The Ronald Press Company, New York, 1962. Chapters 6 and 8 of this textbook discuss determinations of e, N_A, F, and h.

4. E. Cohen, K. Crowe, and J. Dumond, *Fundamental Constants of Physics*, Interscience Publishers, Inc., New York, 1957.

5. J. H. Sanders, *Fundamental Atomic Constants*, Oxford University Press, Fairlawn, N.J., 1961. This and Ref. 4 discuss present methods, as well as earlier methods, of determining the values of fundamental constants.

6. G. Thomson, *J. J. Thomson, Discoverer of the Electron*, Anchor Books, Doubleday & Company, Inc., Garden City, N.Y. An interesting study of J. J. Thomson by his son, G. P. Thomson, also a physicist.

PROBLEMS   SET A

3-1. Calculate the standard deviation σ for Wilson's data in Table 3-1. What percentage of the mean value is σ?

3-2. Using a current of 2 amp, how long does it take to obtain 0.1 gram of copper from electrolysis using $CuSO_4$?

3-3. Given the photoelectric threshold $\lambda_t = 4,000$ Å for a metal, find

(a) The work function ϕ.

(b) The maximum kinetic energy of electrons if incident light of wavelength 3,000 Å is used. What is the stopping potential for this case?

3-4. What is the threshold wavelength λ_t and the work function ϕ for the metal used by Millikan to obtain Figure 3-9?

3-5. Calculate the energy range in electron volts for photons in the visible spectrum (about 4,000 Å to 8,000 Å in wavelength).

3-6. What number of photons per second of frequency $f = 100$ megacycles is needed by an FM radio that can just detect a signal of 10^{-12} watts?

3-7. One mole of rocksalt (a crystal of NaCl) has N_A ions of sodium and N_A ions of chlorine arranged alternately at the corners of a cube. Each ion therefore occupies a volume d^3, where d is the spacing of the ions. Using $M = 58.45$ for the molecular weight and $\rho = 2.164$ g/cm^3 for the density, calculate the volume of 1 mole and the spacing of the ions. What is the energy of a photon that has a wavelength $\lambda = d$?

3-8. An x-ray tube operates at a potential of 40,000 volts. What is the cutoff wavelength of the continuous x-ray spectrum from this tube?

3-9. Data for stopping potential versus wavelength for the photoelectric effect using sodium are

λ (in angstroms)	2,000	3,000	4,000	5,000	6,000
V_0 (in volts)	4.20	2.06	1.05	0.41	0.03

Plot these data in such a way as to be able to obtain from your plot:
(a) The work function
(b) The threshold frequency
(c) The ratio h/e

3-10. Using Eq. (3–46), calculate the value of C_v for a solid at the Einstein temperature $T_E = hf/k$.

SET B

3-11. A mercury source is placed in a magnetic field of $B = 4,000$ gauss $= 0.4$ weber/m^2. The observed splitting of the spectral line $\lambda = 5,791$ Å is $\Delta\lambda = \pm 0.0623$ Å. Calculate e/m from these data.

3-12. (a) Calculate the standard deviation σ for the numbers in column 5, Table 3–2. (If you write the mean as $5,386 \times 10^{-6}$ and use tables of squares, this is not as laborious as it may appear.) What percentage is σ of the mean value?

(b) For a gaussian distribution, the chance of a value differing from the mean by more than 3σ is less than 0.3 percent. The number corresponding to $n' = 9$ differs from the mean by more than any other (except that for $n' = 1$). To investigate the possibility of this being due to the existence of fractional charges, recalculate the number in column 5 assuming n to be $9\frac{1}{3}$. By how many standard deviations does this number differ from the mean? Are these data good evidence for the existence of "quarks," particles with charge $\frac{1}{3}e$ or $\frac{2}{3}e$?

3-13. In J. J. Thomson's first method, the heat capacity of the beam stopper was about 5×10^{-3} cal/°C and the temperature increase was about 2°C. How many 2,000-eV electrons struck the beam stopper?

3-14. In Figure 3–5, the plates D and E are 1.5 cm apart and 5 cm long and are kept at 50 volts potential difference.

(a) If the electrons have kinetic energy of 2,000 eV, find the deflection produced in the 5-cm path between the plates.

(b) What is the total deflection of the spot on the screen, assuming the beam travels an additional 30 cm in a field-free region before striking the screen?

(c) What strength of magnetic field would be needed between the plates for no deflection?

3-15. This problem is one of *estimating* the time lag (expected classically but not observed) for the photoelectric effect. Assume that a point light source gives 1 watt = 1 joule/sec of light energy.

(a) Assuming uniform radiation in all directions, find the light intensity in eV/cm^2-sec at 1 meter from the source.

(b) Assuming some reasonable size for an atom, find the energy/sec falling on the atom for this intensity.

(c) If the work function is 2 eV, how long does it take for this much energy to be absorbed, assuming that all the energy hitting the atom is absorbed?

3-16. Apply the Lorentz transformation for energy and momentum to the case of a photon of frequency f_0 in S (thus $E = hf_0 = pc$) to derive the relativistic Doppler-effect formula for the frequency f' in S'.

3-17. Prove that the photoelectric effect cannot occur with a free electron. (Hint: Consider the reference frame in which the total momentum of the electron and incident photon is zero.)

3-18. What energy photons should be used so that the maximum change in wavelength due to Compton scattering by electrons is 1 percent? Using these photons, what is $\Delta\lambda$ in angstroms for Compton-scattered photons at 60° from the incident beam? What is the energy of the recoil electrons for this case?

3-19. A photon can be absorbed by a system that can have internal energy. Assume that a 15-MeV photon is absorbed by a carbon nucleus initially at rest. The momentum of the carbon nucleus must be 15 MeV/c.

(a) Calculate the kinetic energy of the carbon nucleus. What is the internal energy of this nucleus?

(b) The carbon nucleus comes to rest and then loses its internal energy by emitting a photon. What is the energy of the photon?

3–20. The total energy of radiation in a blackbody is given by $U = \int_0^\infty f(\lambda) \, d\lambda$, where $f(\lambda)$ is given by the Planck formula, Eq. (3–21). Derive the Stefan-Boltzmann law

$$U = \alpha T^4$$

where α is a constant. (Hint: You need not do any integration if you change the variable of integration from λ to the dimensionless variable $x = hc/\lambda kT$. You need only show that U is proportional to T^4.)

3–21. Sketch the histogram of F_n versus n, where

$$F_n = e^{-E_n/kT} = e^{-n(hf/kT)}$$

(a) For the temperature $T = 10(hf/k) = 10T_E$
(b) For the temperature $T = hf/k = T_E$
On each of these histograms, sketch the continuous function

$$f(E) = e^{-E/kT}$$

3–22. The molar heat capacity data given below and arranged in tabular form are taken from *AIP Handbook*, 2d ed., McGraw-Hill Book Company, New York, 1963. Plot the data for these solids all on one graph and sketch in the curves C_v versus T. Estimate the Einstein temperature for each of the solids using the result of Problem 3–10.

$T°K$

	20°	50°	70°	100°	150°	200°	250°	300°	400°	500°	600°	800°	1000°
Au	0.77	3.41	4.39	5.12	5.62	5.84	5.96	6.07	6.18	6.28	6.40	6.65	6.90
Dia.	0.00	0.005	0.016	0.059	0.24	0.56	0.99	1.46	2.45	3.24	3.85	4.66	5.16
Al	0.05	0.91	1.85	3.12	4.43	5.16	5.56	5.82	6.13	6.42	6.72	7.31	7.00
Be	0.003	0.04	0.12	0.43	1.36	2.41	3.30	3.93	4.77	5.26	5.59	6.07	6.51

3–23. From the Einstein temperatures found in Problem 3–22, calculate the frequency of vibration $f = kT_E/h$ of the atoms.

3–24. Show that the expression for C_v given by Eq. (3–46) approaches zero as T approaches zero and approaches $3N_A k$ as T approaches infinity.

3–25. Consider a system which has only two possible energy states, $E_1 = 0$ and $E_2 = \epsilon$. The distribution function is $F_i = Ce^{-E_i/kT}$.

(a) What is C for this case?

(b) Compute the average energy $\bar{E}$, and show that $\bar{E} \to 0$ as $T \to 0$ and $\bar{E} \to \epsilon/2$ as $T \to \infty$.

(c) Show that the heat capacity for N particles is

$$C_v = Nk \left(\frac{\epsilon}{kT}\right)^2 \frac{e^{-\epsilon/kT}}{(1 + e^{-\epsilon/kT})^2}$$

(d) Sketch C_v versus T.

FOUR
THE
NUCLEAR
ATOM

4·1

EMPIRICAL Many data were collected near the turn of the century on the
SPECTRA emission of light by atoms in a gas when excited by an electrical dis-
FORMULAS charge or in a flame. When viewed through a spectroscope, tnis
light appears as a discrete set of lines of different color or wavelength; the spacing and intensities of the lines are characteristic
of the element. (The light appears as lines because the source is
placed at a narrow-slit aperture.) The wavelengths of these lines
could be determined accurately, and much effort went into finding
regularities in the spectra. In 1885 a Swiss schoolteacher, Johann
Balmer, found that the lines in the spectrum of hydrogen could be
represented by the formula

$$\lambda = b \, \frac{m^2}{m^2 - 4}$$

where $m = 3, 4, 5, \ldots$
$b = 3645.6 \times 10^{-8}$ cm

He suggested that this might be a special case of the expression

$$\lambda = b \, \frac{m^2}{m^2 - n^2}$$

145

where m and n are both integers. Rydberg generalized this expression to fit the spectra of heavier elements. He found that many groups of lines could be well represented by

$$\frac{1}{\lambda} = \left(\frac{1}{\lambda}\right)_{\infty} - \frac{R}{(m + u)^2}$$

where R and u are constants and $(1/\lambda)_{\infty}$ is the limiting value of $1/\lambda$ as $m \rightarrow \infty$. The quantity $1/\lambda$ is called the *wave number* and is written $\bar{f}$ since it is proportional to the frequency, f. (The frequency $f = c/\lambda = c\bar{f}$ was not used because c could not be determined nearly as accurately as λ.) Though u and $(1/\lambda)_{\infty}$ vary from series to series, the constant R was the same for all lines of the same element and varied only slightly from element to element. The value of R, now called the *Rydberg constant*, is $R_{\mathrm{H}} = 109{,}677.58$ cm^{-1} for hydrogen. The variation in R is now known to be due to the mass of the atom; for the most massive atoms, R approaches $R_{\infty} = 109{,}737.31$ cm^{-1}.

Ritz, about 1908, noticed that many of the wave numbers in a spectrum equaled the differences between other pairs of numbers of the same spectrum. He suggested that the wave-number formula be written

$$\bar{f} = R\left[\frac{1}{(m + A)^2} - \frac{1}{(n + B)^2}\right] \qquad (4\text{--}1)$$

where R is the Rydberg constant, m and n are integers, and A and B are constants that depend on the element. The Balmer expression is a special case of Eq. (4–1), with $A = B = 0$ and $n = 2(R = 4/b)$. These empirical expressions were successful in predicting other spectra; for example, other lines in hydrogen outside the visible spectrum were predicted and found.

Many attempts were made to construct a model of the atom that would yield these formulas for its radiation spectrum. It was known that an atom was about 10^{-10} meter in diameter, that it contained electrons much lighter than the atom, and that it was electrically

figure 4–1 *The Balmer series of hydrogen. [From G. Herzberg,* Annalen der Physik, **84**, *565 (1927), Leipzig.*]

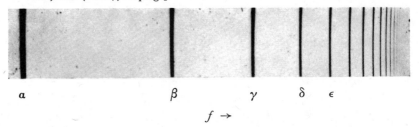

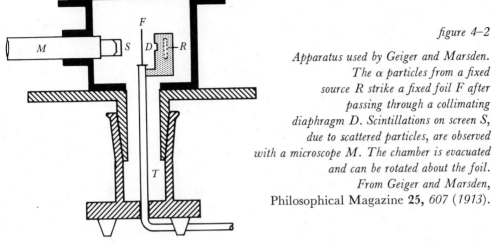

figure 4–2

*Apparatus used by Geiger and Marsden.
The α particles from a fixed
source R strike a fixed foil F after
passing through a collimating
diaphragm D. Scintillations on screen S,
due to scattered particles, are observed
with a microscope M. The chamber is evacuated
and can be rotated about the foil.
From Geiger and Marsden,*
Philosophical Magazine **25**, *607 (1913)*.

neutral. Electromagnetic theory showed that charges radiated when accelerated. In particular, when vibrating, they radiated with the frequency of the vibration. It was natural to assume that the atom was analogous to a sound system whose general motion was made up of a set of vibrations with a discrete frequency spectrum. The atom would thus emit all frequencies simultaneously. The most popular model was due to J. J. Thomson. He considered various arrangements of electrons embedded in some kind of fluid that contained most of the mass of the atom and had enough positive charge to make the atom electrically neutral. He then searched for configurations that were stable and had normal modes of vibration corresponding with the known frequency spectrum. One problem with this model, and all others, was that electrical forces alone could not produce stable equilibrium. Despite rather elaborate mathematical calculations, Thomson was unable to obtain from his model a set of frequencies of vibration that corresponded with the frequencies of the observed spectra.

4·2
RUTHERFORD
SCATTERING

The Thomson model of the atom was essentially ruled out by the results of a set of experiments conducted at the Rutherford laboratory by Rutherford and his students Geiger and Marsden. Rutherford was investigating radioactivity and had shown that the radiations from uranium consisted of two types, which he labeled α and β. He showed, by an experiment similar to that of J. J. Thomson, that q/m for the α particle was half that of the proton. Suspecting that the α particles were doubly ionized helium, Rutherford and his co-workers let a radioactive substance decay in a previously evacuated chamber; then, by spectroscopy they detected ordinary helium gas in the chamber. Realizing that this energetic, massive

Before collision   After collision

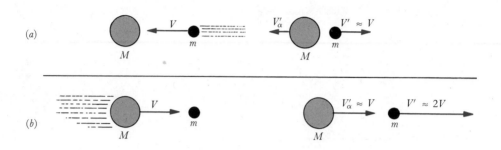

figure 4-3   *Collision of a small particle (electron) and a large one. In (a) the large particle is initially at rest and the electron is turned around with momentum change of approximately 2mV. The velocities of the particles in frame (b) are obtained by adding V to each particle. The momentum change is approximately 2mV for each particle in either frame.*

particle would make an excellent probe to investigate other atoms, Rutherford began a series of experiments for this purpose.

In these experiments, a narrow pencil of α particles fell on a zinc sulfide screen, which gave off visible light scintillations when struck. The distribution of scintillations on the screen was observed when various thin metal foils were placed between it and the source. Most of the particles were either undeflected, or deflected through very small angles of the order of 1°, but much to the surprise of everybody, some were deflected through angles as large as 90° or more. If the atom consisted of a positive sphere of charge of radius 10^{-10} meter, containing electrons as in the Thomson model, a single encounter of a particle with an atom could only result in a very small deflection even if the α penetrated into the atom.

Let us *estimate* the order of magnitude of the deflection of an α particle by such an atom. We first consider the collision of an α with a single electron. Because the mass of the α is about 8,000 times that of an electron, the electron can have little effect on the momentum of the α. Figure 4-3 shows a head-on collision between an electron moving with speed V and an α at rest. This is like the problem of a BB shot hitting a bowling ball. The shot is merely turned around, with a change of momentum of $2mV$. We can obtain the situation of an α, moving with speed V, colliding with an electron at rest (Figure 4-3b) by adding speed V to each particle in Figure 4-3a. The changed momentum of the electron is still

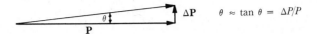

$$\theta \approx \tan \theta = \Delta P/P$$

figure 4-4   *The maximum deflection can be estimated by taking the maximum momentum change to be perpendicular to the original momentum.*

$2mV$. By conservation of momentum, this is also the change in momentum of the α particle, $\Delta P = 2m_e V \approx M_\alpha V/4{,}000$. We can get an upper-limit estimate on the angle of deflection by taking this maximum momentum change $\mathbf{\Delta P}$ to be perpendicular to the original momentum $\mathbf{P}$ of the α, as in Figure 4-4. (Of course, $\mathbf{\Delta P}$ could be perpendicular to $\mathbf{P}$ only for a glancing collision, in which case ΔP would be less than $2m_e V$; however, we are interested only in the order of magnitude of the deflection angle.) Then $\Delta P/P \approx \theta \approx 1/4{,}000$ radian $\approx 0.01°$.

We now consider the possible effect of the positive charge.

The electric force on a point charge, due to a uniformly charged sphere, as a function of r is shown in Figure 4-5. The maximum force occurs at $r = R$. We can estimate the change in momentum of the α particle, ΔP, due to this charge, by assuming that the

figure 4-5   *Force on a point charge versus distance r from the center of a uniformly charged sphere of radius R. Outside the charge, the force is proportional to Q/r^2, where Q is the total charge. Inside the charge, the force is proportional to $q'/r^2 = Qr/R^2$, where $q' = Q(r/R)^3$ is the charge within the sphere of radius r. The maximum force occurs at $r = R$.*

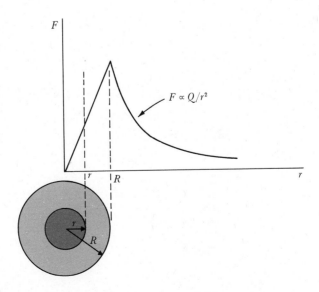

maximum force acts for the time taken in passing the atom at speed V, $\Delta t \approx 2R/V$. Using Coulomb's law for the electrostatic force on the α particle a distance R from a positive charge Q,

$$F = \frac{Kq_\alpha Q}{R^2}$$

where q_α is the charge of the α particle and

$$K = \frac{1}{4\pi\epsilon_0} \approx 9 \times 10^9 \text{ Nm}^2/\text{C}^2$$

is the Coulomb constant, we have

$$\Delta P \approx F \Delta t = \frac{Kq_\alpha Q}{R^2} \frac{2R}{V}$$

Again taking this $\mathbf{\Delta P}$ at right angles to the momentum $M_\alpha V$, we get for the maximum deflection angle,

$$\tan \theta \approx \frac{\Delta P}{P} \approx \frac{2Kq_\alpha Q}{RMV^2} = \frac{Kq_\alpha Q}{R(\frac{1}{2}MV^2)} \qquad (4\text{-}2)$$

Let us evaluate this expression for a typical case of an α particle ($q_\alpha = 2e$) with energy of 5 MeV incident on a gold atom, $Q = 79e$. It is convenient for this calculation and others to express the quantity Ke^2, which has dimensions of energy $\times$ length, in units of eV-Å. We have

$$\begin{aligned} Ke^2 &= (9 \times 10^9 \text{ Nm}^2/\text{C}^2)(1.6 \times 10^{-19} \text{ C})^2 \\ &= (9 \times 10^9)(1.6 \times 10^{-19})^2 \text{ joule-m} \\ &\quad \times \frac{1 \text{ eV}}{1.6 \times 10^{-19} \text{ joule}} \\ &= 14.4 \times 10^{-10} \text{ eV-m} = 14.4 \text{ eV-Å} \qquad (4\text{-}3) \end{aligned}$$

For our example then, Eq. (4–2) gives

$$\frac{\Delta P}{P} = \frac{(2)(79)(14.4) \text{ eV-Å}}{(1 \text{ Å}) 5 \times 10^6 \text{ eV}} \approx 4.5 \times 10^{-4}$$

Thus

$$\tan \theta \approx \theta \approx 4.5 \times 10^{-4} \text{ radian} \approx 0.026°$$

We see from these order-of-magnitude estimates that a deflection even as small as $1°$ must be the result of many collisions. If this is the case, the number of particles scattered through angles greater than some particular angle θ can be predicted by statistics if the average angle of scattering is known. The theory is quite similar to that for combining many small errors, some positive and some negative. Let θ_m be the rms scattering angle; then the number scattered through angles greater than θ is

$$N = N_0 e^{-(\theta/\theta_m)^2} \tag{4-4}$$

where N_0 is the total number of particles. When performing this experiment with gold foil of 10^{-4} cm thick, Geiger and Marsden found θ_m to be about $1°$; thus the expected number scattered through $90°$ or more should be

$$N_{90} = N_0 e^{-(90/1)^2} = N_0 e^{-8,100} \approx N_0 10^{-3,500}$$

The number observed was about 1 in 8,000, a fraction tremendously large compared with $10^{-3,500}$. The chance of observing a deflection of even $10°$ is practically zero according to this theory of multiple scattering, for the fraction that should be observed is only $e^{-100} \approx 10^{-43}$. Rutherford concluded that such large-angle scattering must be the result of a single encounter of the α particle with a massive charge confined to a volume much smaller than the atom. Assuming this "nucleus" to be a point charge, he calculated the expected angular distribution for the scattered α particles.

Figure 4–6 shows the geometry of an α being scattered by a point nucleus which we shall take to be fixed at rest at the origin O. When the α is very far away, it moves with speed V a distance b from a parallel line $\overline{COA}$ drawn through the origin. After the scattering, when the α is again far from the nucleus, it is moving with the same speed V parallel to the line OB and a distance b from it. (Since the potential energy is again zero, the final speed must equal the initial speed by conservation of energy.) The distance b is called the *impact parameter*. We wish to find the scattering angle θ as a function of the impact parameter b. The position of the α at any time can be described by the distance r to the origin and the angle ϕ made with the z' axis, which bisects lines $\overline{OC}$ and $\overline{OB}$. The path can be found by classical mechanics to be a hyperbola, symmetric about the z' axis. We can find the relation between θ and b without going into the details of the determination of the path. [The following derivation was first given by M. M. Gorden, *American Journal of Physics*, **23**, 247 (May, 1955).]

In Figure 4–7, $\mathbf{P}_1$ is the initial momentum of the α and $\mathbf{P}_2$ the final momentum. It is evident from the vector diagram that the total change in momentum $\Delta\mathbf{P} = \mathbf{P}_2 - \mathbf{P}_1$ is along the z' axis. The magnitude of $\mathbf{P}_1$ and $\mathbf{P}_2$ is MV. From the isosceles triangle

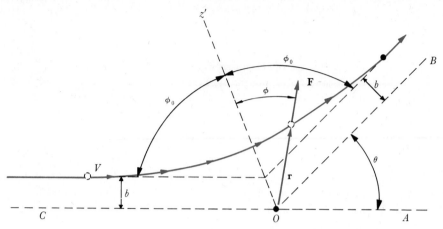

figure 4–6   *Rutherford scattering geometry. The nucleus is at O. The α particle has initial momentum MV parallel to line COA and final momentum of the same magnitude (by conservation of energy) parallel to line OB. The distance b is called the* impact parameter. *The change in momentum is along the symmetry axis z′. The scattering angle θ can be related to the impact parameter by setting this change in momentum equal to the component of the impulse in the z′ direction* $\Delta P = \int F \cos \phi \, dt$.

formed by $\mathbf{P}_1$, $\mathbf{P}_2$, and $\Delta \mathbf{P}$, we find the magnitude of $\Delta \mathbf{P}$ to be $\frac{1}{2}\Delta P/MV = \sin \frac{1}{2}\theta$, or $\Delta P = 2MV \sin \frac{1}{2}\theta$. We now write Newton's law for the α particle:

$$\mathbf{F} = d\mathbf{P}/dt$$

or

$$d\mathbf{P} = \mathbf{F} \, dt$$

The force F is given by Coulomb's law, $Kq_\alpha Q/r^2$, and is in the radial direction. Taking components along the $z′$ axis and integrating, we have

$$\int (dP)_{z'} = \Delta P = \int F \cos \phi \, dt = \int F \cos \phi \, \frac{dt}{d\phi} \, d\phi \qquad (4\text{–}5)$$

where we have changed the variable of integration from t to ϕ. We can write $dt/d\phi$ in terms of the angular momentum of the α about the origin. Since the force is central (i.e., it acts along the line joining the α and the origin), there is no torque about the origin, and the angular momentum is conserved. Initially, the angular momentum is MVb. At a later time, it is $Mr^2 \, d\phi/dt$. Thus conservation of angular momentum implies

$$Mr^2 \frac{d\phi}{dt} = MVb \qquad (4\text{–}6)$$

Using Eq. (4–6) for $d\phi/dt$ in Eq. (4–5) and $Kq_\alpha Q/r^2$ for F, we have

$$\Delta P = \int \frac{Kq_\alpha Q}{r^2} \cos\phi \, \frac{r^2}{Vb} \, d\phi = \frac{Kq_\alpha Q}{Vb} \int \cos\phi \, d\phi$$

or

$$\Delta P = \frac{Kq_\alpha Q}{Vb} (\sin\phi_2 - \sin\phi_1)$$

where ϕ_1 and ϕ_2 are the initial and final values of ϕ. From Figure 4–6 we see that $\phi_1 = -\phi_0$, $\phi_2 = +\phi_0$, where $2\phi_0 + \theta = 180°$. Thus $\sin\phi_2 - \sin\phi_1 = 2\sin(90 - \frac{1}{2}\theta) = 2\cos\frac{1}{2}\theta$. Writing ϕ in terms of θ and using our previous result for the net momentum change, $\Delta P = 2MV \sin\frac{1}{2}\theta$, we have, finally,

$$2MV \sin\tfrac{1}{2}\theta = \frac{Kq_\alpha Q}{Vb} 2\cos\tfrac{1}{2}\theta$$

or

$$b = \frac{Kq_\alpha Q}{MV^2} \cot\tfrac{1}{2}\theta \qquad (4\text{–}7)$$

Of course, it is not possible to choose or to know the impact parameter for any α particle; however, all such particles with impact parameters less than, or equal to, a particular b will be scattered through an angle θ greater than or equal to that given by Eq. (4–7). Let the intensity of the incident α-particle beam be I_0 particles per

figure 4–7   *Momentum diagram for Rutherford scattering. The magnitude of the momentum change* ΔP *is related to the scattering angle* θ *by* $\Delta P = 2MV \sin\frac{1}{2}\theta$.

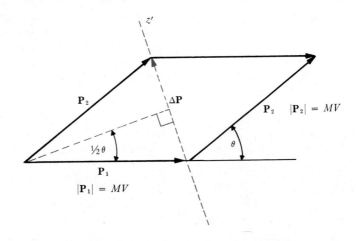

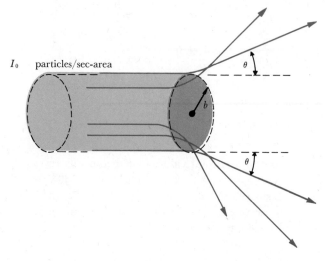

I_0 particles/sec-area

figure 4–8

Particles with impact parameters less than or equal to b are scattered through angles greater than or equal to θ related to b by Eq. (4–7). The area πb^2 is called the cross section for scattering through angles greater than θ.

second per unit area. The number per second scattered by one nucleus through angles greater than θ equals the number per second that have impact parameters less than $b(\theta)$. This number is $\pi b^2 I_0$.

The quantity πb^2 having dimensions of area is called the *cross section for scattering through angles greater than θ*. The total number scattered per second is obtained by multiplying $\pi b^2 I_0$ by the number of nuclei in the scattering foil, assuming the foil to be thin enough so there is negligible chance of overlap. Let n be the number of nuclei per unit volume:

$$n = \frac{\rho(\text{g/cm}^3)\,N_A\,\text{atoms/mole}}{\mathfrak{M}\ \text{g/mole}} = \frac{\rho N_A}{\mathfrak{M}}\,\frac{\text{atom}}{\text{cm}^3} \tag{4–8}$$

For a foil of thickness t the total number of nuclei is nAt, where A is the area of the foil or that of the beam, whichever is smaller. The total number scattered per second through angles greater than θ is thus $\pi b^2 I_0 ntA$. If we divide this by the number of α particles incident per second, $I_0 A$, we get the fraction scattered through angles greater than θ

$$f = \pi b^2 nt \tag{4–9}$$

Let us evaluate this fraction for the gold foil 10^{-4} cm thick, used by Geiger and Marsden, for $\theta = 90°$. Using $\cot(90/2) = 1$ and taking $\frac{1}{2}MV^2 = 5$ MeV for a typical α particle energy, we have

$$b = \frac{(2)(79)Ke^2}{MV^2} = \frac{(2)(79)14.4\ \text{eV-Å}}{2(5 \times 10^6\ \text{eV})} \approx 2.3 \times 10^{-4}\ \overset{\circ}{\text{A}}$$

$$= 2.3 \times 10^{-12}\ \text{cm}$$

and

$$n = \frac{(19.3 \text{ g/cm}^2)(6.02 \times 10^{23} \text{ atoms/mole})}{197 \text{ g/mole}}$$

$$= 5.9 \times 10^{22} \text{ atoms/cm}^3$$

Thus

$$f = \pi (2.3 \times 10^{-12})^2 (5.9 \times 10^{22})(10^{-4}) \approx 10^{-4}$$

This compares favorably with their observation of about 1 in 8,000 in their first trial.

Geiger and Marsden did a series of experiments in which they measured:

1. The number of particles per unit area on the screen, scattered through angles between θ and $\theta + d\theta$
2. The variation in the number scattered with foil thickness
3. The variation in the number scattered with the atomic weight of the foil
4. The variation in the number scattered with incident velocity V, which they varied by placing thin absorbers in the incident beam to slow down the α particles

Let us obtain the predictions of the point-nucleus model for these experiments. The number scattered by one nucleus at angles between θ and $\theta + d\theta$ is the number with impact parameters between $b(\theta)$ and $b + db$. This number is the intensity times the

figure 4–9

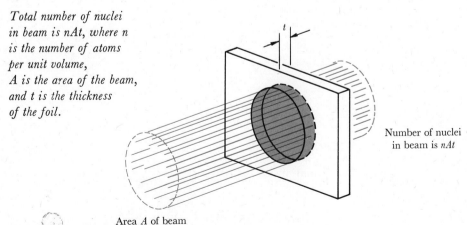

Total number of nuclei in beam is nAt, where n is the number of atoms per unit volume, A is the area of the beam, and t is the thickness of the foil.

Number of nuclei in beam is *nAt*

Area A of beam

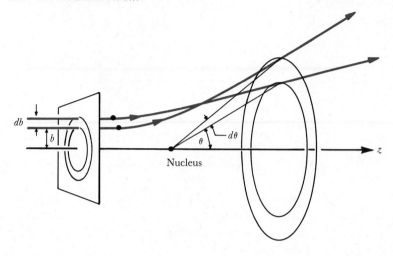

Nucleus

figure 4–10   *The number of particles with impact parameters between b and b + db is proportional to the area 2πb db. These particles are scattered into the range dθ.*

area $2\pi b\,db$. See Figure 4–10. Differentiating Eq. (4–7), we have

$$db = -\frac{Kq_\alpha Q}{mV^2} \operatorname{cosec}^2 \tfrac{1}{2}\theta\, \frac{d\theta}{2}$$

(We shall ignore the minus sign, which just means that an increase in b causes a decrease in θ.) Then

$$|I_0 2\pi b\,db| = I_0\pi \left(\frac{Kq_\alpha Q}{mV^2}\right)^2 \cot \tfrac{1}{2}\theta \operatorname{cosec}^2 \tfrac{1}{2}\theta\, d\theta \qquad (4\text{–}10)$$

If we use

$$\cot \tfrac{1}{2}\theta = \frac{\cos \tfrac{1}{2}\theta}{\sin \tfrac{1}{2}\theta} = \frac{\cos \tfrac{1}{2}\theta \sin \tfrac{1}{2}\theta}{\sin^2 \tfrac{1}{2}\theta} = \frac{\tfrac{1}{2}\sin \theta}{\sin^2 \tfrac{1}{2}\theta}$$

and

$$\operatorname{cosec}^2 \tfrac{1}{2}\theta = \frac{1}{\sin^2 \tfrac{1}{2}\theta}$$
$$q_\alpha = 2e \qquad Q = Ze$$

Equation (4–10) becomes

$$|I_0 2\pi b\,db| = I_0 2\pi \left(\frac{KZe^2}{mV^2}\right)^2 \frac{\sin \theta\, d\theta}{\sin^4 \tfrac{1}{2}\theta} \qquad (4\text{–}11)$$

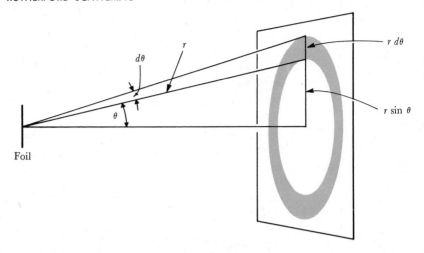

figure 4–11   *Particles scattered into the range dθ fall on the shaded area on the screen. This area is* $(r\,d\theta)(2\pi r\,\sin\theta)$.

The area of the screen, from Figure 4–11, is $(2\pi r\,\sin\theta)(r\,d\theta)$; thus the number scattered by one nucleus per unit area on the screen is given by

$$\frac{N}{\text{area}} = \frac{I_0}{r^2}\left(\frac{KZe^2}{mV^2}\right)^2 \frac{1}{\sin^4 \frac{1}{2}\theta} \qquad (4\text{--}12)$$

The point-nucleus model thus predicts that the observed number of scattered particles per unit area on the screen is proportional to $\sin^{-4}\frac{1}{2}\theta$, Z^2, and V^{-4}. Since the number of scattering nuclei is proportional to the thickness, the number of α particles scattered at a given angle should be proportional to the thickness. Note how this differs from the Thomson-model prediction. If the large-angle deflections were due to a large number N of small deflections θ_i, the chance of a particular deflection θ would be proportional to $N^{1/2}\theta_i$ similar to the random-walk problem because the θ_i's vary in direction, some canceling out others.

We quote the summary from the paper "Deflection of α Particles through Large Angles," by Geiger and Marsden, *Philosophical Magazine*, **25**, 605 (1913).

"The experiments described in the foregoing paper were carried out to test a theory of the atom proposed by Prof. Rutherford, the main feature of which is that there exists at the center of the atom an intense, highly concentrated electrical charge. The verification is based on the laws of scattering which were deduced from this theory. The following relations have been verified experimentally:

"(1) The number of α particles emerging from a scattering foil at angle ϕ with the original beam varies as $1/\sin^4(\phi/2)$, when the α

particles were counted on a definite area at a constant distance from the foil. This relation has been tested for angles varying from 5° to 150°, and over this range the number of α particles varied from 1 to 250,000 in good agreement with the theory.

"(2) The number of α particles scattered in a definite direction is directly proportional to the thickness of the scattering foil for small thicknesses. For larger thicknesses the decrease of velocity of the α particles in the foil causes a somewhat more rapid increase in the amount of scattering.

"(3) The scattering per atom of foils of different materials varies approximately as the square of the atomic weight. This relation was tested for foils of atomic weight from that of carbon to that of gold.

"(4) The amount of scattering by a given foil is approximately proportional to the inverse fourth power of the velocity of the incident α particles. This relation was tested over a range of velocities such that the number of scattered particles varied as $1:10$.

"(5) Quantitative experiments show that the fraction of particles of Ra C, which is scattered through an angle of 45° by a gold foil of 1 mm air equivalent (2.1×10^{-5} cm), is 3.7×10^{-7} when scattered particles are counted on a screen of 1-sq mm area placed at a distance of 1 cm from the scattering foil. From this figure and the foregoing results, it can be calculated that the number of elementary charges composing the center of the atom is equal to half the atomic weight.

figure 4–12   *The number of scattered α particles as a function of θ. The curve is* $\sin^{-4}\frac{1}{2}\theta$. *The data are from Geiger and Marsden. (From Evans,* The Atomic Nucleus, *McGraw-Hill Book Company, New York, 1955.)*

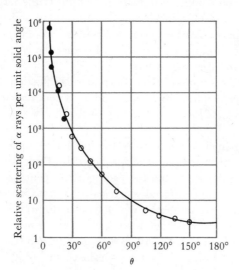

figure 4–13 *Hans Geiger (left) and Ernest Rutherford in the Manchester Laboratory.*
(Courtesy of University of Manchester.)

"We are indebted to Prof. Rutherford for his kind interest in these experiments, and for placing at our disposal the large quantities of radium emanation necessary. We are also indebted to the Government Grant Committee of the Royal Society for a grant to one of us, out of which part of the expenses has been paid."

Figure 4–12 is a plot of their data showing the angular dependence of the scattering using 7.7 MeV α particles. For a given scattering, the distance of closest approach of the α to the nucleus can be calculated from the geometry of the collision. For the largest angle, near 180°, the collision is nearly "head-on." We can calculate the distance D of closest approach for a head-on collision by setting the potential energy at this distance equal to the original kinetic energy:

$$\frac{Kq_\alpha Q}{D} = \tfrac{1}{2}MV^2$$

or

$$D = \frac{Kq_\alpha Q}{\tfrac{1}{2}MV^2} \qquad\qquad (4\text{–}13)$$

For the case of 7.7 MeV α particles, the distance of closest approach for a head-on collision is

$$D = \frac{(2)(79)14.4 \text{ eV-Å}}{7.7 \times 10^6 \text{ eV}} \approx 3 \times 10^{-4} \text{ Å} = 3 \times 10^{-14} \text{ meter}$$

figure 4-14   *If the α particle does not penetrate the nuclear charge, the nucleus can be considered a point charge. If the particle has enough energy to penetrate the nucleus, as in the figure on the right, the Rutherford scattering law does not hold.*

For other collisions, the distance of closest approach is somewhat greater than this but of the same order of magnitude for those scattered at large angles. If the nucleus is not a point charge but a small ball of radius R_0, the point-nucleus calculation will hold only if the α particle does not penetrate the nucleus, i.e., if the distance of closest approach is greater than R_0. The excellent agreement of the data of Geiger and Marsden at large angles thus indicates that the radius of the gold nucleus is less than about 3×10^{-14} meter. If higher-energy α particles could be used, the distance of closest approach would be smaller, and as the energy of the α particles increased, we might expect that eventually the particles would penetrate the nucleus. Since, for this case, the force law is no longer $Kq_\alpha Q/r^2$, the data would not agree with the point-nucleus calculation. Rutherford did not have higher-energy α particles available but he could reduce the distance of closest approach by using targets of lower atomic numbers. For the case of aluminum with $Z = 13$, the most energetic α particles scattered at large angles did not follow the predictions of Eq. (4-12). From these data, Rutherford estimated the radius of the nucleus to be about 10^{-14} meter.

A unit of length convenient for describing nuclear sizes is the fermi, F, defined by $1F = 10^{-15}$ meter $= 10^{-13}$ cm. As we shall see in Chapter 10, the nuclear radius varies from about 1 to 10F from the lightest to the heaviest atoms.

A convenient quantity used to describe scattering experiments is the differential-scattering cross section, written $d\sigma/d\Omega$ and defined as follows: $d\sigma/d\Omega$ = *the number per second scattered by one nucleus into $d\theta$ and $d\phi$ per unit solid angle, divided by the incident intensity.* The differential cross section has units of area/steradian.

The solid angle is defined as the area on the surface of a sphere of radius R divided by R^2. From Figure 4-15 we see that the solid angle subtended by the area between θ and $\theta + d\theta$ and between

ϕ and $\phi + d\phi$ is given by

$$d\Omega \equiv \frac{(R \sin \theta \, d\phi) R \, d\theta}{R^2} = \sin \theta \, d\theta \, d\phi \qquad (4\text{-}14)$$

The unit of solid angle is called the *steradian* and is dimensionless like the radian. The strip between θ and $\theta + d\theta$ subtends a solid angle, $d\Omega_\theta = 2\pi \sin \theta \, d\theta$, obtained from Eq. (4-14) by integrating over $d\phi$. The differential cross section for Rutherford scattering is obtained from Eq. (4-11) by dividing by the intensity I_0 and the solid angle $d\Omega_\theta$:

$$\frac{d\sigma}{d\Omega} = \left(\frac{KZe^2}{mV^2}\right)^2 \frac{1}{\sin^4 \frac{1}{2}\theta} \qquad (4\text{-}15)$$

figure 4–15   *The differential solid angle $d\Omega$ is defined as the area on the sphere in the range $d\theta$ and $d\phi$, $(R \sin \theta \, d\phi)(R \, d\theta)$ divided by R^2. Thus $d\Omega = \sin \theta \, d\theta \, d\phi$.*

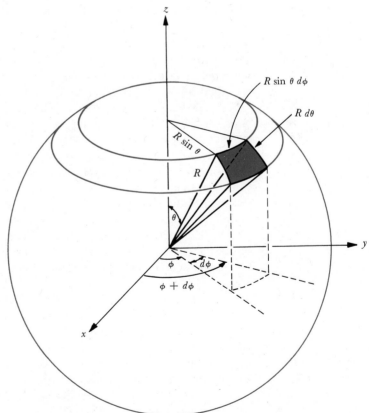

The total cross section σ is the total number scattered by one nucleus divided by the incident intensity. The total cross section represents the "effective area" presented by the nucleus for scattering. It is related to the differential cross section by

$$\sigma = \iint \left(\frac{d\sigma}{d\Omega}\right) \sin\theta \, d\theta \, d\phi$$

and to the impact parameter $b(\theta)$ by $\sigma = \pi b^2(0°)$.

The total cross section for Rutherford scattering is infinite because, no matter how large the impact parameter is, the α particle will be scattered if the force law is assumed to be $K q_\alpha Q/r^2$ for all r. (At distances greater than the radius of the *atom*, the negative electrons shield the nuclear charge and the force on the α drops to zero; thus this force law is not realistic for all r.) The total cross section for scattering of BB's by a bowling ball, for example, is the area presented by the bowling ball, πr^2. (See Problem 4–15.)

4·3
THE BOHR MODEL
OF THE ATOM

In 1913 a Danish physicist, Niels Bohr, proposed a model of the hydrogen atom which had remarkable successes. Since the diameter of the atom is roughly 10^{-10} meter, while the positive charge is concentrated in the nucleus of diameter about 10^{-14} or 10^{-15} meter, the electron must be relatively far from the nucleus, at least on the average. The force law between two point charges is given by Coulomb's law, $F = K q_1 q_2/r^2$.

To achieve mechanical stability the electron must be in motion, and the laws of mechanics for an inverse-square attractive force predict the electron path to be an ellipse with the force center at one focus, as is the case for the motion of the planets about the sun. For such motion, the electron is always accelerating toward the nucleus. The laws of electrodynamics predict that such an accelerating electron will radiate light of a frequency equal to that of the periodic motion which, in this case, is the frequency of revolution. Since energy will be lost to the radiation, the electron's orbit will become smaller and smaller. The time required for the electron to spiral into the nucleus can be calculated from classical mechanics and electrodynamics; it turns out to be less than 10^{-6} sec. Thus, at first sight, this model predicts that the atom will radiate a continuous spectrum (since the frequency of revolution changes continuously as the electron spirals in) and will collapse after a very short time, a result that fortunately does not occur. Bohr showed that one could not deduce stable positions for the electrons in atoms from classical mechanics and electrodynamics. Because the need to modify electrodynamics had already been indicated by Planck's blackbody-radiation theory and by the photoelectric effect, Bohr chose to assume that classical

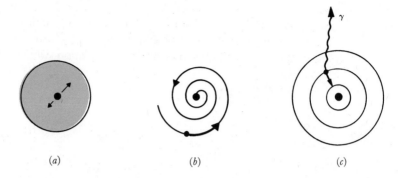

(a)   (b)   (c)

figure 4–16   *Models of an atom. (a) In the Thomson model, the electron is embedded in a large positive charge and oscillates about the center. (b) In the classical orbital model, the electron orbits about the nucleus and spirals into the center because of the energy radiated. (c) In the Bohr model, the electron orbits without radiating until it jumps to another radius, at which time radiation is emitted.*

mechanics applied to atoms but that electrodynamics needed modification. He assumed that there existed certain orbits for the electrons in which they did *not* radiate; that radiation occurred when the electrons somehow changed from one of these stable orbits to another. The frequency of radiation was *not* the frequency of revolution of either orbit but is related to the energies of the orbits by

$$hf = W_1 - W_2 \tag{4-16}$$

where W_1 and W_2 are the total energies in orbits 1 and 2 and h is Planck's constant. This last assumption is the key one of the Bohr theory. Prior to this, all attempts at explaining atomic spectra were directed at finding a model in which the frequencies of motion of the charges were the frequencies of the observed radiation. We shall give a derivation of the spectrum of hydrogen that closely follows Bohr's original line of thought.

For simplicity, Bohr assumed the electron orbits to be circular. The potential energy of an electron of charge e at a distance r from the nucleus of charge Ze is

$$U = -\frac{KZe^2}{r}$$

(Although we are considering the hydrogen atom, for which $Z = 1$, it is convenient not to specify Z at this time. We can then see how the results depend on the nuclear charge and apply them to other one-electron atoms such as ionized helium.) The total energy is

$$W = \tfrac{1}{2}mv^2 + U = \tfrac{1}{2}mv^2 - \frac{KZe^2}{r} \tag{4-17}$$

The kinetic energy can be obtained as a function of r by using Newton's law, $F = ma$. Setting the Coulomb attractive force equal to the mass times the centripetal acceleration, we have

$$\frac{KZe^2}{r^2} = \frac{mv^2}{r} \tag{4-18}$$

or

$$\tfrac{1}{2}mv^2 = \frac{1}{2}\frac{KZe^2}{r}$$

For circular orbits we thus see that the kinetic energy is equal to half the magnitude of the potential energy. The total energy is therefore

$$W = -\frac{1}{2}\frac{KZe^2}{r} \tag{4-19}$$

Using Eq. (4–16) for the frequency of radiation when the electron changes from orbit 1 of radius r_1 to orbit 2 of radius r_2, we have

$$f = \frac{1}{2}\frac{KZe^2}{h}\left(\frac{1}{r_2} - \frac{1}{r_1}\right) \tag{4-20}$$

To obtain the Balmer-Ritz formula $f = c\bar{f} = cR(1/m^2 - 1/n^2)$, it is evident that the radii of the stable orbits must be proportional to the squares of integers, that is,

$$r_n = n^2 r_0 \tag{4-21}$$

This has the effect of quantizing the energies of the atom,

$$W_n = -\frac{1}{2}\frac{KZe^2}{r_0}\frac{1}{n^2} \tag{4-22}$$

We have, then, for the frequency:

$$f = \frac{1}{2}\frac{KZe^2}{hr_0}\left(\frac{1}{n_2{}^2} - \frac{1}{n_1{}^2}\right) \tag{4-23}$$

The constant r_0 is the smallest possible radius. It can be determined by considering the case for very large n. As n approaches infinity, the difference in energy between adjacent orbits approaches zero and quantization should have little effect. Bohr reasoned that for $n \gg 1$, classical physics should give the correct results. This principle is known as Bohr's *correspondence principle: In the region of very large quantum numbers (n, in this case) classical calculations and quantum cal-*

culations must yield the same results. Writing $n_1 = n$ and $n_2 = n - 1$, we have

$$\frac{1}{(n-1)^2} - \frac{1}{n^2} = \frac{2n-1}{n^2(n-1)^2} \approx \frac{2}{n^3}$$

for $n \gg 1$. Equation (4–23) thus gives, for the frequency of radiation,

$$f \approx \frac{KZe^2}{hr_0n^3} \qquad \text{for } n \gg 1 \tag{4-24}$$

The frequency of radiation predicted by classical theory is the frequency of revolution of the electron, which is $f_{\text{rev}} = v/2\pi r$. Using Eq. (4–18) for v^2 and Eq. (4–21) for r, we have

$$f_{\text{rev}}^2 = \frac{v^2}{4\pi^2r^2} = \frac{KZe^2}{4\pi^2mr^3} = \frac{KZe^2}{4\pi^2mr_0^3}\frac{1}{n^6}$$

Setting this classical prediction for f_{rev}^2 equal to f^2 from Eq. (4–24), we obtain

$$\frac{K^2Z^2e^4}{h^2r_0^2n^6} = \frac{KZe^2}{4\pi^2mr_0^3n^6}$$

or

$$r_0 = \frac{h^2}{4\pi^2Ke^2m}\frac{1}{Z} = \frac{a_0}{Z} \tag{4-25}$$

where $a_0 = h^2/(4\pi^2Ke^2m)$ is the smallest radius for $Z = 1$. We can evaluate a_0 from the known values of the constants in Eq. (4–25). The result is

$$a_0 \approx 0.529 \text{ Å} \tag{4-26}$$

Putting this expression for r_0 into Eq. (4–23), we obtain, for the frequencies of radiation,

$$f = Z^2 \frac{2\pi^2mK^2e^4}{h^3}\left(\frac{1}{n_2^2} - \frac{1}{n_1^2}\right) \tag{4-27}$$

Comparing this for $Z = 1$ with the empirical Balmer-Ritz formula, Eq. (4–1), we have for the Rydberg frequency,

$$f_R = cR = \frac{2\pi^2mK^2e^4}{h^3} \tag{4-28}$$

Using the values of m, e, and h, which were known in 1913, Bohr calculated cR to be 3.1×10^{15}, which, within the limits of the uncertainties of the constants, compared well with the value of 3.29×10^{15} obtained from spectroscopy. Bohr noted in his original paper that this equation might be valuable in determining values for the constants e, m, and h, because of the extreme precision possible in measuring R. This has indeed turned out to be the case.

The possible values of the energy of the hydrogen atom predicted by the Bohr model are given by Eq. (4–22), with r_0 given by Eq. (4–25). They are

$$W_n = -\left(\frac{2\pi^2 K^2 e^4 m}{h^2}\right)\frac{Z^2}{n^2} = -Z^2 \frac{E_1}{n^2} \tag{4-29}$$

where $E_1 = (2\pi^2 K^2 e^4 m)/h^2 \approx 13.6$ eV. It is convenient to plot these energies versus n, as in Figure 4–17. Such a plot is called an *energy-level diagram*. Various series of transitions are indicated in this diagram by vertical arrows between the levels. The frequency

figure 4-17 *Energy-level diagram for hydrogen showing a few transitions in each of the Lyman, Balmer, and Paschen series. There is an infinite number of levels. Their energies are given by $E_n = -E_1/n^2$, where $E_1 \approx 13.6$ eV.*

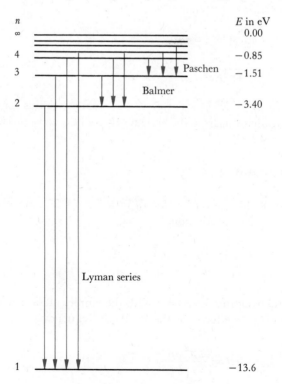

of the light emitted in one of these transitions is the energy difference divided by h according to Bohr's equation (4–16). The energy required to remove the electron from the atom, 13.6 eV, is called the *ionization energy* or *binding energy* of the electron.

The assumption that the nucleus is fixed is equivalent to the assumption that the nucleus has infinite mass. If the nucleus has mass M, its kinetic energy will be $\frac{1}{2}MV^2 = P^2/2M$, where $P = MV$ is the momentum. If we assume that the total momentum of the atom is zero, the momentum of the nucleus and electron must be equal in magnitude. The total kinetic energy is thus

$$E_k = \frac{P^2}{2M} + \frac{P^2}{2m} = \frac{M + m}{2mM}P^2 = \frac{P^2}{2\mu}$$

where

$$\mu = \frac{mM}{m + M} = \frac{m}{1 + m/M} \tag{4–30}$$

This is slightly different from the kinetic energy of the electron because μ, called the *reduced mass*, is slightly different from the electron mass. The results derived above for a nucleus of infinite mass can be applied directly for the case of a nucleus of mass M if we replace the electron mass in the equations by the reduced mass μ, defined by Eq. (4–30). (The validity of this procedure is proved in most intermediate and advanced mechanics books.) This correction amounts to only 1 part in 2,000 for the case of hydrogen and to even less for other nuclei; however, the predicted variation in the Rydberg constant from atom to atom is just that which is observed. For example, the spectrum of a singly ionized helium atom, which has one remaining electron, is just that predicted by Eq. (4–27), with $Z = 2$ and the proper reduced mass.

It is, of course, not surprising that the form of the Bohr formula fits the experimental data, for it was forced to do so; however, the fact that the empirical Rydberg constant was predicted in terms of known constants is certainly significant. The more accurately these constants become known, the more closely Bohr's formula agreed with the spectroscopic measurements. In his original paper, Bohr pointed out that Eqs. (4–18), (4–21), and (4–25) implied that the angular momentum $L = mvr$ of the electron in state n was

$$L = n\frac{h}{2\pi} = n\hbar \tag{4–31}$$

where $\hbar \equiv h/2\pi = 6.58 \times 10^{-16}$ eV-sec. (The combination $h/2\pi$ occurs so often that the symbol $\hbar$, called *h-bar* or *h-cross*, is used for it.) Thus, angular momentum seems to play an important part in

(a)

(b)

(c)

(d)

figure 4–18   (a) *Niels Bohr in 1922. (Courtesy of Culver Pictures, Inc.)* (b) *The Rutherfords and Bohrs in the Rutherfords' garden in 1930. (Courtesy of American Institute of Physics.)* (c) *The Bohrs take a ride on George Gamow's motorcycle at their country house in Tisvilde in the summer of 1930. (Courtesy of George Gamow.)* (d) *Niels Bohr explains a point in front of the blackboard (1956). (Courtesy of American Institute of Physics.)*

the quantization of atomic energies. In fact, if Eq. (4–31) is taken as a postulate along with Eq. (4–16), with the assumption of non-radiating orbits, the rest of the equations follow from classical mechanics. These were soon taken to be the postulates of the Bohr model. We shall state them here and let the reader work out the derivation of Eqs. (4–21), (4–27), and (4–29) from them as an exercise.

Bohr Postulates

1. Electrons move in certain nonradiating, stable, circular orbits, consistent with Coulomb's law and Newton's law and specified by the quantization of angular momentum

$$L = n \frac{h}{2\pi} = n\hbar$$

where h = Planck's constant and n is an integer.
2. Radiation of frequency

$$f = \frac{W_1 - W_2}{h}$$

occurs when the electron jumps from orbit 1 of energy W_1 to orbit 2 of energy W_2.

At the time of Bohr's paper there were two series known for hydrogen: the Balmer series, corresponding to $n_2 = 2$, $n_1 = 3, 4, 5, \ldots$, and another named after its discoverer, Paschen (1908), corresponding to $n_2 = 3$, $n_1 = 4, 5, 6, \ldots$. Equation (4–27) indicates that other series should exist for different values of n_2. In 1916 Lyman found the series corresponding to $n_2 = 1$, and in 1922 and 1924 Brackett and Pfund, respectively, found series corresponding to $n_2 = 4$ and $n_2 = 5$. As can be easily determined by computing the wavelengths for these series, only the Balmer series lies in the visible portion of the electromagnetic spectrum. The Lyman series is in the ultraviolet, and the others are in the infrared.

A natural extension of the Bohr model is the treatment of elliptical orbits. A result of Newtonian mechanics, familiar from planetary motion, is that in an inverse-square force field, the energy depends only on the major axis of the ellipse and not on its eccentricity; thus there is no change at all unless the force differs from inverse square or newtonian mechanics is modified. Sommerfeld considered the effect of special relativity on the Bohr model. Since the relativistic corrections should be of the order of v^2/c^2, it is likely that a highly eccentric orbit would have a larger correction, because v becomes greater as the electron moves near the nucleus. The Sommerfeld calculations are quite complicated, but we can estimate the order of magnitude of the effect of special relativity by calculating v/c for the first Bohr orbit in hydrogen. We have

$$mvr = \hbar$$

$$r = \frac{h^2}{4\pi^2 mKe^2} = \frac{\hbar^2}{mKe^2}$$

$$v = \frac{\hbar}{mr} = \frac{Ke^2}{\hbar} \qquad\qquad (4\text{--}32)$$

$$\frac{v}{c} = \frac{Ke^2}{\hbar c} = \frac{14.4 \text{ eV-Å}}{1{,}970 \text{ eV-Å}} \simeq \frac{1}{137}$$

where we have used another convenient combination

$$\hbar c = \frac{1.24 \times 10^4 \text{ eV-Å}}{2\pi} = 1{,}970 \text{ eV-Å}$$

Though v^2/c^2 is very small, an effect of this magnitude is observable. Upon examination with high resolution, some spectral lines of hydrogen are seen to consist of several closely spaced lines. This is explained in Sommerfeld's theory in the following way. For each allowed circular orbit of radius r_n and energy W_n, there is a set of n elliptical orbits of equal major axis but different eccentricities and so slightly different energies. Thus, the energy radiated when the electron changes orbit depends slightly on the eccentricities of the initial and final orbits as well as on their major axes. The splitting of the energy levels is called *fine-structure splitting*, and the dimensionless constant

$$\alpha = \frac{Ke^2}{\hbar c} = \frac{1}{137} \qquad\qquad (4\text{--}33)$$

is called the *fine-structure constant*. As we shall see in Chapter 7, fine structure is associated with a completely nonclassical property of the electron called *spin*. Though the Sommerfeld explanation does not provide the correct picture, it is remarkable because the result of his calculation agrees perfectly with experiment and also with a detailed and complex calculation based on the Dirac relativistic wave equation, which includes spin.

4·4

X-RAY SPECTRA   The extension of the Bohr theory to atoms more complicated than hydrogen proved difficult. Although quantitative calculations of the energy levels of complex atoms could not be made from the Bohr model, strong evidence was furnished through experiments by

H. Moseley in 1913 and J. Franck and G. Hertz in 1914 to support the general Bohr-Rutherford picture of the atom as a positively charged core surrounded by electrons that moved in quantized energy states relatively far from the core. Moseley's analysis of x-ray spectra will be discussed in this section; the Franck-Hertz measurement of the transmission of electrons through gases will be discussed in the next section.

Using the methods of crystal spectrometry that had just been developed by W. H. and W. L. Bragg, Moseley measured the wavelengths of the characteristic x-ray line spectrum for about 40 different target elements. (Figure 3–15, shows a Bragg crystal spectrometer, and Figure 3–16 shows a typical x-ray spectrum.) He noted that the x-ray line spectrum varied in a regular way from element to element, unlike the irregular variations of optical spectra. He surmised that this regular variation was because characteristic x rays were due to transitions involving the innermost electrons of the atoms. Because of the shielding of the other electrons, the inner-electron energies do not depend on the details of the complex interactions of the outer electrons which are responsible for the complicated optical spectra. Also, the inner electrons are well shielded from the interatomic forces responsible for the binding of the atoms in solids.

According to the Bohr theory (published earlier the same year, 1913), the energy of an electron in the first Bohr orbit was proportional to the square of the nuclear charge. Moseley thus reasoned that the energy, and therefore the frequency, of a characteristic x-ray photon should vary as the square of the atomic number of the target element. He therefore plotted the square root of the frequency of a particular x-ray line versus the atomic number Z of the element. Such a plot, now called a *Moseley plot*, is shown in Figure 4–19. These curves can be fitted by the equation

$$f^{1/2} = A(Z - b) \qquad\qquad (4\text{--}34)$$

where A and b are constants for each line. One family of lines, called the *K series*, has $b = 1$ and different values for A. The other family shown in Figure 4–19, called the *L series*, could be fitted by Eq. (4–34) with $b = 7.4$.

If the bombarding electron in the x-ray tube knocks an electron from the inner orbit $N = 1$ in a target atom completely out of the atom, photons will be emitted corresponding to transitions of other electrons to the vacancy in the $n = 1$ orbit. (This orbit was called the *K shell*; thus the name "*K series*" for these lines.) The lowest-frequency line corresponds to the lowest-energy transition, $n = 2$ to $n = 1$. This line is called the K_α *line*. Using the Bohr relation for a one-electron atom [Eq. (4–27)] for $n_1 = 1$ and using $(Z - 1)$ in

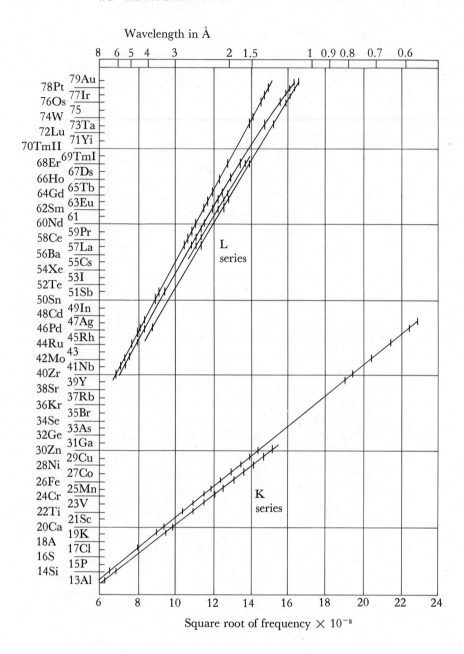

figure 4-19   *Moseley's plots of $f^{1/2}$ versus Z for x rays. When an atom is bombarded by high energy electrons, an inner atomic electron is sometimes knocked out leaving a vacancy in the inner shell. The K series x rays are produced by atomic transitions to vacancies in the $n = 1$ (K) shell, whereas the L series is produced by transitions to vacancies in the $n = 2$ (L) shell. [From Moseley,* Philosophical Magazine, **27**, *713 (1914).]*

place of Z, we obtain for the frequencies of the K series

$$
\begin{aligned}
f &= \frac{2\pi^2 m K^2 e^4}{h^3}(Z-1)^2\left(\frac{1}{1^2}-\frac{1}{n^2}\right) \\
&= f_R(Z-1)^2\left(\frac{1}{1^2}-\frac{1}{n^2}\right)
\end{aligned}
\tag{4–35}
$$

where f_R is the Rydberg frequency. Comparing this expression with Eq. (4–34), we see that A is given by

$$
A^2 = f_R\left(\frac{1}{1^2}-\frac{1}{n^2}\right)
\tag{4–36}
$$

The wavelength for the K_α line of molybdenum, $Z = 42$, calculated from Eq. (4–35) is

$$
\lambda = \frac{c}{f} = \frac{1}{R(1-\frac{1}{4})(42-1)^2} = 0.725 \text{ Å}
$$

which compares well with the value $\lambda = 0.721$ Å measured by Moseley.

The fact that f is proportional to $(Z-1)^2$ rather than to Z^2 is explained by the shielding of the nuclear charge by another electron remaining in the K shell. Using this reasoning, Moseley concluded that, since $b = 7.4$ for the L series, these lines involved electrons farther from the nucleus, which was thus shielded by more electrons. Assuming that the L series was due to transitions to the $n = 2$ shell, the lowest frequency L_α of this series is

$$
f_{L\alpha} = f_R\left(\frac{1}{2^2}-\frac{1}{3^2}\right)(Z-7.4)^2
\tag{4–37}
$$

Before Moseley's work the atomic number was merely the place number of the element in Mendeleev's periodic table of the elements arranged by weight. The atomic number was known to be approximately $A/2$ (where A is the atomic weight). The experiments of Geiger and Marsden showed that the nuclear charge was approximately $A/2$, while x-ray scattering experiments by Barkla showed that the number of electrons in an atom was approximately $A/2$, agreeing with the observation of neutral atoms. Several discrepancies were found in the periodic table as arranged by weight. For example, the eighteenth element by weight (following chlorine) is potassium (39.102) and the nineteenth is argon (39.948). Arrangement by weight puts potassium in the column with the inert gases and argon with the active metals, contrary to their known chemical properties. Moseley showed that for these elements to fall on the line $f^{1/2}$ versus Z, Z for argon had to be 18 and for potassium 19. Arranging the elements by the number Z, obtained from the Moseley plot, gave a

figure 4–20

Henry G. J. Moseley.
(Courtesy of University
of Manchester.)

(a)

(b)

(c)

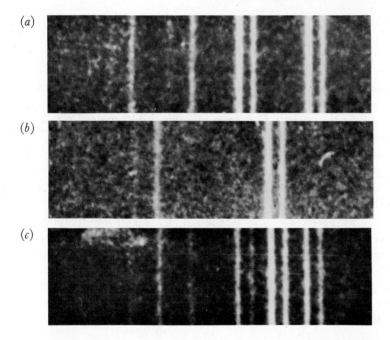

figure 4–21   Characteristic x-ray spectra. (a) Part of the spectra of neodymium ($Z = 60$)
and samarium ($Z = 62$). (b) Part of the spectrum of the synthetic element
promethium ($Z = 61$). This element was first positively identified in 1945
at the Clinton Laboratory (now Oak Ridge). (c) Part of the spectra of the
three elements, neodymium, promethium, and samarium. (Courtesy of Dr.
J. A. Swartout, Oak Ridge National Laboratory.)

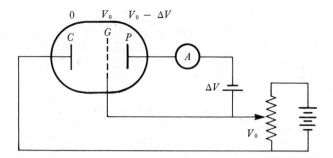

figure 4–22   Schematic diagram of Franck-Hertz experiment. Electrons ejected from heated cathode at zero potential are drawn by the positive grid and reach the plate if they have sufficient energy to overcome the small back potential ΔV.

periodic chart in complete agreement with the chemical properties. We quote from the summary of Moseley's second paper.[1]

"1. Every element from aluminum to gold is characterized by an integer Z which determines its x-ray spectrum. Every detail in the spectrum of an element can therefore be predicted from the spectra of its neighbors.

"2. This integer Z, the atomic number of the element, is identified with the number of positive units of electricity contained in the atomic nucleus.

"3. The atomic numbers for all elements from Al to Au have been tabulated on the assumption that Z for Al is 13.

"4. The order of the atomic numbers is the same as that of the atomic weights, except where the latter disagrees with the order of the chemical properties.

"5. Known elements correspond with all the numbers between 13 and 79 except three. There are here three possible elements still undiscovered.

"6. The frequency of any line in the x-ray spectrum is approximately proportional to $A(Z - b)^2$, where A and b are constants."

4·5

THE FRANCK-HERTZ
EXPERIMENT

An important experiment confirming Bohr's hypothesis of energy quantization in atoms was done in 1914 by J. Franck and G. Hertz. (This is now a standard undergraduate laboratory experiment.) Figure 4–22 is a schematic sketch of the apparatus. Electrons are

[1]*Philosophical Magazine,* **27**, 713 (1914). In this paper Moseley used N for the atomic number. We have changed this to Z in this excerpt to conform with our notation, which is standard today.

ejected from a heated cathode and accelerated toward a grid which is at a potential V_0 (taking the cathode as zero potential). Some electrons pass through the grid and reach the plate P, which is at a slightly lower potential, $V_p = V_0 - \Delta V$. The tube is filled with mercury vapor. The experiment involves measuring the plate current as a function of V_0. As V_0 is increased from 0, the current increases until a critical value (about 4.9 volts for Hg) is reached, at which point the current suddenly decreases. As V_0 is increased further, the current rises again. The explanation of this result is that the first excited state of Hg (i.e., the next to the lowest energy level) is about 4.9 eV above the lowest level (ground state). Electrons of energy less than this amount cannot lose energy to the Hg atoms, but electrons with energy greater than 4.9 eV can make inelastic collisions and lose 4.9 eV. If this happens near the grid, these electrons cannot gain enough energy to overcome the small back voltage ΔV and reach the plate; thus the current decreases. If this explanation is correct, the Hg atoms that are excited to an energy level of 4.9 eV above the ground state should return to the

figure 4–23   *Current versus V_0 in the Franck-Hertz experiment. The current decreases because many electrons lose energy due to inelastic collisions with mercury atoms in the tube and therefore cannot overcome the small back potential indicated in Figure 4–22. The regular spacing of the peaks in this curve indicates that only a certain quantity of energy, 4.9 eV, can be lost to the mercury atoms. This interpretation is confirmed by the observation of radiation of energy 4.9 eV emitted by the mercury atoms, when V_0 is greater than this energy. [From J. Franck and G. Hertz, Verhand. Deut. Physik. Ges., 16, 457 (1914).]*

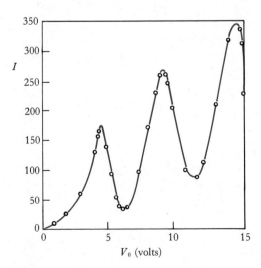

V_0 (volts)

ground state by emitting light of wavelength

$$\lambda = \frac{c}{f} = \frac{hc}{eV_0} = \frac{1.24 \times 10^4 \text{ eV-\AA}}{4.9 \text{ eV}} = 2{,}530 \text{ \AA}$$

There is indeed a line of this wavelength in the mercury spectrum. When the tube is viewed with a spectroscope, this line is seen when V_0 is greater than 4.9 V, while no lines are seen when V_0 is less than this amount. For further increases in V_0, additional sharp decreases in the current are observed, corresponding either to excitation of other levels in Hg or to multiple excitation of the first excited state, i.e., due to an electron losing 4.9 eV more than once. (In the usual setup, multiple excitations of the first level are observed; dips are noticed every 4.9 eV. The probability of observing this, or excitation of other levels, depends on the detailed variation of the potential in the tube. The reader is referred to Melissinos, *Experiments in Modern Physics*, Academic Press, Inc., New York, 1966, page 8, for details of this experiment.) A plot of the data of Franck and Hertz is shown in Figure 4–23.

The Franck-Hertz experiment was an important confirmation of the idea that discrete optical spectra were due to the existence of discrete energy levels in atoms which could be excited by non-optical methods. It is particularly gratifying to be able to detect the existence of discrete energy levels by measurements, using only voltmeters and ammeters.

4·6

WILSON-SOMMERFELD QUANTIZATION RULE

It was peculiar that Bohr could derive the hydrogen spectrum by postulating the quantization of angular momentum $L = n\hbar$, while Einstein and Planck had used the quantization of energy $E = nhf$ to obtain the specific heats of solids and the spectral distribution of blackbody radiation. Certainly there had to be some connection between these quantum postulates; yet just what the connection was, was a mystery for some time. In 1916, Wilson and Sommerfeld announced a general rule for the quantization of periodic systems. Their rule is

$$\oint P \, dq = nh \tag{4–38}$$

where P can be a component of momentum such as P_x, in which case q is the corresponding coordinate x, or P can be a component of angular momentum such as L_z, in which case q is the angle ϕ associated with rotation about the z axis. The symbol $\oint$ indicates that the integral is to be taken over one cycle. For many cases, the evaluation of Eq. (4–38) is somewhat involved. We give three examples in this section.

Example 4–1   *Particle moving in a circle in a central field.* The Wilson-Sommerfeld condition for this problem is

$$\oint L \, d\phi = nh$$

Since the angular momentum is constant, this becomes

$$L \oint d\phi = nh$$

The integration of $d\phi$ for one cycle gives 2π; thus

$$L = \frac{nh}{2\pi} = n\hbar$$

which is the Bohr quantum condition.

*

Example 4–2   *Simple harmonic motion.* Newton's law of motion for a mass m on a spring of force constant K is

$$-Kx = m \frac{d^2x}{dt^2}$$

A solution of this equation is

$$x = A \sin \omega t \tag{4–39}$$

where A is the amplitude and ω is the angular frequency $\omega = 2\pi f = \sqrt{K/m}$. The sum of the potential energy, $\frac{1}{2}Kx^2$ and the kinetic energy $P^2/2m$ is constant and just equal to the maximum value of either:

$$E = \tfrac{1}{2}KA^2 = \tfrac{1}{2}m\omega^2 A^2 \tag{4–40}$$

Using Eq. (4–39), we can calculate dx and the momentum P. We have

$$dx = \omega A \cos \omega t \, dt$$
$$P = m \frac{dx}{dt} = m \, \omega A \cos \omega t$$

Thus

$$\oint P \, dx = \oint m\omega^2 A^2 \cos^2 \omega t \, dt = nh$$

or

$$2E \oint \cos^2 \omega t \, dt = nh$$

where we have used $m\omega^2 A^2 = 2E$. If we let $\theta = \omega t$, the integration over one cycle corresponds to integrating θ from 0 to 2π. We have thus

$$\frac{2E}{\omega} \int_0^{2\pi} \cos^2 \theta \, d\theta = \frac{2E}{\omega} \pi = nh$$

or

$$E = \frac{nh\omega}{2\pi} = nhf = n\hbar\omega \qquad (4\text{-}41)$$

This is the condition used by Planck and Einstein for the quantization of oscillators.

*

Example 4-3 A particle of mass m moves back and forth in a one-dimensional box of size L. No forces act on the particle except when it hits the walls and is reflected elastically. If we consider the particle at the left wall at the beginning of the cycle, we have

$$\oint P \, dx = \int_0^L (+mv) \, dx + \int_L^0 (-mv) \, dx = 2mvL = nh$$

or

$$P = mv = \frac{nh}{2L}$$

Assuming the particle to be nonrelativistic, the energy is

$$E = \tfrac{1}{2}mv^2 = \frac{P^2}{2m} = n^2 \frac{h^2}{8mL^2} \qquad (4\text{-}42)$$

*

figure 4-24 *Particle moving with constant speed in a box of length L. The Wilson-Sommerfeld quantization rule predicts that the momentum is quantized to the values $P_n = nh/2L$, where n is an integer.*

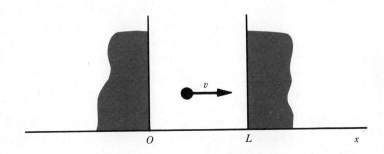

O L x

**4·7
CRITIQUE OF THE
BOHR THEORY AND
OF "OLD
QUANTUM
MECHANICS"**

We have seen in this and the preceding chapters that many phenomena — blackbody radiation, the photoelectric effect, Compton scattering, specific heats, optical spectra of hydrogen, and x-ray spectra of many elements — could be "explained" by various quantum assumptions, all of which could be summarized by the Wilson-Sommerfeld quantum rule. This "theory" is now usually referred to as "old quantum mechanics." It is a strange mixture of classical physics and quantum assumptions. The application of this quantum mechanics in the early years of the twentieth century was more of an art form than a science, for no one knew exactly what the rules were. The successes of the Bohr theory were spectacular. The existence of unknown spectral lines was predicted and later observed. Not only was the Rydberg constant given in terms of known constants, but its slight variation from atom to atom was accurately predicted by the slight variation in the reduced mass. The radius of the first Bohr orbit in hydrogen, 0.53 Å, corresponded well with the known diameter of the hydrogen molecule, about 2.2 Å. The wavelengths of the characteristic x-ray spectra could be calculated from the Bohr theory.

The failures of the Bohr theory and the "old quantum mechanics" were mainly those of omission. There was no way of predicting the relative intensities of spectral lines. There was little success in applying the theory to the optical spectra of more complex atoms. Finally, there was the philosophical problem of the lack of a foundation for the assumptions. There were no a priori reasons to expect that Coulomb's law would work but that the laws of radiation would not, or that Newton's laws could be used even though only certain values of the angular momentum were allowed. Though the Wilson-Sommerfeld quantization rule worked well for periodic systems, it was not known why, and there was no theory at all for nonperiodic systems. In the decade 1920 to 1930, scientists struggled with these difficulties, and a systematic theory, now known as *quantum mechanics* or *wave mechanics*, was formulated by de Broglie, Schroedinger, Heisenberg, Pauli, Dirac, and others. We shall study this theory in the next two chapters and apply it to the study of atoms, nuclei, and solids in the remaining chapters of this book. We shall see that, though this theory is much more satisfying from a philosophical point of view, it is somewhat abstract and difficult to apply in detail to problems. In spite of its shortcomings, the Bohr theory provides a model that is easy to visualize, gives the correct energy levels in hydrogen, and is often useful in describing a quantum-mechanical calculation.

SUMMARY   The scattering of α particles indicates that the positive charge in an atom is concentrated in a small nucleus which, for gold, has a radius of about 10^{-14} meter. The charge on the nucleus is Ze, where Z is the atomic number (place number in the periodic table).

If the incoming intensity is I_0 (particles/sec-area), the number per second scattered by one atom at angles greater than θ is related to the impact parameter b by

$$N_{>\theta} = I_0 \pi b^2(\theta)$$

The cross section σ is defined as the number scattered per atom divided by the incident intensity. The cross section has dimensions of area and represents the effective area of an atom for scattering. The cross section for scattering through angles greater than θ is

$$\sigma_{>\theta} = \frac{N_{>\theta}}{I_0} = \pi b^2(\theta)$$

The impact parameter for Rutherford scattering is related to the scattering angle by

$$b = \tfrac{1}{2}D \cot \tfrac{1}{2}\theta$$

where the distance of closest approach for a head-on collision is

$$D = \frac{Kq_a Q}{\tfrac{1}{2}MV^2}$$

The cross section for scattering between θ and $\theta + d\theta$ is

$$d\sigma = \left(\frac{Z^2 Ke^2}{MV^2}\right)^2 \frac{d\Omega_\theta}{\sin^4 \tfrac{1}{2}\theta}$$

where $d\Omega_\theta = 2\pi \sin \theta \, d\theta$ is the solid angle between θ and $\theta + d\theta$. The number per second scattered into $d\theta$ per solid angle by a foil of n atoms/cm^3 of thickness t and area A is obtained by multiplying $d\sigma/d\Omega_\theta$ by I_0 and the number of atoms in the foil, ntA. Since the number incident per second is $I_0 A$, the fraction scattered per unit solid angle by a foil is $(d\sigma/d\Omega_\theta) \, nt$.

The Bohr postulates are:

1. Electrons move in certain nonradiating, stable, circular orbits consistent with Coulomb's law and Newton's law and specified by the quantization of angular momentum

$$L = mvr = \frac{nh}{2\pi} = n\hbar$$

where $h =$ Planck's constant and n is an integer.

2. Radiation of frequency $f = (W_1 - W_2)/h$ occurs when the electron jumps from orbit 1 of energy W_1 to orbit 2 of energy W_2.

These postulates lead to

$$r_n = n^2 \frac{a_0}{Z}$$

where $a_0 = (\hbar c / Ke^2)(\hbar c / mc^2) \approx 0.529$ Å for the allowed electron-orbits, and

$$E_n = -Z^2 \frac{E_1}{n^2}$$

where $E_n = \frac{1}{2}(Ke^2/\hbar c)^2 mc^2$ and $n = 1, 2, 3, \ldots$.

The Wilson-Sommerfeld quantization rule for periodic systems,

$$\oint P \, dq = nh$$

leads to

$$L = n\hbar \qquad \text{for circular motion}$$
$$E = nhf \qquad \text{for simple harmonic motion}$$
$$E = n^2 \frac{h^2}{8mL^2} \qquad \text{for a particle in a rigid box}$$

Some useful combinations of physical constants are

$$hc = 1.24 \times 10^4 \text{ eV-Å}$$
$$\hbar c = \frac{h}{2\pi} c = 1.97 \times 10^3 \text{ eV-Å}$$
$$Ke^2 = (1/4\pi\epsilon_0)e^2 = 14.4 \text{ eV-Å}$$
$$\alpha = \frac{Ke^2}{\hbar c} \simeq \frac{1}{137}$$

REFERENCES   Many original papers, including those quoted in this and the preceding chapters, can be found in *The World of the Atom* (Ref. 2, Chapter 2) or in *Great Experiments in Physics* (Ref. 2, Chapter 3).

1. A. Melissinos, *Experiments in Modern Physics*, Academic Press, Inc., New York, 1966. Many of the classic experiments that are now undergraduate laboratory experiments are described in detail in this text.
2. Richtmyer, Kennard, and Lauritsen, *Introduction to Modern Physics*, McGraw-Hill Book Company, New York, 1955. This is the fifth

edition of an excellent text originally published in 1928 and intended as a survey course for graduate students.

3. B. Cline, *The Questioners: Physicists and the Quantum Theory,* Thomas Y. Crowell Company, New York, 1965.
4. G. Gamow, *Thirty Years That Shook Physics, the Story of the Quantum Theory,* Doubleday & Company, Inc., Garden City, New York, 1965.

References 3 and 4 are interesting accounts of the development of the quantum theory and the interactions of the people involved.

PROBLEMS

SET A

4-1. If a particle is deflected by 0.01° in each collision, about how many collisions would be necessary to produce an rms deflection of 10°? (Use the results of the one-dimensional random-walk problem.) Compare this result with the number of atomic layers in a gold foil of thickness 10^{-4} cm, assuming the thickness of each atom is 1 Å $= 10^{-8}$ cm.

4-2. (*a*) Calculate the distance of closest approach, D, for a 5-MeV α particle incident on a gold nucleus. (*b*) What is the impact parameter b for scattering of this particle through 10°? (*c*) What fraction of the incident beam is scattered through angles greater than 10° by a gold foil 10^{-4} cm thick?

4-3. Calculate the distance of closest approach for an 8-MeV α particle making a head-on collision with the nucleus of an aluminum atom, $Z = 13$.

4-4. Show that Eq. (4-25) for the radius of the first Bohr orbit and Eq. (4-29) for the magnitude of the lowest energy for hydrogen can be written as

$$a_0 = \frac{\hbar c}{\alpha mc^2} = \frac{\lambda_c}{2\pi\alpha}$$

$$E_1 = \tfrac{1}{2}\alpha^2 mc^2$$

where $\lambda_c = h/mc$ is the Compton wavelength of the electron and $\alpha = Ke^2/\hbar c \approx \frac{1}{137}$ is the fine-structure constant. Use these expressions to check the numerical values of the constants a_0 and E_1.

4-5. Show that the Rydberg constant can be written $R = \tfrac{1}{2}\alpha^2 mc^2/hc$ and use this to calculate R in cm^{-1}. (See Problem 4-4.)

4-6. (*a*) Calculate the three longest wavelengths in the Lyman series ($n_2 = 1$) in angstroms and indicate their position on a horizontal linear scale. Indicate the series limit (shortest wavelength) on this scale. Are any of these lines in the visible spectrum?

(b) What series in hydrogen, other than the Lyman, has the shortest wavelength? What is this wavelength?

4-7. Calculate the longest three wavelengths and the series limit for the Paschen ($n_2 = 3$) and the Brackett ($n_2 = 4$) series, and plot both series on the same linear scale.

4-8. It is possible for a muon to be captured by a proton to form a μ-mesic atom. A muon is identical to an electron except for its mass, which is 105.7 MeV/c^2. (a) Calculate the radius of the first Bohr orbit of a μ-mesic atom. (b) Calculate the magnitude of the lowest energy. (c) What is the shortest wavelength in the Lyman series for this atom?

4-9. The wavelength of the K_α x-ray line for an element is measured as 0.794 Å. What is the element?

4-10. The wavelength of the K_α x-ray line for an element is 3.368 Å. What is the element?

4-11. (a) Calculate the ground-state energy of helium ($Z = 2$), assuming that the two electrons are in the $n = 1$ orbit and neglecting any interaction between them.

(b) The farthest apart these electrons can be while in the same orbit is twice the radius of the orbit. Assuming their mutual repulsion keeps them this far apart, calculate the postive energy of interaction $+Ke^2/2r$.

(c) The ionization energy is the energy needed to remove one electron. Estimate this for helium, based on your results for part a and b. The measured value is about 24.6 eV.

4-12. In the lithium atom ($Z = 3$), two electrons are in the $n = 1$ orbit and the third is in the $n = 2$ orbit. (Only two are allowed in the $n = 1$ orbit because of the exclusion principle discussed in Chapter 8.) The interaction of the inner electrons with the outer one can be approximated by writing the energy of the outer electron as

$$W = -Z'^2 \frac{E_1}{n^2}$$

where $E_1 = 13.6$ eV, $n = 2$, and Z' is the effective nuclear charge, which is less than 3 due to the screening effect of the two inner electrons. Using the measured ionization energy of 5.39 eV, calculate Z'.

SET B

4-13. Show that Eqs. (4–18), (4–21), and (4–25) imply that the angular momentum of the electron in a circular orbit in the hydrogen atom is given by $L = nh/2\pi = n\hbar$.

4–14. Starting with the Bohr postulates stated on page 169, derive the equations

$$r_n = n^2 \frac{a_0}{Z}$$

$$E_n = -Z^2 \frac{E_1}{n^2}$$

where

$$a_0 = \frac{\hbar c}{Ke^2} \frac{\hbar c}{mc^2}$$

$$E_1 = \frac{1}{2}\left(\frac{Ke^2}{\hbar c}\right)^2 mc^2$$

4–15. A small shot of negligible radius hits a stationary smooth hard sphere of radius R, making an angle β with the normal to the sphere, as shown in Figure 4–25. It is reflected at an angle β to the normal. The scattering angle is $\theta = 180 - 2\beta$, as shown.

(a) Show by the geometry of the figure that θ is related to the impact parameter by $b = R \cos \frac{1}{2}\theta$.

(b) If the incoming intensity of the shot is I_0 particle/sec-area, how many are scattered through angles greater than θ?

(c) What is the cross section for scattering through angles greater than θ?

(d) Find the differential cross section $d\sigma/d\Omega$ and show that it is independent of θ or ϕ.

(e) Show that the total scattering cross section σ, defined by

$$\sigma \equiv \iint_\Omega \frac{d\sigma}{d\Omega}\, d\Omega$$

equals πR^2, in agreement with your answer to part c.

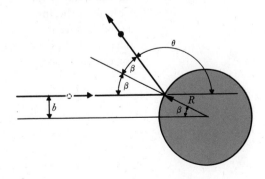

figure 4–25

Small particle scattered by a hard sphere of radius R.

4-16. Assume that a gold nucleus of radius 8×10^{-13} cm acts like a hard sphere for the scattering of uncharged particles (such as neutrons). What fraction of uncharged point particles will be deflected at all by nuclei in a gold foil of thickness 10^{-4} cm? (Use the result of Problem 4–15 that the total cross section for hard-sphere scattering is πR^2.)

4-17. Make an energy-level diagram for a charged-particle oscillator in simple harmonic motion, using the Wilson-Sommerfeld result for the energies $E_n = nhf_0$, where f_0 is the frequency of oscillation. Indicate transitions on this diagram for which $n_2 = n_1 \pm 1$. Show that the frequencies of radiation given by the Bohr condition in Eq. (4–16) for these transitions are the same as those expected classically.

4-18. Make an energy-level diagram for a particle of mass equal to that of an electron in a one-dimensional box of length $L = 1$ Å, using the Wilson-Sommerfeld result for the energies

$$E_n = n^2 \frac{hc}{8mc^2} \frac{hc}{L^2}$$

Calculate the wavelengths for transitions to the ground state $n = 1$ from the states $n = 4$, $n = 3$, and $n = 2$.

4-19. For the energy levels given in Problem 4–18, show that the frequency of radiation emitted for the transition n to $n - 1$ equals the frequency of motion when $n \gg 1$ in accord with Bohr's correspondence principle.

4-20. Show that a small change in the reduced mass of the electron produces a small change in a spectral line given by $\Delta\lambda/\lambda \approx -\Delta m/m$. Use this to calculate the difference $\Delta\lambda$ in the Balmer red line $\lambda = 6,563$ Å between hydrogen and deuterium which has a nucleus with twice the mass of hydrogen.

4-21. What is the magnitude of the lowest energy $(n = 1)$, for a proton in a one-dimensional box of the size of the gold nucleus, $L \approx 16$ F $(= 16 \times 10^{-13}$ cm)? Use $m = 938$ MeV/c^2 for the mass of the proton.

4-22. Calculate the lowest energy for an electron in a one-dimensional box of size $L = 16 \times 10^{-5}$ Å. [Note that Eq. (4–42) does not hold because the electron is relativistic. Use $E \approx pc$ for the electron.]

FIVE
ELECTRON
WAVES

**THE DE BROGLIE
RELATIONS**
In 1924 a French student, L. de Broglie, suggested in his dissertation that, since light was known to have both wave and particle properties, perhaps matter — namely, electrons — might also have wave as well as particle characteristics. This suggestion was highly speculative; there was no evidence at that time for any wave aspects of electrons. For the frequency and wavelength of electron waves, de Broglie chose the equations

$$f = \frac{E}{h} \tag{5-1}$$

$$\lambda = \frac{h}{p} \tag{5-2}$$

where p is the momentum and E the energy of the electron, in analogy with the identical equations that hold for photons. He pointed out that the Bohr quantum condition for angular momentum $L = nh/2\pi$ was equivalent to the condition for standing waves

$$n\lambda = 2\pi r = S$$

where S is the circumference of the circular Bohr orbit. The idea

187

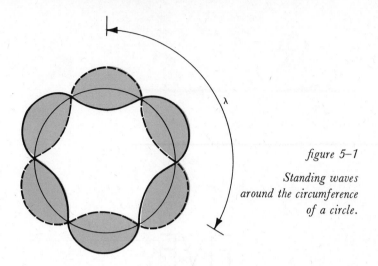

figure 5–1

Standing waves around the circumference of a circle.

of explaining discrete energy states in matter by standing waves seemed quite promising. The Wilson-Sommerfeld quantum rule could be interpreted as the standing-wave condition. For example, the Wilson-Sommerfeld quantum condition for the particle in a one-dimensional box of size L (Example 4–3, in Section 4–6), is $p = nh/2L$; using $p = h/\lambda$, this condition is $n(\lambda/2) = L$. This is identical to the condition for standing waves on a string fixed at both ends.

The ideas of de Broglie were expanded and developed into a complete theory by E. Schroedinger later in 1924. In 1927, Davisson and Germer verified Eqs. (5–1) and (5–2) directly by observing interference patterns with electron beams. It is easy to see why wave properties of matter were not readily observed if we recall that the wave properties of light were not noted until apertures or slits the same size as the wavelength of light could be obtained. When the wavelength of light is much smaller than any aperture, the diffraction and interference effects are not observable and the light obeys geometric or ray optics. Because of the smallness of Planck's constant, the wavelength given by Eq. (5–2) is extremely small for any macroscopic object.

figure 5–2 *Standing waves in a one-dimensional box.*

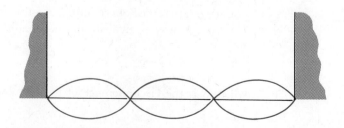

Example 5–1 What is the de Broglie wavelength for a very small but macroscopic object of mass 10^{-9} gram moving with speed 3×10^{-8} m/sec?

$$\lambda = \frac{h}{mv} = \frac{hc}{mc^2 v/c} = \frac{1.24 \times 10^4 \text{ eV-Å}}{(5.61 \times 10^{23} \text{ eV})(10^{-16})}$$

$$= 2 \times 10^{-4} \text{ Å}$$

where we have used $mc^2 = 5.61 \times 10^{32}$ eV/g. This is much smaller than any possible aperture.

*

The case is different for low-energy electrons. Consider an electron that has been accelerated through V_0 volts. Its energy is then

$$E = \frac{p^2}{2m} = eV_0$$

and

$$\lambda = \frac{h}{p} = \frac{hc}{pc} = \frac{hc}{(2mc^2 eV_0)^{1/2}}$$

Putting in $hc = 1.24 \times 10^4$ eV-Å and $mc^2 = 0.51 \times 10^6$ eV, we obtain

$$\lambda = \frac{12.25}{V_0^{1/2}} \text{ Å} \tag{5-3}$$

Example 5–2 What is the de Broglie wavelength of a 10-eV electron? Putting $V_0 = 10$ we have

$$\lambda = \frac{12.25}{\sqrt{10}} \approx 3.9 \text{ Å}$$

Though this wavelength is small, it is just the order of magnitude of the size of the atom and of the spacing of atoms in a crystal.

*

5·2
MEASUREMENTS OF ELECTRON WAVELENGTHS

The first measurements of the wavelengths of electrons were made in 1927 by C. J. Davisson and L. H. Germer, who were studying electron reflection from a nickel target at Bell Telephone Laboratories. After heating their target to remove an oxide coating that had accumulated during an accidental break in their vacuum system, they found that the scattered electron intensity as a function of the scattering angle showed maxima and minima. Their target

figure 5–3   *Louis V. de Broglie.*
(Courtesy of Culver Pictures, Inc.)

figure 5–4

The Davisson-Germer
experiment.
Electrons scattered
at angle φ from a
nickel crystal are detected
in an ionization chamber.

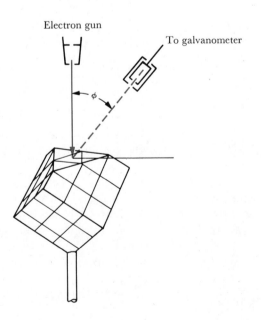

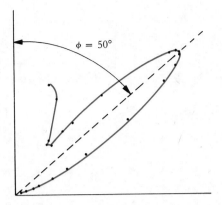

figure 5–5   *Polar plot of the scattering intensity versus angle for 54 eV electrons. (The intensity at a given angle is indicated by the distance of the point from the origin.) There is a maximum intensity at $\phi = 50°$, as predicted by Bragg-scattering of waves having wavelength $\lambda = h/p$. (From* Nobel Prize Lectures: Physics, *Elsevier, Amsterdam, New York, © Nobel Foundation, 1964.)*

had crystallized and they were observing electron diffraction. They then prepared a target consisting of a single crystal of nickel and extensively investigated the scattering of electrons from it. Figure 5–4 illustrates their experimental arrangement. Their data for 54-eV electrons, shown in Figure 5–5, indicate a strong maximum of scattering at $\phi = 50°$. Consider the scattering from a set of Bragg planes, as shown in Figure 5–6. The Bragg condition for constructive interference is $n\lambda = 2d \sin \alpha = 2d \cos \theta$. The spacing of the Bragg planes d is related to the spacing of the atoms D by $d = D \sin \theta$; thus

$$n\lambda = 2D \sin \theta \cos \theta = D \sin 2\theta$$

or

$$n\lambda = D \sin \phi \tag{5–4}$$

where $\phi = 2\theta$ is the scattering angle.

The spacing D is known from x-ray diffraction to be 2.15 Å. The wavelength calculated from Eq. (5–4) is for $n = 1$,

$$\lambda = 2.15 \sin 50° = 1.65 \text{ Å}$$

This compares well with that calculated from the de Broglie relation

$$\lambda = \frac{12.25}{(54)^{1/2}} = 1.67 \text{ Å}$$

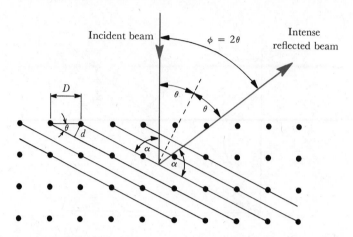

figure 5–6 *Scattering of electrons by a crystal. Electron waves are strongly scattered if the Bragg condition $n\lambda = 2d \sin \alpha$ is met. This is equivalent to the condition $n\lambda = D \sin \phi$.*

Figure 5–7 shows a plot of measured wavelengths versus $V_0^{-1/2}$. The wavelengths measured by diffraction are slightly lower than the theoretical predictions because the refraction of the electron waves at the crystal surface has been neglected. We have seen from the photoelectric effect that it takes work of the order of several eV to remove an electron from a metal. Electrons entering a metal gain kinetic energy; therefore, their de Broglie wavelength is slightly less inside the crystal. It is interesting to read Davisson's account of the connection between de Broglie's predictions and their experimental verification.[1]

"Perhaps no idea in physics has received so rapid or so intensive development as this one. De Broglie himself was in the van of this development, but the chief contributions were made by the older and more experienced Schroedinger.

"In these early days — eleven or twelve years ago — attention was focused on electron waves in atoms. The wave mechanics had sprung from the atom, so to speak, and it was natural that the first applications should be to the atom. No thought was given at this time, it appears, to electrons in free flight. It was implicit in the theory that beams of electrons like beams of light would exhibit the properties of waves, that scattered by an appropriate grating they would exhibit diffraction, yet none of the chief theorists mentioned this interesting corollary. The first to draw attention to it was Elsasser, who pointed out in 1925 that a demonstration of

[1]From *Nobel Prize Lectures: Physics*, Elsevier, Amsterdam, New York, © Nobel Foundation, 1964.

diffraction would establish the physical existence of electron waves. The setting of the stage for the discovery of electron diffraction was now complete.

"It would be pleasant to tell you that no sooner had Elsasser's suggestion appeared than the experiments were begun in New York which resulted in a demonstration of electron diffraction — pleasanter still to say that the work was begun the day after copies of de Broglie's thesis reached America. The true story contains less of perspicacity and more of chance. The work actually began in 1919 with the accidental discovery that the energy spectrum of secondary electron emission has, as its upper limit, the energy of the primary electrons, even for primaries accelerated through hundreds of volts; that there is, in fact, an elastic scattering of electrons by metals.

"Out of this grew an investigation of the distribution-in-angle of these elastically scattered electrons. And then chance again intervened; it was discovered, purely by accident, that the intensity of elastic scattering varies with the orientations of the scattering crystals. Out of this grew, quite naturally, an investigation of elastic scattering by a single crystal of predetermined orientation.

figure 5–7   Test of the de Broglie formula $\lambda = h/p = h/mv$. The wavelength, computed from diffraction data, is plotted against $V_0^{-1/2}$, where V_0 is the accelerating voltage. The straight line is $\lambda = 12.25 V_0^{-1/2}$ predicted from $\lambda = h(2mE)^{-1/2}$. ($\times$ From observations with diffraction apparatus; $\bigcirc$ same, particularly reliable; $\square$ same, grazing beams. $\odot$ From observations with reflection apparatus.) (From Nobel Prize Lectures: Physics, Elsevier, Amsterdam, New York, © Nobel Foundation, 1964.)

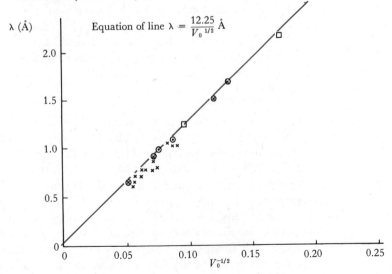

figure 5–8   Clinton J. Davisson (left) and Lester A. Germer. (Courtesy of Bell Telephone Laboratories, Inc.)

The initiation of this phase of the work occurred in 1925, the year following the publication of de Broglie's thesis, the year preceding the first great developments in the wave mechanics. Thus the New York experiment was not, at its inception, a test of the wave theory. Only in the summer of 1926, after I had discussed the investigation in England with Richardson, Born, Franck and others, did it take on this character.

"The search for diffraction beams was begun in the autumn of 1926, but not until early in the following year were any found — first one and then twenty others in rapid succession. Nineteen of these could be used to check the relationship between wavelength and momentum, and in every case the correctness of the de Broglie formula, $\lambda = h/p$, was verified to within the limit of accuracy of the measurements."

Another demonstration of the wave nature of electrons was provided in the same year by G. P. Thomson, who observed the transmission of electrons through thin metallic foils. (G. P. Thomson, son of J. J. Thomson, shared the Nobel Prize in 1937 with Davisson.) The experimental arrangement was similar to that used to obtain Laue patterns with x rays (see Figure 3–11). Because the metal foil contained many tiny crystals randomly oriented, the diffraction pattern consisted of concentric rings. If a crystal is oriented at an angle θ with the incident beam, where θ satisfies the Bragg condition, this crystal will strongly scatter at an equal angle θ; thus

figure 5–9   (a) *Diffraction pattern produced by x rays of wavelength* 0.71 Å *and an aluminum-foil target.* (b) *Diffraction pattern produced by* 600-*eV electrons* (*de Broglie wavelength of about* 0.5 Å) *and an aluminum-foil target. The pattern has been enlarged by* ×1.6 *for comparison with* (a). (*Courtesy of Film Studio, Education Development Center.*)

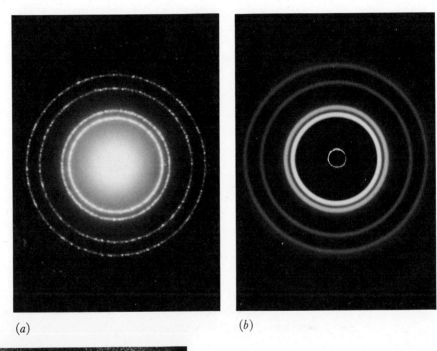

(a)   (b)

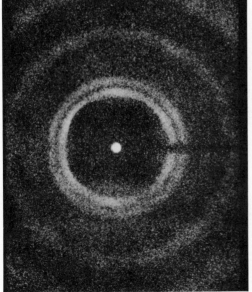

figure 5–10

Diffraction pattern produced by 0.0568 *eV neutrons* (*de Broglie wavelength of* 1.20 Å) *and a target of polycrystalline copper. Note the similarity in the patterns produced by x rays, electrons, and neutrons. (Courtesy of Dr. C. G. Shull.)*

there will be a scattered beam making an angle 2θ with the incident beam. Figures 5–9a and b show the similarities in patterns produced by x rays and electron waves.

In 1930 Stern and Estermann observed diffraction of hydrogen and helium atoms from a lithium fluoride crystal. Since then, diffraction of other atoms and of neutrons has been observed. In all cases the measured wavelengths agree with the de Broglie prediction.

Before we consider the implications of the wave properties of electrons, let us review some properties of classical waves.

5·3
CLASSICAL WAVE
EQUATIONS

A direct application of Newton's second law, $\mathbf{F} = m\mathbf{a}$, to a segment of a string of mass density $\rho = m/LA$, where L and A are the length and area of the string, gives for small displacements y,

$$(\rho A)\frac{\partial^2 y}{\partial t^2} = T\frac{\partial^2 y}{\partial x^2} \tag{5–5}$$

where T is the tension and $y(x,t)$ is the displacement of the string from the horizontal position. (See Figure 5–13.) If we let $v = (T/\rho A)^{1/2}$ we have

$$\frac{\partial^2 y}{\partial x^2} = \frac{1}{v^2}\frac{\partial^2 y}{\partial t^2} \tag{5–6}$$

Equation (5–6) is known as the *wave equation*. The student should verify that any function $y = f(x \pm vt)$ satisfies this equation. The solution $y = f(x - vt)$ represents a wave moving to the right

figure 5–11

Neutron Laue pattern of NaCl.
Compare this with the x-ray
Laue pattern in Figure 3–12.
(Courtesy of Dr. E. O. Wollan.)

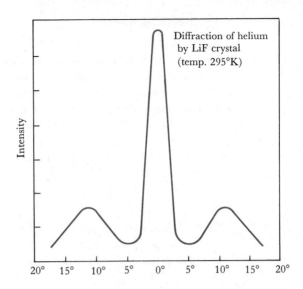

figure 5-12   *The diffraction pattern obtained with helium reflected from a lithium fluoride crystal. (From* Introduction to Atomic and Nuclear Physics, *4th edition, by Henry Semat. Copyright 1939, 1946, 1954, © 1962, 1967 by Henry Semat. Reprinted by permission of Holt, Rinehart and Winston, Inc.)*

(toward positive x) with speed v, since a constant displacement (phase) is maintained if $x - vt =$ constant. A similar application of Newton's law, along with the gas laws, leads to an equation identical to Eq. (5-6) for sound waves. For this case $y(x,t)$ is the displacement from equilibrium of gas particles, the pressure, or the density; and the velocity is given by $v = (\gamma P_0/\rho)^{1/2}$, where $\gamma = C_p/C_v$; P_0 is the equilibrium pressure and ρ the mass density.

figure 5-13   *Wave on a string. The net force in the y direction is $F_y = T \sin \theta_2 - T \sin \theta_1 \approx T \Delta S$, where $S = \tan \theta = \partial y/\partial x$ is the slope of the string. The mass element $\Delta m \approx \rho A \Delta x$ has acceleration $\partial^2 y/\partial t^2$. $F_y = ma_y$ thus gives $T \Delta S = \rho A \Delta x(\partial^2 y/\partial t^2)$. For small Δx, $\Delta S/\Delta x \approx \partial S/\partial x = \partial^2 y/\partial x^2$, thus the wave equation $T(\partial^2 y/\partial x^2) = \rho A(\partial^2 y/\partial t^2)$.*

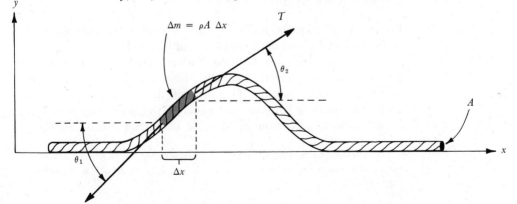

The laws of electrodynamics, summarized by Maxwell's equations, lead to this same equation where now $y(x,t)$ represents the electric or magnetic field and $v = c$, the speed of light. Since the form of the wave equation is identical for these three types of waves, many results obtained from the study of one of the phenomena can be applied to the others.

A particularly useful solution of the wave equation (5–6) is

$$y(x,t) = y_0 \cos 2\pi \left(\frac{x}{\lambda} - ft \right) = y_0 \cos \frac{2\pi}{\lambda} (x - vt) \qquad (5-7)$$

This is a wave traveling to the right with amplitude y_0, wavelength λ, frequency f, and velocity $v = f\lambda$. It is convenient to use the angular frequency, ω and wave number k, defined by[2]

$$\omega = 2\pi f \qquad \text{angular frequency} \qquad (5-8)$$

$$k = \frac{2\pi}{\lambda} \qquad \text{wave number} \qquad (5-9)$$

Equation (5–7) can then be written

$$y(x,t) = y_0 \cos (kx - \omega t) \qquad (5-10a)$$

Other forms of this type of solution are

$$y(x,t) = y_0 \sin (kx - \omega t) \qquad (5-10b)$$

and

$$y(x,t) = y_0 e^{i(kx - \omega t)} \qquad (5-10c)$$

Equation (5–10b) differs from (5–10a) only in the choice or origin of x or t. Equation (5–10c) is a linear combination of Eqs. (5–10a) and (5–10b) since

$$e^{i\theta} = \cos \theta + i \sin \theta \qquad (5-11)$$

Because $y(x,t)$ must be real, it is usually understood that the real or the imaginary part of the right side of Eq. (5–10c) is to be taken.

Consider an element of a string of length Δx, having mass $\Delta m = \rho A \, \Delta x$. As a wave travels along the string, this element undergoes simple harmonic motion. The sum of the kinetic energy and potential energy is constant and equal to the maximum potential energy (which is, of course, also the maximum kinetic energy),

[2]In spectroscopy, the quantity $\lambda^{-1} = k/2\pi$ is called the *wave number*. In the theory of waves, the term "wave number" is used for $k = 2\pi\lambda^{-1}$, which occurs very often.

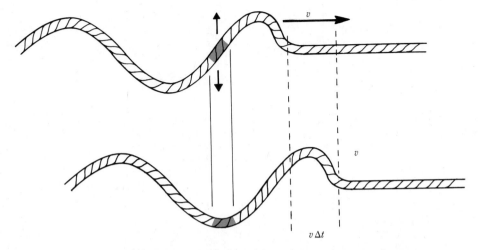

figure 5-14   *A segment of the string is executing simple harmonic motion with energy* $\Delta W = \frac{1}{2}\omega^2 y_0{}^2 \Delta m = \frac{1}{2}\omega^2 y_0{}^2 \rho A \Delta x$. *After time* Δt *the wave has moved distance* $v \Delta t$. *The intensity* $I = \Delta W / A \Delta t$ *is* ηv, *where* $\eta = \frac{1}{2}\omega^2 y_0{}^2$ *is the energy per unit volume.*

$\frac{1}{2}K y_0{}^2$, where y_0 is the maximum displacement, called the *amplitude* of the wave, and K is the force constant. If $\omega = 2\pi f$ is the angular frequency of vibration, $\omega = \sqrt{K/\Delta m}$, or $K = \Delta m \omega^2$. Thus the total energy of this string segment is

$$\Delta W = \tfrac{1}{2}\Delta m \omega^2 y_0{}^2 = \tfrac{1}{2}\omega^2 y_0{}^2 \rho A \Delta x$$

and the energy per unit volume is

$$\eta = \tfrac{1}{2}\rho\omega^2 y_0{}^2 \tag{5-12}$$

It is common to all waves that the energy density is proportional to the square of the amplitude. In a time Δt, the wave progresses along the string a distance $v \Delta t$, and the energy passing a cross section of the string is just that in the volume $Av \Delta t$, which is $\eta Av \Delta t$. The *intensity* is the energy per sec per unit area; thus

$$I = \eta v = \tfrac{1}{2}\rho\omega^2 y_0{}^2 v \tag{5-13}$$

This result is also common to all waves. For example, the intensity of an electromagnetic wave is proportional to the square of the electric field $\mathcal{E}$.

Although these solutions are very useful in discussing many wave phenomena (as can be seen by consulting various elementary physics textbooks), they are not sufficient for all interesting phenomena. The situation of standing waves should be familiar to most students. No *single* traveling wave can satisfy the boundary conditions of a

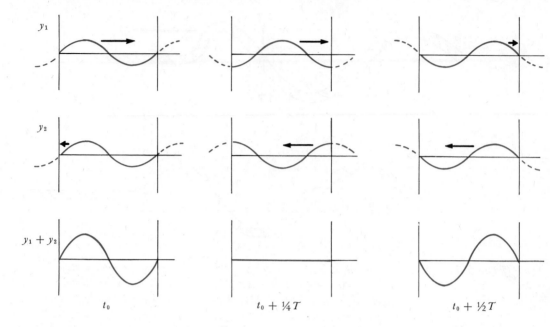

figure 5–15 *A standing wave can be considered to be the sum of a wave moving to the right,* y_1, *plus a wave moving to the left,* y_2.

string held fixed at $x = 0$ and $x = L$; however, the sum of two traveling waves,

$$y_0 \sin (kx - \omega t) + y_0 \sin (kx + \omega t) = 2y_0 \sin kx \cos \omega t$$

$$(5\text{–}14)$$

does for certain values of k and ω, namely,

$$k = n \frac{\pi}{L} \tag{5–15}$$

where n is an integer. Using $k = 2\pi/\lambda = 2\pi f/v$, we see that Eq. (5–15) is equivalent to

$$n \frac{\lambda}{2} = L \tag{5–16}$$

or

$$f = n \frac{v}{2L}$$

Thus the boundary condition that the ends of the string remain fixed, places a restriction on the possible wavelengths and frequencies given by the above equations.

5·4
WAVE PACKETS
Another familiar phenomenon not describable by a single traveling wave is that of a pulse, such as a sudden noise, a flip of one end of a long string, or the brief opening of a shutter in front of a light source. The main characteristic of a pulse is that of localization in time and space. A wave of a single frequency and wavelength such as any of those of Eqs. (5–10) has *no* localization in time or space. In order to describe a pulse, a group of waves of different frequencies and wavelengths must be taken. The range of wavelengths or frequencies needed depends on the extent in space (or time) of the pulse. In general, if the extent in space, Δx, is small, the range of wave numbers Δk must be large. The mathematics of representing arbitrarily shaped pulses by sums of sine or cosine functions involves Fourier series and Fourier integrals. Since this is beyond the scope of this book, we shall illustrate the phenomenon of a group of waves by considering some special cases. Wave groups are particularly important because a wave description of an electron must include the important property of localization of an electron.

Consider two waves of equal amplitude and nearly equal frequencies and wavelengths. Such a group occurs in the phenomenon of beats and is described in most elementary textbooks. Let the wave numbers be k_1 and k_2 and the angular frequencies ω_1 and ω_2. The sum of the two waves is

$$
\begin{aligned}
y(x,t) &= y_0 \cos (k_1 x - \omega_1 t) + y_0 \cos (k_2 x - \omega_2 t) \\
&= 2y_0 \cos \left[\tfrac{1}{2}(k_1 - k_2)x - \tfrac{1}{2}(\omega_1 - \omega_2)t\right] \\
&\quad \times \cos \left[\tfrac{1}{2}(k_1 + k_2)x - \tfrac{1}{2}(\omega_1 + \omega_2)t\right] \\
&= [2y_0 \cos (\tfrac{1}{2}\Delta kx - \tfrac{1}{2}\Delta \omega t)] \cos (\bar{k}x - \bar{\omega}t) \quad (5\text{–}17)
\end{aligned}
$$

where we have written Δk and $\Delta \omega$ for the differences in wave numbers and frequencies and $\bar{k}$ and $\bar{\omega}$ for the mean values. Figure 5–17 shows a sketch of $y(x,t_0)$ versus x for some time t_0. The dotted curve is the envelope of the group of two waves, given by the term in

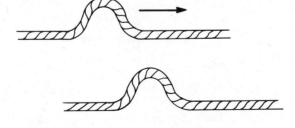

figure 5–16

A pulse moving along a string.

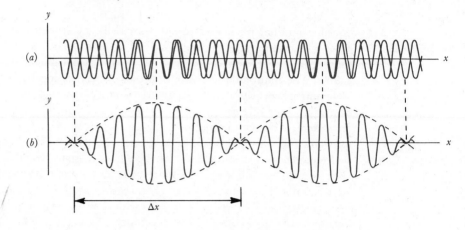

figure 5–17   *Two waves of slightly different wavelength and frequency produce beats.*
(a) Shows y versus x at a given instant for the two waves. The waves are out
of phase at first, but because of the difference in wavelength, they become in
phase and then out of phase again. The sum of these waves is shown in (b).
The spacial extent of the group Δx is inversely proportional to the difference
in wave numbers Δk, where k is related to the wavelength by $k = 2\pi/\lambda$.
Identical figures are obtained if y is plotted versus time t at a fixed point x.
For this case the extent in time Δt is inversely proportional to the frequency
difference $\Delta\omega$.

brackets, [ ]. The individual waves move with speed $\bar{\omega}/\bar{k}$. Examination of the modulating term in brackets shows that the envelope moves with speed $(\frac{1}{2}\Delta\omega)/(\frac{1}{2}\Delta k) = \Delta\omega/\Delta k$. As k_2 approaches k_1, the group velocity becomes

$$v_g = \frac{d\omega}{dk} \tag{5–18}$$

If we take, for the spacial extent of the group $\Delta x = x_2 - x_1$, where x_2 and x_1 are two consecutive values of x for which the envelope is zero, we have

$$\tfrac{1}{2}\Delta k x_2 - \tfrac{1}{2}\Delta k x_1 = \pi$$

or

$$\Delta x\, \Delta k = 2\pi \tag{5–19}$$

For a particular value of x, the function $y(x_0, t)$ versus t is identical to Figure 5–17, with t replacing x. The extent in time Δt is related to $\Delta\omega$ by

$$\Delta t\, \Delta\omega = 2\pi \tag{5–20}$$

The range Δx and Δt that we have used for this particular group of two waves is somewhat artificial because the envelope does not remain small outside these ranges.

It is not possible to obtain a wave group (often called a *wave packet*) that is small everywhere outside a well-defined range, with a finite number of waves. The larger the number of waves, the larger the region in which destructive interference makes the envelope small; however, eventually all the waves will again be in phase, the envelope will be large, and the pattern will be repeated. To represent a pulse such as in Figure 5–16, a range of wave numbers Δk, with an infinite number of values of k, is needed. We shall illustrate one such continuous group. For simplicity, let us ignore the time dependence and consider the group at a particular time.

Example 5–3 Let us consider the wave packet consisting of a large number of waves N, with the wave number equally spaced between k_1 and k_2. The wave packet formed by the sum of these waves is

$$y(x) = \sum_{i=1}^{N} y_0 \cos k_i x$$

In the limit as $N \to \infty$, the distribution of wave numbers becomes a continuous distribution. We can calculate $y(x)$ by integrating

$$y(x) = \int g(k) y_0 \cos kx \, dk \tag{5–21}$$

where $g(k)$ is the distribution of wave numbers. For this case,

$$g(k) = C \qquad \text{for } k_1 \leq k \leq k_2$$
$$g(k) = 0 \qquad \text{for other } k$$

figure 5–18   *Moiré pattern showing beats produced by two sets of parallel lines when the spacing of one set differs slightly from that of the other.*

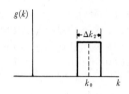

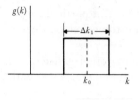

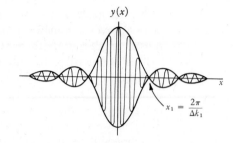

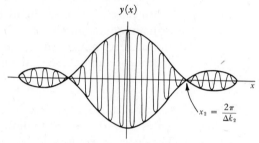

figure 5–19   *A "rectangular" distribution of wave numbers g(k) produces the wave group y(x) shown. The width of y(x) is inversely proportional to the width of g(k).*

Then

$$y(x) = \int_{k_1}^{k_2} Cy_0 \cos kx \, dx$$

$$= \frac{Cy_0}{x} (\sin k_2 x - \sin k_1 x)$$

$$= \frac{2Cy_0}{x} \sin (\tfrac{1}{2}\Delta kx) \cos \bar{k}x$$

where $\Delta k = k_2 - k_1$ and $\bar{k} = \frac{1}{2}(k_1 + k_2)$. If there are N waves, the constant C is given by

$$\int_{k_1}^{k_2} C \, dk = N = C \, \Delta k$$

Thus the wave packet can be written

$$y(x) = Ny_0 \frac{\sin \frac{1}{2}\Delta kx}{\frac{1}{2}\Delta kx} \cos \bar{k}x$$

$$= y_m \frac{\sin \frac{1}{2}\Delta kx}{\frac{1}{2}\Delta kx} \cos \bar{k}x$$

where $y_m = Ny_0$ is the maximum value of y.

Figure 5–19 shows a plot of $y(x)$ versus x. The envelope of this function is large in the region $-(2\pi/\Delta k) < x < (2\pi/\Delta k)$. If we

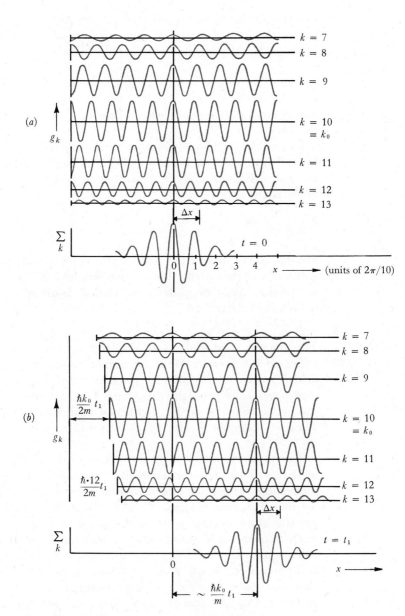

figure 5–20   Wave group produced by seven waves
              with $k = 7$ to $k = 13$. The average wave
              number is $k_0 = 10$. After time t_1, the group
              has moved a distance $(\hbar k_0/m)t_1$.
              (From Introduction to Quantum Mechanics,
              by Chalmers W. Sherwin. Copyright © 1959 by
              Holt, Rinehart and Winston, Inc. Reprinted by
              permission of Holt, Rinehart and Winston, Inc.)

call this range Δx, we again see that the range in x is inversely proportional to the range of wave numbers Δk in the distribution of waves. For this particular packet, $\Delta x \, \Delta k = 4\pi$.

*

Figure 5–20 shows a wave packet made up of seven waves with wave numbers from $k = 7$ to $k = 13$. At a time t_1 later, the packet has moved a distance $(\hbar k_0/m)t_1$, where $k_0 = 10$ is the mean wave number.

In general, if either the form of the wave packet or the distribution of wave numbers is known, the other can be obtained by the method of Fourier analysis. In all cases, the velocity of the wave group is given by

$$V_g = \frac{d\omega}{dk} \qquad (5\text{–}22)$$

and the width in x of the packet is inversely proportional to the width in k of the distribution of wave numbers. The exact value of the product $\Delta x \, \Delta k$ depends on the kind of distribution and on the definition of Δx and Δk.

5·5
ELECTRON WAVE PACKETS

The quantity analogous to the displacement $y(x,t)$ for waves on a string, to the pressure $P(x,t)$ for a sound wave, or to the electric field $\mathcal{E}(x,t)$ for electromagnetic waves is called the *wave function for electron waves* and is usually designated $\Psi(x,t)$. Consider an electron wave containing a single frequency and wavelength such as $\Psi(x,t) = A \cos(kx - \omega t)$, $\Psi(x,t) = A \sin(kx - \omega t)$, or $\Psi(x,t) = Ae^{i(kx-\omega t)}$.

The phase velocity is given by $v = f\lambda = (E/h)(h/p) = E/p$, where we have used the de Broglie relations for the energy and momentum. Using the nonrelativistic expression $E = p^2/2m$, we see that the phase velocity is $v = E/p = p/2m$, which is half the velocity of an electron with momentum p. However, a wave of a single frequency and wavelength is spread out in space and has no localization. To describe an electron which has the property of being localized, $\Psi(x,t)$ must be a wave packet containing more than one wave number k and frequency ω. It is reasonable to expect that the position of the electron corresponds to the position of the maximum of the wave packet. If this is so, the wave packet should move with the same velocity as the electron, i.e., the group velocity rather than the phase velocity should be equal to the velocity of the electron. For the wave packet

$$\Psi(x,t) = \int g(k) \cos(kx - \omega t)\, dk \qquad (5\text{–}23)$$

where $g(k)$ contains a range of wave numbers centered about some value k_0, the group velocity is given by

$$V_g = \frac{d\omega}{dk}$$

where the derivative is evaluated at k_0. Using the de Broglie relations for electron waves

$$E = hf = \frac{h\omega}{2\pi} = \hbar\omega \qquad (5\text{--}24)$$

and

$$p = \frac{h}{\lambda} = \frac{hk}{2\pi} = \hbar k \qquad (5\text{--}25)$$

we can write the nonrelativistic expression for energy in terms of ω and k:

$$E = \frac{p^2}{2m}$$

or

$$\hbar\omega = \frac{\hbar^2 k^2}{2m}$$

Then

$$V_g = \left(\frac{d\omega}{dk}\right)_{k_0} = \frac{\hbar k_0}{m} = \frac{p_0}{m} \qquad (5\text{--}26)$$

Thus the wave packet does move with the particle velocity p_0/m. This was one of de Broglie's motives for choosing Eqs. (5–1) and (5–2). (De Broglie considered the relativistic expression relating energy and momentum which also leads to the equality of the group velocity and particle velocity. See Problem 5–12.)

5·6
THE PROBABILISTIC INTERPRETATION OF THE WAVE FUNCTION

Let us investigate in more detail the relation between the wave function $\Psi(x,t)$ and the location of the electron. We can get a hint as to this relation from the case of light. The wave equation that governs light is Eq. (5–6) with $y = \mathcal{E}$, the electric field. The energy per unit volume in a light wave is proportional to $\mathcal{E}^2$, but the energy in a light wave is quantized in units of hf for each photon. We might expect, therefore, that the number of photons in a unit volume is proportional to $\mathcal{E}^2$. Consider the famous double-slit experiment illustrated in Figure 5–21. The pattern observed on the screen is determined by the interference of the waves from the slits. At a point on the screen where the wave from one slit is

180° out of phase with that from the other slit, the resultant electric field is zero; there is no light energy at this point, and the point is dark. If we reduce the intensity to a very low value, we can still observe the interference pattern if we replace the screen by a film and wait a sufficient length of time to expose the film. The interaction of light with a film is a quantum phenomenon. If we expose the film for only a very short time with a low-intensity source, we do not see merely a weaker version of the high-intensity pattern; we see, instead, "dots" on the film caused by the interactions of individual photons. At points where the waves from the slits interfere destructively, there are no dots, and at points where the waves interfere constructively, there are many dots. However, if the exposure is short with a weak source, random fluctuations from the average predictions of the wave theory are clearly evident. If the exposure is long enough so that many photons interact with the film, the fluctuations even out and the quantum nature of light is not noticed. The interference pattern depends only on the total number of photons interacting with the film and not on the rate. Even if the intensity is so low that only one photon at a time hits the film, the wave theory predicts the correct average pattern. Thus, rather than being proportional to the number of photons in a unit volume, $\mathcal{E}^2$ must be proportional to the *probability* of there being a photon in a unit volume. At points on the film or screen where $\mathcal{E}^2$ is zero, photons are never observed, whereas they are most likely to be observed at points where $\mathcal{E}^2$ is large.

figure 5–21   *Two-slit interference pattern. The first minimum occurs at angle θ such that the path difference d sin θ is λ/2. The interference pattern is produced even if only one photon or electron at a time traverses the slits.*

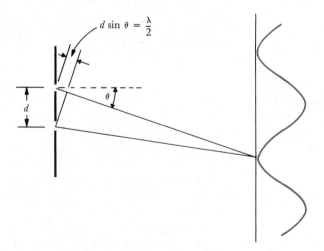

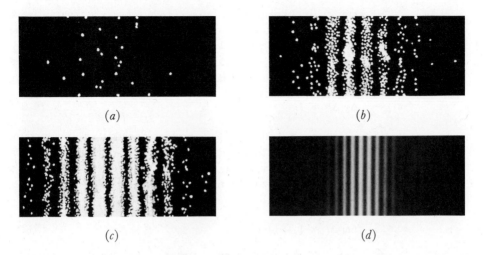

(a) (b)

(c) (d)

figure 5–22   Growth of two-slit interference pattern. The photo (d) is an actual two-slit
electron interference pattern in which the film was exposed to millions of
electrons. The pattern is identical to that usually obtained with photons. If
the film were to be observed at various stages, such as after being struck by
28 electrons, then after about 1,000 electrons, and again after about 10,000
electrons, the patterns of individually exposed grains would be similar to
those shown in (a), (b), and (c), except that the exposed dots would be
smaller than the dots drawn here. Note that there are no dots in the region
of the interference minima. The probability of any point of the film being
exposed is determined by a wave theory, whether the film is exposed by electrons or photons. [Parts (a), (b), and (c) from Physics 1 by Elisha R.
Huggins, copyrighted by W. A. Benjamin, Inc., 1968, p. 510. Photo (d)
courtesy of Dr. Claus Jönsson.]

It is not necessary to use light waves to produce an interference
pattern. Such patterns can be produced with electrons as well.
For electrons, Ψ^2 is proportional to the probability that an electron
is in a unit volume. In one dimension, $\Psi^2\,dx$ is the probability of
an electron being in the interval dx.

5·7
THE UNCERTAINTY
PRINCIPLE

Consider a wave packet $\Psi(x,t)$ representing an electron. The most
probable position of the electron is the value of x for which $\Psi^2(x,t)$
is a maximum. The fact that $\Psi^2(x,t)$ must be interpreted as the
probability that the electron is in dx and that $\Psi^2(x,t)$ is nonzero
for a range of values of x mean that there is an uncertainty in the
value of the position of the electron. If we make a large number of
position measurements on identical electrons — electrons with
the same wave function — we shall obtain a distribution of results.
In fact, the distribution function for the results of such measurements
will be given by $\Psi^2(x,t)$. If the wave packet is very narrow, the

uncertainty in position will be small. However, a narrow wave packet must contain a wide range of wave numbers k. Since the momentum is related to the wave number by $p = \hbar k$, a wide range of k values means a wide range of momentum values. We have seen that for all wave packets the ranges Δx and Δk are related by

$$\Delta x \, \Delta k \approx 1 \qquad (5\text{-}27)$$

(Since the exact value for the product depends on the kind of packet and the exact specification of the meaning of Δx and Δk, we have taken the value 1 for a typical product.) Similarly, a packet that is localized in time Δt must contain a range of frequencies $\Delta \omega$, where these ranges are related by

$$\Delta \omega \, \Delta t \approx 1 \qquad (5\text{-}28)$$

Equations (5–27) and (5–28) are inherent properties of waves. If we multiply these equations by $\hbar$ and use $p = \hbar k$ and $E = \hbar \omega$, we obtain

$$\Delta x \, \Delta p \approx \hbar \qquad (5\text{-}29)$$

and

$$\Delta E \, \Delta t \approx \hbar \qquad (5\text{-}30)$$

Equations (5–29) and (5–30) provide a statement of the *uncertainty principle* first enunciated in 1927 by Heisenberg. Equation (5–29) expresses the fact that the distribution functions for position and momentum cannot both be made arbitrarily narrow; thus measurements of position and momentum will have uncertainties which are related by Eq. (5–29). Of course, because of inaccurate measurements, the product of Δx and Δp can be, and usually is, much larger than $\hbar$. The lower limit is not due to any technical problem in the design of measuring equipment which might be solved at some later date; it is due to the wave and particle nature of both matter and light.

The position distribution function $\Psi^2(x)$ and the wave-number distribution function $g^2(k)$ are related by

$$\Psi(x) = \int g(k) \cos kx \, dk \qquad (5\text{-}31)$$

The functions $\Psi(x)$ and $g(k)$ are called *Fourier transforms* of each other. If one is known, the other can be obtained. A result of Fourier analysis that we shall state but not derive is that the minimum value of the product $\Delta x \, \Delta k$ occurs when $\Psi(x)$ is a gaussian function. For this case, $g(k)$ is also a gaussian and the

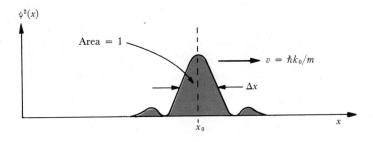

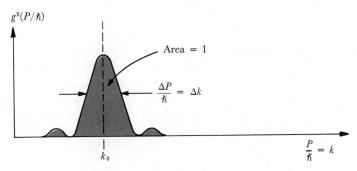

figure 5–23   *Distribution functions for the position and momentum of an electron in one dimension. The product of Δx and Δk is of the order of 1. The minimum product $\Delta x \, \Delta k = \frac{1}{2}$ occurs when the distribution functions are gaussian.*

distributions are gaussian distributions. The standard deviations of these distributions are related by $\sigma_k \sigma_x = \frac{1}{2}$. If we define Δx and Δp to be the standard deviations, the minimum value of their product is $\frac{1}{2}\hbar$. Thus

$$\Delta x \, \Delta p \geq \tfrac{1}{2}\hbar \qquad\qquad (5\text{–}32)$$

Similarly

$$\Delta E \, \Delta t \geq \tfrac{1}{2}\hbar \qquad\qquad (5\text{–}33)$$

Example 5–4   Let us see how a classical physicist might attempt to violate the uncertainty principle. A common way to measure the position of an object is to look at it with light. The momentum can be obtained by looking at it a short time later and computing what velocity it must have had. Our classical physicist knows that he cannot hope to make distance measurements smaller than the wavelength of the light he uses because of diffraction effects; he will thus use the shortest wavelength x ray or ultraviolet light that he can obtain. (There is, in principle, no limit to how short a wavelength of electromagnetic radiation can be found.) He also knows that light carries

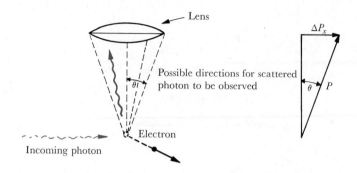

figure 5–24 *"Seeing an electron" with a microscope. Because of the size of the lens, the momentum of the scattered photon is uncertain by $\Delta p_x \approx p \sin \theta = h \sin \theta / \lambda$. Thus the recoil momentum of the electron is also uncertain by at least this amount. The position of the electron cannot be resolved better than $\Delta x \approx \lambda / \sin \theta$ because of diffraction. The product of the uncertainties $\Delta p_x \, \Delta k$ is thus of the order of Planck's constant h.*

momentum and energy; thus, when it scatters off the electron, the electron will be disturbed, spoiling the momentum measurement. Therefore, he will substantially reduce the intensity of the light. Though this might seem like a good idea, it will not be effective; either one photon will be scattered or none, and reducing the intensity merely decreases the number of photons. The momentum of the photon is $hf/c = h/\lambda$; thus the smaller he takes λ to locate the position, the more the photon will disturb the electron and spoil the momentum measurement. The only way to increase the accuracy of the momentum measurement is to use longer wavelengths, thus decreasing the accuracy of the position measurement. Figure 5–24 illustrates the problem. (This illustration was first given by Neils Bohr.) The position of the electron is to be determined by viewing it through a microscope. We shall assume that only one photon is needed. We can take for the uncertainty in position, the separation distance for which two objects can just be resolved; this is[3]

$$\Delta x = \frac{\lambda}{2 \sin \theta}$$

where θ is the half-angle subtended by the aperture, as shown in the figure. Let us assume that the x component of momentum of the

[3]The resolving power of a microscope is discussed in some detail in *Fundamentals of Optics*, by F. A. Jenkins and H. E. White, McGraw-Hill Book Company, New York, 1957 (3d ed.), pages 306–308. The expression for Δx used here is determined by Rayleigh's criterion that two points are just resolved if the central maximum of the diffraction pattern from one falls at the first minimum of the diffraction pattern of the other.

incoming photon is precisely known. The scattered photon can have any x component of momentum from 0 to $p_x = P \sin \theta$, where P is the total momentum of the scattered photon. By conservation of momentum, the uncertainty in the momentum of the electron after the scattering must be at least equal to that of the scattered photon (it would be equal, of course, if the electron's initial momentum were perfectly known); thus we write

$$\Delta P \geq P \sin \theta = \frac{h}{\lambda} \sin \theta$$

and

$$\Delta x \, \Delta P \geq \frac{\lambda}{2 \sin \theta} \cdot \frac{h \sin \theta}{\lambda} = \frac{1}{2} h$$

This example illustrates the essential point of the uncertainty principle — that this product of uncertainties cannot be less than $\hbar$ in *principle*, that is, even in an ideal situation. If electrons were used rather than photons to locate the object, there would be no change in the analysis since the relation $\lambda = h/p$ is the same for both.

*

The example given above provides some insight into the difficulties in measurement imposed by the wave-particle duality of light and matter, but it can be misleading. In this example we assumed that the electron had a definite position and momentum, and in the process of measuring the position, the momentum uncertainty was introduced. However, because of the wave nature of the electron, it must be represented by a wave packet; this implies that there is already an uncertainty in position and momentum corresponding to the spread in x of the packet and the spread in k of the wave numbers. In the process of measuring the position of the electron, such as irradiating the electron with photons, the wave packet of the electron is changed. If photons of very small wavelength are used, the position can be determined accurately. This means that the new wave packet describing the electron is now very narrow in x, but, of course, this also means that the distribution in k is correspondingly wide. Thus the uncertainty in momentum is now large.

5·8
PARTICLE-WAVE DUALITY

We have seen that electrons, which we usually think of as particles, have the normal wave properties of diffraction and interference. In previous chapters we saw that light, which we ordinarily think of as a wave motion, also has the usual particle properties when it interacts with matter, such as in the photoelectric effect or the Compton effect. All phenomena — electrons, atoms, light, sound, etc. — have both particle and wave characteristics. It is sometimes said that an electron, for example, is both a wave and a particle. This is rather confusing since, in classical physics, the concepts of waves and particles are mutually exclusive. A *classical particle* behaves like a BB shot. It can be localized and scattered, it exchanges energy suddenly in a lump, and it obeys the laws of conservation of energy and momentum in collisions; but it does *not* exhibit interference and diffraction. A *classical wave* behaves like a water wave. It exhibits diffraction and interference patterns and has its energy spread out continuously in space and time. Nothing can be both a classical particle and a classical wave.

Until the twentieth century, it was thought that light was a classical wave and an electron was a classical particle. We now see that the concepts of classical waves and classical particles do not adequately describe any phenomena. Every phenomenon behaves like a classical wave when propagation is considered and like a classical particle when its energy exchange is considered. Let us elaborate on this statement.

Every phenomenon is describable by a wave function which is the solution of a wave equation. The wave function for light is the electric field $\mathcal{E}(x,t)$ (in one dimension), which is the solution of a wave equation of the type Eq. (5–6). We have called the wave function for an electron, $\Psi(x,t)$. We shall study the wave equation for an electron, called the *Schroedinger equation*, in the next chapter. The square of the wave function gives the probability (per unit volume) that the electron is in a given region. The wave function exhibits the classical wave properties of interference and diffraction. Thus, in order to determine where an electron is likely to be, we must find the wave function by methods similar to classical wave theory. When the electron (or light) interacts and exchanges energy and momentum, the wave function is changed by the interaction. The interaction can be described by classical particle theory such as is done in the Compton effect.

There are times when the classical particle theory and the classical wave theory give the same results. If the wavelength is much smaller than any object or aperture, particle theory can be used as well as wave theory to describe propagation because diffraction and interference effects are too small to be observed. Common examples are geometrical optics, which is really a particle theory, and the propagation of baseballs. If one is interested only in time averages of energy and momentum exchange, the classical-wave theory works as well as the classical-particle theory. For example, the wave theory of light correctly predicts that the total electron current in the photoelectric effect is proportional to the intensity of the light.

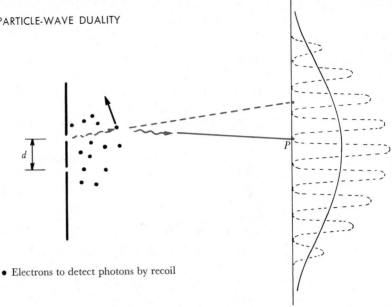

● Electrons to detect photons by recoil

figure 5–25   *The dashed curve is a typical two-slit interference pattern observed when there are no detectors present (electrons indicated by dots). No photons hit the screen at point P, an interference minimum. If electrons are placed near the slits to detect through which slit a photon passes, the interference pattern is destroyed by the scattering of the photons. The resulting pattern is the sum of two independent single-slit diffraction patterns as shown by the solid curve.*

Example 5–5   Let us again consider the double-slit interference example. The slits are separated by a distance d and there is a screen or film far enough away from the slits that we can use small-angle approximations. We shall consider the case of a light beam, though the analysis is identical for an electron beam. The interference pattern has a maximum at $\theta = 0$, and the first minimum at θ given by $d \sin \theta = \lambda/2$. In the usual case θ is small, so we can approximate $\sin \theta \approx \theta$ and write $\theta = \lambda/2d$ for the position of the first minimum. As we have discussed before, the interference pattern does not depend on the intensity of the light, even if only one photon at a time hits the film. If we consider the light to be a beam of photons, we have the following problem. If a photon goes through slit A, how does it know whether slit B is open or closed? If slit B is open, the photon never goes to the interference minimum (point P in Figure 5–25), but if slit B is closed, there is no interference minimum so some photons must go to point P.

Let us examine the statement "the photon goes through slit A." In the description of this problem by classical wave theory, we do not have any difficulty because a wave goes through both slits if they are open, so a wave certainly knows if slit B is open or closed. Light cannot act like a classical particle and a classical wave at the same time. Let us see what happens if we try to observe the particle aspects of light as it goes through the slits. We shall measure which slit the photon goes through. In Figure 5–25, we have placed electrons in the region just beyond the slits. We can tell which slit the photon passed through by observing the recoil electron. To do this we must know the vertical position of the electron within a distance $d/2$. If $\Delta y \ll d/2$, the uncertainty in the vertical momentum of the recoil electron must be greater than $2\hbar/d$, and by conservation of momentum, the vertical momentum of the scattered photon must be uncertain by $\Delta p_y \gg 2\hbar/d$. If the photon was originally heading toward the interference maximum at $\theta = 0$ with momentum $p = h/\lambda$, it will be deflected through an angle that is *uncertain* by

$$\Delta\theta \approx \frac{\Delta p_y}{p} \gg \frac{2\hbar d}{h/\lambda} = \frac{\lambda}{\pi d}$$

Comparing this with the angle of the interference minimum, we see that in the process of measuring which slit the photon goes through, the photon is scattered so much that the interference pattern is washed out.

*

From this example we see that it is impossible to measure both the particle and wave aspects of light at the same time. When we place electrons near the slits to measure the particle properties of light, the wave properties of interference cannot be observed. With no electron detectors near the slit, the experiment is designed to measure the wave properties of light. We cannot, then, say that a photon passed through one slit or the other. This result is known as *Bohr's principle of complementarity* — the particle aspects and wave aspects complement each other. Both are needed, but both cannot be observed at the same time. Whether the wave aspect or the particle aspect is observed depends on the experimental arrangement.

5·9
SOME
CONSEQUENCES
OF THE
UNCERTAINTY
PRINCIPLE

In the next chapter we shall see that the Schroedinger wave equation provides a straightforward method of solving problems in atomic physics. We shall also see that the solution of the Schroedinger equation is often laborious and difficult. A great deal of semi-quantitative information about the behavior of atomic systems can be obtained from the uncertainty principle alone without a detailed solution of the problem. Some examples follow.

Example 5–6   *Minimum energy of a particle in a box.* An important consequence of the uncertainty principle is that a particle confined to a small space cannot have zero kinetic energy. Let us consider the case of a one-dimensional box of length L. If we know that the particle is in the box, Δx is not larger than L. This implies that Δp is at least

$$\Delta p \geq \frac{\hbar}{L}$$

(Since we are interested in orders of magnitude, we shall ignore the $\frac{1}{2}$ in the minimum uncertainty product. In general, distributions are not gaussian anyway, so $\Delta p \, \Delta x$ will be larger than $\frac{1}{2}\hbar$.)

Let us take the standard deviation for Δp,

$$(\Delta p)^2 = (p - \bar{p})^2_{\text{ave}} = (p^2 - 2p\bar{p} + \bar{p}^2)_{\text{ave}} = \overline{p^2} - \bar{p}^2$$

If the box is symmetric, $\bar{p}$ will be zero since the particle moves to the left as often as to the right. Then

$$(\Delta p)^2 = \overline{p^2} \geq \left(\frac{\hbar}{L}\right)^2$$

and the average kinetic energy is

$$\bar{E} = \frac{\overline{p^2}}{2m} \geq \frac{\hbar^2}{2mL^2}$$

(Compare this with the lowest energy state for a particle in a box, obtained in Section 4–6 from the Wilson-Sommerfeld quantum condition.) Let us calculate some numerical examples. Consider a small but macroscopic particle. Taking $m = 10^{-6}$ gram and $L = 10^{-4}$ cm, we find that the minimum kinetic energy is about

$$E \approx \frac{\hbar^2}{2mL^2} = \frac{(\hbar c)^2}{2mc^2L^2} \approx \frac{(1{,}970 \text{ eV} \times 10^{-8} \text{ cm})^2}{2(5.6 \times 10^{26} \text{ eV})(10^{-4} \text{ cm})^2}$$

$$\approx 3.5 \times 10^{-29} \text{ eV}$$

using $c^2 \approx 5.6 \times 10^{32}$ eV/g.

The speed corresponding to this energy is

$$v = \left(\frac{2E}{m}\right)^{1/2} = c\left(\frac{2E}{mc^2}\right)^{1/2} \approx \left(\frac{7 \times 10^{-29}}{5.6 \times 10^{26}}\right)^{1/2} c$$

$$= 3.5 \times 10^{-29} c \approx 10^{-19} \text{ m/sec}$$

We can see from this calculation that the minimum energy is certainly not observable for macroscopic systems even as small as 10^{-6} gram. If we take m to be the mass of an electron and L to be

1 Å (the size of an atom), we find

$$E \approx \frac{(1{,}970 \text{ eV-Å})^2}{2 \times (0.5 \times 10^6 \text{ eV}) \text{ Å}^2} = 4 \text{ eV}$$

This is the correct order of magnitude of the kinetic energy of an electron in an atom.

*

Example 5-7   *Minimum energy of a simple harmonic oscillator.* Consider a particle of mass m on a spring of force-constant K. The potential energy is

$$V(x) = \tfrac{1}{2}Kx^2 = \tfrac{1}{2}m\omega^2 x^2$$

where $\omega = \sqrt{K/m}$ is the angular frequency. The total energy is constant and therefore equal to its average value:

$$E = \bar{E} = \frac{\overline{p^2}}{2m} + \frac{1}{2}m\omega^2\overline{x^2}$$

As in the previous example, $\bar{p}$ and $\bar{x}$ are zero by symmetry; thus

$$(\Delta x)^2 = \overline{x^2}$$

and

$$(\Delta p)^2 = \overline{p^2}$$

Using the uncertainty relation $(\Delta p)^2 \geq \hbar^2/(\Delta x)^2$, the total energy can be written

$$E \geq \frac{\hbar^2}{2m\,(\Delta x)^2} + \frac{1}{2}m\omega^2\,(\Delta x)^2$$

When Δx is small, the first term is large; when Δx is large, the second term is large. The minimum value of E can easily be found (see Problem 5-18). The result is

$$E_{\min} = \hbar\omega$$

We shall see in the next chapter that the shape of the wave packet for this problem is really a gaussian function; thus the uncertainty product actually has its minimum value $\Delta x\,\Delta p = \tfrac{1}{2}\hbar$. If this value were used rather than $\Delta x\,\Delta p = \hbar$, the calculation would yield for the minimum energy $\tfrac{1}{2}\hbar\omega$. It is easy to see that, for the low frequencies observed for macroscopic particles on springs, $E_{\min}$ is negligible; however, for typical frequencies of $f = \omega/2\pi \approx 10^{13}/\text{sec}$ for molecular vibrations, the minimum energy is of the order of 0.1 eV.

*

Example 5–8   *Size of the hydrogen atom.* The energy of an electron of momentum p a distance R from a proton is

$$W = \frac{p^2}{2m} - \frac{Ke^2}{R}$$

If we take for the order of magnitude of the position uncertainty $\Delta x \approx R$, we have $\Delta p^2 = \overline{p^2} > \hbar^2/R^2$. The energy is then

$$W = \frac{\hbar^2}{2mR^2} - \frac{Ke^2}{R}$$

As in Example 5–7, there is a radius R_m which gives a minimum W. Setting $dW/dR = 0$ yields R_m and W_m

$$R_m = \frac{\hbar^2}{Ke^2m} = a_0 \approx 0.529 \text{ Å}$$

and

$$W_m = -\frac{K^2e^4m}{2\hbar^2} = -13.6 \text{ eV}$$

The fact that R_m came out to be exactly the radius of the first Bohr orbit is due to the judicious choice of $\Delta x = R$ rather than $2R$ or $R/2$, which are just as reasonable. It should be clear, however, that any reasonable choice for Δx does give the correct order of magnitude of the size of an atom.

*

Example 5–9   *Widths of spectral lines.* Equation (5–33) implies that the energy of a system cannot be measured exactly unless an infinite time is available for the measurement. If an atom is in an excited state, it does not remain in that state indefinitely but makes transitions to lower energy states until it reaches the ground state. The decay of an excited state is a statistical process. We can take the mean time of decay τ, called the *lifetime*, to be a measure of the time available to determine the energy of the state. For atomic transitions, τ is of the order of 10^{-8} sec. The uncertainty in the energy corresponding to this time is

$$\Delta E \approx \frac{\hbar}{\tau} = \frac{4.14 \times 10^{-15} \text{ eV/sec}}{2\pi \times 10^{-8} \text{ sec}} \approx 10^{-7} \text{ eV}$$

This uncertainty in energy causes a spread in the wavelength of the light emitted, $\Delta\lambda$. For transitions to the ground state, which has a perfectly certain energy E_0 because of its indefinite lifetime, the percentage spread in wavelength can be calculated from

$$E - E_0 = \frac{hc}{\lambda}$$

$$dE = -hc \frac{d\lambda}{\lambda^2}$$

$$\Delta E \approx -hc \frac{\Delta\lambda}{\lambda^2}$$

thus

$$\frac{\Delta\lambda}{\lambda} \approx \frac{\Delta E}{E - E_0}$$

The energy width $\Gamma_0 = \hbar/\tau$ is called the *natural line width*. Other effects that cause broadening of spectral lines are the Doppler effect, the recoil effect, and atomic collisions. (See Problems 5–20, 5–21, and 5–22.) For optical spectra in the eV energy range, the Doppler width D is about 10^{-6} eV at room temperature, roughly 10 times the natural width and the recoil width is negligible. For nuclear transitions in the MeV range, both the Doppler width and the recoil width are of the order of eV, much larger than the natural line width. We shall see in Chapter 10 that, in some special cases of atoms in solids at low temperatures, the Doppler and recoil widths are essentially zero and the width of the spectral line is just the natural width. This effect, called the *Mössbauer effect* after its discoverer in 1958, is extremely important for it provides photons of well-defined energy which are useful in experiments demanding extreme precision. For example, the 14.4-keV photon from Fe^{57} has a natural width of the order of 10^{-10} of its energy.

*

SUMMARY   Electrons and other "particles" exhibit the usual wave properties of interference and diffraction. The frequency and wavelength of electron waves are related to the energy and momentum by the de Broglie relations $E = hf = \hbar\omega$ and $p = h/\lambda = \hbar k$.

If the wavelength is small compared with all apertures and obstacles, wave properties can generally be neglected for electrons as well as for light. All phenomena can be described by wave equations that relate the time and space behavior of the wave function appropriate to the phenomena. The square of the wave function at x and t is proportional to the probability of observing a particle in the region dx at x and t. The description of a wave localized in a region Δx requires a wave function, or wave packet, that contains a range of wave numbers k given by $\Delta k \approx 1/\Delta x$. Because k is related to the momentum by $p = \hbar k$, this implies that the product of the uncertainty in position and uncertainty in momentum cannot be less than $\hbar$. One consequence of this uncertainty principle is that a particle confined in a region of space cannot have zero kinetic energy.

REFERENCES

1. E. Goldwasser, *Optics, Waves, Atoms, and Nuclei*, W. A. Benjamin, Inc., New York, 1965.
2. D. Halliday and R. Resnick, *Physics*, John Wiley & Sons, Inc., New York, 1966.
3. C. Andrews, *Optics of the Electromagnetic Spectrum*, Prentice-Hall, Inc., Englewood Cliffs, N.J., 1960.
4. Grant R. Fowles, *Introduction to Modern Optics*, Holt, Rinehart and Winston, Inc., New York, 1968.

The above references, as well as other elementary physics textbooks or optics textbooks, can be consulted for a review of the properties of classical waves.

5. L. de Broglie, *Matter and Light, The New Physics*, Dover Publications, Inc., New York, 1939. Among this collection of studies in physics is de Broglie's lecture on the occasion of receiving the Nobel Prize, in which he describes his reasoning leading to the prediction of the wave nature of matter.
6. Film of lecture by Richard Feynman, "Probability and Uncertainty — The Quantum Mechanical View of Nature," available from Educational Services, Inc., Film Library, Newton, Mass.

PROBLEMS

SET A

5–1. Calculate the de Broglie wavelength of an 8-MeV α particle.

5–2. Calculate the de Broglie wavelength of an 0.02-eV neutron. (This kinetic energy is of the order of magnitude of kT at room temperature.)

5–3. Calculate the de Broglie wavelength of an electron with kinetic energy of 13.6 eV. What is the ratio of this wavelength to the first Bohr radius?

5-4. Calculate the de Broglie wavelength of an electron with kinetic energy of 100 MeV. What is the wavelength of a photon of this energy?

5-5. In order to observe diffraction of α particles by crystals, the wavelength of the particle must be of the order of 1 Å. What is the energy of an α particle with this wavelength?

5-6. A mass of 10^{-6} gram has a speed of 1 cm/sec. If the speed is uncertain by 0.01 percent, what is the minimum uncertainty in the position of the mass?

5-7. The energy of a certain nuclear state can be measured with an uncertainty of 1 eV. What is the minimum lifetime of this state?

5-8. Show that the relation $\Delta p_s \, \Delta s > \hbar$ can be written $\Delta L \, \Delta \phi > \hbar$ for a particle moving in a circle about the z axis, where p_s is the linear momentum tangential to the circle, s is the arc length, and L is the angular momentum. How well can the angular position of the electron be specified in the Bohr atom?

5-9. From the uncertainty principle, estimate the minimum kinetic energy of a proton confined to a region of (a) $\Delta x \approx$ 1 Å; (b) $\Delta x \approx 5F$.

5-10. From the uncertainty principle, estimate the minimum kinetic energy of an electron confined to a region of space $\Delta x \approx 5F$. (Since the energy is much greater than the rest energy, use $E \approx pc$.)

SET B

5-11. Show that, in general, if the energy of a particle is much greater than its rest energy, its de Broglie wavelength is approximately the same as that of a photon of the same energy.

5-12. Using the relativistic expression $E^2 = p^2c^2 + m^2c^4$,

  (a) Show that the phase velocity of an electron wave is greater than c.

  (b) Show that the group velocity of an electron wave equals the particle velocity of the electron.

5-13. Show that, if y_1 and y_2 are solutions of Eq. (5-6), the function $y_3 = C_1y_1 + C_2y_2$ is also a solution for any constants C_1 and C_2.

5-14. Show that Eq. (5-6) is satisfied by $y = f(\phi)$, where $\phi = x - vt$ for any function f.

5-15. Plug into Eq. (5-6) the trial solution $y(x,t) = g(t)f(x)$, where f is a function of x only and g is a function of t only. Show that

$$\frac{g''(t)}{g(t)} = v^2 \frac{f''(x)}{f(x)}$$

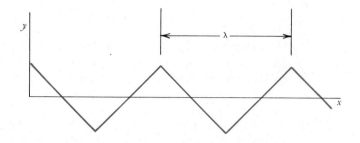

figure 5–26 *Triangular wave Trn λ.*

If a function of t only equals a function of x only, neither function can depend on x or t. Set $g''(t)/g(t)$ equal to the constant $-\omega^2$ and solve for $g(t)$ and $f(x)$.

5–16. Some understanding of wave groups made up of just a few waves can be obtained by adding the waves graphically. The tedious plotting of sine or cosine waves can be avoided without loss of understanding by using "triangular waves," as shown in Figure 5–26. In this and the next problem, the notation Trn λ refers to such a triangular wave. Define $k = 2\pi/\lambda$ just as in sine waves.

(a) Obtain by graphical addition

$$f(x) = \text{Trn } \lambda_1 + \text{Trn } \lambda_2 + \text{Trn } \lambda_3$$

(start with all the waves at maximum at $x = 0$ and plot for positive x only) for $\lambda_1 = 2$ units, $\lambda_2 = 4$ units, $\lambda_3 = 6$ units, and sketch f^2 versus x.

(b) What is the smallest positive value x_1 for which $f(x_1) = 0$?

(c) Find the maximum and minimum values of $k = 2\pi/\lambda$. Using $\Delta k = k_{max} - k_{min}$ and $\Delta x = 2x_1$, find $\Delta x \, \Delta k$ for this group.

(d) What is the first value of x after $x = 0$ for which all the waves are in phase?

(e) Add a fourth wave $\lambda_4 = 5$ units to this group. Now what is the first value of x after $x = 0$ for which the four waves are in phase?

5–17. (See Problem 5–16.) Obtain by graphical addition the group

$$f(x) = \sum_{i=1}^{5} g_i \text{ Trn } \lambda_i$$

where $g_1 = g_5 = 1$, $g_2 = g_4 = 2$, and $g_3 = 3$ and $\lambda_1 = 5$, $\lambda_2 = 6$, $\lambda_i = 4 + i$ up to $i = 5$.

(a) Sketch f^2 versus x.

(b) What is the smallest positive value x_1 for which $f(x_1) = 0$?

(*c*) Sketch the distribution function $g_i(k_i)$.

(*d*) What is the standard deviation σ_k?

(*e*) Using $\Delta x = 2x_1$ and $\Delta k = \sigma_k$, find $\Delta x \, \Delta k$ for this group.

5-18. Show that the minimum energy of a simple harmonic oscillator is $\frac{1}{2}\hbar\omega$ if $\Delta x \, \Delta p = \frac{1}{2}\hbar$. What is the minimum energy in joules of a mass of 10^{-2} kg oscillating on a spring of force constant $K = 1$ N/m?

5-19. A particle is on a table in a uniform gravitational field. The energy is $E = mgz + p^2/2m$, where $z = 0$ at the table. Classically, the minimum energy is $E = 0$. Assume that the particle moves in a small range Δz above $z = 0$. Take for the average height $\bar{z} = \frac{1}{2}\Delta z$ and $\Delta p \geq \hbar/2 \, \Delta z$.

(*a*) Write $\bar{E}$ as a function of $\bar{z}$ and show that $\bar{E}$ has the minimum value

$$\bar{E}_{\min} = \frac{3}{4}\left(\frac{mg^2\hbar^2}{2}\right)^{1/3} = \frac{3}{2} mg\bar{z}_{\min}$$

at $\bar{z}_{\min} = \frac{1}{2}(\hbar^2/2m^2g)^{1/3}$.

(*b*) Find numerical values for $E_{\min}$ and $z_{\min}$ for a mass of 10^{-6} gram and for the mass of a proton and that of an electron.

5-20. Using the first-order Doppler shift formula $f' = f_0(1 \pm V/c)$, calculate the energy shift of a 1-eV photon emitted from an iron atom moving with energy of $\frac{3}{2} kT$ at $T = 300°K$. Do the same for a 1-MeV photon.

5-21. Calculate the shift in energy of a 1-eV photon and a 1-MeV photon due to the recoil of the iron nucleus. (Take the momentum of the nucleus to be equal to that of the photon, then calculate $p^2/2m$.)

5-22. If an atom makes a collision while radiating, the frequency of the radiation may change. Assume the line width due to collisions is given by

$$\Gamma_c \approx \frac{\hbar}{\tau_c}$$

where τ_c is the mean time between collisions which is related to the mean speed $\bar{v}$ and mean free path ℓ by $\tau_c = \ell/\bar{v}$. Using reasonable values for ℓ and $\bar{v}$ for oxygen gas, calculate Γ_c at standard conditions. (See Table 2-3 for ℓ determined from viscosity.) At what pressure is $\tau_c \approx 10^{-8}$ sec?

SIX
THE SCHROEDINGER EQUATION IN ONE DIMENSION

The success of the de Broglie relations in predicting the diffraction of electrons and the realization that classical standing waves lead to a discrete set of frequencies prompted a search for a wave theory of electrons analogous to the wave theory of light. In this electron-wave theory, classical mechanics should appear as the short-wavelength limit, just as geometrical optics is the short-wavelength limit in the wave theory of light.

In 1925, Erwin Schroedinger published his now-famous wave equation which governs the propagation of electron waves. At about the same time, Werner Heisenberg published a seemingly different theory to explain atomic phenomena. In the Heisenberg theory, only measurable quantities appear. Dynamical quantities such as energy, position, and momentum are represented by matrices, the elements of which are the possible results of measurement. Though the Schroedinger and Heisenberg theories appear to be quite different, it was eventually shown that they were equivalent, i.e., each could be derived from the other. The resulting theory, now called *wave mechanics* or *quantum mechanics*, has been amazingly successful. Though its principles may seem strange to us

figure 6–1

Erwin Schroedinger.
(Courtesy of American
Institute of Physics.)

whose experiences are limited to the macroscopic world, and though
the mathematics required to solve even the simplest problem is quite
involved, there seems to be no alternative to describe correctly
the experimental results in atomic and nuclear physics. In this
book, we shall confine our study to the Schroedinger system because
it is easier to learn and is a little more intuitive than the Heisenberg
system.

In this chapter we shall study the Schroedinger wave equation
for one particle in one dimension. (We shall study three-dimensional problems in Chapter 7 and extend the treatment to more
than one particle in Chapter 8.) Although we eventually must consider more complicated systems in three dimensions, many of the
features of quantum mechanics are brought out in the study of
one-dimensional problems. In fact, a considerable understanding
of real physical systems can be obtained from the study of rather
simple one-dimensional models. It should be clearly understood
that the Schroedinger equation, like Newton's equations, cannot
be derived. It would be perfectly logical to begin by stating the
Schroedinger equation as a postulate. However, because students
are often unfamiliar with wave equations or, in fact, partial differential equations in general, we shall begin by giving a plausibility
argument for the form of the Schroedinger equation. We shall show

how this equation leads to energy quantization in all cases in which a particle is confined to a region of space, and then we shall apply it to some problems.

6·1

PLAUSIBILITY ARGUMENT FOR THE SCHROEDINGER EQUATION

The nonrelativistic energy of a particle of mass m and momentum p is the sum of the kinetic energy and the potential energy:

$$E = \frac{p^2}{2m} + V(x) \tag{6-1}$$

Using the de Broglie relations in the form $E = \hbar\omega$ and $p = \hbar k$, Eq. (6–1) can be written

$$\hbar\omega = \frac{(\hbar k)^2}{2m} + V(x) \tag{6-2}$$

We want to find a wave equation for the wave function $\Psi(x,t)$ that is consistent with Eq. (6–2). We shall first consider the special case of $V(x) = 0$ corresponding to no forces acting on the electron. Equation (6–2) becomes, for this case,

$$\hbar\omega = \frac{(\hbar k)^2}{2m} \tag{6-3}$$

Let us consider the wave equation for light

$$\frac{\partial^2 \mathcal{E}(x,t)}{\partial x^2} = \frac{1}{c^2}\frac{\partial^2 \mathcal{E}(x,t)}{\partial t^2} \tag{6-4}$$

where $\mathcal{E}$ is the electric field and c is the speed, which depends only

figure 6–2

Werner Heisenberg. (Courtesy of Wide World Photos.)

on the medium. If we try any of the solutions of the type of Eqs. (5–10), for example,

$$\mathcal{E}(x,t) = \mathcal{E}_0 \cos (kx - \omega t) \tag{6-5}$$

we see that $-k^2 \mathcal{E}(x,t) = 1/c^2[-\omega^2 \mathcal{E}(x,t)]$, or $\omega = kc$. Using $\omega = E/\hbar$ and $p = \hbar k$, we get

$$E = pc \tag{6-6}$$

which is the relation between energy and momentum for light.

By analogy with the wave theory for light, we might try for an electron-wave equation:

$$\frac{\partial^2 \Psi(x,t)}{\partial x^2} = \frac{1}{v^2} \frac{\partial^2 \Psi(x,t)}{\partial t^2} \tag{6-7}$$

where $\Psi(x,t)$ is the wave function and v is the phase velocity. Since the momentum is constant if there are no forces, we expect a solution like $\Psi = A \cos (kx - \omega t)$, $\Psi = A \sin (kx - \omega t)$, or $\Psi = Ae^{i(kx-\omega t)}$ corresponding to a single momentum $p = \hbar k$. However, if we try any of these solutions, we again obtain a relation like Eq. (6–6), with the energy proportional to the momentum rather than to the square of the momentum, as required by Eq. (6–3). It is easy to see why this equation does not work for electron waves. The second time-derivative gives a term proportional to $\omega^2 = E^2/\hbar^2$, while the second space-derivative gives a term proportional to $k^2 = p^2/\hbar^2$.

As our next attempt, let us try setting the first time-derivative proportional to the second space-derivative.

$$\frac{\partial \Psi}{\partial t} \propto \frac{\partial^2 \Psi}{\partial x^2} \tag{6-8}$$

This would work if $(\partial \Psi/\partial t) \propto \omega \Psi$, but this is not the case for $\Psi_1 = A \cos (kx - \omega t)$ because $(\partial \Psi_1/\partial t) = \omega A \sin (kx - \omega t)$, which is not proportional to $A \cos (kx - \omega t)$. The same difficulty occurs for $\Psi_2 = A \sin (kx - \omega t)$, but we note that

$$\psi = Ae^{i(kx-\omega t)} \tag{6-9}$$

does work. We have

$$\frac{\partial \Psi}{\partial t} = -i\omega Ae^{i(kx-\omega t)} = -i\omega \Psi \tag{6-10}$$

and

$$\frac{\partial^2 \Psi}{\partial x^2} = (ik)^2 Ae^{i(kx-\omega t)} = -k^2 \Psi \tag{6-11}$$

Let us multiply Eq. (6–3) by Ψ. Then

$$\hbar\omega\Psi = \frac{\hbar^2 k^2}{2m}\,\Psi$$

or

$$i\hbar(-i\omega\Psi) = \frac{-\hbar^2}{2m}\,(-k^2\Psi)$$

Comparing this with Eqs. (6–10) and (6–11), we see that

$$i\hbar\,\frac{\partial\Psi}{\partial t} = -\frac{\hbar^2}{2m}\,\frac{\partial^2\Psi}{\partial x^2} \tag{6-12}$$

is consistent with Eq. (6–3) for the wave-function equation (6–9). We can generalize Eq. (6–12) for the case in which the potential energy is a constant V_0 rather than being zero. The student can easily check that Eq. (6–9) is a solution of

$$i\hbar\,\frac{\partial\Psi}{\partial t} = -\frac{\hbar^2}{2m}\,\frac{\partial^2\Psi}{\partial x^2} + V_0\Psi$$

if

$$\hbar\omega = \frac{(\hbar k)^2}{2m} + V_0$$

We now postulate the Schroedinger equation in one dimension for arbitrary potential energy $V(x)$:

$$i\hbar\,\frac{\partial\Psi}{\partial t} = -\frac{\hbar^2}{2m}\,\frac{\partial^2\Psi}{\partial x^2} + V(x)\Psi \tag{6-13}$$

The Schroedinger equation is somewhat peculiar in that the imaginary number $i = \sqrt{-1}$ appears explicitly. We should thus expect $\Psi(x,t)$ to be a complex function, a result that we have already seen to be the case for a constant potential:

$$\Psi = Ae^{i(kx-\omega t)} = A\cos(kx - \omega t) + iA\sin(kx - \omega t)$$

We cannot avoid the difficulties of complex numbers by assuming that the real part of this function, $A\cos(kx - \omega t)$, is to be taken, for as we have seen, the real part is not a solution of the Schroedinger equation. Evidently $\Psi(x,t)$ cannot be a measurable function like the electric field $\mathcal{E}$, for measurements always yield real numbers. The probability $\mathcal{E}$ of finding the electron in dx is certainly measurable, however, just as is the probability that a flipped coin will turn up heads. The probability that an electron is in region dx can be measured by counting the fraction of times this occurs in a very large number of identical trials. Thus we must modify slightly the interpretation of the wave function discussed in Chapter 5 so that the probability of finding the electron in dx is real. We take for this probability

$$P(x,t) \; dx \; = \; |\Psi(x,t)|^2 \; dx = \; \Psi^*\Psi \; dx \qquad (6\text{–}14)$$

where Ψ^* is the complex conjugate of Ψ. Ψ^* is obtained from Ψ by replacing i by $-i$.[1] If the wave function happens to be real, as it is in some cases, $\Psi^*\Psi$ is the same as Ψ^2.

The probability of finding the electron in dx at x_1 or in dx at x_2 is the sum of the separate probabilities, $P(x_1) \; dx + P(x_2) \; dx$. Since the electron must certainly be somewhere, the sum of the probabilities over all possible x values must equal 1:

$$\int_{-\infty}^{+\infty} \Psi^*\Psi \; dx \; = \; 1 \qquad (6\text{–}15)$$

Equation (6–15) is called the *normalization condition*. This should be familiar from the distribution functions encountered in Chapter 2. As we shall see, this condition plays an important role in quantum mechanics, for it places the restriction on the possible solutions of the Schroedinger equation $\Psi(x,t) \rightarrow 0$ as $x \rightarrow \pm\infty$. As will be discussed in Section 6·3, it is this restriction that leads to energy quantization.

An important feature of the Schroedinger equation is that it is a linear equation, as is the wave equation for light. [A differential equation is linear if the function and its derivatives appear only to the first power, i.e., no terms such as Ψ^2, $(\partial\Psi/\partial x)^2$, $\Psi \, \partial\Psi/\partial x$ are in the equation.] If $\Psi_1(x,t)$ and $\Psi_2(x,t)$ are any two functions satisfying the Schroedinger equation, the linear combination $\Psi_3(x,t) = C_1\Psi_1(x,t) + C_2\Psi(x,t)$ does also for any constants C_1 and C_2. This is the principle of superposition, which leads to the phenomenon of interference, a common wave phenomenon. We have seen that the function $\Psi = Ae^{i(kx-\omega t)}$ corresponding to a single wave number k and frequency ω is a solution of the Schroedinger equation for the case of a constant potential energy $V(x) = V_0$. Because of the superposition principle, we know that a wave packet consisting of a distribution of more wave numbers k_i,

$$\Psi(x,t) \; = \; \sum_i C(k_i) e^{i(k_i x - \omega_i t)}$$

is also a solution.

---

[1]Every complex number can be written in the form $z = a + bi$, where a and b are real numbers. The magnitude or absolute value of z is defined as $(a^2 + b^2)^{1/2}$. The complex conjugate of z is $z^* = a - bi$; thus $z^*z = (a - bi)(a + bi) = a^2 + b^2 = |z|^2$.

6·2
THE
TIME-INDEPENDENT
SCHROEDINGER
EQUATION

We can separate the time dependence from the space dependence by a technique common in the solution of partial differential equations. We try the solution

$$\Psi(x,t) = f(t)\psi(x) \tag{6-16}$$

where $f(t)$ is a function of time only and $\psi(x)$ is a function of x only. Using $f'(t)$ for df/dt and $\psi''(x)$ for $d^2\psi/dx^2$ the Schroedinger equation (6–13) becomes

$$i\hbar f'(t)\psi(x) = -\frac{\hbar^2}{2m}f(t)\psi''(x) + V(x)f(t)\psi(x)$$

If we divide by $f(t)\psi(x)$, we obtain

$$i\hbar\frac{f'(t)}{f(t)} = -\frac{\hbar^2}{2m}\frac{\psi''(x)}{\psi(x)} + V(x) \tag{6-17}$$

The left side of Eq. (6–17) is constant for all changes in x at fixed t, while the right side is constant for all changes in t for fixed x; thus both sides must be equal to a constant.[2] Let us call this constant C. Considering the left side of Eq. (6–17) first,

$$i\hbar\frac{f'(t)}{f(t)} = C \tag{6-18}$$

The solution of Eq. (6–18) is

$$f(t) = Ae^{-i(C/\hbar)t} = Ae^{-i\omega t} \tag{6-19}$$

where A is a normalization constant and $\omega = C/\hbar$ is the angular frequency of oscillation. Comparing with the de Broglie relation $E = \hbar\omega$, we see that the constant C is the total energy; thus we relabel this constant E. The right side of Eq. (6–17) is then

$$-\frac{\hbar^2}{2m}\psi''(x) + V(x)\psi(x) = E\psi(x) \tag{6-20}$$

Eq. (6–20) is called the time-independent Schroedinger equation. The form of $\psi(x)$ that satisfies Eq. (6–20) depends, of course, on the form of $V(x)$. The superposition principle holds for the time-independent Schroedinger equation also because it is linear. Because any solution $\psi(x)$ can always be multiplied by a constant, we can choose the constant A in Eq. (6–19) to be 1. The complete solution to the

---

[2]It can be seen from Eq. (6–17) that this is true only if the potential energy V is independent of time, as we have assumed. Time-dependent potentials will not be considered here.

time-dependent Schroedinger equation for a particle of energy E can thus be written

$$\Psi(x,t) = e^{-i(E/\hbar)t}\psi(x) \qquad (6\text{-}21)$$

The probability distribution is

$$\Psi^*\Psi = e^{+i(E/\hbar)t}\psi^*(x)e^{-i(E/\hbar)t}\psi(x) = \psi^*(x)\psi(x)$$

Note that the probability distribution is independent of time. This is true only if the wave function contains a single energy. Such a wave function is useful for describing a system with a constant energy; however, in order to describe transitions between energy states such as those that occur when an atom emits light, a more general wave function, containing a distribution of energies, must be used. The most general solution of the time-dependent Schroedinger equation can be written

$$\Psi(x,t) = \sum_n C_n e^{-i(E_n/\hbar)t}\psi_n(x)$$

where E_n is a possible energy of the particle and $\psi_n(x)$ is a solution of Eq. (6–20) for the energy E_n.

In the next few sections we shall study the solutions of the Schroedinger equation corresponding to a single energy E. For a given potential energy function $V(x)$, we need only solve the time-independent equation for the space part of the wave function $\psi(x)$. The total wave function is then given by Eq. (6–21). We shall be considering some problems in which the potential energy $V(x)$ is discontinuous at some point x_1. [This is a useful approximation to real situations in which $V(x)$ varies rapidly over a small region of space, such as is the case for an electron leaving the surface of a metal.] For these problems, the Schroedinger equation can be solved in each of the regions $x < x_1$ and $x > x_1$ separately, and the solutions joined at $x = x_1$. Since the probability of finding the particle cannot vary discontinuously from point to point, the wave function $\psi(x)$ must be continuous. It follows directly from the Schroedinger equation (6–20)[3] that if $V(x_1)$ is not infinite, the slope ψ' must also be continuous, i.e., the function must join smoothly at x_1. The normalization condition [Eq. (6–15)], expressing the fact that the prob-

---

[3]For a small change in x, Δx, the change in the slope, is approximately

$$\Delta\psi' \approx \frac{d\psi'}{dx}\,\Delta x = \psi''\,\Delta x$$

Using the Schroedinger equation for ψ'', we obtain

$$\Delta\psi' \approx \frac{2m}{\hbar^2}\,[V(x) - E]\psi(x)\,\Delta x$$

As $\Delta x \to 0$, $\Delta\psi' \to 0$ as long as $V(x)$ is not infinite.

ability of finding the particle somewhere must be unity, is

$$\int_{-\infty}^{+\infty} \Psi^*(x,t)\Psi(x,t)\ dx = \int_{-\infty}^{+\infty} \psi^*(x)\psi(x)\ dx = 1 \qquad (6\text{-}22)$$

In order for $\psi(x)$ to obey the normalization condition, $\psi(x)$ must approach zero as $x \to \pm\infty$. For future reference, we list the following conditions that the wave function $\psi(x)$ must meet to be acceptable:

1. $\psi(x)$ must satisfy the Schroedinger equation.
2. $\psi(x)$ must be continuous.
3. $\psi'(x)$ must be continuous [unless $V(x)$ is infinite].
4. $\psi(x) \to 0$ as $x \to \pm\infty$, so that $\psi(x)$ can be normalized.

**6·3
ENERGY
QUANTIZATION
FROM THE
SCHROEDINGER
EQUATION**

We shall now show how the Schroedinger equation leads to energy quantization in situations in which the potential energy $V(x)$ is greater than the total energy E for some range of x. For this case, the particle is bound to some region of space and the energy state is called *a bound state*.

In order to make the analysis easier, we consider the somewhat special case of the potential energy $V(x)$ given by:

$$V(x) = 0 \quad \text{for } |x| < a$$
$$V(x) = \text{any function obeying}$$
$$V(x) > E \quad \text{for } |x| > a$$

and

$$V(-x) = V(x)$$

Such a potential-energy function is shown in Figure (6–3). Since this function is symmetric, i.e., since it is the same at $-x$ as at $+x$, the probability of finding the particle in dx at some point $-x_1$

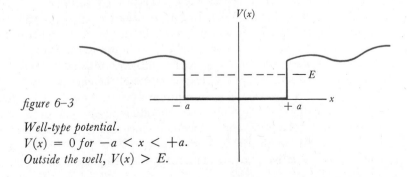

figure 6–3

Well-type potential.
$V(x) = 0$ for $-a < x < +a$.
Outside the well, $V(x) > E$.

must equal that at $+x_1$. Thus $|\psi(-x)|^2 = |\psi(+x)|^2$ and $\psi(x)$ must be either an even function

$$\psi_e(-x) = +\psi_e(+x) \qquad (6\text{--}23)$$

or an odd function

$$\psi_o(-x) = -\psi_o(+x) \qquad (6\text{--}24)$$

Thus we need only to solve the Schroedinger equation for positive x; solutions for negative x can be obtained from Eq. (6–23) or (6–24). (Even functions are said to have even parity or parity of $+1$, whereas odd functions have odd parity or parity of -1.)

For $0 < x < a$, the Schroedinger equation is

$$-\frac{\hbar^2}{2m}\psi''(x) = E\psi(x)$$

or

$$\psi''(x) = -\frac{2mE}{\hbar^2}\psi(x) = -k^2\psi(x) \qquad (6\text{--}25)$$

where $k^2 = 2mE/\hbar^2$. Solutions to Eq. (6–25) are

$$\psi(x) = A\cos kx = A\cos\frac{2\pi x}{\lambda} \qquad \text{(even)} \qquad (6\text{--}26)$$

$$\psi(x) = B\sin kx = B\sin\frac{2\pi x}{\lambda} \qquad \text{(odd)} \qquad (6\text{--}27)$$

where $\lambda = 2\pi/k$ is the wavelength.

The Schroedinger equation for $|x| > a$ is

$$\psi''(x) = \frac{2m}{\hbar^2}[V(x) - E]\psi(x) = \alpha^2\psi(x) \qquad (6\text{--}28)$$

where $\alpha^2 = (2m/\hbar^2)[V(x) - E] > 0$. We cannot solve Eq. (6–28) unless the function $V(x)$ is specified. However, the important feature of this equation is that α^2 is positive; thus ψ'' has the same sign as $\psi(x)$. If $\psi(x)$ is positive, $\psi''(x)$ is positive and $\psi(x)$ is concave upward, as in Figure 6–4a. If $\psi(x)$ is negative, $\psi''(x)$ is negative and $\psi(x)$ is concave downward, as in Figure 6–4b. In general, for arbitrary E, the solutions $\psi(x)$ for $x > a$ do not tend to zero for large x. The wave function approaches either positive or negative infinity at large x except for certain values of the energy E.

Consider the even solution $\psi(x) = A\cos(2\pi x/\lambda)$, for $x < a$, for the case $\frac{1}{4}\lambda = 2a$, corresponding to the energy $E = h^2/2m\lambda^2 = h^2/128ma^2$. The behavior of this solution is shown in Figure 6–5. Although $\psi(x)$ is heading toward zero at $x = a$, that is, the slope is negative, the rate of increase of the slope is so great that the function

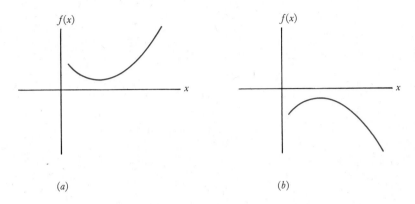

figure 6–4   (a) *Function that is concave up.* (b) *Function that is concave down.*

turns up and approaches $+\infty$ for large x. Figure 6–6 shows what happens as we gradually reduce the wavelength λ. For λ greater than some critical value λ_1, $\psi(x) \to +\infty$ as $x \to +\infty$. For λ just less than λ_1, $\psi(x) \to -\infty$ as $x \to \infty$. At the critical wavelength, $\psi(x)$ and $\psi'(x)$ approach zero together. If we reduce the wavelength even more, $\psi(x)$ approaches $-\infty$ until another critical value λ_2 is reached. For this case, the wave function crosses the axis once and then approaches zero as $x \to \infty$. This function is sketched in Figure 6–7.

figure 6–5   *This function that satisfies the Schroedinger equation with $\lambda = 8a$ inside the well is not an acceptable wave function because it becomes infinite at large x. Although the function is heading toward zero at $x = a$ (slope is negative), the rate of increase of the slope ψ'' is so great that the slope becomes positive before the function becomes zero, and the function then increases. Since ψ'' has the same sign as ψ, the slope always increases (once it becomes positive) and the function increases without bound.*

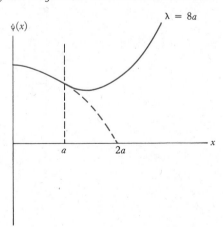

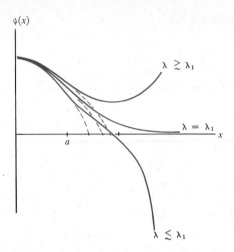

$$\psi(x)$$

$$\lambda \gtrsim \lambda_1$$

$$\lambda = \lambda_1$$

$$a$$

$$\lambda \lesssim \lambda_1$$

figure 6–6   *Functions satisfying the Schroedinger equation with wavelengths near the critical wavelength λ_1. If λ is slightly greater than λ_1, the function approaches infinity similarly to that in Figure 6–5. At the critical wavelength λ_1, the function and its slope approach zero together. This is an acceptable wave function. The energy corresponding to this wave function is $E_1 = h^2/2m\lambda_1{}^2$. If λ is slightly less than λ_1, the function crosses the x axis while the slope is still negative. The slope becomes more negative because its rate of change ψ'' is now negative. This function approaches negative infinity at large x.*

figure 6–7   *There is a second critical wavelength for functions which cross the x axis between 0 and a. At this wavelength λ_2, the function and its slope approach zero together from below the axis. The energy corresponding to this acceptable wave function is $E_2 = h^2/2m\lambda_2{}^2$, which is greater than E_1 because λ_2 is less than λ_1. If the wavelength is slightly greater or slightly less than λ_2, the function does not approach zero at large x.*

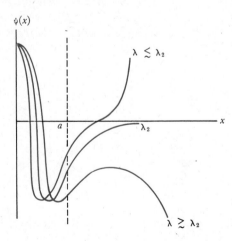

$$\psi(x)$$

$$\lambda \lesssim \lambda_2$$

$$a$$

$$\lambda_2$$

$$\lambda \gtrsim \lambda_2$$

We see by this analysis that the Schroedinger equation has well-behaved solutions obeying condition 4 on page 233 only for certain values of the energy, such as

$$E_1 = \frac{h^2}{2m\lambda_1{}^2}$$

or

$$E_2 = \frac{h^2}{2m\lambda_2{}^2}$$

There are other well-behaved even solutions for which $\psi(x)$ crosses the axis more than once, and there is a set of well-behaved odd solutions. The lowest energy odd solution is sketched in Figure 6–8.

In this example we have chosen $V(x) = 0$ for $x < a$ so that the wave functions could easily be sketched. For other potential-energy functions, the momentum, and therefore the wavelength, varies with position, and the shape of $\psi(x)$ depends on the particular function $V(x)$. For a more general $V(x)$, the above analysis will apply if E is greater than $V(x)$ for some region $|x| < a$ and is less than $V(x)$ outside this region. The Schroedinger equation for $|x| < a$ will be

$$\psi'' = -k^2(x)\psi \qquad (6\text{–}29)$$

with $k^2(x) = 2m[E - V(x)]/\hbar^2 > 0$. This type of equation leads to solutions $\psi(x)$ which oscillate since ψ'' and ψ have opposite signs; however, unless $V(x)$ is zero or constant, the wavelength will not be constant. The Schroedinger equation for $|x| > a$ is Eq. (6–28). As we have seen, the solutions in this region do not oscillate, and $\psi(x)$ will be well-behaved only for certain values of the energy E.

figure 6–8

A well-behaved odd solution for the well-type potential of Figure 6–3.

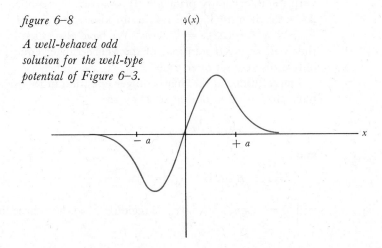

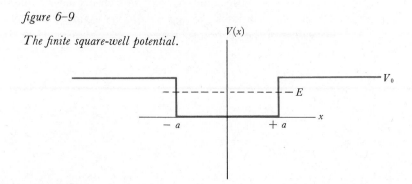

figure 6–9

The finite square-well potential.

The solution of the Schroedinger equation for any particular potential energy function $V(x)$ is usually quite difficult mathematically.
In this section we shall consider an example called the *square-well
potential*, for which the mathematics is relatively easy. The square-
well potential is shown in Figure 6–9 and is defined by

$$V(x) = 0 \qquad \text{for } -a < x < +a$$
$$V(x) = V_0 \qquad \text{for } |x| > a \tag{6–30}$$

We shall consider the problem of a particle of mass m with total
energy E less than V_0. The classical solution of this problem is
very simple: The particle is confined to the region inside the well
$|x| \le a$ and can have any energy. If $E = 0$, the particle simply
rests at some point; while if $E > 0$, the particle moves back and
forth, being reflected at the walls ($x = +a$ or $x = -a$) where the
force $F = -dV/dx$ is infinite. (This is a force that provides an
impulse just large enough to reverse the particle's momentum.)

We have already noted in Chapter 5 that $E = 0$ is inconsistent
with the uncertainty principle. If a particle is confined to a region
$\Delta x = 2a$, it must have a minimum kinetic energy of the order of
$E_{\min} \approx \hbar^2/2m\,(\Delta x)^2 = \hbar^2/8ma^2$. We have also noted in Section 6·3
that well-behaved solutions of the Schroedinger equation exist for
only a discrete set of energies.

The solutions of the Schroedinger equation in the region $|x| < a$
have already been obtained. They are

$$\psi(x) = A \cos kx \tag{6–31}$$

and

$$\psi(x) = B \sin kx \tag{6–32}$$

with $k = (2mE/\hbar^2)^{1/2}$. In the region $x > a$, the Schroedinger equation is similar to Eq. (6–28):

$$\psi''(x) = \alpha^2 \psi(x) \tag{6–33}$$

where $\alpha^2 = (2m/\hbar^2)(V_0 - E)$. Since α is a constant for this problem, Eq. (6–33) is not difficult to solve. The solutions are of the form

$$\psi(x) = Ce^{\pm \alpha x}$$

where C is a constant. Since α is positive and $\psi(x)$ must approach zero for large x, the $+$ sign in the exponent of this equation is unacceptable for $x > 0$. Thus, for $x > a$, the wave function is

$$\psi(x) = Ce^{-\alpha x} \tag{6–34}$$

If we try to join this solution to either $A \cos kx$ or $B \sin kx$ at $x = a$ such that $\psi(x)$ and $\psi'(x)$ are continuous, we find that this is possible for only a discrete set of energies, in agreement with the general discussion in Section 6·3. Even for this somewhat simple form of potential-energy function, it is difficult to carry out the mathematical details and find the allowed energies for arbitrary V_0. We shall thus consider first the limiting case $V_0 \rightarrow \infty$, which is much simpler mathematically. This limiting case is called the *infinite square well*.

If V_0 is very large, α is very large and $\psi(x)$ approaches zero rapidly for $x > a$. In the limit $V_0 = \infty$, $\psi(x)$ is zero everywhere outside the well. Thus, for the infinite square-well problem, we need only find the solutions inside the well, $|x| \leq a$, and apply the boundary condition

$$\psi(x) = 0 \quad \text{at } x = \pm a \tag{6–35}$$

For the even solutions,

$$A \cos ka = 0,$$

if

$$k_n = n(\pi/2a) \qquad n = 1, 3, 5, \dots$$

and for the odd solutions,

$$A \sin ka = 0$$

if

$$k_n = n(\pi/2a) \qquad n = 2, 4, 6, \dots$$

Thus the boundary condition $\psi(x) = 0$ at $x = \pm a$ places the restriction on the possible values of k, namely,

$$k_n = n\frac{\pi}{2a} \qquad n = 1, 2, 3, \dots \tag{6–36}$$

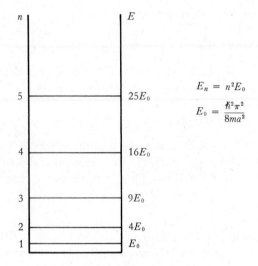

figure 6–10 *Energy-level diagram for the infinite square-well potential. Classically, a particle can have any value of energy. However, quantum mechanically, only certain values of energy given by $E_n = n^2(\hbar^2\pi^2/8ma^2)$ yield well-behaved solutions of the Schroedinger equation.*

The energy is correspondingly restricted to

$$E_n = \frac{\hbar^2 k_n^2}{2m} = n^2 \frac{\hbar^2 \pi^2}{8ma^2} \tag{6–37}$$

Figure 6–10 is an energy level diagram for the infinite square-well potential.

In terms of the wavelength $\lambda = 2\pi/k$, Eq. (6–36) can be written

$$n\frac{\lambda}{2} = 2a \tag{6–38}$$

This condition is the same as that for standing waves on a string fixed at both ends. The solutions $\psi_n(x)$ are also the same as the solutions $y(x)$ for the vibrating-string problem.

The number n is called a quantum number. It specifies the energy and the wave function. If we are given the value of n for this problem, we can immediately write down the wave function and the energy of the system. The quantum number n occurs because of the boundary condition $\psi(x) = 0$ at $x = \pm a$. We shall see in Chapter 7 that for problems in three dimensions, three quantum numbers arise, one associated with each dimension.

The constants A and B in Eqs. (6–31) and (6–32) are determined by the normalization condition. For the even solutions,

$$\int_{-\infty}^{+\infty} \psi_n^* \psi_n \, dx = \int_{-a}^{+a} A^2 \cos^2 \frac{n\pi x}{2a} \, dx = 1$$

Performing the integration gives $A = 1/\sqrt{a}$. The result for the odd solutions is the same, $B = 1/\sqrt{a}$; thus the normalized solutions are

$$\psi_n(x) = a^{-1/2} \cos \frac{n\pi x}{2a} \qquad \text{for } n \text{ odd}$$

$$\psi_n(x) = a^{-1/2} \sin \frac{n\pi x}{2a} \qquad \text{for } n \text{ even}$$

$$(6\text{–}39)$$

The wave functions and the distribution functions

$$P_n(x) = |\psi_n(x)|^2$$

are sketched in Figure 6–11 for the lowest energy state, $n = 1$, called the *ground state*, and the first two excited states, $n = 2$ and $n = 3$. These distributions are quite different from what we expect classically for a particle in a one-dimensional box. The classical expectation is that the chance of finding the particle in dx is proportional to the time spent in dx, which is dx/v where v is the speed. Since the speed is constant, the classical distribution function is just a constant inside the well. According to Bohr's correspondence

figure 6–11 *Wave function $\psi_n(x)$ and probability densities $\psi_n^2(x)$, for $n = 1, 2,$ and 3, for the infinite square-well potential.*

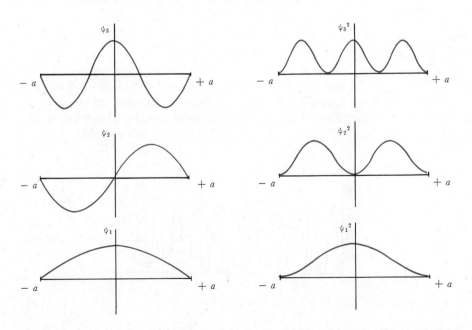

principle, the quantum-mechanical distribution should approach the classical distribution when n is large. For any state n, the quantum distribution has n peaks. The distribution for $n = 10$ is shown in Figure 6–12. For very large n, the peaks are close together, and if there are many peaks in a small distance Δx, only the average corresponding to the classical distribution will be observed.

We shall not present the details of the determination of the allowed energies for the case of the finite square well. The wave functions and probability distributions for the ground state and the first two excited states for finite V_0 are sketched in Figure 6–13. We can see from these sketches that since $\psi(a)$ is not zero, the wavelengths are larger than the corresponding ones for the infinite well; thus the energies

$$E = \frac{\hbar^2 k^2}{2m} = \frac{h^2}{2m\lambda^2}$$

are slightly lower. (In order to calculate these energies, approximate or graphical methods must be used. A complete solution is outlined in Problem 6–17.)

Note that, contrary to the classical case, there is some probability of finding the particle outside the box in the region $|x| > a$. In this region, the total energy is less than the potential energy V_0, so it would seem that the kinetic energy must be negative. Since negative kinetic energy is a meaningless concept in classical physics, it is interesting to speculate about the meaning of this penetration of the wave function beyond $x = a$. Does quantum mechanics predict that we should measure a negative kinetic energy? If this were so, it would be a serious defect in the theory. The uncertainty principle provides us with a way out of this dilemma. In order to measure such a negative kinetic energy, we must be able to measure

figure 6–12   *Probability distribution for $n = 10$ for the infinite square-well potential. The dotted line is the classical probability $P = 1/2a$ which equals the quantum mechanical distribution averaged over a region Δx containing several oscillations. A physical measurement with resolution Δx will yield the classical result if n is so large that $\psi^2(x)$ has many oscillations in Δx.*

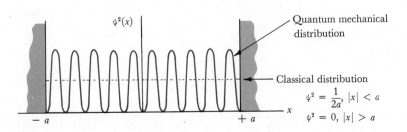

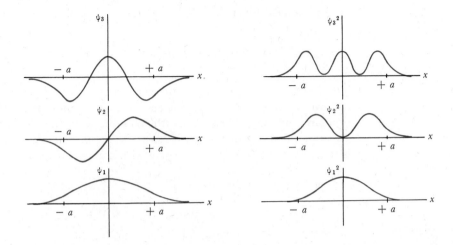

figure 6–13   Wave functions $\psi_n(x)$ and probability distributions $\psi_n{}^2(x)$, for $n = 1, 2,$ and 3, for the finite square well. Compare these to Figure 6–11. For finite V_0, $\psi_n(x)$ and $\psi_n{}^2(x)$ are not zero at the edges of the well $\pm a$. The wavelengths are slightly longer than the corresponding ones for infinite V_0, thus the allowed energies are somewhat smaller.

the kinetic energy with an uncertainty less than $V_0 - E$. Let us estimate the uncertainty in the kinetic energy when a determination is made that the particle is in the region $x > a$. In this region the wave function is very small. It decreases from its maximum value $\psi(a)$ at $x = a$ to e^{-1} times this value in the distance $\Delta x = \alpha^{-1}$; thus the probability $\psi^2(x)$ decreases by e^{-2} in this distance. If we consider $\psi^2(x)$ to be negligible beyond $x = a + \alpha^{-1}$, it is reasonable to say that observing the particle in the region $x > a$ is roughly equivalent to localizing the particle within the region $\Delta x \approx \alpha^{-1}$. The uncertainty in the momentum is then $\Delta p > \hbar/\Delta x = \hbar\alpha$. As we have seen in Chapter 5, this implies a minimum kinetic energy of the order of $T \approx (\Delta p)^2/2m = \hbar^2\alpha^2/2m = V_0 - E$. We thus have no chance (fortunately) of measuring a negative kinetic energy.

6·5
CALCULATION OF
EXPECTATION
VALUES FROM
THE WAVE
FUNCTION

The solutions of the time-dependent Schroedinger equation can be written

$$\Psi_n(x,t) = e^{-i\omega_n t}\,\psi_n(x)$$

where $\omega_n = E_n/\hbar$, E_n is one of the possible energies, and $\psi_n(x)$ is the corresponding solution of the time-independent equation. The expectation value of the position of the particle is usually written

$\langle x \rangle$ and defined by

$$\langle x \rangle \equiv \int_{-\infty}^{+\infty} x \Psi^*(x,t) \Psi(x,t)\ dx \tag{6-40}$$

The expectation value of x is the same as the average value of x that we would expect to obtain from a measurement of the position of a large number of particles with the same wave function $\Psi(x,t)$. As we pointed out in Section 6·2, the probability density $|\Psi(x,t)|^2$ is independent of time for a particle with a given energy:

$$|\Psi_n(x,t)|^2 = \Psi_n^*(x,t)\Psi_n(x,t) = [e^{+i\omega_n t}\psi_n^*(x)][e^{-i\omega_n t}\psi_n(x)]$$
$$= \psi_n^*(x)\psi_n(x)$$

Thus the expectation value of x is

$$\langle x \rangle = \int_{-\infty}^{+\infty} x\psi_n^*(x)\psi_n(x)\ dx \tag{6-41}$$

For the case of the even solutions for the infinite square well,

$$\psi_n = a^{-1/2} \cos k_n x \qquad \text{for } |x| \le a$$
$$= 0 \qquad \qquad \text{for } |x| \ge a$$

where $k_n = n(\pi/2a)$, $n = 1, 3, 5, \ldots$, the expectation value of x is

$$\langle x \rangle = \int_{-\infty}^{+\infty} x\psi_n^*(x)\psi_n(x)\ dx = \int_{-a}^{+a} xa^{-1} \cos^2 k_n x\ dx = 0$$

The expectation value of x^2 for this wave function is

$$\langle x^2 \rangle = \int_{-a}^{+a} x^2 a^{-1} \cos^2 k_n x\ dx$$

It is left as an exercise to show that

$$\langle x^2 \rangle = \frac{a^2}{3}\left(1 - \frac{6}{\pi^2 n^2}\right) \tag{6-42}$$

for both the even and the odd solutions for the infinite square well.

   We would now like to find the expectation value for the momentum of the particle. This problem is not difficult for the special case of the infinite square well. Since the potential energy is zero inside the well and the energy is constant, $E_n = p_n^2/2m$, we expect $\langle p^2 \rangle$ to be $2mE_n$ and $\langle p_n \rangle = 0$ because p_n is negative as often as it is positive. However, we would like to find a general expression for $\langle p \rangle$ similar to Eq. (6–41). If we could find p as a function of x, $p(x)$, we could calculate $\langle p \rangle$ from

$$\langle p \rangle = \int p(x) \psi^* \psi \, dx$$

However, it is impossible *in principle* to find $p(x)$, for p and x cannot be determined at the same time. This is because of the wave nature of the electron as expressed in the uncertainty principle. We thus need to know the distribution of momenta. This turns out to be not too difficult. Consider again the even solutions for the infinite square-well problem. We can write $\cos k_n x$ as

$$\cos k_n x = \tfrac{1}{2}(e^{+ik_n x} + e^{-ik_n x})$$

and

$$a^{-1/2} e^{-i\omega_n t} \cos k_n x = \tfrac{1}{2} a^{-1/2} (e^{i(k_n x - \omega_n t)} + e^{-i(k_n x + \omega_n t)})$$

$$= \frac{1}{\sqrt{2}} \phi_R + \frac{1}{\sqrt{2}} \phi_L \qquad (6\text{--}43)$$

where $\phi_R = (2a)^{-1/2} e^{i(k_n x - \omega_n t)}$ and $\phi_L = (2a)^{-1/2} e^{-i(k_n x + \omega_n t)}$

The function ϕ_R is a plane wave corresponding to a particle with a definite momentum $p = \hbar k_n$ moving to the right, while ϕ_L corresponds to a particle with a definite momentum $p = -\hbar k_n$ moving to the left. These functions have the properties

$$\int_{-a}^{+a} \phi_R^* \phi_R \, dx = \int_{-a}^{+a} \phi_L^* \phi_L \, dx = 1 \qquad (6\text{--}44)$$

$$\int_{-a}^{+a} \phi_R^* \phi_L \, dx = \int_{-a}^{+a} \phi_L^* \phi_R \, dx = 0 \qquad (6\text{--}45)$$

If we measure the momentum of a particle in a box, we expect to find either $p = +\hbar k_n$ or $p = -\hbar k_n$, and the two possibilities are equally likely. If we write Eq. (6–43) as $\Psi = C_1 \phi_R + C_2 \phi_L$, we see that $C_1{}^2 = \tfrac{1}{2}$ is the probability of measuring $p = +\hbar k_n$ and $C_2{}^2 = \tfrac{1}{2}$ is the probability of measuring $p = -\hbar k_n$. For potentials more complicated than the infinite square well, the wave function $\psi(x)$ will be, in general, more complicated than a simple sine or cosine function; however, it can still be written as a sum (or integral) of exponential functions [like Eq. (6–43)] with different values of k. This sum is called a *Fourier sum*. The square of the coefficient of the exponential corresponding to a particular k value is

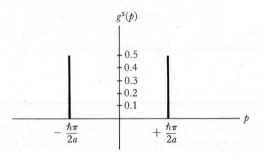

figure 6–14   *Momentum distribution function for the ground state of infinite square well. There are two possible values of the momentum, $\hbar\pi/2a$ and $-\hbar\pi/2a$, each with probability $\frac{1}{2}$. This is the same as the classical distribution.*

the probability of measuring the momentum to be $\hbar k$. Thus, in general, if we write

$$\psi(x) = \sum_n C_n \phi_n(x) \tag{6–46}$$

where $\phi_n(x) = C e^{ik_n x}$, the probability of measuring a particular momentum $\hbar k_n$ is $|C_n|^2$. Thus the expectation value of momentum is

$$\langle p \rangle = \sum_n \hbar k_n |C_n|^2 \tag{6–47}$$

In principle, given the function $\psi(x)$, the momentum distribution $|C_n|^2$ can be found by the methods of Fourier analysis. Fortunately it is not necessary to do this in order to calculate $\langle p \rangle$. We shall now show that Eq. (6–46) and (6–47) are equivalent to

$$\langle p \rangle = \int \psi^*(x) \frac{\hbar}{i} \frac{d}{dx} \psi(x) \, dx \tag{6–48}$$

The proof involves some assumptions about the functions similar to Eqs. (6–44) and (6–45). We assume

1. ϕ_n are normalized; $\int \phi_n^* \phi_n \, dx = 1.$

2. ϕ_n are orthogonal; $\int \phi_n^* \phi_m \, dx = 0$ if $m \neq n.$

It is easiest to begin with Eq. (6–48) and show that it implies Eq. (6–47). We note that

$$\frac{\hbar}{i} \frac{d}{dx} \phi_n = \frac{\hbar}{i} \frac{d(e^{ik_n x})}{dx} = \hbar k_n \phi_n$$

Then

$$\frac{\hbar}{i}\frac{d}{dx}\psi(x) = \frac{\hbar}{i}\frac{d}{dx}\sum_m C_m\phi_m = \sum_m \hbar k_m C_m\phi_m$$

and

$$\int \psi^* \frac{h}{i}\frac{d}{dx}\psi\, dx = \int \left(\sum_n C_n^*\phi_n^*\right)\left(\sum_m \hbar k_m C_m\phi_m\right) dx$$

$$= \sum_n \sum_m C_n^* C_m \hbar k_m \int \phi_n^*\phi_m\, dx$$

$$= \sum_n C_n^* C_n \hbar k_n = \sum_n |C_n|^2 \hbar k_n$$

In the last step, we summed over m. Each term is zero except for $m = n$, for which case $\int \phi_n^*\phi_n\, dx = 1$.

We see thus that we can calculate $\langle p \rangle$ directly from the wave function by Eq. (6–48), and we need not find the momentum distribution. To find the expectation value of p^2, we take

$$\langle p^2 \rangle = \int \psi^* \left(\frac{\hbar}{i}\frac{d}{dx}\right)\left(\frac{\hbar}{i}\frac{d}{dx}\right)\psi\, dx$$

$$= \int \psi^* \left(-\hbar^2 \frac{d^2\psi}{dx^2}\right) dx \qquad (6\text{–}49)$$

From the time-independent Schroedinger equation, we have

$$-\hbar^2 \frac{d^2\psi}{dx^2} = 2m[E - V(x)]\psi$$

We thus see that Eq. (6–49) implies that

$$\langle p^2 \rangle = \int \psi^* 2m[E - V(x)]\psi\, dx$$

$$= 2m\left[E\int \psi^*\psi\, dx - \int \psi^* V(x)\psi\, dx\right]$$

or

$$E = \frac{1}{2m}\langle p^2 \rangle + \langle V(x) \rangle \qquad (6\text{–}50)$$

This is the same as the classical relation with the classical values of p^2 and $V(x)$ replaced by expectation values. In the classical limit, the ranges Δx and Δp of the wave packets are much smaller than experimental uncertainties, and the expectation value of a quantity is the same as the classically measured value. (See Problem 6–8.)

6·6
OPERATORS,
EIGENVALUES, AND
EIGENFUNCTIONS

It is convenient to call the differential expression $(\hbar/i)(d/dx)$, which operates on the wave function in Eq. (6–48), the momentum operator P_{op}. (An operator can be anything that does something to a function, such as differentiate it or multiply it by another function.) The expectation value of the momentum can then be written

$$\langle p \rangle = \int \psi^* P_{op} \psi \, dx \tag{6-51}$$

When we write P_{op} we always assume there is a function following it to be operated on. The meaning of P_{op}^2 is $P_{op}P_{op}$, that is,

$$P_{op}^2 f(x) \equiv P_{op}[P_{op} f(x)] = \frac{\hbar}{i} \frac{d}{dx} \left[\frac{\hbar}{i} \frac{d}{dx} f(x) \right] = -\hbar^2 \frac{d^2 f(x)}{dx^2}$$

Using this notation, the time-independent Schroedinger equation is written

$$\left[\frac{1}{2m} P_{op}^2 + V(x) \right] \psi(x) = E\psi(x) \tag{6-52}$$

or

$$E_{op}\psi(x) = E\psi(x) \tag{6-53}$$

where the energy operator is defined by

$$E_{op} \equiv \frac{1}{2m} P_{op}^2 + V(x) \tag{6-54}$$

An equation such as (6–53), in which an operation on a function gives a constant times the function, is called an *eigenvalue equation*. (From the German *eigen*, meaning "proper." The English term "characteristic value" is sometimes used.) The function is called an *eigenfunction* of the operator, and the constant is called an *eigenvalue*. The "eigenvalue problem" is to find both the eigenfunctions and the eigenvalues, given the operator and boundary conditions on the functions. The Schroedinger equation is just such a problem. The eigenfunctions of E_{op} are the possible wave functions, and the eigenvalues are the possible values of the energy. We have just studied another eigenvalue problem:

$$P_{op}f_n(x) = p_n f_n(x)$$

Using the definition of P_{op}, this equation is

$$\frac{\hbar}{i} \frac{d}{dx} f_n(x) = p_n f_n(x)$$

The solutions of this eigenvalue problem are

$$f_n(x) = Ce^{\pm ik_n x}$$

with the eigenvalues $p_n = \pm \hbar k_n$. Thus, for both the momentum and energy operators just defined, the eigenvalues of the operator are the possible values of the corresponding variable (momentum or energy).

In general, the wave function is not an eigenfunction of the momentum operator. For example, in the infinite square-well problem, the wave function which *is* an eigenfunction of E_{op} is a linear combination of two eigenfunctions of P_{op}, one with eigenvalue $+\hbar k_n$ and one with eigenvalue $-\hbar k_n$. For example,

$$\cos k_n x = \tfrac{1}{2}(e^{ik_n x} + e^{-ik_n x})$$

or

$$\sin k_n x = \frac{1}{2i}(e^{ik_n x} - e^{-ik_n x})$$

Thus, for these wave functions, there are two possibilities for the results of a measurement of momentum.

In the next chapter, when we study the Schroedinger equation in three dimensions, we shall find it convenient to define other operators, in particular those associated with the components of the angular momentum of a particle. Just as the eigenvalues of the momentum operator are the possible results of a measurement of momentum, the eigenvalues of any other quantum-mechanical operator are the possible results of a measurement of the associated variable. We shall make some general assertions here about quantum-mechanical operators which we have seen to be true for the energy and momentum operators and which we can take to be postulates of quantum mechanics.

Consider a general operator A_{op} associated with some variable a which has eigenfunctions f_n and eigenvalues a_n, that is,

$$A_{op}f_n = a_n f_n.$$

The wave function can be written as a linear combination of eigenfunctions f_n similar to a Fourier expansion:

$$\psi = \sum_n C_n f_n$$

The distribution function for the variable a is $|C_n|^2$. For the special case in which ψ is an eigenfunction of A_{op}, C_n will be 1 for one particular n and zero for all others, and a measurement of a will always yield the corresponding eigenvalue a_n. In general, the expectation value of a is

$$\langle a \rangle = \int \psi^* A_{\text{op}} \psi \, dx \tag{6-55}$$

6·7
TRANSITIONS BETWEEN ENERGY STATES

We have shown how the Schroedinger equation leads to energy quantization in one dimension. In the next chapter we shall consider three-dimensional problems — in particular, the hydrogen atom. We shall see that the hydrogen energy states predicted by the Schroedinger equation are just those predicted by the Bohr model. The existence of these energy levels is determined directly by observation of electromagnetic radiation emitted or absorbed when the system changes from one energy state to another. In this section we shall study some aspects of these transitions in one dimension. The results will be readily applicable to more complicated situations.

In classical physics, a charged particle radiates when it accelerates. If the charge oscillates, the frequency of the radiation is equal to the frequency of oscillation. A stationary charge distribution does not radiate.

Consider a particle with charge q in a quantum state n defined by the wave function

$$\Psi_n(x,t) = e^{-i(E_n/\hbar)t} \psi_n(x) \tag{6-56}$$

where E_n is the energy and $\psi_n(x)$ is a solution of the time-independent Schroedinger equation for some potential energy $V(x)$. The probability of finding the charge in dx is $\Psi_n^* \Psi_n \, dx$. If we make many measurements on identical systems (i.e., particles with the same wave function), the average amount of charge found in dx will be $q\Psi_n^* \Psi_n \, dx$. It is thus reasonable to call $q\Psi_n^* \Psi_n$ the *charge density*. As we have already pointed out, the probability density is independent of time if the wave function contains a single energy. Thus the charge density for this state is also independent of time:

$$\rho_n = q\Psi_n^*(x,t)\Psi(x,t) = q\psi_n^*(x)\psi_n(x)$$

We would thus expect that this stationary charge distribution would not produce radiation. (This argument, for the case of the hydrogen atom, is the quantum-mechanical explanation of Bohr's postulate of nonradiating orbits.) However, we do observe that systems make transitions from one energy state to another with the emission or absorption of radiation. The cause of the transition is the interaction of the electromagnetic field with the charged particle. A detailed treatment of this interaction, well beyond the scope of this book, is necessary in order to obtain rates of emission and absorption. However, we can learn a great deal about the frequencies of radiation emitted and absorbed from a semiclassical treatment which we shall now discuss.

Let us write the wave function for a particle making a transition from state n to state m as a mixture of the two states Ψ_n and Ψ_m:

$$\Psi_{nm}(x,t) = a\Psi_n(x,t) + b\Psi_m(x,t) \tag{6-57}$$

We need not be concerned with the numbers a and b. We wish only to show that if neither a nor b is zero, the probability density, and thus the charge density, oscillates with the angular frequency ω_{nm} given by the Bohr relation

$$\omega_{nm} = \frac{E_n - E_m}{\hbar} \tag{6-58}$$

In order to simplify the notation, it is convenient to assume that the time-independent functions $\psi_n(x)$ and $\psi_m(x)$ are real. The probability density for the wave function $\Psi_{nm}(x,t)$ is then

$$\Psi_{nm}^*\Psi_{nm} = a^2\Psi_n^*\Psi_n + b^2\Psi_m^*\Psi_m + ab(\Psi_n^*\Psi_m + \Psi_m^*\Psi_n) \tag{6-59}$$

The first two terms are independent of time:

$$\Psi_n^*(x,t)\Psi_n(x,t) = \psi_n^*(x)\psi_n(x) = \psi_n^2(x)$$

assuming $\psi_n(x)$ is real, with a similar expression for the second term. The third term in Eq. (6-59) contains the quantities

$$\Psi_n^*(x,t)\Psi_m(x,t) = e^{i(E_n/\hbar)t}\psi_n^*(x)e^{-i(E_m/\hbar)t}\psi_m(x)$$
$$= e^{i\omega_{nm}t}\psi_n(x)\psi_m(x)$$

and

$$\Psi_m^*(x,t)\Psi_n(x,t) = e^{i(E_m/\hbar)t}\psi_m^*(x)e^{-i(E_n/\hbar)t}\psi_n(x)$$
$$= e^{-i\omega_{nm}t}\psi_m(x)\psi_n(x)$$

where ω_{nm} is the Bohr angular frequency given by Eq. (6-58). Adding these and using $e^{i\omega_{nm}t} + e^{-i\omega_{mm}t} = 2\cos\omega_{nm}t$, we see that the probability density is

$$|\Psi_{nm}(x,t)|^2 = a^2\psi_n^2(x) + b^2\psi_m^2(x)$$
$$+ 2ab\cos(\omega_{nm}t)\psi_n(x)\psi_m(x) \tag{6-60}$$

Thus the wave function consisting of a mixture of two energy states does lead to a charge distribution which oscillates with the Bohr frequency. We can describe the radiation of a system somewhat loosely as follows. At some time, a system is in an excited state n, described by Eq. (6–57), with $a = 1$ and $b = 0$. Because of an interaction of the system with the electromagnetic field (which we have not included in the Schroedinger equation), a decreases and b is no longer zero. At this time the charge density oscillates with angular frequency ω_{nm}. The system does not, however, radiate energy continuously as predicted by classical theory. Instead, the oscillating charge density implies a probability that a photon of energy $\hbar\omega_{nm} = E_n - E_m$ will be emitted, after which the system will be in the state m with $a = 0$, $b = 1$. The emission of an individual photon is a statistical process.

The most elementary classical radiation system is an oscillating electric dipole. The dipole moment qx for a particle with wave function Ψ has the expectation value

$$q\langle x \rangle = q \int \Psi^* x \Psi \, dx$$

It can be seen from the previous discussion that if the wave function is of the type of Eq. (6–56), containing a single energy, the expectation value of the dipole moment will be independent of time. However, if Ψ is the mixture given by Eq. (6–57), $q\langle x \rangle$ will be

$$q\langle x \rangle = qab \left[e^{i\omega_{nm}t} \int \psi_n^*(x) x \psi_m(x) \, dx \right.$$
$$\left. + e^{-i\omega_{nm}t} \int \psi_m^*(x) x \psi_n(x) \, dx \right] + \text{stationary terms}$$

This can be written

$$q\langle x \rangle = 2qab \cos \omega_{nm}t \int \psi_n^* x \psi_m \, dx + \text{stationary terms} \quad (6\text{–}61)$$

[The two integrals in the above equation are equal whether or not the wave functions $\psi_n(x)$ and $\psi_m(x)$ are real, a result we shall not prove here.] The integral in Eq. (6–61) is called a *matrix element*. There are many cases for which this integral is identically zero. For example, if $\psi_n(x)$ and $\psi_m(x)$ are both even functions or odd functions [see Eqs. (6–23) and (6–24) for the definition of even and odd functions], the integral is zero. An even function is said to have even parity, and an odd function, odd parity. If $\psi_n(x)$ and $\psi_m(x)$ have the same parity, electric-dipole radiation cannot occur. The transition is then called a *forbidden transition*. We have what is called a *selection rule:*

For electric-dipole radiation, the parity of the state must change.

Example 6–1   Let us consider a particle in the state $n = 3$ of an infinite square well. The transition $n = 3$ to $n = 1$ is forbidden because the integral

$$\int_{-a}^{+a} (a^{-1/2} \cos k_3 x) x (a^{-1/2} \cos k_1 x)\, dx = 0$$

for $k_3 = 3\pi/2a$ and $k_1 = 1\pi/2a$. This transition might occur by mechanisms other than electric-dipole radiation. These are usually less probable than the transition $n = 3$ to $n = 2$ followed by $n = 2$ to $n = 1$. (Other mechanisms include higher-order radiation, such as electric quadrupole, or a nonradiative energy loss due to a collision with another particle if there were many particles in the well.)

*

6·8
THE SIMPLE
HARMONIC
OSCILLATOR

We now consider the problem of a mass on a spring. The force on the particle is $F = -Kx$, and the potential energy for this problem is

$$V(x) = \tfrac{1}{2}Kx^2 = \tfrac{1}{2}m\omega^2 x^2 \tag{6–62}$$

where K is the force constant and ω is the angular frequency of vibration defined by $\omega = \sqrt{K/m} = 2\pi f$. This is a particularly important problem. If a particle is in stable equilibrium at $x = 0$, the restoring force is approximately proportional to the displacement for small displacements. The solution of the Schroedinger equation for the potential-energy function Eq. (6–62) can be applied to a variety of problems, such as the vibrations of molecules in gases and solids.

The classical equation of motion is obtained from Newton's law:

$$m\frac{d^2 x}{dt^2} = -Kx = -m\omega^2 x$$

The solution is $x = A \cos(\omega t + \phi)$, where A and ϕ are constants determined by the initial conditions. The maximum displacement A is related to the total energy by

$$E = \tfrac{1}{2}KA^2 = \tfrac{1}{2}m\omega^2 A^2 \tag{6–63}$$

The particle moves back and forth, confined to the region $|x| < A$. The classical probability of finding the particle in dx is proportional to the time spent in dx, which is dx/v. The speed of the particle can be obtained from the conservation of energy

$$\tfrac{1}{2}mv^2 + \tfrac{1}{2}m\omega^2 x^2 = E$$

The classical probability is thus

$$P_c(x)\, dx \propto \frac{dx}{v} = \frac{dx}{\sqrt{(2/m)(E - \frac{1}{2}m\omega^2 x^2)}} \tag{6-64}$$

Any value of the energy E is possible. The lowest energy is $E = 0$, corresponding to the particle at rest at the origin.

The Schroedinger equation for this problem is

$$-\frac{\hbar^2}{2m}\frac{d^2\psi(x)}{dx^2} + \frac{1}{2}m\omega^2 x^2\psi(x) = E\psi(x) \tag{6-65}$$

Since $V(x)$ is greater than E for $x > A$, where A is the classical turning point defined by Eq. (6–63), the second derivative of the wave function $\psi''(x)$ has the same sign as the wave function $\psi(x)$ for large x. Thus we know from our considerations in Section 6·3 that solutions of the Schroedinger equation will be well-behaved as $x \to \infty$ only for certain values of the energy E_n. The problem is thus to solve Eq. (6–65) and obtain these eigenvalues E_n and the corresponding well-behaved eigenfunctions $\psi_n(x)$. We have already seen in Chapter 5, that the minimum energy for this problem consistent with the uncertainty principle is of the order of $\hbar\omega$. In fact, if the uncertainty product $\Delta x\, \Delta p$ has its minimum value of $\frac{1}{2}\hbar$, we found the minimum energy to be $\frac{1}{2}\hbar\omega$.

It is convenient to change the variable in Eq. (6–65) from x to a dimensionless variable u proportional to x and defined by

$$u = \left(\frac{m\omega}{\hbar}\right)^{1/2} x = \gamma x$$

where $\gamma \equiv (m\omega/\hbar)^{1/2}$. Then $d\psi/dx = \gamma\, d\psi/du$ and $d^2\psi/dx^2 = \gamma^2\, d^2\psi/dx^2$. Equation (6–65) then becomes

$$-\frac{\hbar^2}{2m}\frac{m\omega}{\hbar}\psi''(u) + \frac{1}{2}m\omega^2\frac{\hbar}{m\omega}u^2\psi = E\psi$$

where we have written $\psi''(u)$ for $d^2\psi/du^2$. Simplifying this equation and defining

$$\alpha \equiv \frac{2E}{\hbar\omega} \tag{6-66}$$

we obtain

$$\psi''(u) = (u^2 - \alpha)\psi(u) \tag{6-67}$$

Although Eq. (6–67) looks relatively simple, it is not at all easy to solve. The mathematical techniques involved in solving this type

of equation are standard in mathematical physics but they are beyond the experience of most students at this level. We shall first
state and discuss the results and then outline the method of obtaining these results.

Since $\psi(x)$ must obey the normalization condition

$$\int \psi^*(x)\psi(x)\ dx\ =\ 1$$

and u is proportional to x, $\psi(u)$ must go to zero as $u \to \pm\infty$ to be
an acceptable solution of Eq. (6–67). The acceptable or well-
behaved solutions of Eq. (6–67) can be written

$$\psi_n(u)\ =\ C_n e^{-(1/2)u^2} f_n(u) \tag{6–68}$$

where C_n is a constant determined by normalization to be

$$C_n\ =\ \left(\frac{\gamma}{\sqrt{\pi}\ 2^n n!}\right)^{1/2}$$

$n = 0, 1, 2, 3, \ldots$, and $f_n(u)$ is a polynomial in u of order n called
a *Hermite polynomial*. The first four Hermite polynomials are

$$\begin{aligned}
f_0(u)\ &=\ 1\\
f_1(u)\ &=\ 2u\\
f_2(u)\ &=\ 2 - 4u^2\\
f_3(u)\ &=\ 12u - 8u^3
\end{aligned} \tag{6–69}$$

The well-behaved solutions [Eq. (6–68)] occur only for the values

figure 6–15   *Wave functions for the ground state and first excited state of the simple-
harmonic-oscillator potential.*

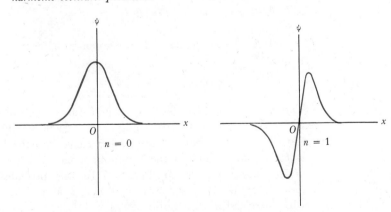

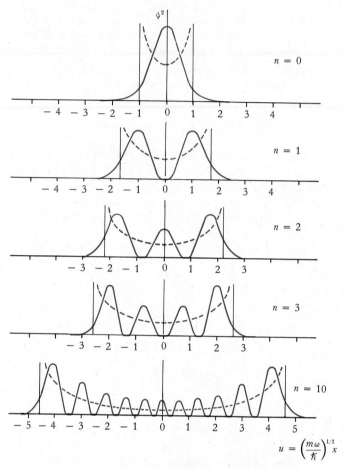

figure 6–16   *Probability density $\psi^2(x)$ for the simple harmonic oscillator. The dotted curves are the classical probability densities for the same energy. (From* Introduction to Quantum Mechanics, *by Chalmers W. Sherwin. Copyright © 1959 by Holt, Rinehart and Winston, Inc. Reprinted by permission of Holt, Rinehart and Winston, Inc.)*

of α given by $\alpha_n = 2n + 1$, corresponding to the energy eigenvalues $(E = \frac{1}{2}\hbar\omega\alpha)$:

$$E_n = (n + \tfrac{1}{2})\hbar\omega \tag{6–70}$$

The ground-state and the first excited-state wave functions ($n = 0$ and $n = 1$) are sketched in Figure 6–15. The ground-state wave function has the shape of a gaussian curve and the lowest energy is $E_0 = \frac{1}{2}\hbar\omega$, which is the minimum energy consistent with the uncertainty principle. In Figure 6–16, the probability distributions $\psi_n{}^2(x)$ are sketched for $n = 0, 1, 2, 3,$ and 10, to be compared with the classical distribution.

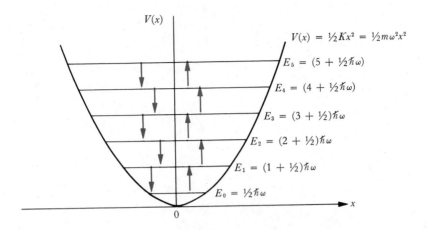

figure 6–17   *Energy levels in the simple-harmonic-oscillator potential. Transitions obeying the selection rule $\Delta n = \pm 1$ are indicated by the arrows (those pointing up indicate absorption). Since the levels have equal spacing, all the transitions have the same energy $\hbar\omega$. For this special potential, the frequency of the emitted or absorbed photon equals the frequency of oscillation as predicted by classical theory.*

The Hermite polynomials contain only odd powers of u if n is odd and only even powers of u if n is even; thus $\psi_n(x)$ has even parity for n even and odd parity for n odd. A property of these wave functions that we shall state but not prove[4] is that

$$\int_{-\infty}^{+\infty} \psi_n^*(x)\, x \psi_m(x)\, dx = 0 \qquad \text{unless } n = m \pm 1 \qquad (6\text{–}71)$$

Equation (6–71) is thus a selection rule for electric-dipole radiation emitted or absorbed by a simple harmonic oscillator. The energy of the photon emitted or absorbed is always given by

$$\Delta E_n = \hbar\omega$$

Thus the frequency of the photon equals the classical frequency of the oscillator, as was assumed by Planck in his derivation of the blackbody radiation formula. Figure 6–17 shows an energy-level diagram for the simple harmonic oscillator, with the allowed energy transitions indicated by vertical arrows.

[4]This result follows from the properties of Hermite polynomials. A derivation can be found in L. I. Schiff, *Quantum Mechanics*, 2d ed., McGraw-Hill Book Company, New York, 1955, page 65.

Outline of the method of solving the equation

$$\psi''(u) = (u^2 - \alpha)\psi(u) \qquad (6\text{-}67)$$

1. Consider the behavior of the solution at large u. For sufficiently large u, we can neglect $\alpha\psi$ compared with $u^2\psi$, and we write Eq. (6-67) approximately

$$\psi''(u) \approx u^2\psi(u)$$

The function $\psi_0(u) = Ce^{-(1/2)u^2}$ is an approximate solution of this equation. We have

$$\psi'_0 = -uCe^{-(1/2)u^2} = -u\psi_0 \qquad (6\text{-}72)$$

and

$$\psi''_0 = -u\psi'_0 - \psi_0 = (u^2 - 1)\psi_0 \qquad (6\text{-}73)$$

and for large u, $\psi''_0 \approx u^2\psi_0$. Note that ψ_0 is a solution of Eq. (6-67) for *any* value of u if $\alpha = 1$; that is,

$$\psi''_0 = (u^2 - 1)\psi_0 = (u^2 - \alpha)\psi_0 \qquad \text{if } \alpha = 1$$

The energy corresponding to $\alpha = 1$ is, by Eq. (6-66),

$$E_0 = \tfrac{1}{2}\hbar\omega$$

2. To obtain other well-behaved solutions, try

$$\psi(u) = \psi_0 f(u) \qquad (6\text{-}74)$$

If we put this function into Eq. (6-67), we obtain an equation for $f(u)$. We have

$$\psi' = \psi'_0 f + \psi_0 f'$$
$$\psi'' = \psi''_0 f + 2\psi'_0 f' + \psi_0 f''$$

and, using Eqs. (6-72) and (6-73),

$$\psi'' = (u^2 - 1)\psi_0 f - 2u\psi_0 f' + \psi_0 f''$$

Equation (6-67) is then

$$[(u^2 - 1)f - 2uf' + f'']\psi_0 = (u^2 - \alpha)\psi_0 f$$

or

$$f'' - 2uf' + (\alpha - 1)f = 0 \qquad (6\text{-}75)$$

Equation (6–75) is called the *Hermite equation*. In addition to satisfying this equation, $f(u)$ must satisfy

$$e^{-(1/2)u^2}f(u) \rightarrow 0 \qquad \text{as } u \rightarrow \infty$$

so that the wave function can be normalized.

3. Try an infinite-power-series solution for the Hermite equation. Let

$$f(u) = a_0 + a_1u + a_1u^2 + \cdots$$

$$= \sum_{n=0}^{\infty} a_n u^n$$

Since $\psi(x)$ must be either an even function or an odd function, the series for $f(u)$ can contain either only even powers of u or only odd powers of u. For the even solution, we can choose $a_0 = 1$ since this is just a matter of normalization and we already have a normalization constant C in Eq. (6–74). Similarly, for the odd solution, we can choose $a_1 = 1$. The other values of a_n are found by putting this series into Eq. (6–75). When this is done, we get a relation giving the coefficient $a_n + 2$ in terms of a_n. We can thus generate both the even and the odd solutions. We have

$$f' = \sum_{n=0}^{\infty} n a_n u^{n-1}$$

and

$$-2uf' = -2 \sum_{n=0}^{\infty} n a_n u^n$$

The second derivative is (using m for the summation index)

$$f'' = \sum_{m=0}^{\infty} m(m-1) a_m u^{m-2}$$

By changing the summation index, this can be written

$$f'' = \sum_{n=0}^{\infty} (n+2)(n+1) a_{n+2} u^n$$

Putting these into the Hermite equation, we have

$$\sum_{n=0}^{\infty} [(n+2)(n+1)a_{n+2} - 2na_n + (\alpha - 1)a_n]u^n = 0$$

If this equation holds, the coefficient of each power of u must be zero, giving

$$a_{n+2} = \frac{2n + 1 - \alpha}{(n+2)(n+1)} a_n \qquad (6\text{--}76)$$

Equation (6–76) is called a *recursion relation*.

4. Investigate convergence of the series obtained. We do not require the series for $f(u)$ to converge, but only that

$$e^{-(1/2)u^2} f(u) \rightarrow 0 \qquad \text{as } u \rightarrow \infty$$

However, the series satisfying Eq. (6–76) does not even meet this requirement. We can see this by examining a_{n+2}/a_n for large values of n:

$$\frac{a_{n+2}}{a_n} \rightarrow \frac{2}{n} \qquad \text{as } n \rightarrow \infty$$

This series behaves like the series

$$e^{+u^2} = 1 + u^2 + \frac{u^4}{2!} + \cdots + \frac{u^n}{(\frac{1}{2}n)!} + \frac{u^{n+2}}{(\frac{1}{2}n + 1)!}$$

For this series,

$$\frac{b_{n+2}}{b_n} = \frac{(\frac{1}{2}n)!}{(\frac{1}{2}n + 1)!} = \frac{1}{\frac{1}{2}n + 1} \rightarrow \frac{2}{n} \qquad \text{for large } n$$

Thus the infinite series that satisfies Eq. (6–75) does not yield a wave function that is well behaved at $u \rightarrow \infty$.

5. Terminate the series. If $f(u)$ is a *polynomial* $f_n(u)$ with only a finite number of terms, there is no convergence problem because

$$e^{-(1/2)u^2} f_n(u) \rightarrow 0 \qquad \text{as } u \rightarrow \infty$$

for any polynomial $f_n(u)$. We see from the recurrence relation [Eq. (6–76)] that if $a_{n+2} = 0$ for some n, a_{n+4} and all higher coefficients will also be zero. We also see that a_{n+2} will be zero if $2n + 1 - \alpha = 0$, or using Eq. (6–66) for α, $E_n = (n + \frac{1}{2})\hbar\omega$. For this value of E, the wave function is

$$\psi_n(u) = C_n e^{-(1/2)u^2} f_n(u)$$

where $f_n(u)$ is a polynomial of order n containing only even powers of u if n is even, and only odd powers if n is odd.

6·9
REFLECTION AND TRANSMISSION OF WAVES

Up to this point, we have been concerned with bound-state problems in which the potential energy is larger than the total energy for large values of $|x|$. In this section, we shall consider some simple examples of unbound states for which E is greater than $V(x)$. For these problems, $\psi''(x)$ always has the opposite sign of the wave function; thus $\psi(x)$ always curves toward the axis and does not become infinite at large values of $|x|$. Normalization, therefore, is not

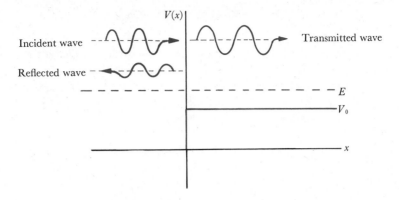

figure 6–18
Step potential. A classical particle incident from the left, with total energy E greater than V_0, is always transmitted. The potential change at $x = 0$ merely provides an impulsive force which reduces the speed of the particle. A wave incident from the left is partially transmitted and partially reflected because the wavelength changes abruptly at $x = 0$. The wavelength of the transmitted wave is less than that of the incident and reflected waves. The amplitudes of the waves are such that the energy per second arriving at $x = 0$ equals that leaving $x = 0$.

an important problem; all values of E are allowed. The wave nature of the Schroedinger equation does, however, lead to some interesting consequences.

STEP POTENTIAL Consider a particle of energy $E > V_0$ moving in a region in which the potential energy is the step function:

$$V(x) = 0 \qquad \text{for } x < 0$$
$$V(x) = V_0 \qquad \text{for } x \geq 0$$

as shown in Figure 6–18. We are interested in what happens when a particle moving from left to right with energy $E > V_0$ encounters the step. The classical result is simple. For $x < 0$, the speed is $v = \sqrt{2E/m}$. At $x = 0$, the particle receives an impulsive force that changes the speed to $v = \sqrt{2(E - V_0)/m}$ for $x > 0$. The particle is never turned around by this force so long as V_0 is less than E. The result is different, however, when we consider the situation of a *wave* incident from the left. The wavelength changes abruptly from

$$\lambda_1 = \frac{h}{p_1} = \frac{h}{\sqrt{2mE}} \qquad \text{for } x < 0$$

to

$$\lambda_2 = \frac{h}{p_2} = \frac{h}{\sqrt{2m(E - V_0)}} \qquad \text{for } x > 0$$

We know from optics that when the wavelength changes suddenly (in a distance small compared with the wavelength), part of the wave is reflected and part is transmitted. Thus, because of its wave properties, an electron or other "particle" will sometimes be transmitted and sometimes reflected.

The time-independent Schroedinger equation for $x < 0$ is

$$-\frac{\hbar^2}{2m}\psi''(x) = E\psi(x)$$

Solutions of this equation have the form

$$\psi_1(x) = Ae^{+ik_1x} + Be^{-ik_1x} \qquad (6\text{--}77)$$

where $k_1 = (2mE/\hbar^2)^{1/2}$. As we saw at the beginning of this chapter, Ae^{ik_1x} describes a wave moving to the right corresponding to a particle which has a definite value of momentum $\hbar k_1$. To describe a particle that has some localization, we should construct a wave packet containing a range of k values. However, we need only localize the particle in the range $-\infty < x < 0$ in order to find the relative probability of reflection or transmission at $x = 0$. Thus the range of k can be very narrow and we can use the wave function Ae^{ik_1x} to represent a particle incident from the left. Similarly, the function Be^{-ik_1x} is a wave traveling to the left, which we shall interpret as the reflected wave. For $x > 0$, the Schroedinger equation is

$$-\frac{\hbar^2}{2m}\psi''(x) = (E - V_0)\psi(x)$$

with the solution

$$\psi_2(x) = Ce^{ik_2x} + De^{-ik_2x} \qquad (6\text{--}78)$$

with $k_2 = [2m(E - V_0)/\hbar^2]^{1/2}$. The function Ce^{+ik_2x} describes the transmitted wave. The function De^{-ik_2x} describes a wave moving to the left. Since there are no sources at $x > 0$ and no boundaries to produce reflected waves moving to the left for $x > 0$, we must choose $D = 0$ for this problem. Since the wave function and its slope must be continuous at $x = 0$, we have the boundary conditions

$$\psi_1(0) = \psi_2(0) \qquad \text{and} \qquad \psi_1'(0) = \psi_2'(0)$$

Using Eqs. (6–77) and (6–78) with $D = 0$, these imply

$$A + B = C \qquad \text{and} \qquad ik_1A - ik_1B = ik_2C$$

Solving for B and C in terms of A, we have

$$B = \frac{k_1 - k_2}{k_1 + k_2} A \qquad (6\text{-}79)$$

and

$$C = \frac{2k_1}{k_1 + k_2} A \qquad (6\text{-}80)$$

It should be evident that these boundary conditions could not be satisfied without a reflected wave, that is, $B = 0$ is not possible. We can interpret

$$|Ae^{ik_1 x}|^2 = |A|^2$$

as the probability density for the incoming particle. Similarly, $|B|^2$ is the probability density for the reflected particle and $|C|^2$ is the probability density for the transmitted particle. (Since we are using unlocalized wave functions, we cannot normalize them. However, this is not a serious problem because we need only find the ratios $|B|^2/|A|^2$ and $|C|^2/|A|^2$ to determine the relative probability of reflection and transmission.) If we think of N particles incident from the left, the number density NA^2 times their speed v_1 is the incident current density. Similarly, $N|B|^2 v_1$ is the reflected current density and $N|C|^2 v_2$ is the transmitted current density. The speeds are given by

$$v_1 = \frac{p_1}{m} = \frac{\hbar k_1}{m}$$

and

$$v_2 = \frac{p_2}{m} = \frac{\hbar k_2}{m}$$

We can just as well divide by N and think of these currents as probability currents for one particle. The reflection coefficient is defined as the reflected current density divided by the incident current density:

$$R = \frac{v_1 |B|^2}{v_1 |A|^2} = \left(\frac{k_1 - k_2}{k_1 + k_2}\right)^2 \qquad (6\text{-}81)$$

The transmission coefficient is the ratio of the transmitted current density to the incident current density

$$T = \frac{v_2 |C|^2}{v_1 |A|^2} = \frac{k_2}{k_1} \left(\frac{2k_1}{k_1 + k_2}\right)^2 \qquad (6\text{-}82)$$

Since we do not have a source at $x = 0$, we expect $T + R = 1$, that is, each particle arriving at $x = 0$ is either reflected or transmitted. The probability of the reflection of one particle plus the probability of the transmission of one particle equals unity. It is left as an exercise to show that this is true for this problem.

For the problem in which the potential is V_0 for negative x and drops to 0 at $x = 0$, the analysis is the same except that k_1 and k_2 are interchanged. Since the reflection coefficient depends only on $(k_1 - k_2)^2$, it is the same for this problem. Thus the probability of reflection does not depend on whether $V(x)$ increases or decreases but only on the magnitude of the discontinuity.

SQUARE-WELL
POTENTIAL

Let us now consider the square-well potential shown in Figure 6–19 for the case $E > 0$. (This problem is not significantly different if V_0 is positive and $E > V_0$. It is then called the *square-barrier problem*.) For this problem there are two abrupt changes in $V(x)$, at $x = -a$ and $x = +a$; thus reflection occurs at each of these points. The quantum-mechanical solution is similar to that above, except there are now three regions in which to solve the Schroedinger equation and two boundaries at which to match solutions. The algebra is quite tedious, so we shall discuss the interesting features qualitatively.

A wave incident from the left is partially transmitted and partially reflected at $x = -a$. The transmitted wave proceeds to $x = +a$, where again there is partial transmission and partial reflection. The reflected wave from $x = +a$ returns to $x = -a$, where the

figure 6–19 *Square-well potential. A wave from the left is partially reflected and partially transmitted at each boundary. (Only the first few reflections are indicated in this figure.)*

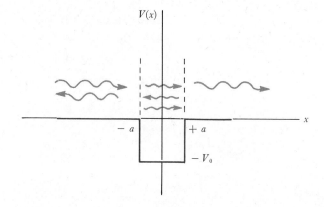

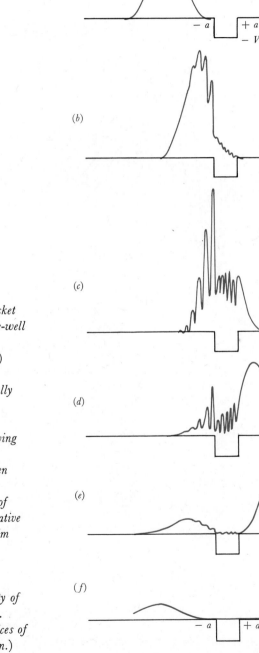

figure 6–20

*Behavior of a gaussian wave packet
incident from the left on a square-well
potential. The oscillations
evident in (b), (c), (d), and (e)
are due to multiple reflections
at the edges of the well. Eventually
two packets are formed:
a transmitted packet moving to
the right, and a reflected one moving
to the left. For this case, in
which the mean energy was chosen
to be $\frac{1}{2}V_0$, the probability of
transmission is larger than that of
reflection, as indicated by the relative
size of the packets. (From the film
by A. Goldberg, H. Schey, and
J. Schwartz, Scattering in
One Dimension, Lawrence
Radiation Laboratory, University of
California, Berkeley, California.
Work performed under the auspices of
U.S. Atomic Energy Commission.)*

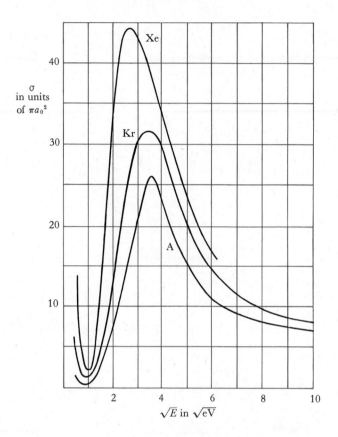

σ in units of $\pi a_0{}^2$

$\sqrt{E}$ in $\sqrt{eV}$

figure 6–21   *The cross section for scattering of electrons by inert gases. The dip in the cross section at $E \approx 1\ eV$ corresponds to nearly perfect transmission. This effect, called the* Ramsauer-Townsend *effect, can be understood in terms of a one-dimensional model of scattering of a wave by a square-well potential.* (*From H. Massey and E. Burhop*, Electronic and Ionic Impact Phenomena, *Clarendon Press, Oxford, 1952.*)

process is repeated. Figure 6–20 shows the behavior of a gaussian wave packet incident from the left on a square-well potential. Eventually, two packets are formed, a transmitted packet moving to the right and a reflected packet to the left. For the case shown, in which the mean energy of the packet is $\frac{1}{2}V_0$, the probability of transmission is greater than that of reflection, as indicated by the relative sizes of the packets.

An interesting phenomenon occurs if the well size $2a$ is just equal to half the wavelength of the particle in the well. The wave reflected at $x = +a$ has traveled just one full wavelength when it returns to $x = -a$. Because there is a phase change of 180° in the reflection at $x = -a$ (this is analogous to the phase change when light is reflected from glass), the two waves are out of phase and tend to cancel. (These waves are not, in general, of equal amplitude, and thus the cancellation is not complete.) For a given size of well, there will be a certain energy for which the reflection is nearly zero; thus the transmission is perfect for this energy wave. Although atoms do not usually look like square-well potentials to incoming electron waves, the atoms of the inert gases have relatively sharp boundaries because of their closed-shell electron structure. Figure 6–21 shows the scattering cross section versus speed for electrons incident on argon, krypton, and xenon. At a speed corresponding to an energy of 1 eV, the cross section dips sharply, corresponding to nearly perfect transmission. This effect is called the *Ramsauer-Townsend effect*.

PENETRATION OF A BARRIER — Consider the step potential of Figure 6–22a for the case $E < V_0$. The classical expectation is that a particle incident from the left is always reflected at $x = 0$. It cannot penetrate beyond $x = 0$ because the potential energy function is greater than the total energy in this region.

The wave theory also predicts total reflection for this problem. This is somewhat analogous to total reflection in optics for angles greater than the critical angle. Figure 6–22b shows the behavior of the wave function for this problem. The wave function does not go to zero at $x = 0$ but decays exponentially, as in the case of the wave function for the bound state in a finite square-well problem,

figure 6–22   (a) *Step potential.* (b) *The wave function for total energy E less than V_0 penetrates slightly into the region $x > 0$. However, the probability of reflection for this case is 1 and no energy is transmitted.*

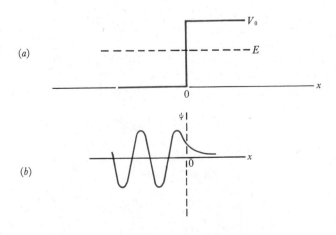

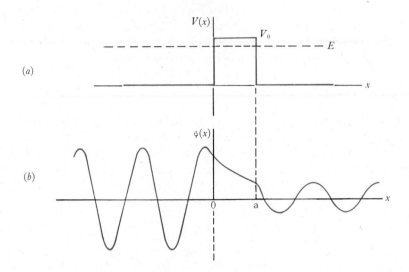

figure 6–23   (a) *Square-barrier potential.* (b) *Penetration of the barrier by a wave with energy less than the barrier energy. Part of the wave gets through the barrier even though, classically, the particle cannot enter the region 0 < x < a in which the potential energy is greater than the total energy.*

discussed earlier in this chapter. The particle thus penetrates into the classically forbidden region $x > 0$, but it is always eventually reflected. As was discussed in Section 6·4, if the particle is observed in the forbidden region, the uncertainty in the kinetic energy is greater than $V_0 - E$; thus there is no prediction that negative kinetic energy can be observed.

We can calculate the reflection coefficient for this problem. The wave function for $x < 0$ is

$$\psi_1 = A e^{ik_1 x} + B e^{-ik_1 x}$$

For $x > 0$, the solution of the Schroedinger equation is

$$\psi_2 = C e^{-k_2 x} + D e^{+k_2 x} \tag{6–83}$$

with $k_2 = [2m(V_0 - E)/\hbar^2]^{1/2}$. We must choose $D = 0$ so that ψ_2 does not become infinite as $x \to \infty$. Matching the solutions at $x = 0$ gives $A + B = C$ and $ik_1 A - ik_1 B = -k_2 C$. It is difficult to find the transmission coefficient because the kinetic energy for $x > 0$ is negative corresponding to an imaginary velocity. We can, however, compute the reflection coefficient. Eliminating C from the above equations, we obtain

$$B = \frac{ik_1 + k_2}{ik_1 - k_2} A$$

$$|B|^2 = B^*B = \frac{-ik_1 + k_2}{-ik_1 - k_2} A^* \frac{ik_1 + k_2}{ik_1 - k_2} A = |A|^2$$

Thus the reflection coefficient is

$$R = |B|^2/|A|^2 = 1$$

A much more interesting case of barrier penetration is that for a particle of energy $E < V_0$ incident on the rectangular barrier, shown in Figure 6–23a and given by

$$V = 0 \qquad x < 0$$
$$V = V_0 \qquad 0 \leq x \leq a$$
$$V = 0 \qquad x > a$$

This problem is more complicated because there are two boundaries where solutions must be matched. In the region $0 < x < a$, the wave function is that of Eq. (6–83), but since x does not become infinite, we cannot set $D = 0$. For the situation of a wave incident from the left, the algebra involved in calculating the reflection and transmission is too tedious to reproduce here but the qualitative results are interesting. The reflection coefficient is not equal to 1 for this case. A sketch of the wave function is shown in Figure 6–23b. It can be seen that part of the wave gets through the barrier. For the case $k_2a = [2ma^2(V_0 - E)/\hbar^2]^{1/2} \gg 1$, the wave function for $x > a$ is proportional to e^{-k_2a}; thus the probability of transmission through the barrier is proportional to e^{-2k_2a}.

The penetration of a barrier is not a unique property of matter waves. In Figure 6–24 a light ray is incident on a glass-to-air sur-

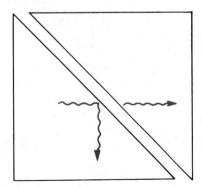

figure 6–24

Optical-barrier penetration.
Part of the wave penetrates
the air barrier even though the
angle of incidence
in the prism is greater than
the critical angle. This effect can
easily be demonstrated with
two 45° prisms and a laser.

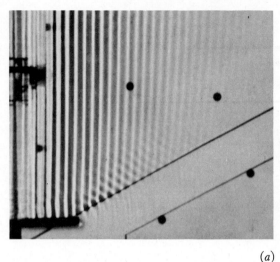

(a)

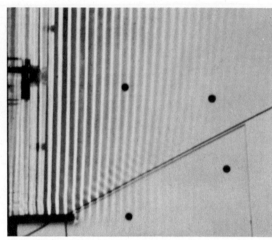

(b)

figure 6–25   *Barrier penetration by waves in a ripple tank. In* (a) *the waves are totally reflected from a gap of deeper water. When the gap is very narrow as in* (b), *a transmitted wave appears. (Courtesy of Film Studio, Education Development Center.)*

face. At an angle greater than the critical angle, total reflection occurs. This is analogous to the barrier of Figure 6–22. Because of the wave nature of light, the electric field $\mathcal{E}$ is not identically zero in the air but decreases exponentially and becomes negligible within a few wavelengths of the surface. If another piece of glass is brought near the surface, the situation is analogous to that shown in Figure 6–23. Some of the light is transmitted across the barrier. (This can easily be demonstrated with a laser beam and two prisms.) Figure 6–25 shows barrier penetration by water waves in a ripple tank.

The theory of penetration of a barrier by particles was used by George Gamow in 1928 to explain the enormous variation in the mean life for α decay. In general, the smaller the energy of the α radioactive source, the larger the mean life. The energies of the α particles from natural sources range from about 4 MeV to 7 MeV, whereas the mean lifetimes range from about 10^{10} years to 10^{-6} sec. Gamow assumed that a radioactive nucleus could be described by a potential well containing an α particle, as in Figure 6–26.

For r less than the nuclear radius R, the α particle is attracted by the nuclear force. Without knowing much about this force, we can estimate the velocity of the α particle inside the nucleus from the uncertainty principle. If we take $R \approx 10$ fermis $= 10^{-14}$ meter and use $mv \approx \hbar/R$, we obtain for the speed, $v \approx 10^7$ m/sec. For a point α particle of charge ze a distance $R = 10$ fermis from a nucleus of charge Ze, the Coulomb energy $KZze^2/R$ is about 28 MeV for $Z = 100$. Classically, the α particle can never get out because its total energy is less than the potential energy in the region $R < r < r_1$ in the figure. However, because of the wave properties of the α, there is a small probability that the α will leak through the barrier rather than be reflected. Assuming that the α particle bounces back and forth inside the nucleus with speed 10^7 m/sec, it hits the barrier with a frequency of about

$$\frac{v}{2R} \approx \frac{10^7 \text{ m/sec}}{2 \times 10^{-14} \text{ m}} \sim 10^{22} \text{ times/sec}$$

If the barrier were rectangular, as in Figure 6–23a, the probability of penetration for each "attempt" would be proportional to $e^{-2k_2 a}$, where a is the width of the barrier. The probability per second of escaping would be

$$P \approx \frac{v}{2R} e^{-2k_2 a}$$

figure 6–26   *Model of potential-energy function for an α particle and a nucleus. The strong attractive nuclear force for r, less than the nuclear radius R, can be approximately described by the potential well shown. Outside the nucleus the nuclear force is negligible, and the potential is given by Coulomb's law, $V(r) = +KZze^2/r$, where Ze is the nuclear charge and ze is the charge of the α particle. An α particle inside the nucleus oscillates back and forth, being reflected at the barrier at R. Because of its wave properties, when the α particle hits the barrier there is a small chance that it will penetrate and appear outside the well at $r = r_1$. The wave function is similar to that shown in Figure 6–23b.*

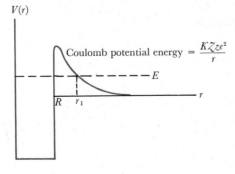

and the mean life would be

$$\tau = \frac{1}{P} \approx \frac{2R}{v} e^{+2k_2a} \approx 10^{-22} e^{2k_2a} \qquad (6\text{-}84)$$

Because the barrier is not rectangular, the theory is somewhat more complicated. The exponent k_2a is replaced by

$$k_2a \rightarrow \overline{k_2a} = \int_R^{r_1} \left(\frac{2m[V(r) - E]}{\hbar^2} \right)^{1/2} dr$$

Without going further into the details of Gamow's calculation, we can see how a small variation in energy E leads to a large variation in the mean life τ because the energy, and r_1 which depends on the energy, are in the exponent of Eq. (6-84). For example, r_1 is about 70 fermis for $E = 4$ MeV and about 47 fermis for $E = 6$ MeV. The mean lifetime for $E = 4$ MeV is of the order of 10^{10} years $= 10^{17}$ sec. For $E = 4$ MeV, then, the factor e^{2k_2a} must be about $10^{39} \approx e^{90}$ from Eq. (6-84). Let us estimate the half-life from this if $E = 6$ MeV. We shall make the very crude approximation that the exponent $\overline{2k_2a}$ is proportional to the width of the barrier $\Delta r = r_1 - R$. We then have

$$(\overline{2k_2a})_{6\text{ MeV}} \approx \frac{(\Delta r)_{6\text{ MeV}}}{(\Delta r)_{4\text{ MeV}}} (\overline{2k_2a})_{4\text{ MeV}} \approx \left(\frac{47 - 10}{70 - 10} \right) 90 = 55.5$$

Using $e^{55.5} \approx 10^{24}$, we obtain for the mean life, for $E = 6$ MeV,

$$\tau_{6\text{ MeV}} \approx 10^{-22} \times 10^{24} = 2 \text{ sec}$$

This rough estimation shows how critical the dependence of the mean life is on the energy of decay. A slight change in E or in the nuclear radius for a given E leads to a change in an exponential, which implies a large change in τ. Detailed calculations give the dependence of τ on E in excellent agreement with experiment, thus showing that α decay is indeed an example of barrier penetration.

SUMMARY   The Schroedinger wave equation in one dimension is

$$-\frac{\hbar^2}{2m} \frac{\partial^2 \Psi(x,t)}{\partial x^2} + V(x)\Psi(x,t) = i\hbar \frac{\partial \Psi}{\partial t}(x,t)$$

The distribution function for position measurements is $|\Psi(x,t)|^2$. The expectation value of x is

$$\langle x \rangle = \int |\Psi|^2 x \, dx$$

The Schroedinger equation can be written in terms of operators:

$$P_{\text{op}} \equiv \frac{\hbar}{i} \frac{\partial}{\partial x}$$

$$E_{\text{op}} \equiv i\hbar \frac{\partial}{\partial t} = \frac{1}{2m} P_{\text{op}}^2 + V(x)$$

$$\frac{1}{2m} P_{\text{op}}^2 \Psi(x,t) + V(x)\Psi(x,t) = E_{\text{op}}\Psi(x,t)$$

The expectation value of momentum is

$$\langle p \rangle = \int \Psi^*(x,t) P_{\text{op}} \Psi(x,t) \, dx = \int \Psi^*(x,t) \frac{\hbar}{i} \frac{\partial \Psi}{\partial x} \, dx$$

The time dependence can be separated by letting

$$\Psi(x,t) = f(t)\psi(x)$$

resulting in

$$f(t) = Ce^{-(E/\hbar)t}$$

and the time-independent Schroedinger equation

$$-\frac{\hbar^2}{2m} \psi''(x) + V(x)\psi(x) = E\psi(x)$$

Given the potential $V(x)$, the time-independent Schroedinger equation can be solved for the wave functions $\psi_n(x)$ and the allowed energies E_n. When $V(x)$ is larger than the total energy outside some range of x, only certain values of E lead to well-behaved wave functions, and thus the energy is quantized.

For the infinite square-well potential of total length L, the allowed energies are

$$E_n = n^2 \frac{h^2}{8mL^2} \qquad n = 1, 2, 3, \ldots$$

This is equivalent to quantizing the de Broglie wavelength

$$n(\lambda/2) = L$$

For the simple-harmonic-oscillator potential, the allowed energies are

$$E_n = (n + \tfrac{1}{2})\hbar\omega \qquad n = 0, 1, 2, \ldots$$

where ω is the classical angular frequency.

A system can make a transition from state n_1 to state n_2 by emission or absorption of electric-dipole radiation only if the matrix element

$$\int \psi_{n_1} x \psi_{n_2} \, dx$$

is not zero. This requirement leads to selection rules. An example of a selection rule is $\Delta n = \pm 1$ for the simple harmonic oscillator. Transitions not obeying a selection rule either do not occur or involve some process other than electric-dipole radiation, and they are usually much less probable than electric-dipole transitions.

When the potential changes abruptly in a distance that is small compared with the de Broglie wavelength, a particle may be reflected even though $E > V(x)$. A particle may also penetrate a region in which $E < V(x)$. Reflection and barrier penetration of de Broglie waves are similar to those for any kind of waves. The decay of α particles provides an example of barrier penetration. Because the probability of penetration decreases rapidly with the size of the barrier, the mean lifetime of α decay depends strongly on the energy of decay.

REFERENCES
1. R. Eisberg, *Fundamentals of Modern Physics*, John Wiley & Sons, Inc., New York, 1961.
2. C. Sherwin, *Introduction to Quantum Mechanics*, Holt, Rinehart and Winston, Inc., New York, 1960.
3. P. Matthews, *Introduction to Quantum Mechanics*, McGraw-Hill Book Company, New York, 1963.
4. V. Rojansky, *Introductory Quantum Mechanics*, Prentice-Hall, Inc., Englewood Cliffs, N.J., 1938.

PROBLEMS

SET A

6-1. Show that $\Psi(x,t) = A \sin (kx - \omega t)$ does *not* satisfy the time-dependent Schroedinger equation (6–13).

6-2. Find $\bar{x}$, $\overline{x^2}$, $\bar{p}$, $\overline{p^2}$, and $\sigma_x \sigma_p = \sqrt{(\overline{x^2} - \bar{x}^2)(\overline{p^2} - \bar{p}^2)}$ for the ground-state wave function for an infinite square well.

6-3. A particle is in the ground state in an infinite well of size $2a$. What is the probability of finding the particle in $\Delta x = 0.01a$ at

(a) $x = 0$

(b) $x = \frac{1}{2}a$

(c) $x = \frac{2}{3}a$

(Since Δx is very small, you need not do any integration.)

6-4. Do Problem 6–3 for a particle in the first excited state in an infinite square well and for a particle in the second excited state.

6-5. Using arguments about the concavity of a function similar to those in Section 6·3, sketch the solution $y(t)$ of the equation

$$y''(t) = -\omega^2 y(t)$$

6-6. Assuming that an inert-gas atom of radius R can be approximated by a one-dimensional square well of length $L = 2R$, calculate R from the data on electron scattering shown in Figure 6–21. At what higher energy might there be another scattering minimum?

6-7. A mass of 10^{-6} gram is moving with a speed of about 10^{-1} cm/sec in a box of length 1 cm. Considering this to be a one-dimensional infinite square-well problem, calculate the approximate value of n.

6-8. For the classical particle in Problem 6–7, show that reasonable experimental uncertainties Δx and Δp give a product $\Delta x \, \Delta p$ which is much greater than the minimum allowed by the uncertainty principle. Equation (6–50) is thus the same as the classical equation for this situation.

SET B

6-9. Solve the time-dependent Schroedinger equation (6–13) by the separation of variables for the constant potential energy $V(x) = V_0$ and $E > V_0$ to obtain solutions of the form of Eq. (6–9).

6-10. For the wave functions

$$\psi_n(x) = a^{-1/2} \cos \frac{n\pi x}{2a} \qquad n = 1, 3, 5, \ldots$$

corresponding to an infinite square well of size $2a$,
(a) Show that $\overline{x^2} = (a^2/3)[1 - (6/n^2\pi^2)]$.
(b) Show that $\overline{x^2}$ approaches the classically expected value for $n \gg 1$.

6-11. A particle of mass m on a table at $z = 0$ can be described by the potential energy

$$\begin{aligned} V &= mgz \qquad \text{for } z > 0 \\ V &= \infty \qquad \text{for } z < 0 \end{aligned}$$

For some positive value of total energy E, indicate the classically allowed region on a sketch of $V(z)$ versus z. Sketch also the kinetic energy versus z. The Schroedinger equation for this problem is quite difficult to solve. Using arguments similar to those in Section 6·3 about the concavity of the wave function as given by the Schroedinger equation, sketch your "guesses" for the shape of the wave function for the ground state and the first two excited states.

6–12. (a) Find the normalization constant for the ground-state wave function for the simple harmonic oscillator.

(b) Determine $\bar{x}$, $\overline{x^2}$, $\bar{p}$, and $\overline{p^2}$ for this wave function.

(c) What is $\Delta x \, \Delta p$ for this state?

6–13. Plot a few points and then sketch the probability density $\psi^2(x)$ versus x for the ground state of the simple-harmonic-oscillator problem. Estimate the probability that the particle is outside the classically allowed region by counting squares on your graph.

6–14. Show that if the wave function is an eigenfunction of A_{op}, the uncertainty in a, Δa defined by $(\Delta a)^2 = \overline{a^2} - \bar{a}^2$ is zero.

6–15. Plug the polynomial $f(u) = u$ directly into the Hermite equation (6–75) and determine α from this.

6–16. Do Problem 6–15 for the polynomials

(a) $f_2 = 1 + a_2 u^2$

(b) $f_3 = u + a_3 u^3$

and determine a_2 and a_3 as well as the values of α.

6–17. The wave function for the finite-square-well problem is given by [see Eqs. (6–31), (6–32), and (6–34)]

$$\psi_{out}(x) = Ce^{-\alpha x} \qquad x \geq a$$

and

$$\psi_{in}(x) = \begin{cases} A \cos kx & x \leq a, \text{ even} \\ \\ B \sin kx & x \leq a, \text{ odd} \end{cases}$$

where $k^2 = 2mE/\hbar^2$ and

$$\alpha^2 = 2m(V_0 - E)/\hbar^2 = (2mV_0/\hbar^2) - k^2$$

Considering the even solution first, use the boundary conditions $\psi_{out}(a) = \psi_{in}(a)$ and $\psi'_{out}(a) = \psi'_{in}(a)$ to obtain the equation $ka \tan ka = \alpha a$.

Sketch the functions $y_1(z) = z \tan z$ and $y_2(z) = \alpha a = (\beta^2 - z^2)^{1/2}$, where $z = ka$ and $\beta^2 = 2ma^2 V_0/\hbar^2$.

The intersections $y_1 = y_2$ are the values of z corresponding to the allowed values of E. Show that for large V_0, the allowed energies are approximately the same as those for the infinite well.

SEVEN
ANGULAR
MOMENTUM
AND
THE HYDROGEN
ATOM

7·1

THE SCHROEDINGER EQUATION IN SPHERICAL COORDINATES

We now turn to the consideration of the Schroedinger equation in three dimensions. We shall confine our discussion to problems in which the potential energy is a function only of r, the radial distance from the origin. In classical mechanics this means that the force is radial. There is no torque about the origin, so angular momentum is conserved. We should thus expect angular momentum to play an important role in the solution of the Schroedinger equation for these problems, just as it does in classical mechanics problems and in the Bohr model of the hydrogen atom.

The Schroedinger equation in three dimensions for a particle of mass M with potential energy $V(x,y,z)$ is

$$-\frac{\hbar^2}{2M}\left(\frac{\partial^2 \psi}{\partial x^2} + \frac{\partial^2 \psi}{\partial y^2} + \frac{\partial^2 \psi}{\partial z^2}\right) + V(x,y,z)\psi = E\psi \tag{7-1}$$

Note that this can be written

$$\frac{1}{2M} P_{\text{op}}^2 \psi + V\psi = E\psi \tag{7-2}$$

where $P_{\text{op}}^2 = P_{x,\text{op}}^2 + P_{y,\text{op}}^2 + P_{z,\text{op}}^2$ and $P_{x,\text{op}} = \frac{\hbar}{i}\frac{\partial}{\partial x}$, with

277

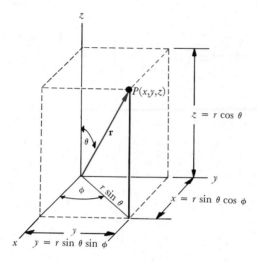

figure 7–1

Geometrical relation between spherical and rectangular coordinates.

similar equations for $P_{y,\text{op}}$ and $P_{z,\text{op}}$. If the potential energy depends only on $r = (x^2 + y^2 + z^2)^{1/2}$, it is convenient to write Eq. (7–1) in terms of the spherical coordinates r, θ, and ϕ, which are related to x, y, z by

$$
\begin{aligned}
z &= r \cos \theta \\
x &= r \sin \theta \cos \phi \\
y &= r \sin \theta \sin \phi
\end{aligned}
\tag{7–3}
$$

These relations are shown in Figure 7–1. The transformation of the Schroedinger equation into spherical coordinates involves a lot of algebra that we shall not include here.[1] The resulting Schroedinger equation in spherical coordinates is

$$
-\frac{\hbar^2}{2M} \left[\frac{1}{r^2} \frac{\partial}{\partial r} \left(r^2 \frac{\partial \psi}{\partial r} \right) \right] - \frac{\hbar^2}{2Mr^2} \left[\frac{1}{\sin \theta} \frac{\partial}{\partial \theta} \left(\sin \theta \frac{\partial \psi}{\partial \theta} \right) + \frac{1}{\sin^2 \theta} \frac{\partial^2 \psi}{\partial \phi^2} \right]
$$
$$
+ V(r)\psi = E\psi
\tag{7–4}
$$

Equation (7–4) appears quite formidable. Before we consider the important features of the well-behaved solutions of this equation,

[1] This transformation is most easily done by noting that $P_{\text{op}}{}^2 = -\hbar^2 \nabla^2$ and finding $\nabla^2 = $ divergence of the gradient directly in spherical coordinates. The calculation of ∇^2 in spherical coordinates can be found in most intermediate books on electricity and magnetism; e.g., J. Reitz and F. Milford, *Foundations of Electromagnetic Theory*, 2d ed., Addison-Wesley Publishing Company, Inc., Reading, Mass., 1967, Chap. 1.

let us compare the equation with that for the energy of a classical particle in a central field.

The energy of a particle in a central field is

$$E = \frac{p^2}{2M} + V(r)$$

It is convenient to write the momentum in terms of its component p_r along the radius $\mathbf{r}$ and its component $p_\perp$ perpendicular to $\mathbf{r}$. The angular momentum has the magnitude $L = rp_\perp$. Since the angular momentum is conserved, it is convenient to express the energy in terms of the constant L. We have

$$p^2 = p_r{}^2 + p_\perp{}^2 = p_r{}^2 + \frac{L^2}{r^2}$$

Thus

$$E = \frac{p_r{}^2}{2M} + \frac{L^2}{2Mr^2} + V(r) \tag{7-5}$$

Comparing this equation with Eq. (7–4), it is natural to expect that the first term in brackets in Eq. (7–4) is associated with radial motion and the second term in brackets is associated with the angular momentum. Equation (7–4) can, in fact, be written more simply in terms of angular-momentum operators which we shall define in the next section.

figure 7–2   *Classical particle with momentum* $\mathbf{p}$ *at position* $\mathbf{r}$ *from origin. The magnitude of the angular momentum is* $L = rp_\perp$. *It is convenient to write the kinetic energy in terms of the angular momentum which is a constant if the force is along* $\mathbf{r}$. $E_k = (1/2M)(p_r{}^2 + p_\perp{}^2) = (p_r{}^2/2M) + L^2/2Mr^2$.

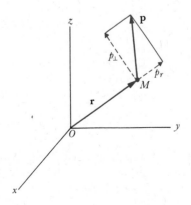

**7·2
ANGULAR-
MOMENTUM
OPERATORS**

In classical mechanics, the definition of angular momentum **L** is

$$\mathbf{L} = \mathbf{r} \times \mathbf{p} \qquad (7\text{-}6)$$

Equation (7–6) defines the three components of angular momentum: L_x, L_y, and L_z. For example, L_x is

$$L_x = yp_z - zp_y \qquad (7\text{-}7)$$

We can define quantum-mechanical operators for angular momentum from the definitions of the operators for linear momentum. For example, the operator for the x component of angular momentum is

$$L_{x,\mathrm{op}} \equiv y\frac{\hbar}{i}\frac{\partial}{\partial z} - z\frac{\hbar}{i}\frac{\partial}{\partial y} \qquad (7\text{-}8)$$

with similar equations for $L_{y,\mathrm{op}}$ and $L_{z,\mathrm{op}}$. Once again, the transformation to spherical coordinates involves uninteresting algebra, which we shall not include. In spherical coordinates, the operators for L_x, L_y, and L_z are

$$L_{x,\mathrm{op}} = \frac{\hbar}{i}\left(-\sin\phi\,\frac{\partial}{\partial\theta} - \cot\theta\cos\phi\,\frac{\partial}{\partial\phi}\right)$$

$$L_{y,\mathrm{op}} = \frac{\hbar}{i}\left(\cos\phi\,\frac{\partial}{\partial\theta} - \cot\theta\sin\phi\,\frac{\partial}{\partial\phi}\right) \qquad (7\text{-}9)$$

$$L_{z,\mathrm{op}} = \frac{\hbar}{i}\frac{\partial}{\partial\phi}$$

We can use these results to calculate the operator

$$L_{\mathrm{op}}^2 = L_{x,\mathrm{op}}^2 + L_{y,\mathrm{op}}^2 + L_{z,\mathrm{op}}^2$$

the result is

$$L_{\mathrm{op}}^2 = -\hbar^2\left[\frac{1}{\sin\theta}\frac{\partial}{\partial\theta}\left(\sin\theta\,\frac{\partial}{\partial\theta}\right) + \frac{1}{\sin^2\theta}\frac{\partial^2}{\partial\phi^2}\right] \qquad (7\text{-}10)$$

Comparing this with Eq. (7–4), we see that the Schroedinger equation can be written

$$-\frac{\hbar^2}{2M}\left[\frac{1}{r^2}\frac{\partial}{\partial r}\left(r^2\frac{\partial\psi}{\partial r}\right)\right] + \frac{L_{\mathrm{op}}^2}{2Mr^2}\psi + V(r)\psi = E\psi \qquad (7\text{-}11)$$

The Schroedinger equation in this form should be compared with Eq. (7–5) for the classical expression for the energy of a particle in a central force field.

We could separate the variables r, θ, ϕ in the Schroedinger equation in the usual way by letting

$$\psi(r,\theta,\phi) = R(r)f(\theta)g(\phi)$$

At this stage, however, because L_{op}^2 involves only the angular variables, θ and ϕ, it is convenient to keep these variables together and let

$$\psi(r,\theta,\phi) = R(r)Y(\theta,\phi) \qquad (7\text{--}12)$$

Putting Eq. (7–12) into Eq. (7–11) and writing $R'(r)$ for $dR(r)/dr$, we have

$$-\frac{\hbar^2}{2Mr^2} Y(\theta,\phi) \frac{d}{dr}[r^2 R'(r)] + \frac{R(r)}{2Mr^2} L_{op}^2 Y(\theta,\phi)$$
$$+ V(r)R(r)Y(\theta,\phi) = ER(r)Y(\theta,\phi)$$

Dividing by $R(r)Y(\theta,\phi)$ and rearranging, we obtain

$$\frac{1}{\hbar^2 Y(\theta,\phi)} L_{op}^2 Y(\theta,\phi) = \frac{2Mr^2}{\hbar^2}[E - V(r)] + \frac{1}{R(r)} \frac{d}{dr}[r^2 R'(r)]$$
$$(7\text{--}13)$$

Since the left side of Eq. (7–13) depends only on the angles θ and ϕ while the right side depends only on r, each side of this equation must equal a constant. Let us call this constant α. Then

$$L_{op}^2 Y(\theta,\phi) = \alpha\hbar^2 Y(\theta,\phi) \qquad (7\text{--}14)$$

and

$$-\frac{\hbar^2}{2Mr^2} \frac{d}{dr}(r^2 R') + \left[\frac{\alpha\hbar^2}{2Mr^2} + V(r)\right] R = ER \qquad (7\text{--}15)$$

Equation (7–15) is called the *radial equation*. Its solution depends on the form of the potential-energy function $V(r)$. In the next section we shall discuss the solutions of this equation for the case of the hydrogen-atom potential-energy function $V(r) = -Ke^2/r$.

Equation (7–14) is independent of the form of the potential energy[2] $V(r)$. The standard method of solution is to separate the variables θ and ϕ. Before we give any details of the solution of this

[2]This occurs whenever the potential energy depends only on r, which we have assumed in order to separate the variables.

equation, we shall state and discuss the results. Equation (7–14) is an eigenvalue equation for the operator $L_{op}{}^2$, corresponding to the square of the angular momentum. As is generally true for such equations, well-behaved solutions exist only for certain values of the eigenvalue $\alpha\hbar^2$; thus the square of the angular momentum is quantized. The values of α which lead to well-behaved solutions are

$$\alpha = 0, 2, 6, 12, \ldots$$

or

$$\alpha = l(l + 1) \tag{7–16}$$

where $l = 0, 1, 2, 3, \ldots$. The possible values of the magnitude of the angular momentum are thus

$$L = \sqrt{l(l + 1)}\,\hbar \tag{7–17}$$

For other values of α, the solutions $Y(\theta,\phi)$ become infinite at the ends of the range of θ, $\theta = 0$, and $\theta = 180°$. This behavior is analogous to that of the one-dimensional wave functions $\psi(x)$, which become infinite at $x = \pm\infty$ except for certain values of the energy. The well-behaved solutions of Eq. (7–14), corresponding to the angular momentum characterized by the quantum number l, are of the form

$$Y_{lm}(\theta,\phi) = e^{im\phi}f_{l|m|}(\theta) \tag{7–18}$$

where $f_{l|m|}(\theta)$ is called an *associated Legendre function* and m is a constant restricted to the $2l + 1$ values,

$$m = 0, \pm 1, \pm 2, \ldots, \pm l \tag{7–19}$$

The constant m arises from the separation of the variables θ and ϕ, just as the constant α arises from the separation of the radial dependence from the angular dependence. The restriction $|m| \leq l$ is a result of the requirement that $f_{l|m|}(\theta)$ be well-behaved. The requirement that m be zero or an integer is connected with the geometric properties of the angle ϕ. If we increase ϕ by 2π, we get back to the same point in space. Setting $Y_{lm}(\theta,\phi + 2\pi)$ equal to $Y_{lm}(\theta,\phi)$, we obtain

$$e^{im(\phi+2\pi)} = e^{im\phi}e^{im2\pi} = e^{im\phi}$$

or

$$e^{im2\pi} = 1 \tag{7–20}$$

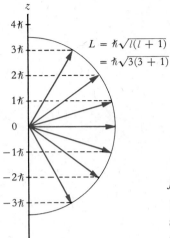

$$L = \hbar\sqrt{l(l+1)}$$
$$= \hbar\sqrt{3(3+1)}$$

figure 7–3

Vector model illustrating the possible values of the z component of the angular momentum for the case l = 3.

Equation (7–20) is satisfied only if m is a positive or negative integer, or zero.

It is important to note that, in addition to being eigenfunctions of $L_{op}{}^2$, the functions $Y_{lm}(\theta,\phi)$, given by Eq. (7–18), are eigenfunctions of $L_{z,op} = (\hbar/i)(\partial/\partial\phi)$. We have

$$L_{z,op}Y_{lm}(\theta,\phi) = \frac{\hbar}{i}\frac{\partial}{\partial\phi}[e^{im\phi}f_{l|m|}(\theta)] = m\hbar\,Y_{lm}(\theta,\phi) \qquad (7\text{–}21)$$

The eigenvalues of $L_{z,op}$ are thus $m\hbar$. The condition that m be a positive or negative integer or zero is therefore a quantization condition on the z component of the angular momentum. (The z component is simpler than the x or y component because the z axis is used to define the spherical coordinate θ. In order to observe the quantization of the z component of angular momentum for some physical system such as an atom, there must be some way of defining the z direction in space such as an external magnetic field.)

Figure 7–3 shows a vector-model diagram illustrating the possible orientations of the angular-momentum vector. We have the somewhat peculiar result that the angular-momentum vector never points in the z direction, for the maximum z component $l\hbar$ is always less than the magnitude $\sqrt{l(l+1)}\,\hbar$. This result is related to an uncertainty principle for angular momentum (which we shall not derive) that implies that no two components of angular momentum can be precisely known, except in the case of zero angular momentum.

The general form of the functions $f_{l|m|}(\theta)$ is rather complicated and will not be given in detail here. Some of these functions for

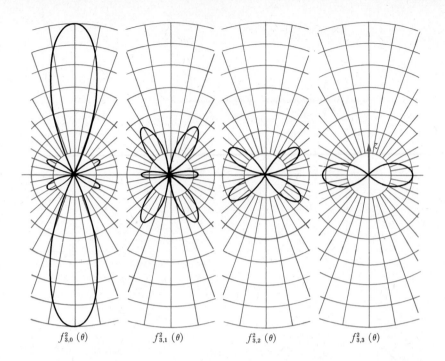

$$f^2_{3,0}(\theta) \qquad\qquad f^2_{3,1}(\theta) \qquad\qquad f^2_{3,2}(\theta) \qquad\qquad f^2_{3,3}(\theta)$$

figure 7–4 *Polar graph of the angular part of the distribution function $f_{3,|m|}{}^2(\theta)$ for the four possible values of $|m|$. (From L. Pauling and E. B. Wilson,* Introduction to Quantum Mechanics, *McGraw-Hill Book Company, Inc., New York, 1935.)*

small l and m are given below. (The constants a_{lm} are normalization constants which need not concern us.)

$$f_{0,0} = a_{0,0}$$

$$f_{1,0} = a_{1,0} \cos\theta$$

$$f_{1,1} = a_{1,1} \sin\theta$$

$$f_{2,0} = a_{2,0}(3\cos^2\theta - 1) \qquad\qquad (7\text{--}22)$$

$$f_{2,1} = a_{2,1} \sin\theta\cos\theta$$

$$f_{2,2} = a_{2,2} \sin^2\theta$$

Figure 7–4 shows a polar graph of $f_{3|m|}{}^2(\theta)$ for the four possible values of $|m|$. Figure 7–5 shows polar graphs for the case $f_{ll}{}^2(\theta)$ for several values of l. The functions f_{ll} are proportional to $\sin^l\theta$; thus for large l, $f_{ll}{}^2(\theta)$ is large only for values of θ near 90°. For this case, the angular part of the wave function $Y_{lm}(\theta,\phi)$ corresponds to circulation confined roughly to the xy plane.

The function $e^{im\phi}$ is similar to the one-dimensional wave function e^{ikx} for a particle of linear momentum k moving in the direction

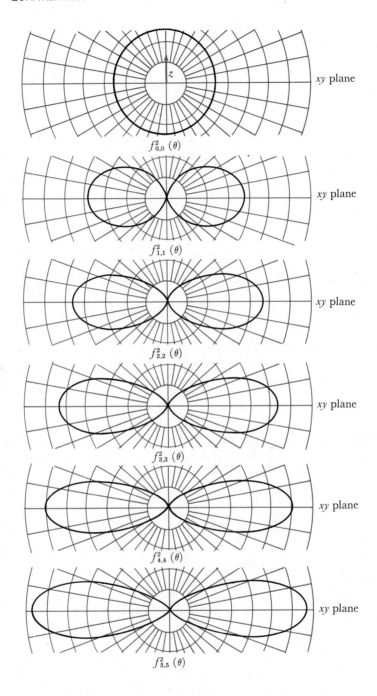

figure 7–5   *Polar graph of the angular part of the distribution function $f_{l,l}{}^2(\theta)$ for the case $m = l$. When l is large, the function is concentrated near the xy plane.* (*From L. Pauling and E. B. Wilson,* Introduction to Quantum Mechanics, *McGraw-Hill Book Company, Inc., New York, 1935.*)

of increasing x. We can bring out this similarity by considering a particle moving around the z axis in a circle of radius ρ. If the linear momentum in the direction of increasing ϕ is $\hbar k_\phi$, the angular momentum in the z direction is $\hbar k_\phi \rho = \hbar m$. The function $e^{im\phi}$ can thus be written

$$e^{im\phi} = e^{ik_\phi \rho \phi} = e^{ik_\phi s}$$

where $s = \rho\phi$ is the linear distance along the circle.

We shall now give some of the details of the solution of Eq. (7–14) by separation of the variables. We let $Y(\theta,\phi) = g(\phi)f(\theta)$. Substituting this into Eq. (7–14), with L_{op}^2 given by Eq. (7–10), we obtain

$$\frac{g(\phi)}{\sin\theta} \frac{d}{d\theta}\left[\sin\theta \frac{df(\theta)}{d\theta}\right] + \frac{f(\theta)g''(\phi)}{\sin^2\theta} = -\alpha f(\theta)g(\phi)$$

Dividing by $f(\theta)g(\phi)$ and rearranging, we obtain

$$\frac{g''(\phi)}{g(\phi)} = -\alpha \sin^2\theta - \frac{\sin\theta}{f(\theta)}\frac{d}{d\theta}\left[\sin\theta \frac{df(\theta)}{d\theta}\right] \tag{7–23}$$

Once again, each side must equal a constant. Calling this constant K, we have

$$g''(\phi) = Kg(\phi) \tag{7–24}$$

The solution of this equation is an exponential function that becomes infinite as $\phi \to \infty$ unless K is a negative number. If we let $K = -m^2$, the solution of Eq. (7–24) is $g(\phi) = e^{im\phi}$. (If we allow m to be negative or positive, this equation includes the solution $e^{-im\phi}$.) We have already shown that the requirement $g(\phi + 2\pi) = g(\phi)$ implies that m is a positive or negative integer or zero.

The equation for θ is obtained by setting the right side of Eq. (7–23) equal to $-m^2$. This equation is not easy to solve. It can be put into a standard form called *Legendre's equation* if the variable is changed to $u = \cos\theta$. Then

$$\frac{df}{d\theta} = \frac{df}{du}\frac{du}{d\theta} = -\sin\theta f'$$

where $f' = df/du$, and this equation becomes

$$(1 - u^2)f'' - 2uf' + \left(\alpha - \frac{m^2}{1 - u^2}\right)f = 0 \tag{7–25}$$

Equation (7–25) can be solved by a power-series method similar to that used in Section 6·8 for the harmonic-oscillator problem. At the extreme ranges of the variable $u = \pm 1$, corresponding to $\theta = 0$ and $\theta = 180°$, the infinite-power series satisfying Eq. (7–25) becomes infinite, thus leading to a wave function that cannot be normalized. However, for certain values of α, the series terminates, becoming a polynomial. The values of α for which well-behaved solutions exist are $\alpha = l(l + 1)$, where $l = 0, 1, 2, 3, \ldots$, and $l \geq |m|$. Let us consider the special case $m = 0$. The well-behaved solutions of

$$(1 - u^2)f'' - 2uf' + \alpha f = 0 \tag{7–26}$$

are polynomials called *Legendre polynomials*. These contain only even powers or only odd powers of u. It is instructive to try to satisfy Eq. (7–26) with some simple polynomials.

The simplest polynomial is $f_0 = 1$. (We need not worry about normalization here.) This clearly satisfies Eq. (7–26) only if $\alpha = 0$.

The next simplest is $f_1 = u$, $f_1' = 1$. Equation (7–26) is then $-2u + \alpha u = 0$, or $\alpha = 2 = 1(1 + 1)$.

Let us now try $f_2 = 1 + au^2$. Then $f_2' = 2au$ and $f_2'' = 2a$. Equation (7–26) is then

$$(1 - u^2)2a - 2u(2au) + \alpha(1 + au^2) = 0$$
$$au^2(\alpha - 6) + (\alpha + 2a) = 0$$

This holds for all u only if $\alpha = 6 = 2(1 + 2)$ and $a = -3$. It is left as an exercise to try other polynomials such as $f_3 = u + bu^3$ and show that Eq. (7–26) is satisfied if $\alpha = 12 = 3(3 + 1)$. For each of these polynomials f_l, we see that α must be given by $\alpha = l(l + 1)$.

7·4 HYDROGEN-ATOM WAVE FUNCTIONS

The solution of the radial equation (7–15) depends on the form of the potential energy function $V(r)$. For an electron a distance r from a nucleus of charge Ze, the potential energy is

$$V(r) = -\frac{KZe^2}{r} \tag{7–27}$$

where $K = 1/4\pi\epsilon_0$ is the Coulomb constant. (For hydrogen, $Z = 1$, but we shall leave it variable so the results can be applied to ionized helium.) We can correct for the motion of the nucleus by replacing the mass of the electron m_e by the reduced mass μ:

$$\mu = \frac{m_e}{1 + (m_e/M_N)}$$

where M_N is the mass of the nucleus. The radial equation for the hydrogen atom is then Eq. (7–15) with $\alpha = l(l + 1)$, $V(r)$ given by Eq. (7–27), and M replaced by μ:

$$-\frac{\hbar^2}{2\mu r^2} \frac{d}{dr} (r^2 R') + \left[\frac{l(l + 1)\hbar^2}{2\mu r^2} - \frac{KZe^2}{r}\right] R = ER \quad (7\text{–}28)$$

Figure 7–6 shows a sketch of the potential-energy function $V(r)$. If the total energy is positive, the electron is not bound to the atom. We are interested only in the bound-state solutions for which E is negative. For this case, the potential energy is greater than the total energy for large r, as shown in the figure. We saw in Chapter 6 (Section 6·3) that whenever $V(x) > E$ for large x, the Schroedinger equation has well-behaved solutions for only certain values of E. A similar result holds for solutions of Eq. (7–28). Except for certain values of E, the solutions $R(r)$ approach ∞ at large r, and the wave function

$$\psi(r,\theta,\phi) = R(r)Y_{lm}(\theta,\phi)$$

cannot be normalized.

Equation (7–28) can be solved by a method similar to that used to solve the harmonic-oscillator problem (and Legendre's equation for θ in the previous section). The details of the general solution of Eq. (7–28) are too involved to include in this book. We shall, however, find one solution to this equation corresponding to the lowest energy, the ground state. Since the energy E is negative, let us define the parameter λ by

$$\lambda^2 = -\frac{2\mu E}{\hbar^2} \qquad\qquad (7\text{–}29)$$

We shall assume λ to be positive. We shall consider only the case $l = 0$. Other values of l correspond to greater angular momentum and therefore greater kinetic energy. For this case, Eq. (7–28) can be written

$$\frac{1}{r^2} \frac{d}{dr} (r^2 R') + \frac{2\mu KZe^2}{\hbar^2} \frac{R}{r} = \lambda^2 R$$

or

$$R'' + \left(\frac{2R'}{r} + \frac{2\mu KZe^2}{\hbar^2} \frac{R}{r}\right) = \lambda^2 R \qquad\qquad (7\text{–}30)$$

We would like to find a solution of Eq. (7–30) that approaches

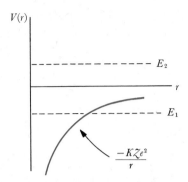

$$V(r)$$

$$----------- E_2$$

$$r$$

$$--------- E_1$$

$$\frac{-KZe^2}{r}$$

figure 7–6   *Potential energy of an electron in a hydrogen atom. If the total energy is greater than zero, as in E_2, the electron is not bound. If the total energy is less than zero, as in E_1, the electron is bound. As in one-dimensional problems, only certain values of $E < 0$ lead to well-behaved wave functions.*

zero as r approaches ∞. For very large r, the terms in parentheses in Eq. (7–30) are small compared with the other two terms; thus the equation can be written approximately

$$R'' \approx \lambda^2 R \qquad \text{for large } r \tag{7–31}$$

Equation (7–31) is satisfied by the functions $e^{-\lambda r}$ and $e^{+\lambda r}$. The latter becomes infinite at large r if we assume λ to be positive, so it is not acceptable. We thus see that, at very large r, the solution of Eq. (7–30) is approximately

$$R \approx e^{-\lambda r} \tag{7–32}$$

The solution (7–32) will satisfy Eq. (7–30) for *all* r if the terms in parentheses in this equation cancel. This occurs for one value of λ and thus for one value of E related to λ by Eq. (7–29). Using $R' = -\lambda e^{-\lambda r} = -\lambda R$ and setting the quantity in brackets in Eq. (7–30) equal to zero, we obtain

$$-2\lambda \frac{R}{r} + \frac{2\mu K Z e^2}{\hbar^2} \frac{R}{r} = 0$$

or

$$\lambda = \frac{\mu K Z e^2}{\hbar^2} = \frac{Z}{a_0}$$

where $a_0 = \hbar^2/\mu K e^2 \approx 0.529$ Å is the Bohr radius. The energy corresponding to this value of λ is, by Eq. (7–29),

$$E = -\frac{\hbar^2\lambda^2}{2\mu} = -\frac{Z^2(Ke^2)^2\mu}{2\hbar^2} = -Z^2E_1$$

where

$$E_1 = \frac{1}{2}\left(\frac{Ke^2}{\hbar c}\right)^2 \mu c^2 \approx 13.6 \text{ eV} \tag{7–33}$$

In general, the well-behaved solutions of the radial equation (7–28) can be written

$$R_{nl} = e^{-Zr/na_0}\left(\frac{2Zr}{na_0}\right)^l L_{nl}\frac{2Zr}{na_0} \tag{7–34}$$

where L_{nl} is a polynomial called a *Laguerre polynomial* and n is an integer which must be greater than l. The energy eigenvalues corresponding to the eigenfunctions in Eq. (7–34) are

$$E_n = -\frac{Z^2E_1}{n^2} \tag{7–35}$$

where E_1 is given by Eq. (7–33). These values of allowed energies are identical to those in the Bohr model. The complete wave function for the hydrogen atom is thus

$$\psi_{nlm}(r,\theta,\phi) = C_{nlm}R_{nl}(r)f_{l|m|}(\theta)e^{im\phi} \tag{7–36}$$

where R_{nl} is given by Eq. (7–34), $f_{l|m|}(\theta)$ are the associated Legendre functions discussed in the previous section, and C_{nlm} are normalization constants. The quantum numbers n, l, and m are restricted to

$$n = 1, 2, 3, \ldots$$
$$l = 0, 1, \ldots, (n-1)$$
$$m = -l, -l+1, \ldots, 0, 1, 2, \ldots, +l$$

This wave function is an eigenfunction of the operators E_{op}, L_{op}^2, and $L_{z,op}$:

$$E_{op}\psi_{nlm} = -\frac{Z^2E_1}{n^2}\psi_{nlm}$$
$$L_{op}^2\psi_{nlm} = l(l+1)\hbar^2\psi_{nlm} \tag{7–37}$$
$$L_{z,op}\psi_{nlm} = m\hbar\psi_{nlm}$$

DEGENERACY   The wave function depends on the three quantum numbers n, l, and m. The number m is associated with a boundary condition on ϕ, l with a boundary condition on θ, and n with a boundary condition on r. The energy, however, depends only on n. The phenomenon of several different wave functions having the same energy is called *degeneracy*. The fact that the energy does not depend on l is a peculiarity of the inverse-square force. It is related to the classical-mechanics result for inverse-square forces that the energy in an elliptical orbit depends only on the major axis, not on the eccentricity. A highly eccentric orbit corresponds to a small value of angular momentum and thus to a small l value (zero angular momentum corresponds to oscillation through the force center), while a circular orbit corresponds to the largest possible angular momentum. For central forces that are not exactly inverse square, the energy does depend on the angular momentum, both classically and quantum-mechanically. We have seen that $m\hbar$ is the z component of angular momentum. Since there is no preferred direction for the z axis for any central force, the energy cannot depend on m.

GROUND STATE   The lowest energy state has $n = 1$. Thus l and m must both be
OF HYDROGEN   zero. The wave function is

$$\psi_{100} = C_{100} e^{-Zr/a_0}$$

The constant C_{100} is determined by normalization:

$$\int \psi^* \psi \, d\tau = \iiint \psi^* \psi r^2 \sin \theta \, d\theta \, dr \, d\phi = 1$$

using for the volume element in spherical coordinates

$$d\tau = (r \sin \theta \, d\phi)(r \, d\theta)(dr)$$

Because $\psi^* \psi$ is spherically symmetric (no θ or ϕ dependence), the integration over the angles gives 4π. Performing the integration over r gives

$$C_{100} = \frac{1}{\sqrt{\pi}} \left(\frac{Z}{a_0} \right)^{3/2}$$

The probability of finding the electron in volume $d\tau$ is $\psi^* \psi \, d\tau$. It is more interesting to determine the probability of finding the electron between r and $r + dr$. This probability, $P(r) \, dr$, is just $\psi^* \psi$ times the volume of the spherical shell of thickness dr:

$$P(r) \, dr = \psi^* \psi 4\pi r^2 \, dr = 4\pi r^2 C_{100}^2 e^{-2Zr/a_0} \, dr \qquad (7\text{--}38)$$

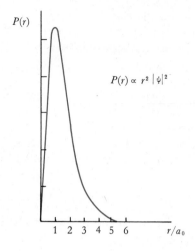

$P(r) \propto r^2 |\psi|^2$

figure 7-7

Probability density $P(r)$ versus r/a_0 for the electron in the ground state of hydrogen. $P(r)$ is proportional to $r^2\psi^2$. The most probable radius is the Bohr radius, a_0.

(Note the similarity of this calculation to the determination of the speed distribution from the velocity distribution done in Chapter 2.) Figure 7-7 shows a sketch of $P(r)$ vs r/a_0. It is left as an exercise (see Problems 7-3 and 7-13) to show that $P(r)$ has its maximum value at $r_m = a_0/Z$ and that the expectation value of $\langle r \rangle$ is

$$\langle r \rangle = \int_0^\infty rP(r) \, dr = \frac{3}{2} \frac{a_0}{Z}$$

In contrast to the Bohr model, in which the electron stays in a well-defined orbit at $r = a_0$, we see that it is *possible* for the electron to be found at any r from zero to infinity; however, the most probable radius is a_0, and the chance of finding the electron at a much different radius is small. It is useful to think of the electron as a charged cloud of charge density $\rho = e\psi^*\psi$. (It should be remembered, however, that the electron is always observed as one charge.) The angular momentum in the ground state is zero, contrary to the Bohr-model assumption of $1\hbar$ for the ground state.

FIRST EXCITED STATE For $n = 2$, there are two possibilities for l: either $l = 0$ or $l = 1$. For $l = 0$, $m = 0$, and we again have a spherically symmetric wave function:

$$\psi_{200} = C_{200}\left(2 - \frac{Zr}{a_0}\right) e^{-Zr/2a_0} \tag{7-39}$$

For $l = 1$, m can be $+1$, 0, or -1. The corresponding wave

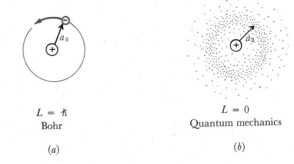

$$L = \hbar$$
Bohr

$$L = 0$$
Quantum mechanics

(a)

(b)

figure 7-8 *Comparison of the Bohr model (a) and the quantum-mechanical model (b) of hydrogen. In (a) the electron orbits about the proton at radius a_0 with angular momentum $1\hbar$. In (b) the electron is represented by a spherically symmetrical probability distribution function. The radial distribution $P(r)$ has a maximum at $r = a_0$ and does not rotate.*

functions are

$$\psi_{210} = C_{210} \frac{Zr}{a_0} e^{-Zr/2a_0} \cos \theta \qquad (7\text{-}40)$$

$$\psi_{21\pm1} = C_{211} \frac{Zr}{a_0} e^{-Zr/2a_0} \sin \theta \, e^{\pm i\phi} \qquad (7\text{-}41)$$

Figure 7-9 shows sketches of $P(r)$ for these wave functions. The distribution for $n = 2$, $l = 1$ is maximum at the second Bohr radius,

$$r_m = (2)^2 a_0$$

while for $n = 2$ and $l = 0$, $P(r)$ has 2 maxima, the largest of which is near this radius.

figure 7-9 · *Probability density $P(r)$ versus r/a_0 for the $n = 2$ states in hydrogen. $P(r)$ for $l = 1$ has a maximum at the Bohr value $2^2 a_0$. For $l = 0$ there is a maximum near this value and a smaller maximum near the origin.*

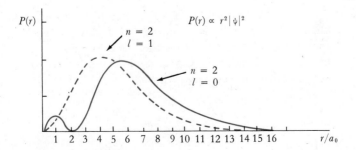

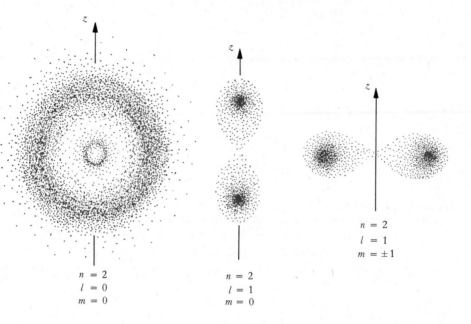

$n = 2$
$l = 0$
$m = 0$

$n = 2$
$l = 1$
$m = 0$

$n = 2$
$l = 1$
$m = \pm 1$

*figure 7-10   Quantum-mechanical model of hydrogen in the states $n = 2$. The proba-
bility function $r^2|\psi|^2$ is indicated by the density of the points. The probability
is spherically symmetrical for $l = 0$. It is proportional to $\cos^2 \theta$ for $l = 1$,
$m = 0$, and to $\sin^2 \theta$ for $l = 1$, $m = \pm 1$. These probability functions
have rotational symmetry about the z axis.*

Similar radial-probability distributions can be obtained for the
other excited states of hydrogen. The main radial dependence of ψ
is contained in the factor e^{-Zr/na_0} except near the origin. A detailed
examination of the Laguerre polynomials shows that $\psi \rightarrow r^l$ as
$r \rightarrow 0$. Thus, for a given n, ψ_{nlm} is smaller near the origin for
large l than for small l.

7·5

**SELECTION RULES
FOR TRANSITIONS
IN HYDROGEN**

The time-dependent wave function for the state n, l, m is

$$\Psi_{nlm}(r,\theta,\phi,t) = e^{-iE_n t/\hbar}\psi_{nlm}(r,\theta,\phi)$$

As was discussed in Section 6·7 for one-dimensional problems, the
charge density $e\psi^*\psi$ is independent of time; thus we expect no
radiation. If we assume that the wave function is a combination
of the two functions $\Psi_{n_1 l_1 m_1}$ and $\Psi_{n_2 l_2 m_2}$, the charge density
oscillates with angular frequency

$$\omega = \frac{|E_{n_2} - E_{n_1}|}{\hbar}$$

As in Section 6·7, we can determine if an electric-dipole radiation transition is possible between two states by computing the average dipole moment $e\mathbf{r}$. The time-dependent part of $e\mathbf{r}$ will be zero if all three components of the matrix element

$$\iiint \psi^*_{n_2 l_2 m_2} \mathbf{r} \psi_{n_1 l_1 m_1} \, d\tau \tag{7-42}$$

are zero. This leads to selection rules for electric-dipole transitions. We shall illustrate the derivation of the selection rule for m and merely state the result for l. Let us consider only the integration over ϕ. The matrix element, Eq. (7-42) will be zero if

$$\int_0^{2\pi} (e^{im_2\phi})^* \mathbf{r} e^{im_1\phi} \, d\phi \tag{7-43}$$

is zero.

The components of $\mathbf{r}$ in rectangular coordinates are

$$r_x = x = r \sin\theta \cos\phi = r \sin\theta \tfrac{1}{2}(e^{i\phi} + e^{-i\phi})$$

$$r_y = y = r \sin\theta \sin\phi = r \sin\theta \frac{1}{2i}(e^{i\phi} - e^{-i\phi})$$

$$r_z = z = r \cos\theta$$

Since z does not involve ϕ, the z component of (7-43) is proportional to

$$\int_0^{2\pi} e^{i(m_1-m_2)\phi} \, d\phi$$

This integral is zero unless $m_1 - m_2 = 0$. The x and y components each involve the two integrals

$$\int_0^{2\pi} e^{i(m_1-m_2+1)\phi} \, d\phi$$

and

$$\int_0^{2\pi} e^{i(m_1-m_2-1)\phi} \, d\phi$$

The first is zero unless $m_1 - m_2 + 1 = 0$, while the second is zero unless $m_1 - m_2 - 1 = 0$. We see, from considering only the integration over ϕ, that all three components of (7-43) are zero unless

$$\Delta m = 0 \text{ or } \pm 1 \tag{7-44}$$

A similar consideration of the integration over θ shows that (7–42) is also zero unless

$$\Delta l = \pm 1 \qquad\qquad (7\text{--}45)$$

There is no selection rule for n.

Let us consider the parity of the wave functions. In one dimension, we described even functions $f_e(-x) = f_e(x)$ as having even parity and odd functions $f_o(-x) = -f_o(x)$ as having odd parity. In three dimensions, a function is said to have even parity if

$$f_e(-x,-y,-z) = +f_e(x,y,z) \qquad \text{even parity}$$

and odd parity if

$$f_o(-x,-y,-z) = -f_o(x,y,z) \qquad \text{odd parity}$$

In spherical coordinates, if r_1, θ_1, ϕ_1 refer to point (x,y,z), the spherical coordinates of point $(-x,-y,-z)$ are $r_2 = r_1$, $\theta_2 = \pi - \theta_1$, and $\phi_2 = \phi_1 + \pi$. Thus the parity of a hydrogen-atom wave function is determined only by the angular part $Y(\theta,\phi)$. A detailed examination of these functions shows that the *parity of a state is even if l is even and odd if l is odd*. Thus, the selection rule $\Delta l = \pm 1$ implies that the parity of the wave function must change.

Figure 7–11 is an energy-level diagram for hydrogen, with some of the allowed transitions shown. This diagram is similar to Figure 4–17 except that the states with the same n but different l are shown separately. These states, called *terms*, are referred to by giving the number n and a letter S (for $l = 0$), P (for $l = 1$), D (for $l = 2$), and F (for $l = 3$). These code letters are remnants from the spectroscopist's descriptions of the various series as *Sharp*, *Principal*, *Diffuse*, and *Fundamental*. (For higher values of l, the letters follow alphabetically: G for $l = 4$, etc.)

7·6
MAGNETIC MOMENTS AND ELECTRON SPIN

As we mentioned in Chapter 4, when viewed with high resolution, a spectral line in an atom is seen to consist of a set of lines; this splitting is called *fine structure*. Although the Sommerfeld relativistic theory, using the Bohr model, agrees perfectly with experiments for hydrogen, it does not agree for any other atom. In other atoms, more lines are seen than predicted by Sommerfeld's theory. In 1925 Pauli suggested that in addition to the quantum numbers n, l, and m, an electron possessed a fourth quantum number which could have two values. As we have seen, quantum numbers arise because of boundary conditions on some coordinate. Pauli originally expected that the fourth quantum number would be associ-

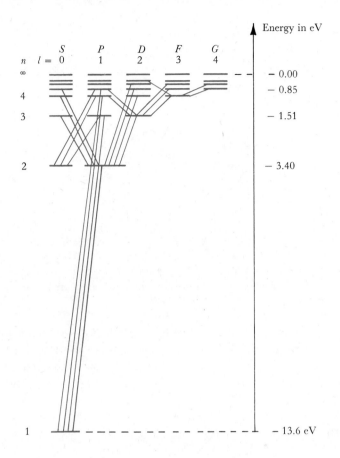

figure 7–11   *Energy level diagram for the hydrogen atom showing transitions obeying the selection rule $\Delta l = \pm 1$. States with the same n value but different l value have the same energy, given by $E_n = -E_1/n^2$, where $E_1 \approx 13.6\ eV$ as in the Bohr theory.*

ated with the time coordinate in a relativistic theory, but this was not pursued. In the same year S. Goudsmit and G. Uhlenbeck, graduate students at Leiden, suggested that this fourth quantum number was the z component, m_s, of an intrinsic-spin angular momentum of the electron. If the spin quantum number is s, we expect $2s + 1$ possible z components, in analogy with the $2l + 1$ possible m components of the orbital angular momentum with quantum number l. If m_s is to have just two values, s must be $\frac{1}{2}$. The proposal of electron spin not only explained fine structure but cleared up several problems such as the arrangement of the periodic table and the results of an interesting experiment by O. Stern and W. Gerlach in 1922 which we shall describe in this section. We shall

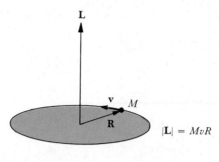

$$|\mu| = IA = \left(q\,\frac{v}{2\pi R} \right)(\pi R^2) = \frac{qvR}{2} = \frac{qL}{2M}$$

figure 7–12 *A charged particle moving in a circle has angular momentum of magnitude MvR and a magnetic moment of magnitude IA, where $I = qv/2\pi R$ is the current, and $A = \pi R^2$ is the area. The angular momentum $\mathbf{L}$ and the magnetic moment $\boldsymbol{\mu}$ are in the same direction. They are related by $\boldsymbol{\mu} = q\mathbf{L}/2M$.*

discuss the periodic table in the next chapter.[3] In order to understand the effects of electron spin, we must study the connection between the angular momentum of a charged system and its magnetic properties.

MAGNETIC MOMENT When any charged system is rotating, it has a magnetic moment, i.e., it behaves like a little current loop or bar magnet when placed in a magnetic field. There is a close connection between the magnetic moment of a system and the angular momentum of the system, both classically and quantum-mechanically. Consider a particle with mass M and charge q moving with speed v in a circle of radius R. The angular momentum of the particle is $L = MvR$ and is in the direction of $\mathbf{R} \times \mathbf{v}$. The magnetic moment of a current loop is the product of the current times the area of the loop. Its direction is also $\mathbf{R} \times \mathbf{v}$ if the charge is positive. For a charge moving in a circle, the current is the charge q times the frequency, which is $v/2\pi R$; thus the magnetic moment is

$$\mu = \frac{qv}{2\pi R}\,\pi R^2 = \tfrac{1}{2}qvR = \frac{q}{2M}\,MvR = \frac{q}{2M}\,L$$

---

[3]Most students are probably aware of the Pauli exclusion principle, which states that no two electrons in an atom can have the same values for their quantum numbers. The extra quantum number m_s, with two values, allows two electrons in the $n = 1$ shell corresponding to the two values of m_s and eight electrons in the $n = 2$ shell — two with $l = 0$ and six with $l = 1$, two each for the three possible values of m_l.

Since the directions are the same if q is positive and opposite if q is negative, we can write

$$\boldsymbol{\mu} = \frac{q}{2M}\mathbf{L} \tag{7-46}$$

For a system of charges, we consider each part of charge q_i and mass M_i moving in a circle R_i. Then

$$\boldsymbol{\mu} = \sum_i \frac{q_i}{2M_i}\mathbf{L}_i$$

If the charge-to-mass ratio q_i/M_i is the same throughout the system,

$$\boldsymbol{\mu} = \frac{q}{2M}\sum \mathbf{L}_i = \frac{q}{2M}\mathbf{L}$$

and Eq. (7–46) holds for the system. The results we have found for charges moving in circles also hold for any type of motion.

Applying these results to the hydrogen atom, we have for the magnitude of the magnetic moment,

$$\mu = \frac{e}{2m_e}L = \frac{e\hbar}{2m_e}\sqrt{l(l+1)} \tag{7-47}$$

and for the z component,

$$\mu_z = -\frac{e\hbar}{2m_e}m \tag{7-48}$$

where m_e is the mass of the electron and m is the z component of the angular momentum. There is a minus sign in Eq. 7–48 because the electron has a negative charge $-e$. The magnetic moment is therefore in the opposite direction of the angular momentum. The unit $e\hbar/2m_e$ is called *a Bohr magneton* and has the value

$$\frac{e\hbar}{2m_e} = 9.27 \times 10^{-28} \text{joule/gauss} = 5.79 \times 10^{-9} \text{ eV/gauss}$$

We see that quantization of angular momentum implies quantization of magnetic moments.

The behavior of a system with a magnetic moment in a magnetic field can be visualized by considering a bar magnet of length X_0 and magnetic-pole strength q_m, giving a magnetic moment

$$\boldsymbol{\mu} = q_m\mathbf{X}_0 \tag{7-49}$$

where the direction of the vector $\mathbf{X}_0$ is from the south pole to the north pole.[4] When placed in an external magnetic field $\mathbf{B}$, there

---

[4]The pole strength of a bar magnet is defined by Eq. (7–49), since $\boldsymbol{\mu}$ and $\mathbf{X}_0$ are quantities that can be measured.

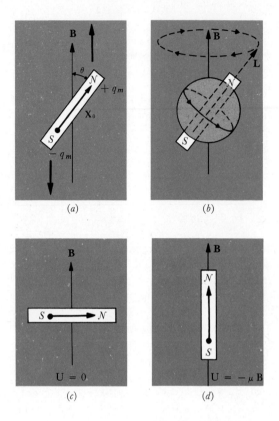

figure 7–13   *Bar-magnet model of magnetic moment. (a) Torque twists the magnet counterclockwise. (b) If the magnet is spinning, torque causes it to precess. (c) Energy is chosen to be zero when moment is perpendicular to* **B**. *(d) Energy is minimum when moment is aligned with* **B**.

is a torque $\boldsymbol{\Gamma} = \boldsymbol{\mu} \times \mathbf{B}$ that tries to line up the magnet with the field **B**. If the magnet is spinning about its axis, the effect of the torque is to make the spin axis precess about the direction of the external field. In order to rotate the magnet through an angle $d\theta$, work must be done:

$$dW = \boldsymbol{\Gamma}\, d\theta = \mu B \sin \theta\, d\theta = d(-\mu B \cos \theta) = d(-\boldsymbol{\mu} \cdot \mathbf{B})$$

Setting this work equal to the increase in potential energy and choosing the zero of potential energy when the magnet is perpendicular to the field gives

$$U = -\boldsymbol{\mu} \cdot \mathbf{B} \qquad\qquad (7\text{--}50)$$

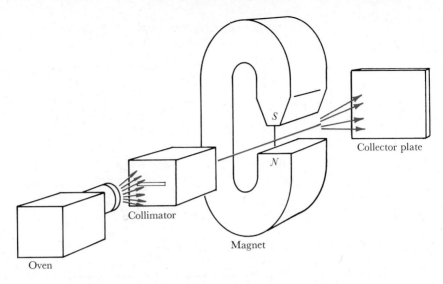

Collector plate

Collimator

Magnet

Oven

figure 7–14   *In the Stern-Gerlach experiment atoms from an oven are collimated, passed through an inhomogeneous magnetic field, and detected on a collector plate.*

If **B** is in the z direction, the potential energy is

$$U = -\mu_z B$$

If the magnetic field is not homogeneous, the force on one pole may be greater than that on the other, depending on the orientation; thus there will be a net force on the magnet.

STERN-GERLACH
EXPERIMENT

In 1922, Stern and Gerlach passed a beam of silver atoms between the poles of a magnet, as shown in Figure 7–14. The poles were shaped to give a magnetic field which was inhomogeneous; B_z was a function of z. Figure 7–15 shows the effect of a field that increases with z on several bar magnets of different orientations. In addition to the torque, the field produces a net force in the positive or negative z direction. This force deflects the magnets up or down by an amount that depends on the field strength B and on the z component of the magnetic moment u_z. Classically, one would expect a continuum of deflections for the beam of silver atoms corresponding to the continuum of possible values of u_z between $+u$ and $-u$; however, we see from Eq. (7–48) that quantum mechanics predicts that u_z can have only $2l + 1$ values corresponding to the $2l + 1$ values of m. Thus, we expect that there will be $2l + 1$ deflections (counting 0 as a deflection). For example, if $l = 0$, there should be one line on the collector plate corresponding to no deflection; while if $l = 1$, there should be three lines corresponding to the three values $m = -1$, $m = 0$, and

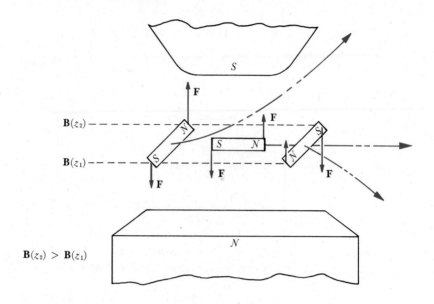

figure 7–15 *Effect of an inhomogeneous magnetic field on path of magnets. In addition to the torque, there is a net force up or down, depending on the orientation of the magnet.*

$m = +1$. When the experiment was done with silver atoms, there were two lines.

In 1927 the same result was obtained by Phipps and Taylor using hydrogen atoms. Since the ground state of hydrogen has $l = 0$, we would expect only one line if it were not for the electron spin. If the electron has spin angular momentum of magnitude $\sqrt{s(s+1)}\,\hbar$, where $s = \frac{1}{2}$, the z component can be either $+\frac{1}{2}\hbar$ or $-\frac{1}{2}\hbar$. Since the orbital angular momentum is zero, the total angular momentum of the atom is just the spin.[5] Thus the magnetic moment of the electron is quantized to two positions. This is called *space quantization*. Figure 7–16 shows a sketch of the pattern observed by Stern and Gerlach. From quantitative measurement of the deflection, the magnitude of the magnetic moment due to the spin angular momentum can be determined. The result is *not* $\frac{1}{2}$ Bohr magneton as predicted by Eq. (7–48), with $m = m_s = \frac{1}{2}$, but twice this value. (This type of experiment is not an accurate way to measure magnetic moments, although the measurement of

[5]The nucleus of an atom also has angular momentum and therefore a magnetic moment, but the mass of the nucleus is about 2,000 times that of the electron for hydrogen, and greater for other atoms. From Eq. (7–47) we expect the magnetic moment of the nucleus to be of the order of 1/2,000 of a Bohr magneton. This small effect does not show up in the Stern-Gerlach experiment.

angular momentum is, of course, accurate because it only involves counting the number of lines.) This result, and the fact that s is not an integer like the orbital quantum number l, makes it clear that the classical model of the electron as a spinning ball is not to be taken too literally. Like the Bohr model of the atom, the classical model is useful in describing results of quantum-mechanical calculations, and it often gives useful guidelines as to what to expect from an experiment. It is customary to write the relation between the z component of the angular momentum, J_z, and the z component of the magnetic moment, μ_z, as

$$\mu_z = -g \frac{e\hbar}{2m_e} \frac{J_z}{\hbar}$$

where $g_l = 1$ for orbital angular momentum and $g_s = 2$ for spin. More precise measurements indicate that $g_s = 2.00232$. The phenomenon of spin and the value of g_s are predicted by the Dirac relativistic wave equation, a subject beyond the scope of this book.

SPIN OPERATORS AND EIGENFUNCTIONS
Our description of the hydrogen atom in terms of the wave functions given by Eq. (7–36) is not complete because these functions do not include spin. The wave function must also be characterized by the quantum number m_s, giving the z component of spin. (The quantum number for the total spin s has the same value, $s = \frac{1}{2}$, for all states of the atom; thus we need not explicitly include this quantum number.) Let us define an operator for spin, S_{op}, analogous to L_{op} for orbital angular momentum. We cannot give a

figure 7–16   *Results of the Stern-Gerlach experiment. Rather than a continuous distribution at the collector, the atoms are split into two lines, indicating space quantization of the magnetic moments. The shape of the upper line is due to the greater inhomogeneity of the magnetic field near the upper-pole face.*

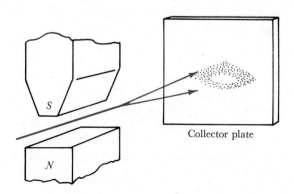

Collector plate

definition of S_{op} in terms of ordinary three-dimensional space coordinates because spin has no classical counterpart, i.e., it is not related to any classical motion (despite the spinning-ball model of an electron which we find useful for picturing this abstract quantity). Similarly, we cannot write spin eigenfunctions as functions in ordinary space. However, we do know that S_{op}^2 has the single eigenvalue $\frac{1}{2}(1 + \frac{1}{2})\hbar^2$, and $S_{z,op}$ has two eigenvalues, $+\frac{1}{2}\hbar$ and $-\frac{1}{2}\hbar$. Let us call the two eigenfunctions of $S_{z,op}$ α and β. α corresponds to the eigenvalue $m_s = +\frac{1}{2}$, and β corresponds to $m_s = -\frac{1}{2}$.

$$S_{z,op}\alpha = +\tfrac{1}{2}\hbar\alpha$$
$$S_{z,op}\beta = -\tfrac{1}{2}\hbar\beta$$
$$S_{op}^2\alpha = \tfrac{1}{2}(1 + \tfrac{1}{2})\hbar^2\alpha \qquad (7\text{-}51)$$
$$S_{op}^2\beta = \tfrac{1}{2}(1 + \tfrac{1}{2})\hbar^2\beta$$

We can then include the spin in the wave functions by multiplying the wave functions [Eq. (7–36)] by α or β. For example, there are now two wave functions for the ground state of the hydrogen atom which are eigenfunctions of E_{op}, L_{op}^2, $L_{z,op}$, S_{op}^2, and $S_{z,op}$. They are

$$\psi_{000+1/2} = C_{000}R_{00}(r)Y_{00}(\theta,\phi)\alpha$$

and

$$\psi_{000-1/2} = C_{000}R_{00}(r)Y_{00}(\theta,\phi)\beta$$

In general, the ground state of a hydrogen atom is a linear combination of these eigenfunctions:

$$\psi = C_1\psi_{000+1/2} + C_2\psi_{000-1/2}$$

The probability of measuring $m_s = +\frac{1}{2}$ (such as observing to which spot the atom goes in the Stern-Gerlach experiment) is $|C_1|^2$. Unless the atoms have been preselected in some way (e.g., by passing them through a previous inhomogeneous magnetic field), C_1 and C_2 will each be $1/\sqrt{2}$, so that the probability of measuring the spin "up" ($m_s = +\frac{1}{2}$) is $\frac{1}{2}$, as is the probability of measuring the spin "down" ($m_s = -\frac{1}{2}$).

Example 7–1   What are the eigenfunctions of L_{op}^2, $L_{z,op}$, S_{op}^2, and $S_{z,op}$ for the hydrogen atom in the state with $n = 2$ and $l = 1$? Let us ignore the normalization constants and the radial part of the wave function R_{nl}. For $l = 1$, there are three eigenfunctions of L_{op}^2 and $L_{z,op}$ corresponding to the values of $m_l = +1, 0, -1$. Since there are two spin eigenfunctions, there are six combinations, which are $f_{1,1}(\theta)e^{i\phi}\alpha$, $f_{1,0}(\theta)e^{0}\alpha$, $f_{1,1}(\theta)e^{-i\phi}\alpha$, $f_{1,1}(\theta)e^{i\phi}\beta$, $f_{1,0}(\theta)e^{0}\beta$, and $f_{1,1}(\theta)e^{-i\phi}\beta$.

*

7·7

THE ADDITION OF ANGULAR MOMENTUM

In general, the orbital angular momentum of the electron in an excited state of hydrogen is not zero. For other atoms, this angular momentum is often not zero even in the ground state. Thus, an electron in an atom generally has both orbital angular momentum **L** and spin angular momentum **S**. In classical mechanics, the total angular momentum is an important quantity, for the resultant torque on a system equals the rate of change of the total angular momentum. (An example of a classical system with two kinds of angular momentum analogous to orbital and spin is a precessing gyroscope, such as a spinning wheel pivoted at a point on the axle. In addition to the spin, there is angular momentum due to the precession of the wheel.) In classical mechanics, the total angular momentum of an electron would be just the vector sum of the orbital angular momentum **L** and the spin angular momentum **S**. We have already seen that, in quantum mechanics, angular momentum is more complicated. For example, both orbital and spin angular momenta are quantized, and their directions cannot be precisely specified.

The meaning of the statement "an electron has orbital angular momentum **L**" is that the wave function of the electron is an eigenfunction of $L_{\mathrm{op}}{}^{2}$ with eigenvalue $L^2 = l(l + 1)\hbar^2$. Let us define the operator for total angular momentum by

$$\mathbf{J}_{\mathrm{op}} = \mathbf{L}_{\mathrm{op}} + \mathbf{S}_{\mathrm{op}} \qquad (7\text{--}52)$$

Since **J** is an angular momentum, we expect it to obey quantum rules similar to those governing **L** and **S**; namely, we expect that the eigenvalues of $J_{\mathrm{op}}{}^{2}$ can be written $j(j + 1)\hbar^2$, where j is a quantum number, and that the eigenvalues of J_x are $m_j\hbar$, where m_j has the $2j + 1$ values from $+j$ to $-j$ in integral steps. This is indeed the case. We can find the values of the quantum number j by considering the z component of Eq. (7–52):

$$J_{z,\mathrm{op}} = L_{z,\mathrm{op}} + S_{z,\mathrm{op}} \qquad (7\text{--}53)$$

In terms of the eigenvalues, this equation is

$$m_j = m_l + m_s \qquad (7\text{--}54)$$

There are two possible values of m_s and $2l + 1$ possible values of m_l. The $2 \times (2l + 1)$ combinations are shown in Table 7–1 for

		\multicolumn{5}{c}{m_l for $l = 2$}
		$+2$	$+1$	0	-1	-2
m_s for $s = \frac{1}{2}$	$+\frac{1}{2}$	$2\frac{1}{2}$	$1\frac{1}{2}$	$\frac{1}{2}$	$-\frac{1}{2}$	$-1\frac{1}{2}$
	$-\frac{1}{2}$	$1\frac{1}{2}$	$\frac{1}{2}$	$-\frac{1}{2}$	$-1\frac{1}{2}$	$-2\frac{1}{2}$

table 7-1   *Possible combinations of $J_z = L_z + S_z$ for $l = 2$ and $s = \frac{1}{2}$.*

the special case of $l = 2$. The maximum value of m_j is $l + s$, which is $2\frac{1}{2}$ for this special case. If $j = 2\frac{1}{2}$, there should be $2j + 1 = 6$ values of m_j: $2\frac{1}{2}, 1\frac{1}{2}, \frac{1}{2}, -\frac{1}{2}, -1\frac{1}{2}, -2\frac{1}{2}$. We see from Table 7-1 that, in addition to these values, there are four other combinations corresponding to $j = 1\frac{1}{2}$. We can generalize this to any value of l. The possible values of j are given by

$$j = l + \tfrac{1}{2}$$

or

$$j = l - \tfrac{1}{2} \tag{7-55}$$

except if $l = 0$, in which case only $j = \frac{1}{2}$ is possible.

In Example 7-1 we saw that there were six eigenfunctions of $L_{op}{}^2$, $L_{z,op}$, $S_{op}{}^2$, and $S_{z,op}$, for $l = 1$ and $s = \frac{1}{2}$. These are not all eigenfunctions of $J_{op}{}^2$. However, there are six independent linear combinations of these eigenfunctions which are eigenfunctions of $J_{op}{}^2$. Four of these have the eigenvalue $j(j + 1)\hbar^2$ with $j = l + \frac{1}{2} = 1\frac{1}{2}$, and the other two with $j = l - \frac{1}{2} = \frac{1}{2}$. In order to find these linear combinations, we would have to go more deeply into the study of the angular-momentum operators than we can do here.

Equation (7-55) is a special case of a more general rule for combining two angular momenta; this is useful when dealing with more than one particle. For example, there are two electrons in the helium atom, each with spin, orbital, and total angular momenta. The rule for combining the angular momenta of two particles is obtained in a way similar to the way in which Eq. (7-55) was obtained. We shall merely state the general rule and give some examples.

If $\mathbf{J}_1$ is one angular momentum (orbital, spin, or a combination) and $\mathbf{J}_2$ is another, the resulting angular momentum $\mathbf{J} = \mathbf{J}_1 + \mathbf{J}_2$ has the value $\sqrt{j(j + 1)}\,\hbar$ for its magnitude, where j can be any of the values

$$j_1 + j_2, \; j_1 + j_2 - 1, \ldots, |j_1 - j_2| \tag{7-56}$$

Let us construct another table for a special case to see how this rule comes about. Let us consider the two orbital angular momenta with quantum numbers 1 and 2. Table 7–2 gives the possible combinations of z components. The z components corresponding to the resultant values of $j = 3$, $j = 2$, and $j = 1$ are indicated. We see that there are generally more than two possible values of j. It is left as a problem to show that the number of possible values of j is either $2j_1 + 1$ or $2j_2 + 1$, whichever is smaller.

Example 7–2 Find the possible values for the magnitude of the resultant angular momentum for two electrons, one with $j_1 = \frac{3}{2}$ and the other with $j_2 = \frac{5}{2}$. By our rule, Eq. (7–56), the possible values of the quantum number j range in integral steps from $j_1 + j_2 = 4$ to $|j_1 - j_2| = 1$. Thus j can be 4, 3, 2, or 1. The number of j values is $2j_1 + 1 = 4$, since $j_1 < j_2$. The possible magnitudes of the resultant angular momenta are

$$j = 4: \ J = \sqrt{j(j + 1)}\,\hbar = \sqrt{20}\,\hbar$$
$$j = 3: \ J = \sqrt{12}\,\hbar$$
$$j = 2: \ J = \sqrt{6}\,\hbar$$
$$j = 1: \ J = \sqrt{2}\,\hbar$$

*

THE VECTOR MODEL Because of the rather complicated rules obeyed by angular momenta in quantum mechanics, it is helpful to picture a semiclassical model. In Figure 7–3 we pictured the orbital angular momentum as a vector of magnitude $\sqrt{l(l + 1)}\,\hbar$, which could have $2l + 1$ orientations relative to the z axis corresponding to the values of the z component $m_l\hbar$. It is customary to think of this vector precessing about the z axis, for such a precession would take place in the presence of a magnetic field in the z direction because of the

table 7–2 Possible Combinations of $J_z = L_{z1} + L_{z2}$ for $l_1 = 2$ and $l_2 = 1$.

		m_{l1} for $l = 2$				
		+2	+1	0	−1	−2
m_{l2} for $l = 1$	+1	3	2	1	0	−1
	0	2	1	0	−1	−2
	−1	1	0	−1	−2	−3

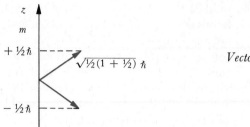

figure 7–17

Vector model illustrating
the possible values
of the z component
of spin-angular
momentum.

torque exerted on the magnetic moment. Figure 7–17 shows a similar vector-model picture for the spin vector. Since the magnitude of the spin is always $\sqrt{\frac{1}{2}(1 + \frac{1}{2})}\,\hbar$, the angle made with the z axis is given by $\cos\theta = \pm\frac{1}{2}/\sqrt{\frac{1}{2}(1 + \frac{1}{2})} = \pm 1/\sqrt{3}$.

Figure 7–18 illustrates the possible combinations of **L** and **S** to give **J** for the case $l = 1$, $s = \frac{1}{2}$. Figure 7–19 shows the combination of two spin vectors to give the possible resultant spins $S = 1$ and $S = 0$.

7·8
FINE STRUCTURE
OF HYDROGEN

Since the ground state of hydrogen is an S state ($l = 0$), the total angular-momentum quantum number has only the one value $j = \frac{1}{2}$. In spectroscopic notation, the j value of a level is written after the code letter indicating the l value; thus the ground state is written $1S_{1/2}$, where the 1 indicates the value of n. The first excited state has $n = 2$ and either $l = 0$ or $l = 1$. For $l = 0$ (S state), j must again be $\frac{1}{2}$; but for $l = 1$ (P state), j can be either $\frac{3}{2}$ or $\frac{1}{2}$. In general, all states except S states have the two possible values of j: $l + \frac{1}{2}$ or $l - \frac{1}{2}$. The $n = 2$ states are written $2S_{1/2}$, $2P_{3/2}$, and $2P_{1/2}$. As we have mentioned, when spin is neglected, the Schroedinger equation leads to degeneracy of the $2P$ and $2S$ states; i.e., they both have the same energy $E = -E_1/2^2 = 13.6/4 \approx$

figure 7–18   *Vector model illustrating the addition of orbital and spin angular momenta for the case $l = 1$ and $s = \frac{1}{2}$. There are two possible values of the quantum number for total angular momentum, $j = \frac{3}{2}$ and $j = \frac{1}{2}$.*

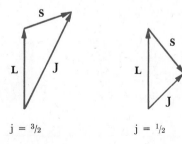

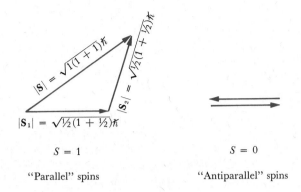

$S = 1$ $S = 0$

"Parallel" spins   "Antiparallel" spins

figure 7–19   *Vector model illustrating the addition of two spin-angular momenta, each*
with $s = \frac{1}{2}$.

3.4 eV. This degeneracy is due to the special nature of a $1/r^2$ force
and is not found in atoms other than hydrogen because of the
interactions of the other electrons. We mentioned in Chapter 4
that Sommerfeld's relativistic theory, based on the Bohr model,
predicted a separation of the $2P$ and $2S$ states of the order of magnitude of the square of the fine-structure constant

$$\left(\frac{e^2}{\hbar c}\right)^2 \approx \left(\frac{1}{137}\right)^2$$

We shall show in this section how the orientation of the electron's
spin magnetic moment relative to its orbital angular momentum
leads to a splitting of the $2P_{1/2}$ and $2P_{3/2}$ states. This splitting is
called *spin-orbit effect*. We shall use the Bohr model to get an estimate
of the order of magnitude of this splitting for hydrogen. For atoms
other than hydrogen, states with the same n but different l have
quite different energies due to the interactions of the other electrons.
Relativistic effects for other atoms are negligible, and the fine
structure is due solely to the spin-orbit effect. Hydrogen is somewhat more complicated. A complete relativistic treatment of hydrogen, using the Dirac relativistic wave equations, leads to the correct
splitting of the $2P_{1/2}$ and $2P_{3/2}$ states and predicts that states with
the same n and j values, such as the $2P_{1/2}$ and $2S_{1/2}$ states, have
the same energy.[6]

[6]If the magnetic moment of the electron were exactly 1 Bohr magneton—that
is, if g_s were exactly 2—the $2P_{1/2}$ and $2S_{1/2}$ states would be degenerate. A
quantum-electrodynamic correction leading to $g_s = 2.00232$, in agreement
with experiment, predicts a difference in these levels of about 10^{-6} eV. This
difference was accurately measured in 1951 by W. E. Lamb and is called the
Lamb shift.

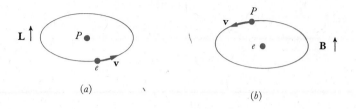

(a) (b)

figure 7–20   *An electron moving about a proton with angular momentum L up. The magnetic field seen by the electron due to the apparent relative motion of the proton (b) is also up, as indicated.*

Let us estimate the order of magnitude of the spin-orbit effect for the 2P state of hydrogen, using the Bohr model and neglecting relativity. Consider an electron moving with speed u in a circle of radius r about a fixed proton. We shall assume that the electron can be considered to be at rest and the proton moving with this speed at this radius. The current due to the moving proton is the charge times the frequency of revolution, $I = e(u/2\pi r)$. The magnetic field at the center of a circular loop carrying a current I is, in MKS units,

$$B = 10^{-7} \frac{2\pi I}{r} = 10^{-7} \frac{2\pi}{r} \frac{eu}{2\pi r} = \frac{10^{-7} eu}{r^2} \qquad (7\text{-}57)$$

The radius of the second Bohr orbit is $r = 2^2 a_0 = 2.12$ Å $= 2.12 \times 10^{-10}$ meter. The energy of this orbit is -3.4 eV, consisting of -6.8 eV potential energy and $+3.4$ eV kinetic energy. From $\frac{1}{2}mu^2 = 3.4$ eV, we can calculate the speed u. The result is $u = 1.1 \times 10^6$ m/sec. Putting these numbers into Eq. (7-57), we can get an order-of-magnitude estimate of the magnetic field seen by the electron. We have

$$B \approx \frac{10^{-7}(1.6 \times 10^{-19})1.1 \times 10^6}{(2.12 \times 10^{-10})2}$$

$$\approx 0.4 \text{ weber/m}^2 = 4 \times 10^3 \text{ gauss}$$

The energy of a magnetic moment $\boldsymbol{\mu}$ in a magnetic field $\mathbf{B}$ is $W = -\boldsymbol{\mu} \cdot \mathbf{B} = -\mu B \cos \theta$. The energy is least when $\boldsymbol{\mu}$ is parallel to $\mathbf{B}$. Since the charge of the electron is negative, its magnetic moment is in the direction opposite to that of its spin. From Figure 7–20, we see that the direction of the magnetic field seen by the electron is parallel to the orbital angular momentum $\mathbf{L}$. For the case $j = \frac{1}{2}$, the spin and orbital angular momenta are roughly antiparallel (see Figure 7–18); thus the magnetic moment of the electron

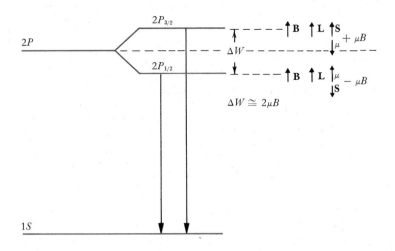

figure 7–21 *Fine-structure energy-level diagram. Because of the spin-orbit force, the $2P$ level is split into two energy levels, with the $j = \frac{3}{2}$ level having slightly greater energy than the $j = \frac{1}{2}$ level. The spectral line, due to the $2P$, $1S$ transition, is thus split into two lines of slightly different wavelengths.*

is roughly parallel to **L** and to **B**. We therefore see that the state $2P_{1/2}$ has a lower energy than the state $2P_{3/2}$, for which μ and **B** are roughly antiparallel. The order of magnitude of this energy splitting is

$$\Delta W \approx \mu B = (5.79 \times 10^{-9} \, \text{eV/gauss})(4 \times 10^3 \, \text{gauss})$$
$$\approx 2.3 \times 10^{-5} \, \text{eV}$$

This calculation is rather crude, but the result is not too different from the measured splitting of about 4.5×10^{-5} eV. We see that, compared with the energy differences of the order of several eV for states of different n, the spin-orbit, fine-structure splitting is quite small. For most other atoms, the fine-structure splitting is larger than that for hydrogen. The most familiar example is the sodium doublet. The two yellow lines, 5,890 Å and 5,896 Å, are due to transitions from the states $3P_{3/2}$ and $3P_{1/2}$ to the ground state $3S_{1/2}$ of the valence electron.

SUMMARY The Schroedinger equation in spherical coordinates can be written

$$-\frac{\hbar^2}{2M} \left[\frac{1}{r^2} \frac{d}{dr} \left(r^2 \frac{d\psi}{dr} \right) \right] + \frac{L_{\text{op}}^2}{2Mr^2} \psi + V\psi = E\psi$$

where L_{op}^2 is the operator corresponding to the square of the angular momentum. When the potential energy is independent of θ and ϕ, the wave function is an eigenfunction of L_{op}^2 and $L_{z,op}$; thus the square of the angular momentum is quantized to the eigenvalues $l(l + 1)\hbar^2$, $l = 0, 1, \ldots$, and the z component is quantized to the eigenvalues $m_l\hbar$, where $m_l = 0, \pm 1, \ldots, \pm l$.

The allowed values of the energy for the hydrogen-atom potential

$$V(r) = -\frac{KZe^2}{r}$$

are the same as given by the Bohr model:

$$E_n = -\frac{Z^2 E_1}{n^2} \qquad \text{where } E_1 = \frac{mk^2 e^4}{2\hbar^2} \text{ and } n = 1, 2, \ldots$$

The values of l in the hydrogen atom are restricted to $l < n$. The hydrogen-atom wave functions vary as r^l near the origin. The probability density is large in the region of the Bohr orbits $r = n^2 a_0$.

Electric-dipole transitions in hydrogen obey the selection rules $\Delta l = \pm 1$ and $\Delta m_l = \pm 1$ or 0.

The electron has, in addition to its orbital angular momentum, an intrinsic angular momentum called *spin* of magnitude $\sqrt{s(s + 1)}\,\hbar$, where $s = \frac{1}{2}$. The magnetic moment associated with orbital angular momentum is

$$\boldsymbol{\mu}_l = -\frac{e\hbar}{2m_e}\frac{\mathbf{L}}{\hbar}$$

and that associated with spin angular momentum is

$$\boldsymbol{\mu}_s = -2\frac{e\hbar}{2m_e}\frac{\mathbf{S}}{\hbar}$$

The quantity

$$\mu_B = \frac{e\hbar}{2m_e}$$

is called a *Bohr magneton*.

The result of combining two angular moments $\mathbf{J} = \mathbf{J}_1 + \mathbf{J}_2$ is quantized to the values $\sqrt{j(j + 1)}\,\hbar$, where j can be any of the values $j_1 + j_2, j_1 + j_2 - 1, \ldots, |j_1 - j_2|$. The z component of $\mathbf{J}$ follows the usual rule for angular momenta. J_z can have any of the $2j + 1$ values from $+j\hbar$ to $-j\hbar$ in integral steps of $\hbar$. For the case $\mathbf{J} = \mathbf{L} + \mathbf{S}$ where $s = \frac{1}{2}$, these rules allow the two values of j, $j = l + \frac{1}{2}$ or $j = l - \frac{1}{2}$.

If $j = l + \frac{1}{2}$, the spin and orbital angular momenta are said to be parallel, while for $j = l - \frac{1}{2}$, they are said to be antiparallel. Because of the small interaction of the electron's spin magnetic moment with the internal magnetic field (the field is seen because of the electron's orbital motion), the state with the higher j value is slightly higher in energy than that with the same n and l values but lower j value. This splitting in the energy levels causes a splitting in the spectral lines called *fine-structure splitting*.

REFERENCES   1. G. Herzberg, *Atomic Spectra and Atomic Structure*, Dover Publications, Inc., New York, 1944.
   2. L. Pauling and E. B. Wilson, *Introduction to Quantum Mechanics*, McGraw-Hill Book Company, New York, 1935.

See also the references in Chapter 6.

PROBLEMS   SET A

7–1. If a rigid body has moment of inertia I and angular velocity ω, its kinetic energy of rotation is

$$E = \tfrac{1}{2}I\omega^2 = \frac{(I\omega)^2}{2I} = \frac{L^2}{2I}$$

where L is the angular momentum. The Schroedinger equation for the body,

$$\frac{1}{2I} L_{op}^{\;2}\psi(\theta,\phi) = E\psi(\theta,\phi)$$

was solved in Section 7–4.

(a) What are the possible values of the energies of rotation E_l for the body?

(b) Draw an energy-level diagram and indicate the transitions allowed by the selection rule $\Delta l = \pm 1$.

(c) The separation of the protons in the H_2 molecule is about $r = 0.74$ Å. The moment of inertia about the center of mass is $I = \tfrac{1}{2}m_p r^2$, where m_p is the mass of the proton. What is the energy of rotation for the first excited state $l = 1$ for H_2?

(d) What is the wavelength of the radiation emitted in the transition $l = 1$ to $l = 0$?

7–2. The moment of inertia of a record is about 10^{-3} kg-m^2.

(a) If it is rotation with $\omega/2\pi = 33\tfrac{1}{3}$/min, what is the approximate value of the angular-momentum quantum number l?

(b) What is the least value (greater than zero) of $2\pi\omega$ in rev/min that the record can have?

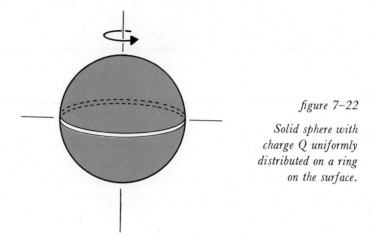

figure 7–22

Solid sphere with charge Q uniformly distributed on a ring on the surface.

7–3. Show that the most probable value of r for the ground-state hydrogen atom is $r_m = a_0/Z$.

7–4. Show that the functions $\sin m_l \phi$ and $\cos m_l \phi$ are *not* eigenfunctions of L_z but that each is a linear combination of eigenfunctions.

7–5. If a classical system does not have a constant charge-to-mass ratio throughout the system, the magnetic moment can be written

$$\mathbf{u} = g \frac{Q}{2M} \mathbf{L}$$

where Q is the total charge, M the mass, and $g \neq 1$.

(a) Show that $g = 2$ for a solid cylinder $(I = \frac{1}{2}MR^2)$ that spins about its axis and has a uniform charge on the cylindrical surface.

(b) Find g for a solid sphere $(I = \frac{2}{5}MR^2)$ which has a ring of charge on the surface, as shown in Figure 7–22.

7–6. A hydrogen atom is in a $3D$ state $(n = 3, l = 2)$.

(a) What are the possible values of the *magnitude* of the total angular momentum, including spin?

(b) What are the possible z components of the total angular momentum?

7–7. A deuteron (nucleus with one proton and one neutron, each with spin $\frac{1}{2}$) has $l = 0$ and $s = 1$.

(a) What is the magnitude of the angular momentum of the deuteron?

(b) What is the angle made between the spins of the neutron and proton?

(c) What is the angle between the spin of the deuteron and the z axis when $m = 1$?

7-8. Construct a table, similar to Tables 7-1 and 7-2, of the possible values of m_l for the case $\mathbf{L} = \mathbf{L}_1 + \mathbf{L}_2$, where $l_1 = 2$ and $l_2 = 3$, and indicate the values corresponding to the possible values of l.

7-9. There are two electrons, each with $l = 1$ and $s = \frac{1}{2}$.

   (a) Neglecting spin, what are the possible values of the quantum number l for the total orbital angular momentum?

   (b) What are the possible values of the quantum number S for the total spin?

   (c) Using the results of parts a and b, find the possible quantum numbers j for the combination $\mathbf{J} = \mathbf{L} + \mathbf{S}$.

   (d) What are the possible quantum numbers j_1 and j_2 for the total angular momentum for *each* particle?

   (e) Use the results of part d to calculate the possible values of j from the combination of j_1 and j_2. Are these the same as in part c?

7-10. An electron has orbital quantum number $l = 2$ and spin $s = \frac{1}{2}$. Draw a vector diagram of $\mathbf{J} = \mathbf{L} + \mathbf{S}$ roughly to scale. On the same diagram indicate the magnetic moment $\boldsymbol{\mu}_j = \boldsymbol{\mu}_l + \boldsymbol{\mu}_s$ and show that $\boldsymbol{\mu}_j$ is not parallel to $\mathbf{J}$.

7-11. A convenient unit for the magnetic moment of nuclei is the nuclear magneton $e\hbar/2m_p$, where m_p is the mass of the proton. Calculate the magnitude of the nuclear magneton in eV/gauss.

SET B

7-12. Separate the three-dimensional Schroedinger equation (7-1) in rectangular coordinates for the case when the potential energy can be written $V(x,y,z) = V_1(x) + V_2(y) + V_3(z)$, and obtain three equations of the form

$$-\frac{\hbar^2}{2m} f''(x) + V_1(x)f(x) = E_1 f(x)$$

where the wave function is $\psi(x,y,z) = f(x)g(y)h(z)$ and the total energy is $E = E_1 + E_2 + E_3$.

   Using these results to solve the problem of a three-dimensional, infinite, cubic square well,

$$V_1(x) = 0 \qquad \text{for } |x| \leq a$$
$$V_1(x) = \infty \qquad \text{for } |x| > a$$

with similar equations for y and z,

   (a) What is the ground-state wave function?

(b) Show that the allowed energies are given by

$$E = (n_1{}^2 + n_2{}^2 + n_3{}^2) \frac{h^2}{32ma^2}$$

where n_1, n_2, n_3 are integers.

7–13. (a) Show that the expectation value of r for the ground-state hydrogen atom is $\langle r \rangle = \frac{3}{2}a_0/Z$.

(b) Show that the expectation value of r^{-1} for the ground-state hydrogen atom is $\langle r^{-1} \rangle = (a_0/Z)^{-1}$.

7–14. Show by substitution that the first excited state of the hydrogen atom with $l = 0$ [Eq. (7–39)] satisfies the radial part of the Schroedinger equation (7–30).

7–15. The radius of a proton is about $R_0 = 10^{-13}$ cm. The probability that the hydrogen-atom electron is inside the proton is

$$p = \int_0^{R_0} P(r) \, dr$$

where $P(r)$ is the probability density [Eq. (7–38)]. Calculate the probability that, in the ground state, the electron is inside the proton. (Hint: Show that the approximation $e^{-r/a_0} \approx 1$ is valid for this calculation.)

7–16. Legendre's equation (7–25) for $m = 0$ is $(1 - u^2)f'' - 2uf' + \alpha f = 0$.

(a) Show that $f_3 = u + a_3u^3$ is a solution if $\alpha = 12 = 3(3 + 1)$, and find a_3.

(b) Show that $f_4 = 1 + a_2u^2 + a_4u^4$ is a solution if $\alpha = 20 = 4(4 + 1)$, and find a_2 and a_4.

7–17. The *Legendre polynomials* $P_n(u)$ are proportional to the solutions of Eq. 7–25, f_n, found in Section 7·3 and in Problem 7–16.

$$P_n(u) = C_n f_n(u)$$

Determine C_n for f_1, f_2, f_3, and f_4 from the condition $P(1) = 1$.

7–18. Show by substitution that the functions $f_{l|m|}(\theta)e^{im\phi}$, where $f_{l|m|}(\theta)$ are given by Eq. (7–22), are eigenfunctions of $L_{op}{}^2$ given by Eq. (7–10). [Doing this problem for each of the six functions given in Eq. (7–22) involves a considerable amount of tedious algebra. The writing can be shortened somewhat by using a simplified notation, such as $u = \cos \theta$, $v = \sin \theta$, $u' = -v$, $v' = u$, and remembering that $u^2 + v^2 = 1$.]

7–19. If the angular momentum of the nucleus is $\mathbf{I}$ and that of the atomic electrons is $\mathbf{J}$, the total angular momentum of the atom is $\mathbf{F} = \mathbf{I} + \mathbf{J}$.

    (a) What are the possible quantum numbers f for the total angular momentum of the hydrogen atom in the ground state? (The proton has spin $\frac{1}{2}$.)

    (b) Explain why two spots are seen in the Stern-Gerlach experiment for hydrogen, even though the total angular momentum f is not $\frac{1}{2}$. (See Problem 7–11.)

7–20. Show that the number of possible values for the quantum number j for the total angular momentum $\mathbf{J} = \mathbf{J}_1 + \mathbf{J}_2$ is

    (a) $2j_1 + 1$ if $j_1 < j_2$.

    (b) $2j_2 + 1$ if $j_2 < j_1$.

(Because of the very small interaction of the nuclear magnetic moment with that of the electrons, a hyperfine splitting of the spectral lines is observed. When $I < J$, the value of I can be determined by counting the number of lines.)

EIGHT
ATOMIC SYSTEMS WITH MORE THAN ONE PARTICLE

The application of quantum mechanics to atoms with two or more electrons is complicated by the interaction of the electrons with each other and by the fact that the electrons are identical. The interaction of the electrons with each other is electromagnetic and is just that expected classically for two charged particles (except for the effect of spin). The Schroedinger equation for an atom with two or more electrons cannot be solved exactly, and approximate methods must be used. However, this is not too different from the situation in classical problems with three or more particles.

The complications arising because of the identity of electrons are purely quantum-mechanical and have no classical counterpart. They are due essentially to the fact that it is impossible to keep track of which electron is which. Classically, identical particles can be identified by their positions, which can be determined with unlimited accuracy. This is impossible quantum-mechanically because of the uncertainty principle. Figure 8–1 is a schematic illustration of the problem. In *a*, the particles come close to each other and then

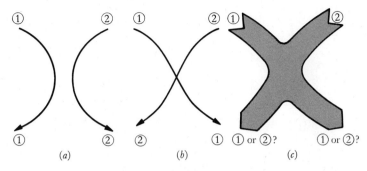

figure 8–1   *Two possible classical electron paths are shown in (a) and (b). The electrons can be distinguished classically. Because of the wave properties of the electrons, the paths are uncertain, as indicated by the shaded region in (c). Thus it is impossible to distinguish which electron is which after they separate.*

separate, while in *b*, their paths cross. In *c*, the particles are represented by shaded regions corresponding to the uncertainty in their positions. (The corresponding uncertainty in their momenta has been omitted for simplicity.) There is no way, even in principle, to know which particle is which after they separate. It might be expected that the inability to distinguish identical particles would have but minor consequences, but this is not the case. As we shall see, this effect is connected with the Pauli exclusion principle, which is of major importance in determining the properties of atoms, nuclei, and matter in bulk. We shall begin by considering a simple case which brings out the important features of the problem of identical particles without involving any complicated mathematics.

8·1
EXCHANGE SYMMETRY OF WAVE FUNCTIONS FOR TWO PARTICLES

For simplicity, we shall consider the particles to be noninteracting and we shall neglect spin. Let $\Psi(x_1,x_2)$ be the time-independent wave function for the two particles, where x_1 is the position of particle 1 and x_2 that of particle 2. The probability of finding particle 1 in dx_1 at x_1 and particle 2 in dx_2 at x_2 is thus

$$|\Psi(x_1,x_2)|^2 \, dx_1 \, dx_2$$

Although we have numbered the particles for this discussion, their identity imposes the restriction on the wave function that this numbering can have no physical consequence; i.e., if we interchange the labels, the probability cannot change. Thus

$$|\Psi(x_1,x_2)|^2 \, dx_1 \, dx_2 = |\Psi(x_2,x_1)|^2 \, dx_1 \, dx_2 \tag{8–1}$$

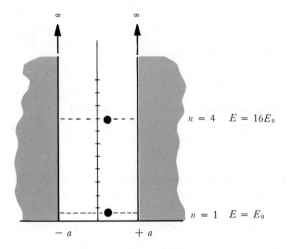

figure 8-2 *Two identical particles in a square well. One is in the state n = 4, and the other in the state n = 1, but it is impossible to distinguish which particle is in which state.*

Equation (8–1) holds if

$$\Psi(x_2,x_1) = +\Psi(x_1,x_2) \qquad \text{symmetric} \qquad (8\text{–}2)$$

or

$$\Psi(x_2,x_1) = -\Psi(x_1,x_2) \qquad \text{antisymmetric} \qquad (8\text{–}3)$$

Example 8–1   Let us consider two identical particles in the infinite square well:

$$V(x) = 0 \qquad \text{for } -a < x < +a$$
$$V(x) = \infty \qquad \text{for } |x| > a$$

Because the well is infinite, the particles are confined to the region $-a < x < +a$, where the classical expression for the energy is

$$E = \frac{P_1{}^2}{2m} + \frac{P_2{}^2}{2m}$$

The time-independent Schroedinger equation for this system is

$$\left(\frac{P_{1,\text{op}}^2}{2m} + \frac{P_{2,\text{op}}^2}{2m}\right)\Psi(x_1,x_2) = E\Psi(x_1,x_2) \qquad (8\text{–}4)$$

where $P_{1,op} = (\hbar/i)(\partial/\partial x_1)$ and $P_{2,op} = (\hbar/i)(\partial/\partial x_2)$. Thus

$$-\frac{\hbar^2}{2m}\frac{\partial^2\Psi}{\partial x_1{}^2} - \frac{\hbar^2}{2m}\frac{\partial^2\Psi}{\partial x_2{}^2} = E\Psi \tag{8-5}$$

We can separate the variables as usual by putting $\Psi(x_1,x_2) = \psi(x_1)\psi(x_2)$, dividing by $\psi(x_1)\psi(x_2)$, and transposing one term to yield

$$-\frac{\hbar^2}{2m}\frac{\psi''(x_1)}{\psi(x_1)} = E + \frac{\hbar^2}{2m}\frac{\psi''(x_2)}{\psi(x_2)} \tag{8-6}$$

Each side of Eq. (8-6) must equal a constant, which we shall call E_1. We then have the two equations

$$-\frac{\hbar^2}{2m}\psi''(x_1) = E_1\psi(x_1) \tag{8-7}$$

$$-\frac{\hbar^2}{2m}\psi''(x_2) = (E - E_1)\psi(x_2) = E_2\psi(x_2) \tag{8-8}$$

where $E_2 = E - E_1$. Solutions of these equations, which are zero at the edges of the well, have already been discussed in Chapter 6. They are

$$\psi_n(x) = a^{-1/2}\cos\frac{n\pi x}{2a} \qquad \text{for } n = 1, 3, 5, \ldots$$

$$\psi_n(x) = a^{-1/2}\sin\frac{n\pi x}{2a} \qquad \text{for } n = 2, 4, 6, \ldots$$

with $E_n = n^2 E_0$, $E_0 = \hbar^2\pi^2/8ma^2$. The total wave function is thus

$$\Psi_{n_1 n_2}(x_1,x_2) = C\psi_{n_1}(x_1)\psi_{n_2}(x_2) \tag{8-9}$$

where C is a normalization constant. The total energy is just $E = E_1 + E_2 = (n_1{}^2 + n_2{}^2)E_0$. An example with $n_1 = 1$ and $n_2 = 4$ is

$$\Psi_{1,4} = C\cos\frac{\pi x_1}{2a}\sin\frac{4\pi x_2}{2a} \tag{8-10}$$

with $E = (1 + 16)E_0 = 17E_0$. It is clear that $\Psi_{1,4}$ does not satisfy either of the conditions (8-2) or (8-3); that is, $\Psi_{1,4}$ is neither symmetric nor antisymmetric, for

$$\Psi_{4,1} = C\sin\frac{4\pi x_1}{2a}\cos\frac{\pi x_2}{2a} \neq \pm\Psi_{1,4}$$

Note that if the functions $\Psi_{1,4}$ and $\Psi_{4,1}$ are added or subtracted, we do obtain a symmetric or an antisymmetric function. If we add them, we obtain

$$\Psi_S(x_1,x_2) = \Psi_{1,4} + \Psi_{4,1} \qquad (8\text{--}11)$$

$$= C\left(\cos\frac{\pi x_1}{2a}\sin\frac{4\pi x_2}{2a} + \cos\frac{\pi x_2}{2a}\sin\frac{4\pi x_1}{2a}\right)$$

which is clearly symmetric upon exchange of x_1 and x_2. If the plus signs in Eq. (8–11) are replaced by minus signs, the function is antisymmetric. We know from the superposition principle that Eq. (8–11) satisfies the Schroedinger equation.

*

The Schroedinger equation for two noninteracting particles can always be separated as was done in the above example if the potential energy can be written $V(x_1,x_2) = V_1(x_1) + V_2(x_2)$. The equations analogous to Eqs. (8–7) and (8–8) are then

$$-\frac{\hbar^2}{2m}\psi''(x_1) + V_1(x_1)\psi(x_1) = E_1\psi(x_1) \qquad (8\text{--}12)$$

and

$$-\frac{\hbar^2}{2m}\psi''(x_2) + V_2(x_2)\psi(x_2) = E_2\psi(x_2) \qquad (8\text{--}13)$$

The solutions $\psi_n(x_1)$ and $\psi_n(x_2)$ are called *single-particle wave functions*. From such wave functions we can always construct a symmetric total-wave function

$$\Psi_S = C_S[\psi_{n_1}(x_1)\psi_{n_2}(x_2) + \psi_{n_1}(x_2)\psi_{n_2}(x_1)] \qquad (8\text{--}14)$$

and an antisymmetric total-wave function

$$\Psi_A = C_A[\psi_{n_1}(x_1)\psi_{n_2}(x_2) - \psi_{n_1}(x_2)\psi_{n_2}(x_1)] \qquad (8\text{--}15)$$

Note that we have, in general, two quite different possibilities, ψ_S or ψ_A for the wave function for two particles. As an example of the differences in Ψ_S and Ψ_A, consider the case where both particles have the same quantum numbers. For $n_1 = n_2$, Ψ_A is identically zero for all x_1, x_2, whereas Ψ_S is not. Nonrelativistic quantum theory gives no indication as to whether two identical particles should have a symmetric or antisymmetric wave function, but experiment does. Experiments with electrons show that two electrons cannot have the same quantum numbers; therefore electrons

figure 8–3

George Gamow and Wolfgang Pauli on a Swiss lake in 1930. (Courtesy of George Gamow.)

must have antisymmetric wave functions. This is an example of the Pauli exclusion principle stated in 1925 for electrons in atoms:

> *No two electrons in an atom can be in the same quantum state. Since each atomic quantum state is characterized by a set of quantum numbers (n, l, m_l, m_s) an alternative statement is that no two electrons can have the same set of quantum numbers.*

Not all particles obey the exclusion principle. Particles that do obey it have antisymmetric wave functions, while those that do not, have symmetric wave functions. There is an important connection between the intrinsic spin of a particle and the exchange symmetry of wave functions describing systems of the particles. We quote from Wolfgang Pauli, Nobel Prize address, Stockholm, 1945:[1]

"In order to prepare for the discussion of more fundamental questions, we want to stress here a law of Nature which is generally valid, namely, the connection between spin and symmetry class.

[1] *Nobel Prize Lectures: Physics,* Elsevier Publishing Company, Amsterdam, New York. © Nobel Foundation, 1964.

A *half-integer value of the spin quantum number is always connected with antisymmetrical states (exclusion principle), an integer spin with symmetrical states.* This law holds not only for protons and neutrons but also for photons and electrons. Moreover, it holds for compound systems, if it holds for all of its constituents. If we search for a theoretical explanation of this law, we must pass to the discussion of relativistic wave mechanics, since we saw that it can certainly not be explained by nonrelativistic wave mechanics."

8·2

SYMMETRY OF SPIN FUNCTIONS

Since the particles that have antisymmetric wave functions always have half-integer spin, the example in the previous section does not conform with any real situation. We now want to consider the wave function for two identical particles such as electrons, each of which has the spin quantum number $s = \frac{1}{2}$. In Chapter 7 we used α and β to denote the spin eigenfunctions of a particle corresponding to spin up ($m_s = +\frac{1}{2}$) and spin down ($m_s = -\frac{1}{2}$), respectively. The eigenfunctions for the resultant spin of two particles consist of linear combinations of the four products $\alpha_1\alpha_2$, $\alpha_1\beta_2$, $\beta_1\alpha_2$, and $\beta_1\beta_2$, where the subscript denotes particle 1 or particle 2. Note that two of these products, $\alpha_1\alpha_2$ and $\beta_1\beta_2$, are symmetric upon exchange of the subscripts. From the other two products, a symmetric combination $\alpha_1\beta_2 + \alpha_2\beta_1$ and an antisymmetric combination $\alpha_1\beta_2 - \alpha_2\beta_1$ can be formed. Thus there are three symmetric combinations and one antisymmetric combination. According to the rules for combining angular momentum, stated on page 306, the quantum number S for the resultant spin of two particles, each with $s = \frac{1}{2}$, can have the possible values $S = 1$ or $S = 0$. It is customary to describe the spins as being parallel when $S = 1$ and antiparallel when $S = 0$. (See Figure 7–19.) For $S = 1$, there are three values of m_s, $+1$, 0, and -1; while for $S = 0$, there is only one value, $m_s = 0$. *The three-spin eigenfunctions corresponding to spin $S = 1$ are symmetric, and the one-spin eigenfunction corresponding to spin $S = 0$ is antisymmetric.* [In order to prove that the three symmetric combinations are indeed eigenfunctions of the operator $S_{op}^2 = (\mathbf{S}_{1,op} + \mathbf{S}_{2,op})^2$ with eigenvalue $\sqrt{1(1 + 1)}^2$, we would need to go more deeply into the properties of these operators. The result stated above should be plausible since there must be three eigenfunctions for $S = 1$ corresponding to the three values of m_s; there are, in fact, three symmetric eigenfunctions and just one that is antisymmetric.] Let us call the spin function for two electrons χ_A for the antisymmetric state $S = 0$ and χ_S for the symmetric state $S = 1$. We can write the total wave function for two spin-$\frac{1}{2}$ particles as the product of a "space function" $\psi(x_1,x_2)$ and a spin function χ:

$$\Psi_T = \Psi(x_1,x_2)\chi$$

If we exchange the labels on the particles, the total wave function will be antisymmetric if either the space part is antisymmetric *and* the spin part symmetric or the space part is symmetric *and* the spin part antisymmetric. If both the space part and the spin part are symmetric or both are antisymmetric, the total wave function will be symmetric. Thus the total wave function for two electrons must be either

$$\Psi_T = \Psi_A(x_1, x_2)\chi_S \qquad (8\text{-}16)$$

or

$$\Psi_T = \Psi_S(x_1, x_2)\chi_A \qquad (8\text{-}17)$$

We see that because of the two possible symmetries of the spin functions, the *space* function for two electrons may be either symmetric or antisymmetric. The symmetry character of the space part of the wave function has important consequences. If we examine the symmetric and antisymmetric *space* wave functions given by Eq. (8-14) and (8-15), we can see that if $x_1 = x_2$, $\Psi_A(x_1, x_2)$ is identically zero, whereas $\Psi_S(x_1, x_2)$ is not. If $|x_1 - x_2|$ is small, $\Psi_A(x_1, x_2)$ will, in general, be much smaller in magnitude than $\Psi_S(x_1, x_2)$. The expectation value of $|x_1 - x_2|$ is in general smaller for electrons with symmetric space functions than for those with antisymmetric space functions. Thus, if the space function for two electrons is symmetric, the electrons will be closer together on the average than if their space function is antisymmetric. Since electrons repel each other and the positive repulsion energy is inversely proportional to their separation, the interaction energy of two electrons will, in general, be greater for symmetric space functions than for antisymmetric space functions, other things being equal. We shall see that this result is important for understanding atomic spectra.

For our example of two spin-$\frac{1}{2}$ particles in a square well, the state of each particle is described by the quantum numbers n and m_s. The requirement that the total wave function be antisymmetric is equivalent to the requirement that the two particles cannot have identical quantum numbers. The quantum numbers n_1 and n_2 can be equal only for symmetric wave functions [by Eq. (8-15), $\Psi_A = 0$ if $n_1 = n_2$]; thus the spin function must be antisymmetric corresponding to $S = 0$. If $S = 0$, m_{s_1} cannot equal m_{s_2}. It is customary, and simpler, not to include the spin functions explicitly in the wave function but merely to require that two particles in the same space state $n_1 = n_2$ have different spin quantum numbers $m_{s_1} \neq m_{s_2}$.

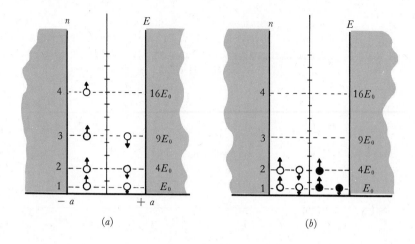

figure 8-4 (a) *Seven neutrons in an infinite square well. In accordance with the exclusion principle, only two neutrons can be in a given space state. The total energy is* $16E_0 + (2 \times 9E_0) + (2 \times 4E_0) + (2 \times 1E_0) = 44E_0$. (b) *Four neutrons and three protons in the same infinite square well. Because protons and neutrons are not identical, four particles (two neutrons and two protons) can be in the state* $n = 1$. *The total energy is* $(3 \times 4E_0) + (4 \times 1E_0) = 16E_0$. *This is much less than in* (a).

8·3

SYSTEMS WITH THREE OR MORE PARTICLES

The total wave function for three or more particles must be antisymmetric upon exchange of any two particles. As discussed above, this is equivalent to saying that no two particles can have the same quantum numbers. Since there are only two possibilities for m_s — namely, $+\frac{1}{2}$ or $-\frac{1}{2}$ — this means that there can be only two particles in one space state. When a particular space state is filled with two particles, the total spin must be zero.

Example 8-2 Find the minimum energy of seven noninteracting neutrons in a one-dimensional, infinite square well of length L. The single-particle energy levels are given by $E_n = n^2 E_0$, where $E_0 = h^2/8mL^2$ and n is the quantum number. Since only two neutrons can have a particular quantum number, the least energetic arrangement consistent with the uncertainty principle is two neutrons with $n = 1$, two with $n = 2$, two with $n = 3$, and one with $n = 4$, giving a total energy of

$$E = 2(1)^2 E_0 + 2(2)^2 E_0 + 2(3)^2 E_0 + 1(4)^2 E_0 = 44E_0$$

The resultant spin of this state is $s = \frac{1}{2}$, due to the unpaired neutron since the spins of the other six add to zero in pairs.

*

Example 8-3   Find the minimum energy of four neutrons and three protons (assumed to be noninteracting) in the same square well.

Because a proton is *not* identical to a neutron, we can have a proton and a neutron with the same quantum numbers. The least energetic arrangement is two neutrons and two protons with $n = 1$ and two neutrons and the other proton with $n = 2$, giving for the total energy

$$E = 4(1)^2 E_0 + 3(2)^2 E_0 = 16 E_0$$

Thus (neglecting the repulsion of the protons), considerably less energy is needed to put four neutrons and three protons in a well than to put seven neutrons in a well. The spin of this state must also be $\frac{1}{2}$ due to the unpaired neutron.

*

We can understand from these simple examples why the numbers of neutrons and protons are approximately equal in stable nuclei.

8·4
INTERACTIONS
OF PARTICLES

In the examples we have discussed so far, we have assumed that the particles do not interact with each other. The Schroedinger equation could be separated into individual equations for each particle and the total wave function obtained by taking combinations of individual-particle wave functions, such as Eq. (8–11) in Example 8–1. If the particles interact with each other, the problem is much more difficult. Let us consider again the example of two particles in a one-dimensional, infinite square well. We shall assume that the potential energy of interaction is $Ke^2/|x_1 - x_2|$, which is the one-dimensional form of Coulomb's law for two electrons or protons. The classical expression for the energy of this system for $-a < x < +a$ is

$$E = \frac{P_1{}^2}{2m} + \frac{P_2{}^2}{2m} + \frac{Ke^2}{|x_1 - x_2|}$$

The Schroedinger equation for this problem is

$$\left(\frac{P_{1,op}^2}{2m} + \frac{P_{2,op}^2}{2m} \right) \Psi(x_1,x_2) + \frac{Ke^2}{|x_1 - x_2|} \Psi(x_1,x_2)$$
$$= E\Psi(x_1,x_2) \qquad (8\text{--}18)$$

Unlike Eq. (8–4), this equation cannot be solved by separation of the variables x_1 and x_2 because of the interaction term, which contains both variables. In fact, Eq. (8–15) cannot be solved exactly by any method; thus an approximation technique must be used. We shall discuss a method of approximation which is not necessarily the most accurate method of obtaining the energy eigenvalues for a particular problem, but it is useful for the general understanding of the energy levels of atomic systems. The method is as follows:

1. Neglect the interaction term. The Schroedinger equation can then be separated and solved. Symmetric and antisymmetric space-wave functions can be obtained from combinations of products of single-particle wave functions. For the example of two particles in an infinite square well, the Schroedinger equation, neglecting the interaction term, is Eq. (8–4), which was solved in Example 8–1. The lowest-energy solution for this case is for $n_1 = n_2 = 1$, for which case the ground-state wave function is

$$\Psi(x_1, x_2) = C \cos \frac{\pi x_1}{2a} \cos \frac{\pi x_2}{2a}$$

and the energy is $E_{1,1} = E_1 + E_1 = 2E_1$. Since the space part of the ground-state wave function is symmetric, the spin must be 0.

2. Use the wave function obtained to calculate the expectation value of the interaction energy, and add this to the energy obtained by neglecting the interaction energy. For the Coulomb repulsion-interaction energy in Eq. (8–18), this correction would be

$$E_{\text{int}} = \left\langle \frac{Ke^2}{|x_1 - x_2|} \right\rangle = \iint \Psi^* \frac{Ke^2}{|x_1 - x_2|} \Psi \, dx_1 \, dx_2$$

It should be noted that this is an approximation because the wave function used to calculate the energy of interaction is only an approximate solution of Eq. (8–18), i.e., it is the solution obtained neglecting the interaction term. The approximation will be good if the magnitude of the correction E_{int} is small compared with the total energy.

We do not need to go into any of the involved details of an actual application of this method, which is known as the *time-independent perturbation theory*. With only a qualitative understanding of this method, we can comprehend many of the important features of the energy levels in atoms, which we shall discuss in the next three sections.

We can now discuss, qualitatively, the wave functions and energy levels for atoms more complicated than the hydrogen atom. We shall discuss the ground states of atoms in this section and consider the excited states and spectra for some of the less complicated cases in the next two sections. To a good approximation, we can describe the wave function for a complicated atom, using single-particle wave functions obtained by neglecting the interaction energy of the electrons. These wave functions are just those obtained for the hydrogen atom except that Z is not equal to 1. The states of the electrons can be characterized by the quantum numbers n and l, corresponding to the radial and orbital angular momentum quantum numbers of the states in the hydrogen atom. This specification of n and l for each electron in an atom is called the *electron configuration*. The specification of l is customarily done by giving a letter rather than the value. The code is:

Letter: s p d f g h
l value: 0 1 2 3 4 5

This is the same code as that used to label the states of the hydrogen atom. The n values are referred to as shells; $n = 1$ is called the K shell, $n = 2$ the L shell, and so on.

Helium $(Z = 2)$

If we neglect the interaction of the electrons, the Schroedinger equation for the helium atom can be separated into two equations, one for each electron. Each equation is identical to that for the hydrogen atom except that $Z = 2$. The energy eigenvalues are given by

$$E = -\frac{Z^2 E_1}{n_1{}^2} - \frac{Z^2 E_1}{n_2{}^2} \qquad \text{where } E_1 = 13.6 \text{ eV}$$

The lowest energy, $E_0 = -2(2)^2 E_1 \approx -108.8$ eV, occurs for $n_1 = n_2 = 1$. For this case, $l_1 = l_2 = 0$. The total wave function is antisymmetrical if the total spin for the two electrons is zero. If the approximate ground-state wave function

$$\psi_{100}(r_1,\theta_1,\phi_1)\psi_{100}(r_2,\theta_2,\phi_2)$$

is used to calculate the expectation value of the interaction energy of the two electrons, the result is $E_{\text{int}} \approx +34$ eV. With this correction, the ground-state energy is $E \approx -108.8 + 34 = -74.8$ eV. The experimental value of the energy needed to remove both electrons is about 79 eV. The discrepancy between this result and the

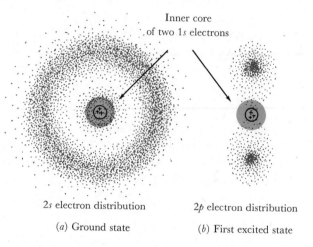

Inner core
of two 1s electrons

2s electron distribution   2p electron distribution

(a) Ground state   (b) First excited state

figure 8–5   *Quantum-mechanical model of the lithium atom. The outer electron is shielded by the inner core of two 1s electrons (shaded circle). The distribution function for the outer electron is indicated by the dots for the 2s state in (a) and for the 2p state in (b). In the 2s state, the distribution function penetrates the inner core more than it does in the 2p state. Thus, the effective nuclear charge is greater for the 2s state, and this state has a lower energy. (The size of the nucleus has been greatly exaggerated relative to the electron distributions in order to indicate the positive charge. On this scale the nucleus would not be visible.)*

value 74.8 eV is due to the inaccuracy of the approximation used to calculate E_{int}, as indicated by the rather large value of the correction (about 30 percent). (It should be pointed out that there are better methods of calculating the interaction energy which give much closer agreement with experiment.) The helium ion He^+, formed by removing one electron, is identical to the hydrogen atom except that $Z = 2$; thus the ground-state energy is

$$-Z^2(13.6) = -54.4 \text{ eV.}$$

The energy needed to remove the first electron from the helium atom is 24.6 eV. The corresponding potential, 24.6 volts, is called the *first ionization potential* of the atom.

The configuration of the ground state of the helium atom is written $1s^2$. The 1 signifies $n = 1$, the s signifies $l = 0$, and the 2 signifies that there are two electrons in this state. Since l can only be zero for $n = 1$, the two electrons fill the K shell ($n = 1$).

Lithium ($Z = 3$)

Lithium has three electrons. Two are in the K shell ($n = 1$), but the third cannot have $n = 1$ because of the exclusion principle.

The next-lowest energy state for this electron is $n = 2$. The possible l values for $n = 2$ are $l = 1$ or $l = 0$. In the hydrogen atom, these l values have the same energy because of the inverse-square nature of the force. This is not the case in other atoms because of the interaction of the electrons with each other. On the average, the $n = 2$ electron is much farther from the origin than the two with $n = 1$; thus the nuclear charge ($Z = 3$) is often shielded by the two inner electrons. The effective charge is more nearly $Z_{eff} \approx 1$, but this is not a point charge. The nuclear charge $+3e$ can be considered a point charge, but the charge distribution of the two electrons in the K shell is spread out in space. We can, in fact, take for the charge density of each, $\rho = -e|\Psi|^2$, where Ψ is a hydrogenlike, $1s$ wave function (neglecting the interaction of the two electrons in the K shell). The $2s$ ($n = 2, l = 0$) wave function penetrates this shielding more than the $2p$ ($n = 2, l = 1$) wave function. (Recall that the hydrogen-atom wave functions behave like r^l for very small r.) Thus Z_{eff} is greater for an electron in the $2s$ state, and this energy is lower than in the $2p$ state. (The energy of the third electron is approximately proportional to $-Z_{eff}^2$.) The configuration of the lithium atom is thus $1s^2 2s$. The total angular momentum of the electrons in this atom is $\frac{1}{2}$ due to the spin of the outer electron. The first ionization potential for lithium is only 5.39 volts.

Beryllium ($Z = 4$)

The fourth electron has the least energy in the $2s$ state. The exclusion principle requires that its spin be antiparallel to the other electron in this state; thus the angular momentum of the four electrons in this atom is 0. The electron configuration of beryllium is $1s^2 2s^2$. The first ionization potential is 9.32 volts. This is greater than that for lithium because of the greater value of Z.

Boron to Neon ($Z = 5$ to $Z = 10$)

Since the $2s$ subshell is filled, the fifth electron goes into the $2p$ subshell, that is, $n = 2$ and $l = 1$. Since there are three possible values of m_l ($+1$, 0, and -1) and two values of m_s for each, there can be six electrons in this subshell. The electron configuration for boron is $1s^2 2s^2 1p$. Although it might be expected that boron would have a greater ionization potential than beryllium because of the greater Z, the $2p$ wave function penetrates the shielding of the core electrons to a lesser extent and the ionization potential of boron is actually about 8.3 volts, slightly less than that of beryllium. The electron configuration of the elements carbon ($Z = 6$) to neon ($Z = 10$) differs from boron only by the number of electrons in the $2p$ subshell. The ionization potential increases slightly with Z

for these elements, reaching the value of 21.6 volts for the last element in the group, neon. This element has the maximum number of electrons allowed in the $n = 2$ shell and is chemically inert. The element just before this, fluorine, has a "hole" in this shell, i.e., it has room for one more electron. It readily combines with elements such as lithium, which has one outer electron that is donated to the fluorine atom, making a $-F$ ion and a $+Li$ ion, which bond together. This is an example of ionic bonding, which will be discussed in the next chapter. The configuration of neon is $1s^2 2s^2 2p^6$.

Sodium to Argon ($Z = 11$ to $Z = 18$)

The eleventh electron must go into the $n = 3$ shell. This electron is weakly bound in the Na atom; thus Na combines readily with atoms such as F. The ionization potential for sodium is only 5.14 volts. Because of the lowering of the energy due to penetration of the electronic shield formed by the other 10 electrons — similar to that discussed for Li — the $3s$ state is lower than the $3p$ or $3d$ states. (With $n = 3$, l can have the values 0, 1, or 2.) This effect of energy difference between subshells of the same n value becomes greater as the number of electrons increases. The configuration of Na is thus $1s^2 2s^2 2p^6 3s^1$. As we move to higher Z elements, the $3s$ subshell and then the $3p$ subshell begin to fill up. These two subshells can accommodate $2 + 6 = 8$ electrons; thus the configuration of argon ($Z = 18$) is $1s^2 2s^2 2p^6 3s^2 3p^6$. One might expect that the nineteenth electron would go into the third subshell, but this is not the case. The shielding or penetration effect is now so strong that the energy is lower in the $4s$ shell than in the $3d$ shell. There is another large energy difference between the eighteenth and nineteenth electrons, and argon, with its $3p$ subshell filled, is stable and inert.

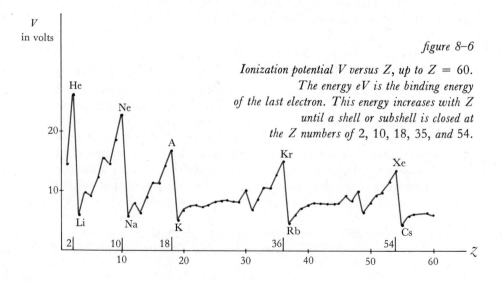

figure 8–6

Ionization potential V versus Z, up to Z = 60. The energy eV is the binding energy of the last electron. This energy increases with Z until a shell or subshell is closed at the Z numbers of 2, 10, 18, 35, and 54.

Atoms with Z > 18

The nineteenth electron in potassium $(Z = 19)$ and the twentieth electron in calcium $(Z = 20)$ go into the $4s$ rather than the $3d$ subshell. The electron configurations of the next 10 elements, scandium $(Z = 21)$ to zinc $(Z = 30)$, differ only in the number of electrons in the $3d$ shell except for chromium $(Z = 24)$ and copper $(Z = 29)$, which have only one $4s$ electron. These elements are called *transition elements*; because their chemical properties are mainly due to their $4s$ electrons, they are quite similar chemically.

Figure 8–6 shows a plot of the first ionization potential of an atom versus Z up to $Z = 60$. The sudden decrease in ionization potential after the Z numbers 2, 10, 18, 36, and 54 mark the closing of a shell or subshell.

Table 8–1 gives the electron configuration for all the elements.

8·6
EXCITED STATES AND SPECTRA OF ALKALI ATOMS

In order to understand atomic spectra we need to understand the excited states of atoms. The situation for an atom with many electrons is, in general, much more complicated than that for hydrogen. An excited state of the atom may involve a change in the state of any one of the electrons or even two or more electrons. Even in the less complicated case of the excitation of only one electron, the change in the state of this electron changes the energies of the others. Fortunately, there are many cases where this effect is negligible, and the energy levels can be calculated accurately from a relatively simple model of one electron plus a stable core. This model works particularly well for the alkali atoms, Li, Na, K, Rb, and Cs. The optical spectra of these elements are not too different from that of hydrogen.

Another simplification is possible because of the wide difference in energies between the excitation of a core electron and the excitation of an outer electron. Consider the case of sodium. We can think of this atom as a neon core (except with $Z = 11$ rather than 10) and the outer $3s$ electron. If this electron did not penetrate the core, it would see an effective nuclear charge of $Z' = 1$, and we would expect the ionization energy to be the same as the energy of the $n = 3$ electron in hydrogen, about 1.5 eV. Penetration of the core will lower the energy of the electron because the effective nuclear charge is greater; thus the ionization energy should be greater than this amount. The measured ionization energy of sodium is about 5 eV. The energy needed to remove one of the outermost core electrons, a $2p$ electron, is about 31 eV, whereas that needed to remove one of the inner core $1s$ electrons is about 1,041 eV. An electron in the inner core cannot be excited to any of the filled $n = 2$ states because of the exclusion principle. Thus the minimum excitation of an $n = 1$ electron is to the $n = 3$ shell. This requires

table 8–1 *Electron configurations of the atoms in the ground state. For some of the rare earth elements ($Z = 57$ to 71) and the heavy elements ($Z > 89$) the configurations are not firmly established.*

Z	element	K n:1 l:s	L 2 s p	M 3 s p d	N 4 s p d f	O 5 s p d f	P 6 s p d	Q 7 s
1	H hydrogen	1						
2	He helium	2						
3	Li lithium	2	1					
4	Be beryllium	2	2					
5	B boron	2	2 1					
6	C carbon	2	2 2					
7	N nitrogen	2	2 3					
8	O oxygen	2	2 4					
9	F fluorine	2	2 5					
10	Ne neon	2	2 6					
11	Na sodium	2	2 6	1				
12	Mg magnesium	2	2 6	2				
13	Al aluminum	2	2 6	2 1				
14	Si silicon	2	2 6	2 2				
15	P phosphorus	2	2 6	2 3				
16	S sulfur	2	2 6	2 4				
17	Cl chlorine	2	2 6	2 5				
18	Ar argon	2	2 6	2 6				
19	K potassium	2	2 6	2 6 .	1			
20	Ca calcium	2	2 6	2 6 .	2			
21	Sc scandium	2	2 6	2 6 1	2			
22	Ti titanium	2	2 6	2 6 2	2			
23	V vanadium	2	2 6	2 6 3	2			
24	Cr chromium	2	2 6	2 6 5	1			
25	Mn manganese	2	2 6	2 6 5	2			
26	Fe iron	2	2 6	2 6 6	2			
27	Co cobalt	2	2 6	2 6 7	2			
28	Ni nickel	2	2 6	2 6 8	2			
29	Cu copper	2	2 6	2 6 10	1			
30	Zn zinc	2	2 6	2 6 10	2			
31	Ga gallium	2	2 6	2 6 10	2 1			
32	Ge germanium	2	2 6	2 6 10	2 2			
33	As arsenic	2	2 6	2 6 10	2 3			
34	Se selenium	2	2 6	2 6 10	2 4			
35	Br bromine	2	2 6	2 6 10	2 5			
36	Kr krypton	2	2 6	2 6 10	2 6			

table 8–1 (*continued*)

Z	element	K	L		M			N				O				P			Q
	n:	1	2		3			4				5				6			7
	l:	s	s	p	s	p	d	s	p	d	f	s	p	d	f	s	p	d	s
37	Rb rubidium	2	2	6	2	6	10	2	6	.	.	1							
38	Sr strontium	2	2	6	2	6	10	2	6	.	.	2							
39	Y yttrium	2	2	6	2	6	10	2	6	1	.	2							
40	Zr zirconium	2	2	6	2	6	10	2	6	2	.	2							
41	Nb niobium	2	2	6	2	6	10	2	6	4	.	1							
42	Mo molybdenum	2	2	6	2	6	10	2	6	5	.	1							
43	Tc technetium	2	2	6	2	6	10	2	6	6	.	1							
44	Ru ruthenium	2	2	6	2	6	10	2	6	7	.	1							
45	Ph rhodium	2	2	6	2	6	10	2	6	8	.	1							
46	Pd palladium	2	2	6	2	6	10	2	6	10	.	.							
47	Ag silver	2	2	6	2	6	10	2	6	10	.	1							
48	Cd cadmium	2	2	6	2	6	10	2	6	10	.	2							
49	In indium	2	2	6	2	6	10	2	6	10	.	2	1						
50	Sn tin	2	2	6	2	6	10	2	6	10	.	2	2						
51	Sb antimony	2	2	6	2	6	10	2	6	10	.	2	3						
52	Te tellurium	2	2	6	2	6	10	2	6	10	.	2	4						
53	I iodine	2	2	6	2	6	10	2	6	10	.	2	5						
54	Xe xenon	2	2	6	2	6	10	2	6	10	.	2	6						
55	Cs cesium	2	2	6	2	6	10	2	6	10	.	2	6	.	.	1			
56	Ba barium	2	2	6	2	6	10	2	6	10	.	2	6	.	.	2			
57	La lanthanum	2	2	6	2	6	10	2	6	10	.	2	6	1	.	2			
58	Ce cerium	2	2	6	2	6	10	2	6	10	1	2	6	1	.	2			
59	Pr praseodymium	2	2	6	2	6	10	2	6	10	3	2	6	.	.	2			
60	Nd neodymium	2	2	6	2	6	10	2	6	10	4	2	6	.	.	2			
61	Pm promethium	2	2	6	2	6	10	2	6	10	5	2	6	.	.	2			
62	Sm samarium	2	2	6	2	6	10	2	6	10	6	2	6	.	.	2			
63	Eu europium	2	2	6	2	6	10	2	6	10	7	2	6	.	.	2			
64	Gd gadolinum	2	2	6	2	6	10	2	6	10	7	2	6	1	.	2			
65	Tb terbium	2	2	6	2	6	10	2	6	10	9	2	6	.	.	2			
66	Dy dysprosium	2	2	6	2	6	10	2	6	10	10	2	6	.	.	2			
67	Ho holmium	2	2	6	2	6	10	2	6	10	11	2	6	.	.	2			
68	Er erbium	2	2	6	2	6	10	2	6	10	12	2	6	.	.	2			
69	Tm thulium	2	2	6	2	6	10	2	6	10	13	2	6	.	.	2			
70	Yb ytterbium	2	2	6	2	6	10	2	6	10	14	2	6	.	.	2			
71	Lu lutetium	2	2	6	2	6	10	2	6	10	14	2	6	1	.	2			
72	Hf hafnium	2	2	6	2	6	10	2	6	10	14	2	6	2	.	2			
73	Ta tantalum	2	2	6	2	6	10	2	6	10	14	2	6	3	.	2			
74	W wolfram (tungsten)	2	2	6	2	6	10	2	6	10	14	2	6	4	.	2			

table 8–1 (*continued*)

Z	element	K $n: 1$ $l: s$	L 2 $s\ p$	M 3 $s\ p\ d$	N 4 $s\ p\ d\ f$	O 5 $s\ p\ d\ f$	P 6 $s\ p\ d$	Q 7 s
75	Re rhenium	2	2 6	2 6 10	2 6 10 14	2 6 5 .	2	
76	Os osmium	2	2 6	2 6 10	2 6 10 14	2 6 6 .	2	
77	Ir iridium	2	2 6	2 6 10	2 6 10 14	2 6 7 .	2	
78	Pt platinum	2	2 6	2 6 10	2 6 10 14	2 6 9 .	1	
79	Au gold	2	2 6	2 6 10	2 6 10 14	2 6 10 .	1	
80	Hg mercury	2	2 6	2 6 10	2 6 10 14	2 6 10 .	2	
81	Tl thallium	2	2 6	2 6 10	2 6 10 14	2 6 10 .	2 1	
82	Pb lead	2	2 6	2 6 10	2 6 10 14	2 6 10 .	2 2	
83	Bi bismuth	2	2 6	2 6 10	2 6 10 14	2 6 10 .	2 3	
84	Po polonium	2	2 6	2 6 10	2 6 10 14	2 6 10 .	2 4	
85	At astatine	2	2 6	2 6 10	2 6 10 14	2 6 10 .	2 5	
86	Rn radon	2	2 6	2 6 10	2 6 10 14	2 6 10 .	2 6	
87	Fr francium	2	2 6	2 6 10	2 6 10 14	2 6 10 .	2 6 .	1
88	Ra radium	2	2 6	2 6 10	2 6 10 14	2 6 10 .	2 6 .	2
89	Ac actinium	2	2 6	2 6 10	2 6 10 14	2 6 10 .	2 6 1	2
90	Th thorium	2	2 6	2 6 10	2 6 10 14	2 6 10 .	2 6 2	2
91	Pa protactinium	2	2 6	2 6 10	2 6 10 14	2 6 10 1	2 6 2	2
92	U uranium	2	2 6	2 6 10	2 6 10 14	2 6 10 3	2 6 1	2
93	Np neptunium	2	2 6	2 6 10	2 6 10 14	2 6 10 4	2 6 1	2
94	Pu plutonium	2	2 6	2 6 10	2 6 10 14	2 6 10 6	2 6 .	2
95	Am americium	2	2 6	2 6 10	2 6 10 14	2 6 10 7	2 6 .	2
96	Cm curium	2	2 6	2 6 10	2 6 10 14	2 6 10 7	2 6 1	2
97	Bk berkelium	2	2 6	2 6 10	2 6 10 14	2 6 10 8	2 6 1	2
98	Cf californium	2	2 6	2 6 10	2 6 10 14	2 6 10 10	2 6 .	2
99	Es einsteinium	2	2 6	2 6 10	2 6 10 14	2 6 10 11	2 6 .	2
100	Rm fermium	2	2 6	2 6 10	2 6 10 14	2 6 10 12	2 6 .	2
101	Md mendelevium	2	2 6	2 6 10	2 6 10 14	2 6 10 13	2 6 .	2
102	No nobelium	2	2 6	2 6 10	2 6 10 14	2 6 10 14	2 6 .	2
103	Lw lawrencium	2	2 6	2 6 10	2 6 10 14	2 6 10 14	2 6 1	2

an energy only slightly less than that needed to remove this electron completely from the atom. Since the energies of photons in the visible range (about 4,000 to 8,000 Å) vary only from about 1.5 to 3 eV, the *optical* spectrum of sodium must be due to transitions involving only the outer electron. Transitions involving the core electrons produce radiation in the x-ray region of the electromagnetic spectrum.

If sodium is bombarded with electrons or photons of energy greater than 1,041 eV, a $1s$ electron can be knocked out of the atom, leaving a vacancy in the $1s$ shell. The K_α x-ray line results from a $2p$ electron dropping into the $1s$ shell, and the filling of the vacant $2p$ shell results in an L x-ray line. (The $2s$ electron cannot make a transition to the $1s$ state because of the selection rule $\Delta l = \pm 1$.) If sodium had a $3p$ electron, it could fill the $1s$ shell and emit the K_β line seen in the x-ray spectrum of heavier elements. We can see why the x-ray spectra are simpler than optical spectra; the energies of the electrons in the inner $n = 1$ and $n = 2$ shells vary uniformly with Z^2 from element to element and do not depend on the position of the element in the periodic chart as do the energies of the outer electrons responsible for optical spectra.

Figure 8–7 shows an energy-level diagram for the optical transitions of sodium. Since the spin of the neon core is zero, the spin of each state is $\frac{1}{2}$; thus each state is a doublet (except the S states).

figure 8–7

Energy level diagram for sodium with transitions indicated. The energy of the ground state has been chosen to be zero for the scale on the left.
(*From Kuhn,* Atomic Spectra, *Academic Press, Inc., New York, 1962.*)

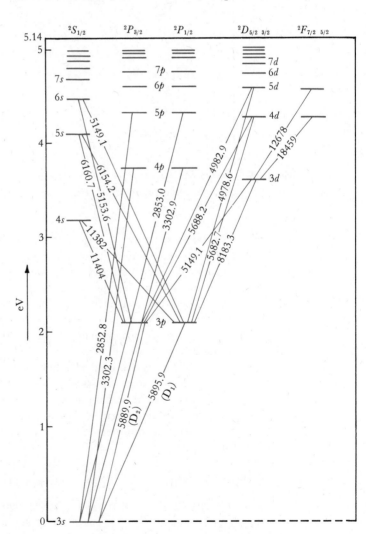

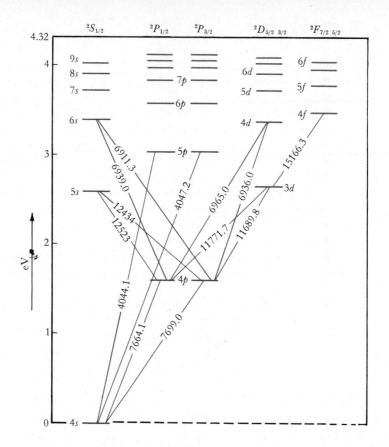

figure 8–8   Energy level diagram for potassium with transitions indicated. (*From Kuhn,* Atomic Spectra, *Academic Press, Inc., New York, 1962.*)

The states with $j = l - \frac{1}{2}$ have slightly lower energy due to the spin-orbit interaction, than those with $j = l + \frac{1}{2}$. The doublet splitting is very small and not evident with this energy scale. The states are labeled by the usual spectroscopic notation, with the 2 before the letter indicating that the state is a doublet. Thus $^2P_{3/2}$, read as "doublet P three halves," means that $l = 1$ and $j = 3/2$. The S states are customarily labeled as if they were doublets even though they are not.

    Capital letters are used to label the states of the atom, whereas small letters denote the state of a single electron. In this case, of course, the orbital and total angular momenta of the state are just those of the outer electron. Transitions beginning or ending on an S state are thus doublets. The most familiar of these is the yellow-line doublet

$$3p(^2P_{1/2}) \rightarrow 3s(^2S_{1/2}) \qquad \lambda = 5{,}896 \text{ Å}$$
$$3p(^2P_{3/2}) \rightarrow 3s(^2S_{1/2}) \qquad \lambda = 5{,}890 \text{ Å}$$

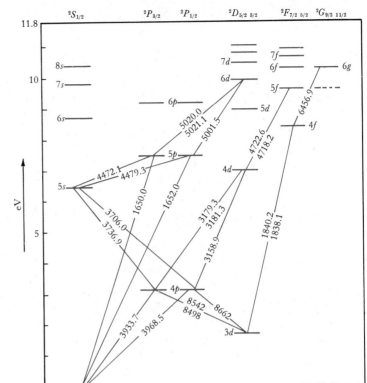

figure 8–9

Energy level diagram for the calcium ion Ca$^+$ with transitions indicated. Note the similarity of Figures 8–7, 8–8, and 8–9. From Kuhn, Atomic Spectra, *Academic Press, Inc., New York, 1962.)*

In addition to the selection rules $\Delta l = \pm 1$ and $\Delta m = \pm 1$ or 0, which were stated in Chapter 7, there is the selection rule[2]

$$\Delta j = \pm 1 \text{ or } 0 \qquad (\text{but not } j = 0 \text{ to } j = 0) \qquad (8\text{–}19)$$

Transitions not involving S states are from one doublet *level* to another. These transitions are triplet *lines* because one of the transitions is eliminated by the selection rule on j. The energy levels and spectra of other alkali atoms are similar to those for sodium. Figures 8–8 and 8–9 show energy-level diagrams for the potassium atom ($Z = 19$), which has an argon core plus one outer electron, and for the Ca$^+$ ion, which has the same electron configuration with $Z = 20$.

[2]We can think of this rule in terms of conservation of angular momentum. The intrinsic-spin angular momentum of a photon has the quantum number $s = 1$. For electric-dipole radiation, the photon spin is its total angular momentum relative to the center of the mass of the atom. If the initial angular-momentum quantum number of the atom is j_1 and the final is j_2, the rules for combining angular momentum imply that $j_2 = j_1 + 1, j_1$, or $j_1 - 1$, if $j_1 \neq 0$. If $j_1 = 0$, j_2 must be 1.

The energy levels and optical spectra are much more complicated for atoms with more than one electron in the outer shell. We shall discuss qualitatively in this section the energy levels for helium and the alkaline earths, atoms in the second column of the periodic table. These atoms all consist of a core of electrons plus two electrons in an outer s shell. Most of the observed spectra can be understood in terms of energy levels due to the raising of one of these electrons to a shell or subshell of higher energy. These are called *normal levels*. Energy levels involving excitation of both outer electrons are called anomalous and will not be discussed here.

The model used to calculate the energy levels for these atoms consists of two identical electrons moving in a potential due to the nucleus and the core. Even though only one of the electrons is in an excited state, we cannot specify which one, so the total wave function for the two electrons must be antisymmetric. The discussion (in Section 8·2) on the symmetries of the space functions and spin functions for two identical particles in a potential well, is applicable here.

Let us consider the case of Mg ($Z = 12$). The configuration in the ground state is $(1s^2 2s^2 2p^6)3s^2$. In the ground state, both outer electrons have the same space quantum numbers; therefore their resultant spin must be $S = 0$. If one of the electrons is excited to a higher energy state, the space quantum numbers of the two electrons will not be the same; thus the spin can be either $S = 0$ or $S = 1$. For the case $S = 1$, the quantum number for the total angular momentum can be $j = l + 1, j = l$, or $j = l - 1$ (except when $l = 0$, in which case there is only one possibility, $j = 1$). Because of the spin-orbit interaction, states with different j values have slightly different energies, i.e., there is fine-structure splitting. The states with $S = 1$ are therefore called *triplet states*. As discussed earlier, the space part of the wave function must be antisymmetric for the triplet state $S = 1$. For the case $S = 0$, j can have only the single value $j = l$; these states are called *singlet states*. The space part of the wave function must be symmetric for singlet states.

The first excited state has one of the outer electrons in the $3p$ state and the other in the $3s$ state. If we neglect the electrostatic interaction of these two electrons, the singlet state $^1P_1$ ($j = 1$ since $l = 1$ and $S = 0$) and the triplet state ^3P_j (j can be 2, 1, or 0, for $l = 1$ and $S = 1$) have the same energy, except for the small fine-structure splitting of the triplet state. The interaction energy due to the electrostatic repulsion of the electrons is *not* the same for the singlet and triplet states. Since the space part of the wave function is antisymmetric for the triplet state, the average separation of the electrons is greater than that for the symmetric space function of the singlet state. Thus the electrostatic repulsion energy is lower for the triplet state than for the singlet state with the same configuration.

figure 8–10

*Probability distribution versus
separation for outer two
electrons in a potential due to
nucleus and electron core.
The average separation is smaller
in the singlet state with
a space-symmetric wave function,
(a), than it is in the
triplet state with a space-
antisymmetric wave function,
(b). The interaction
potential energy, $+Ke^2/|\mathbf{r}_1 - \mathbf{r}_2|$,
is thus greater for the
singlet state than for
the triplet state.*

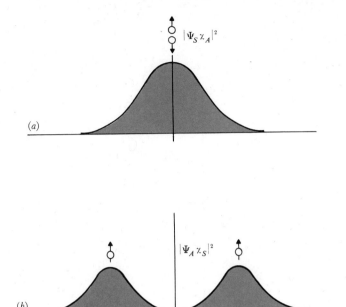

figure 8–11   *Energy level diagram for magnesium. On this scale the separation of the
triplet levels (fine structure) is not evident. Note that the energy of each
singlet level is greater than that of the corresponding triplet level. This is
due to the greater average separation of the outer two electrons in the triplet
states, compared to the singlet state as illustrated in Figure 8–10. (From
Kuhn,* Atomic Spectra, *Academic Press, Inc., New York, 1962.)*

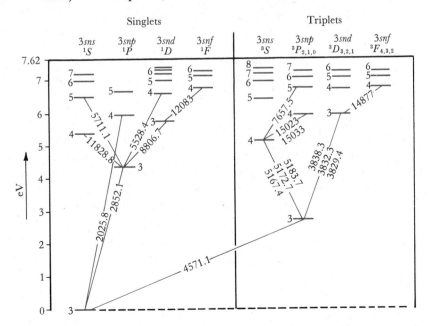

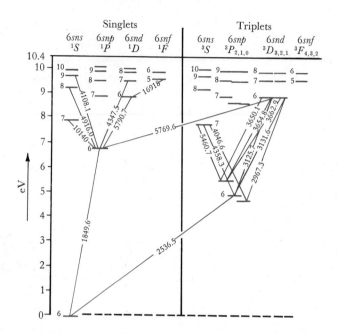

figure 8–12 *Energy level diagram for mercury. The triplet levels 6s6p are separated on this scale. Note the similarity in Figures 8–12 and 8–11. Both* **Mg** *and* **Hg** *have two electrons in an outer shell. (From Kuhn,* Atomic Spectra, *Academic Press, Inc., New York, 1962.)*

This energy difference is of the order of 1 eV, which is much greater than the fine-structure splitting.[3] Figures 8–11 and 8–12 show energy-level diagrams for Mg and Hg with some of the main transitions indicated. Most of the transitions follow the selection rule $\Delta S = 0$; thus the singlet and triplet states do not usually mix. Those transitions for which $\Delta S \neq 0$ are called *intercombination lines.*

8·8

ABSORPTION, STIMULATED EMISSION, AND SCATTERING

When a gas is irradiated with a continuous spectrum of light, the transmitted light shows dark lines corresponding to absorption. Absorption spectra were the first spectra observed. Fraunhofer in 1817 labeled alphabetically the most prominent lines in the absorption spectra of sunlight; it is for this reason that the two intense

[3]This is true for nearly all two-electron atoms such as He, Be, Mg, and Ca, except for the triplet P states in the very heavy atom, mercury. The fine-structure splitting for these states is about the same order of magnitude as the singlet-triplet splitting.

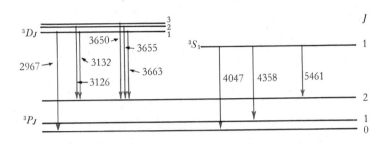

figure 8–13   *Part of a spectrograph of mercury showing lines corresponding to the transitions from the triplet D and S levels, to the triplet P levels as indicated in the energy level diagram at the right. These transitions are also indicated in Figure 8–12. (Courtesy of Dr. E. H. Pinnington.)*

yellow lines in the sodium spectrum are called the *Fraunhofer D lines.* Since, at normal temperatures, nearly all atoms are in their ground state, the absorption spectra are simpler than emission spectra, for only those lines are seen that correspond to transitions from the ground state to an excited state. Thus in hydrogen, for example, only those lines corresponding to the Lyman emission series are seen in the absorption spectrum at normal temperatures. Consider one atom in the ground state and one incident photon. In addition to the possibility of "resonance absorption," the following events may occur (depending on the energy of the incident photon): (1) coherent scattering, (2) inelastic Raman scattering, (3) the photoelectric effect, (4) Compton scattering. These processes are illustrated in Figure 8–14.

If the atom is initially in an excited state, all these processes can occur, with the addition of another process, that of stimulated emission as illustrated in Figure 8–14*f*. This process occurs if the incident photon has just the energy $E_2 - E_1$, where E_2 is the excited energy of the atom and E_1 is the energy of a lower state or the ground state. In this case, the oscillating electromagnetic field of the incident frequency stimulates the excited atom, which emits a

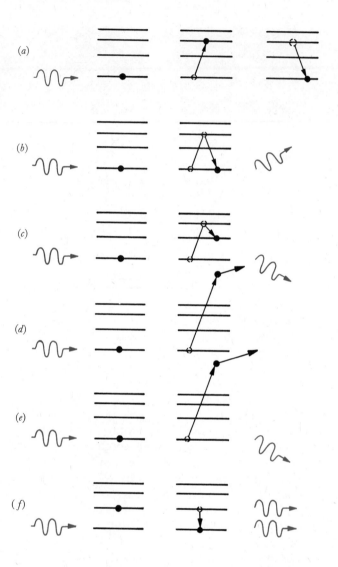

figure 8–14 Descriptions of photon interactions with an atom. In (a) the photon is absorbed and the atom, in an excited state, later emits a photon as it decays to a state of lower energy. This is a two-step process and the emitted photon is uncorrelated with the incident photon. The scattering processes (b) and (c) differ from (a) in that they are one-step processes and there is a correlation between the incident and emitted photons. Parts (d) and (e) illustrate the photoelectric effect and Compton scattering discussed in Chapter 3. In (f) the atom, in an excited state, is stimulated to make a transition to a lower state by an incident photon of just the right energy. The emitted and incident photons have the same energy and are coherent.

photon in the same direction as the incident photon and in phase with it. The relative probabilities of stimulated emission and absorption were first worked out by Einstein. He showed that the probability of stimulating a transition from E_2 to E_1 is the same as that of absorption from state E_1 to E_2.

Stimulated emission is important because the resulting light is coherent, i.e., the phase of the light emitted from one atom is related to that from each other atom. Because of this phase relation, interference of light from different atoms can be observed. In the more usual case of spontaneous emission, the phase of the light from one atom is unrelated to that from another atom and the light is called *incoherent*. Important applications of stimulated emission are the maser (Microwave Amplification by Stimulated Emission of Radiation) and the laser (Light Amplification by Stimulated Emission of Radiation). We shall describe only the basic idea of these important devices. (For more detailed discussion, see Refs. 4 and 5.)

The laser and maser do not differ in theory but in the range of frequency of the electromagnetic spectrum in which they operate. The frequency is determined by the energy levels involved. Consider a system of atoms with the fractions f_1 in the ground state and f_2 in the first excited state with incident radiation of frequency $f = (E_2 - E_1)/h$. The three processes of interest are absorption transitions from E_1 to E_2, stimulated emission from E_2 to E_1, and spontaneous emission from E_2 to E_1. If the second state has a long mean lifetime or if the incident radiation is very intense, we can neglect spontaneous transitions. Since the probabilities of absorption and stimulated emission are equal, the number of each kind of event will depend on the fractions f_1 and f_2. If there are more atoms in the excited state, there will be more emissions with two coherent photons coming out than there will be absorption with the disappearance of a photon; thus there will be amplification. However, the population of the upper state will be more reduced by the emissions than increased by the lesser number of absorptions, so that, eventually, both states will be equally populated and equilibrium will result. For energy differences of the order of 1 eV corresponding to optical frequencies, the fraction in the upper state, without any incident radiation, will be very small at normal temperatures because kT is much less than 1 eV. The ratio of the fraction in the upper state to that in the lower state is

$$\frac{f_2}{f_1} = e^{-(E_2 - E_1)/kT}$$

which is always less than 1 and approaches 1 as T approaches infinity.

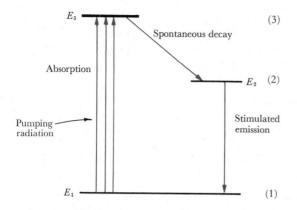

figure 8–15

Energy levels of a three-level laser. In order to obtain amplification, the population of level (2) must be greater than that of the ground state. Thus, an intense auxiliary radiation is necessary to excite atoms from the ground state to the band of levels (3) which decay into level (2).

Amplification by stimulated emission depends on the possibility of obtaining more electrons in the higher state than in the lower state. This situation is called *population inversion*. The most common way of achieving population inversion is by a method called *optical pumping*, which is essentially the intense irradiation of the maser or laser with auxiliary radiation in order to excite many atoms into a higher energy state. Figure 8–15 shows the important energy levels for a three-level laser (such as the ruby laser). The energy level labeled (2) has a long mean life; such a state is called a *metastable state*. Intense incident radiation of frequency $f = (E_3 - E_1)/h$ (this is green light for the ruby laser) causes many atoms initially in the ground state to make transitions to level (3), from which they decay quickly to the metastable level (2) or back to the ground state (1).

figure 8–16   *Energy levels of a four-level laser. Since level (2) is above the ground state, it is sparsely populated if the temperature is low enough. Then population inversion between levels (2) and (3) is easily obtained by exciting just a few atoms from the ground state to the band of levels (4) which decay into level (3).*

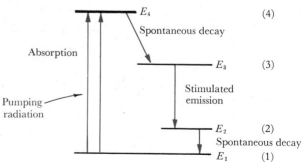

figure 8–17 *Laser used for student laboratory experiments. (Courtesy of Dr. L. Velinsky.)*

[The level labeled (3) is actually a band of levels of nearly equal energy in a solid; thus the incident radiation need not be monochromatic.] If the incident radiation is intense enough, more atoms can be transferred to state (2) than are in the ground state; thus the population of these two states is inverted. Incident photons of energy $E_2 - E_1$ from another source cause stimulated emission from the more populated level (2) to the ground state (1); thus there is amplification. In the ruby laser, the ends of the crystal are polished, with one end totally reflecting and the other partially reflecting, so that some of the beam is transmitted. If the ends are parallel, an intense parallel beam of coherent light emerges. Figure 8–16 illustrates a four-level laser. In this case, transitions are stimulated between levels (3) and (2). Level (2) is sufficiently above the ground state so that there are few atoms in this state at low temperatures. Atoms in the ground state are excited to the level (or band of levels) (4) by absorption of the auxiliary incident radiation of frequency $f = (E_4 - E_1)/h$. Spontaneous transitions then populate level (3), and since (2) is not the ground state, population inversion between these two levels is quickly accomplished. Incident radiation of frequency $f = (E_3 - E_2)/h$ stimulates transitions to state (2), and amplification results. In both types of laser, the population of the upper state is maintained by "pumping" with the auxiliary radiation.

8·9
THE ZEEMAN EFFECT   As we mentioned in Chapter 3, the splitting of spectral lines when an atom is placed in an external magnetic field was looked for by

Faraday and first observed by Zeeman, for whom the effect is now named. With no knowledge of the internal structure of an atom, the magnitude of the frequency change due to the action of the magnetic field on an oscillating charge can be calculated classically. The result, discussed in Chapter 3, is $\Delta\omega = \pm\frac{1}{2}(e/m)B$, or $\Delta\omega = 0$, where e is the charge, m the mass of the charge, and B the external field strength.

The observation of spectral lines split into three components — one of higher frequency, one of lower frequency, and one unchanged — provided one of the earliest estimates of the charge-to-mass ratio of the electron. Though this classical calculation is in agreement with experiment in many cases, it is more usual to find that a spectral line is split into more than three components, with none of the frequency shifts given by the classical calculation. The splitting of a spectral line into three components in a magnetic field is called the *normal Zeeman effect*, whereas the more common splitting into more than three components is called the *anomalous Zeeman effect*. Such terminology is a bit confusing today, for, with the understanding of electron spin, both effects are well understood.

We shall discuss the normal Zeeman effect first because it is somewhat easier to treat. This effect occurs for spectral lines resulting from transitions between singlet states. For these states, the spin is zero and the total angular momentum J is just equal to the orbital

figure 8–18   *Energy-level splitting in the normal Zeeman effect for singlet levels $l = 2$ and $l = 1$. Each level is split into $2l + 1$ terms. The nine transitions consistent with the selection rule $\Delta m = 0, \pm 1$ give only three different energies because the energy difference between two consecutive terms is $e\hbar B/2m$, independent of l.*

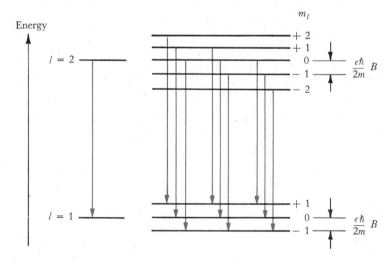

angular momentum L. The magnetic moment of the atom is (see Section 7·6) $\mu = -\mu_B (\mathbf{L}/\hbar)$, where $\mu_B = e\hbar/2m$ is the Bohr magneton. When placed in an external magnetic field $\mathbf{B}$, which we shall choose to be in the z direction, the energy level changes by an amount

$$\Delta E = -\boldsymbol{\mu} \cdot \mathbf{B} = -\mu_z B$$

$$\Delta E = +\mu_B \frac{L_z}{\hbar} B = m_l(\mu_B B) \tag{8-20}$$

Since there are $2l + 1$ values of m_l, each energy level splits into $2l + 1$ levels. Consider a transition between a state with $l = 2$ and one with $l = 1$. Figure 8–18 shows the splitting of these levels in a magnetic field. The allowed transitions obeying the selection rule $\Delta m = 0$ or ± 1 are also shown in the figure. Although there are nine lines shown, there are only three different energies because the energy intervals between any two components are all the same, $\mu_B B$. It is easy to see that this is the case for any initial and final values of l. The energy shifts are thus $\Delta E = \pm\mu_B B = \pm e\hbar B/2m$, or $\Delta E = 0$.

The change in angular frequency $\Delta \omega$ is just the change in energy divided by $\hbar$,

$$\Delta \omega = \frac{\Delta E}{\hbar} = \pm \frac{eB}{2m}, \text{ or } 0 \tag{8-21}$$

in agreement with the classical calculation.

When a magnetic moment is in a magnetic field, there is a torque $\boldsymbol{\mu} \times \mathbf{B}$ on the moment which causes it to precess around the field. It is interesting to calculate the frequency of this precession, which is called the *Larmor frequency*. The torque is equal to the rate of change of angular momentum

$$\boldsymbol{\tau} = \boldsymbol{\mu} \times \mathbf{B} = \frac{d\mathbf{L}}{dt} \tag{8-22}$$

Using $\boldsymbol{\mu} = -\mu_B \mathbf{L}/\hbar = -(e/2m)\mathbf{L}$, Eq. (8–22) becomes

$$-\frac{e}{2m} \mathbf{L} \times \mathbf{B} = \frac{d\mathbf{L}}{dt} \tag{8-23}$$

Equation (8–23) implies that the change in $\mathbf{L}$ is perpendicular to $\mathbf{L}$; thus the magnitude of $\mathbf{L}$ does not change. Figure 8–19 shows the motion of $\mathbf{L}$ about the direction of the field. The tip of the $\mathbf{L}$ vector describes a circle of radius $L \sin \theta$. From the figure, we have

$$d\phi = \frac{|d\mathbf{L}|}{L \sin \theta}$$

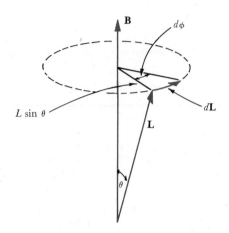

figure 8-19

*Precession of the angular momentum
vector **L** around the magnetic field **B**.
By geometry, $d\phi = |d\mathbf{L}|/L \sin\theta$.
The magnitude of the torque is
$|\boldsymbol{\mu} \times \mathbf{B}| = (e/2m)LB \sin\theta =
|d\mathbf{L}|/dt = L \sin\theta \, d\phi/dt$.
The precession frequency is
$\omega_p = d\phi/dt = eB/2m$.*

Thus the angular frequency of precession is

$$\omega_P = \frac{d\phi}{dt} = \frac{|d\mathbf{L}|/dt}{L \sin\theta} = \frac{(e/2m)LB \sin\theta}{L \sin\theta} = \frac{eB}{2m} \tag{8-24}$$

This equals the frequency shift of the spectral lines in the normal Zeeman effect.

When the spin of a state is not zero, the situation becomes more complicated. The complication is due entirely to the fact that, because the magnetic moment due to spin is 1 rather than $\frac{1}{2}$ Bohr magneton, the total magnetic moment is not parallel to the total angular momentum. Consider an electron with orbital angular momentum **L** and spin **S**. The total angular momentum is

$$\mathbf{J} = \mathbf{L} + \mathbf{S} \tag{8-25}$$

whereas the total magnetic moment is

$$\boldsymbol{\mu} = -g_l \mu_B \frac{\mathbf{L}}{\hbar} - g_s \mu_B \frac{\mathbf{S}}{\hbar} \tag{8-26}$$

Since $g_l = 1$ and $g_s = 2$, we have

$$\boldsymbol{\mu} = -\frac{\mu_B}{\hbar} (\mathbf{L} + 2\mathbf{S}) \tag{8-27}$$

Figure 8-20 shows a vector-model diagram of the addition of $\mathbf{L} + \mathbf{S}$ to give **J**. The magnetic moments are indicated by the dotted vectors. We have seen that the spin-orbit splitting of energy levels with different J values is due to the interaction of the spin magnetic moment with the internal magnetic field in the direction of **L**, seen by the electron due to its orbital motion. From the order-of-magnitude calculation given in Section 7·8 and from the fact that the spin-orbit splitting is much greater than the Zeeman-effect splitting for the usual external laboratory magnetic fields, we can see that this internal magnetic field is very strong. The internal magnetic field causes the spin vector of the electron to precess rapidly around **L**. Since the total angular momentum **J** is constant if there is no external field, the vectors **L** and **S**, and therefore **μ**, all precess rapidly around **J**. When an external magnetic field is turned on, this whole system precesses around **B**. For the usual case, the external field is weak compared with the internal field; thus the precession about **B** is much slower than that of **μ** about **J**.

Before we describe a calculation of the Zeeman splitting for this case based on the vector model, we shall discuss the results. Each energy level characterized by the quantum numbers n, l, s, and j is split into $2j + 1$ levels corresponding to the possible values of m_j. For normal external magnetic fields that are weak compared with the internal fields, the separation of these $2j + 1$ levels is much less than the separation of the levels with the same n and l but different j, which are split because of the spin-orbit interaction (this is the fine-structure splitting). Unlike the case of singlet levels, the Zeeman splitting of these levels depends on j, l, and s. In general,

figure 8–20   (a) *The magnetic moment is not parallel to the angular momentum if the spin is not zero.* (b) *Because of the large internal magnetic field, the magnetic moment precesses rapidly around* **J**. *In a weak external field, the magnetic moment also precesses slowly around* **B**. *The Zeeman energy splitting is proportional to the average component of* **μ** *in the* **B** *direction. Because the precession about* **J** *is so great, compared with that about* **B**, *this energy splitting can be calculated by first finding the projection of* **μ** *on* **J**, *and then finding the projection of* **J** *on* **B**.

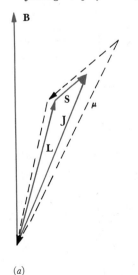

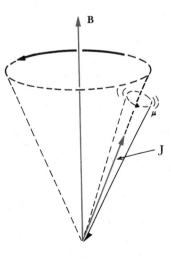

(a)   (b)

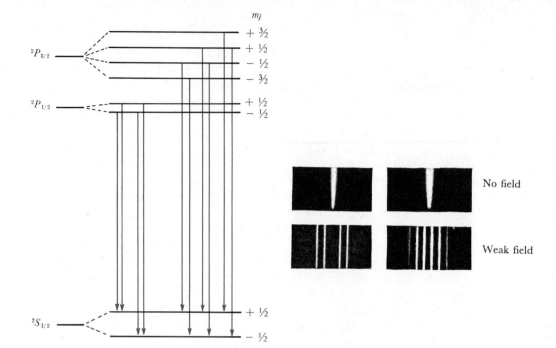

m_j

$^2P_{3/2}$ — + ³⁄₂, + ½, − ½, − ³⁄₂

$^2P_{1/2}$ — + ½, − ½

No field

Weak field

$^2S_{1/2}$ — + ½, − ½

figure 8–21   *Energy-level splitting in a magnetic field for the $^2P_{3/2}$, $^2P_{1/2}$, and $^2S_{1/2}$ states for sodium. Since the splitting depends on both L and J, each of the transitions indicated corresponds to a different energy. Thus the $^2P_{1/2} \rightarrow$ $^2S_{1/2}$ transition splits into four lines, and the $^2P_{3/2} \rightarrow$ $^2S_{1/2}$ splits into six lines, as shown in the photograph on the right. (Photo from* Introduction to Atomic Spectra *by H. E. White. Copyright 1934, McGraw-Hill Book Co. Used by permission of McGraw-Hill Book Co.)*

there are more than three different transition energies. The level splitting can be written

$$\Delta E = g m_j \mu_B B \qquad (8\text{–}28)$$

where

$$g = 1 + \frac{j(j+1) + s(s+1) - l(l+1)}{2j(j+1)} \qquad (8\text{–}29)$$

is called the *Landé g factor*. Equation (8–28) also holds for the singlet levels, for if $s = 0$ (as in the case of helium or the alkaline earths, for example), $j = l$ and $g = 1$, giving the same result as Eq. (8–21). Figure 8–21 shows the splitting of the $^2P_{1/2}$, the $^2P_{3/2}$, and the $^2S_{1/2}$ levels of sodium. The g factor for the $^2P_{1/2}$ state is

$$g_{P_{1/2}} = 1 + \frac{\frac{1}{2}(\frac{1}{2}+1) + \frac{1}{2}(\frac{1}{2}+1) - 1(1+1)}{2(\frac{1}{2})(\frac{1}{2}+1)} = \frac{2}{3}$$

whereas that for the $^2S_{1/2}$ level is

$$g_{S_{1/2}} = 1 + \frac{\frac{1}{2}(\frac{1}{2} + 1) + \frac{1}{2}(\frac{1}{2} + 1) - 0(1)}{2(\frac{1}{2})(\frac{1}{2} + 1)} = 2$$

Thus the splitting is not the same, and there are four different transition energies. It is left as an exercise to compute the Zeeman splitting of the other yellow line of this doublet, $^2P_{3/2} \rightarrow {}^2S_{1/2}$, and to show that there are six different transition energies.

The quantum-mechanical treatment of the problem of an atom such as the sodium atom in a magnetic field involves the solution of the Schroedinger equation. This equation includes a term for the interaction of the magnetic moment with the internal field (spin-orbit interaction) and a term for the interaction of the magnetic moment with the external field, in addition to the main interaction of the outer electron with the electrostatic field of the nucleus and the core electrons. As we have discussed before, approximate methods must be used to solve such a problem. We can describe this calculation semiclassically in terms of the vector model illustrated in Figure 8–20. Despite the complexity of the motion of $\boldsymbol{\mu}$, it is not too difficult to calculate the average component in the direction of $\mathbf{B}$ for the usual case of external fields that are weak compared with the internal fields. Since the precession of $\mathbf{L}$ and $\mathbf{S}$ around $\mathbf{J}$ is then so rapid compared with that of $\mathbf{J}$ around $\mathbf{B}$, we first find the component μ_J parallel to $\mathbf{J}$ and then take the component in the $\mathbf{B}$ direction. We can do this by using Eqs. (8–25) and (8–27) and remembering that the value of J^2 is $j(j + 1)\hbar^2$, with similar relations for L^2 and S^2.

The component of $\boldsymbol{\mu}$ in the $\mathbf{J}$ direction is

$$\mu_J = \frac{\boldsymbol{\mu} \cdot \mathbf{J}}{|\mathbf{J}|} = -\frac{(\mu_B/\hbar)(\mathbf{L} + 2\mathbf{S}) \cdot (\mathbf{L} + \mathbf{S})}{|\mathbf{J}|}$$

$$= -\frac{\mu_B}{\hbar|\mathbf{J}|}(L^2 + 2S^2 + 3\mathbf{S} \cdot \mathbf{L})$$

We can compute $\mathbf{S} \cdot \mathbf{L}$ from $J^2 = (\mathbf{L} + \mathbf{S}) \cdot (\mathbf{L} + \mathbf{S}) = L^2 + S^2 + 2\mathbf{S} \cdot \mathbf{L}$; thus $\mathbf{S} \cdot \mathbf{L} = \frac{1}{2}(J^2 - L^2 - S^2)$ and

$$\mu_J = -\frac{\mu_B}{\hbar|\mathbf{J}|}(L^2 + 2S^2 + \tfrac{3}{2}J^2 - \tfrac{3}{2}L^2 - \tfrac{3}{2}S^2)$$

$$= -\frac{\mu_B}{2\hbar|\mathbf{J}|}(3J^2 + S^2 - L^2)$$

If we take $\mathbf{B}$ to be in the z direction, the component of $\mathbf{J}$ in this

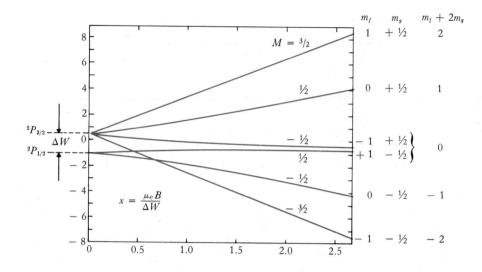

figure 8–22   Paschen-Back effect; splitting of energy levels versus magnetic field **B**. At very large magnetic fields, the levels split into five approximately equally spaced levels, and three spectral lines are seen, as in the normal Zeeman effect. (From Richtmeyer, Kennard, and Lauritsen, Introduction to Modern Physics, 5th ed., McGraw-Hill Book Company, New York, 1955.)

direction is J_z; thus the component of μ_J parallel to **B** is

$$\mu_z = \mu_J \frac{J_z}{|\mathbf{J}|} = -\frac{\mu_B}{\hbar} \frac{3J^2 + S^2 - L^2}{2J^2} J_z$$

$$= -\mu_B \left(1 + \frac{J^2 + S^2 - L^2}{2J^2}\right) \frac{J_z}{\hbar}$$

If we now write J^2, S^2, and L^2 in terms of the quantum numbers j, s, and l, and $J_z = m_j \hbar$, we obtain

$$\mu_z = -g\mu_B m_j$$

where g is given by Eq. (8–29). The energy splitting $\Delta E = -\mu_z B$ is thus given by Eq. (8–28).

It is possible to produce an external magnetic field that is large compared with the internal field for some atoms, such as lithium, which have relatively small internal fields. For this case, the spin-orbit splitting can be neglected in the first approximation. In terms of the vector model, the precession of **L** and **S** around **J** is slow compared with the precession around **B**. We can then calculate μ_z by ignoring the precession about **J** and treating the precession of **L** and **S** about **B** independently. From Eq. (8–27) we then have

$$\mu_z = -\mu_B \frac{L_z + 2S_z}{\hbar}$$
$$= -\mu_B(m_l + 2m_s)$$

and $\Delta E = \mu_B B(m_l + 2m_s)$.

Figure 8–22 shows the Zeeman splitting of a doublet P state as a function of external field B. For very large B, the levels split into five equally spaced energy levels, and as in the normal Zeeman effect, there are only three different transition energies. This behavior in large magnetic fields is called the *Paschen-Back effect* after its discoverers F. Paschen and E. Back.

SUMMARY   The wave function for identical particles must be either symmetric or antisymmetric upon interchanging any two particles. If the wave function is antisymmetric, the particles obey the Pauli exclusion principle. Particles with half-odd integral spin ($\frac{1}{2}$, $\frac{3}{2}$, etc.), called *fermions*, are found to obey the exclusion principle. These particles have antisymmetric wave functions. Particles with zero or integral spin, called *bosons*, do not obey the exclusion principle and have symmetric wave functions.

The Schroedinger equation for two or more interacting particles in a potential field cannot usually be separated and solved exactly. An approximate method for dealing with interacting particles is to solve the Schroedinger equation neglecting the interactions and to use the resulting wave functions to calculate the interaction energy.

Two spin-$\frac{1}{2}$ particles can have a total spin of 0 (*singlet state*), or 1 (*triplet state*). The singlet spin function is antisymmetric; thus the space wave function in the singlet state must be symmetric, so that the total wave function is antisymmetric. The triplet spin function is symmetric, requiring that the space wave function in the triplet state be antisymmetric.

The periodic table is built up by starting with hydrogen and adding one electron to the preceding atom (while increasing the nuclear charge by one) in the quantum state of lowest energy consistent with the exclusion principle. Because of the greater penetration of the outer-electron wave functions into the inner-electron shielding of the nuclear charge, outer electrons with low angular momentum have lower energies than do those in the same n shell with larger angular momentum.

The energy levels of alkali atoms, with one electron outside a closed-shell core, are similar to those of the hydrogen atom except that the l degeneracy is removed because of the penetration of the outer electron into the core electrons.

The energy levels of atoms with two electrons outside a closed-shell core can be separated into singlet states (two outer electrons in spin-0 state) and triplet states (two outer electrons in spin-1 state). Because the average separation of the electrons is greater when they are in the triplet state with antisymmetric space wave function, the average interaction energy is lower; thus the triplet-state energy levels have a lower energy than do the singlet energy levels. The normal excited states are due to the excitation of just one of the outer two electrons.

A photon incident on an atom can be absorbed or scattered elastically or inelastically. If the photon is greater than the ionization energy of the atom, Compton scattering or the photoelectric effect can occur. If the atom is initially in an excited state, an incident photon of the proper energy can cause stimulated emission of another photon of the same energy. The two photons are emitted parallel to each other and in phase. Masers and lasers are important applications of stimulated emission.

The energy levels of an atom are split into $2j + 1$ components in a magnetic field because of the interaction of the field with the magnetic moment. If the spin of the original state is 0, the magnitude of the splitting is $m_j(e\hbar B/2m)$, independent of j and l. Because of the selection rule $\Delta m_j = \pm 1$ or 0, only three different transition lines are seen corresponding to the angular frequency changes of $\pm eB/2m$ or 0. This is called the *normal Zeeman effect*. If the spin of the original state is not zero, the magnitude of the splitting depends on j and l, and more than three lines are seen. Though this is the most common case, it is called the *anomalous Zeeman effect* because it could not be understood using classical physics. The complication of the anomalous Zeeman effect is due to the fact that the magnetic moment is not parallel to the angular momentum when the spin is not zero.

REFERENCES   References in other chapters that are particularly useful for the material in this chapter are Eisberg (1) and Rojansky (4) in Chapter 6 and Hertzberg (1) and Pauling and Wilson (2) in Chapter 7.

Atomic Energy Levels and Spectra

1. H. G. Kuhn, *Atomic Spectra*, Academic Press, Inc., New York, 1962.
2. L. Pauling and S. Goudsmit, *The Structure of Line Spectra*, McGraw-Hill Book Company, New York, 1930.
3. H. White, *Introduction to Atomic Spectra*, McGraw-Hill Book Company, New York, 1934.

Masers and Lasers

4. B. Lengyel, *Introduction to Laser Physics*, John Wiley & Sons, Inc., New York, 1966.

5. The following *Scientific American* articles are available in reprint form, published by W. H. Freeman and Company, San Francisco:

J. Gordon, "The Masers," December, 1958, reprint 215.

A. Schawlow, "Optical Masers," June, 1961, reprint 274.

————, "Advances in Optical Masers," July, 1963, Reprint 294.

E. Leith and J. Upatnieks ,"Photography by Laser," June, 1965, Reprint 300.

PROBLEMS

SET A

8–1. Using the Bohr model for helium and the result that the average interaction energy for the two electrons is about 30 eV, calculate the average separation of the electrons.

8–2. An alternative one-dimensional model to the infinite square well for neutrons and protons in a nucleus is the simple harmonic-oscillator potential $V(x) = \frac{1}{2}M\omega^2 x^2$. (See Examples 8–2 and 8–3.)

    (*a*) What is the ground-state energy of seven noninteracting neutrons in this potential?

    (*b*) What is the ground-state energy of four neutrons and three protons (assumed to be noninteracting) in this potential?

8–3. Indicate which of the following elements should have an energy-level diagram similar to sodium and which should be similar to mercury: Li, He, Ca, Ti, Rb, Ag, Cd, Mg, Cs, Ba, Fr, Ra.

8–4. What is the minimum fraction of the atoms that must be excited in a ruby laser to obtain amplification? Is this also true for a four-level laser?

8–5. Why does cooling increase the efficiency of a four-level laser but not a three-level laser?

8–6. Which of these elements H, He, Li, Mg, and Na might exhibit the normal Zeeman effect?

SET B

8–7. (*a*) Calculate the fine-structure energy splitting of the lowest P state in sodium from the measured wavelengths $\lambda = 5,896$ and $5,890$ Å. (Hint: Use $E = hc/\lambda$ and compute dE using $d\lambda = 6$ Å.)

    (*b*) Taking $\Delta E = e\hbar B/2m$, where B is the internal magnetic field seen by the $3p$ electron, calculate the order of magnitude of B for sodium.

8-8. Two single-particle wave functions are said to be nonoverlapping if, for every value of x_1, either $\psi_{n_1}(x_1)$ or $\psi_{n_2}(x_1)$ is zero. Show that for the case of nonoverlapping single-particle wave functions, $|\Psi_S|^2$ and $|\Psi_A|^2$ from Eqs. (8–14) and (8–15) are the same.

8-9. When there are many identical spin-$\frac{1}{2}$ particles in a square well, the energy of the last particle (called the Fermi energy) may be quite large because of the exclusion principle. Assume that N particles fill the lowest $n = \frac{1}{2}N$ energy levels in an infinite square well of length L.

    (a) Calculate the energy of the nth level (Fermi energy) for the case of 4.4×10^7 electrons/cm. (The number of free electrons/cm^3 in copper is approximately 85×10^{21}.)

    (b) The number of neutrons in a nucleus (in one dimension) is about 1 per 10^{-13} cm. Using $m = 938 \text{ MeV}/c^2$ for the mass of the neutron, calculate the Fermi energy for the neutrons in a nucleus.

8-10. The state E_2 (see Figure 8–16) of the Pr^{3+} ion used in a four-level laser is about 4.2×10^{-2} eV above the ground state. What is the ratio of the number of ions in this level to the number in the ground state at $T = 300°K$ (with no excitation radiation)? What is this ratio at $T = 77°K$?

8-11. Calculate the energy splitting in the normal Zeeman effect for a magnetic field of 4,000 gauss. Calculate the splitting in the wavelength $\Delta\lambda$ for the singlet mercury line $\lambda = 5,791$ Å in this field.

8-12. Calculate the Landé g factor for the $^2P_{3/2}$ level and show that the transition between this and the $^2S_{1/2}$ level, splits into six lines.

NINE
PROPERTIES
OF
MATTER

In this chapter we shall study some of the properties of molecules and solids. The methods of quantum mechanics are readily applicable to these systems because the forces involved are mainly electrostatic. However, as is the case with complex atoms, detailed calculations are quite difficult. For this reason much of the discussion in this chapter will be qualitative. Even a qualitative discussion, with simple quantum-mechanical models, is often far superior to a classical calculation for the understanding of many phenomena. For example, the bonding of two hydrogen atoms is the result of an electron wave-interference effect which has no classical counterpart. The mechanism for covalent bonding can thus be understood by considering qualitatively the interference of electron waves, whereas a classical calculation does not even indicate that the atoms should bind together. Molecular bonding will be examined in Section 9·1, and the energy levels and spectra of diatomic molecules will be discussed in Section 9·3.

The subject of solid-state physics has grown enormously in the last 15 years. In order to give a brief introduction to this subject, a few topics have been selected. We shall discuss the conduction of electricity and heat and the heat capacity of metals using the classical free-electron theory in Section 9·3. These phenomena will be discussed again in Section 9·5 using the results of quantum statistics, which we shall discuss and compare with classical statistics in Section 9·4. In Sections 9·6 and 9·7, the band theory of solids and superconductivity will be treated briefly. Finally, in Section 9·8, liquid helium II will be discussed as an application of Bose-Einstein statistics.

9·1 MOLECULAR BONDING

In this section we shall describe the various ways in which atoms are bound together to form molecules and solids. Molecular bonds can be classified as one of four types: ionic, covalent, van der Waals, and metallic, or a mixture of these.

IONIC BONDING

The easiest type of bond to understand is the ionic bond, found in most salts. Consider NaCl as an example. The sodium atom has one $3s$ electron outside a neon core, $1s^2 2s^2 2p^6$. The ionization energy for Na is low, as it is for all the alkali metals; for Na, only 5.1 eV is required to remove the outer electron from the atom. The removal of one electron from Na leaves a positive ion with a spherically symmetric, closed-shell electron core. Chlorine, on the other hand, lacks just one electron to have a closed argon core. The energy released by the acquisition of one electron is called the *electron affinity*. The electron affinity of Cl is 3.8 eV. The acquisition of one electron by chlorine leaves a negative ion with a spherically symmetric, closed-shell electron core. Thus the formation of a Na^+ ion and a Cl^- ion by the donation of one electron of Na to Cl requires just $5.1 - 3.8 = 1.3$ eV. The electrostatic potential energy of the two ions a distance r apart is $-Ke^2/r$. When the ions are separated by less than R_1, as defined by

$$\frac{Ke^2}{R_1} = 1.3 \text{ eV} \qquad \text{or} \qquad R_1 = 11 \text{ Å}$$

the negative potential energy of attraction is of greater magnitude than the energy needed to create the ions. Since the electrostatic attraction increases as the ions get closer, it would seem that equilibrium could not exist. For very small separation of the ions, however, there is a strong repulsion due to the exclusion principle. The "exclusion-principle repulsion" is responsible for the repulsion of the atoms in all molecules (except H_2) no matter what the bonding mechanism is. When the ions are greatly separated, the wave function for a core electron of one ion does not overlap with that of the other ion. We can distinguish the electrons by the ion

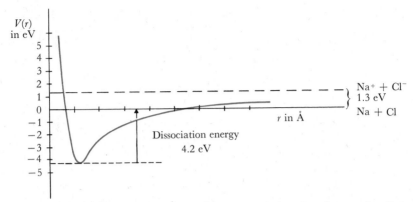

figure 9–1 *Potential energy for* Na^+ *and* Cl^- *ions as a function of separation distance. The energy at infinite separation is chosen to be 1.3 eV corresponding to the energy needed to form the ions from the neutral Na and Cl atoms.*

to which they belong, and the electrons of one ion can have the same quantum numbers as in the other ion. However, when the ions are close, the core-electron wave functions begin to overlap, and some of the electrons must go into higher-energy quantum states because of the exclusion principle. This is not a sudden process. As we shall see below when we study covalent bonding, the energy states of the electrons are gradually changed as the ions are brought together. A sketch of the potential energy of the Na^+ and Cl^- ions versus separation is shown in Figure 9–1. The energy is minimum at a separation of about 2.4 Å. At smaller separations, the energy rises steeply due to the exclusion principle. The energy required to separate the ions and form Na and Cl *atoms*, called the *dissociation energy*, is about 4.2 eV.

The separation distance of 2.4 Å is for gaseous diatomic NaCl (which can be obtained by evaporation of solid NaCl). Normally, NaCl exists in a cubic crystal structure, with Na^+ and Cl^- at alternate corners of a cube. The separation of the ions in a crystal is somewhat larger — about 2.8 Å. Because of the presence of neighboring ions of opposite charge, the Coulomb energy per ion pair is lower when the ions are in a crystal. This energy is usually expressed as $-MKe^2/r_0$, where r_0 is the separation distance and M, called the *Madelung constant*, depends on the crystal structure. For NaCl, $M = 1.75$.

COVALENT
BONDING

A completely different mechanism is responsible for the bonding of molecules such as H_2, N_2, and CO. If we calculate the energy needed to form the ions $H_1{}^+$ and $H_1{}^-$ by the transfer of one electron from one atom to the other and then add this energy to the electrostatic energy, we find that there is no separation distance for which the total energy is negative. The attraction of two hydrogen atoms is a completely quantum-mechanical effect. The decrease in energy when two hydrogen atoms approach each other is due to the sharing of the two electrons by both atoms and is intimately connected with the symmetry properties of the electron wave functions. We can gain some insight into this phenomenon by studying a simple, one-dimensional quantum-mechanics problem — that of two finite square wells each containing one electron. The behavior of the wave functions as the wells are brought together is similar to the behavior of the hydrogen-atom wave functions as the atoms are brought together. Each well can have two electrons in the ground state without violating the exclusion principle (this would be analogous to two He atoms far apart). We shall first consider each well with one electron in the ground state. Let us label the wells a and b and the electrons 1 and 2. Figure 9–2b shows the ground-state wave functions $\psi_a(x_1)$ and $\psi_b(x_2)$ corresponding to electron 1 in well a and electron 2 in well b. The total energy is approximately that of two particles in the ground state of an infinite well

$$E \approx 2E_0 \qquad \text{where } E_0 = \frac{h^2}{8mL^2}$$

When the wells are moved closer together, the electron wave functions begin to overlap, and because the electrons are identical, it is impossible to know if they exchange positions or not. We must

figure 9–2   (a) *Two square wells far apart. If there is one electron in each well, the electrons can have* (b) *antiparallel spins with a symmetric space wave function, or* (c) *parallel spins with an antisymmetric space wave function. The probability distributions and energies are the same for the two wave functions when the wells are far apart.*

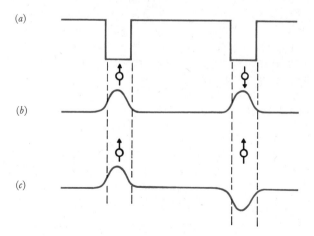

therefore use wave functions that are antisymmetric. The total wave function is antisymmetric if the space function is antisymmetric and the spins parallel (symmetric spin state, $S = 1$) or if the space function is symmetric and the spins antiparallel (antisymmetric spin state, $S = 0$). Note that exchanging the electrons in the wells is the same as exchanging the wells, or changing the coordinates x_1 to $-x_1$ and x_2 to $-x_2$. Thus, for the case of two particles, exchange symmetry is the same as space symmetry. Figure 9–2b is symmetric in space, and it can be taken to represent the wave function for two particles with antiparallel spins. Figure 9–2c is antisymmetric and so represents the wave function for the case of parallel spins. The energies of these two cases are the same when the wells are far apart. We can write the wave functions formally, as we did in Chapter 8, for two particles in a single well. The symmetric (space) wave function is

$$\Psi_S = \frac{1}{\sqrt{2}} [\psi_a(x_1)\psi_b(x_2) + \psi_a(x_2)\psi_b(x_1)] \tag{9-1}$$

and the antisymmetric wave function is

$$\Psi_A = \frac{1}{\sqrt{2}} [\psi_a(x_1)\psi_b(x_2) - \psi_a(x_2)\psi_b(x_1)] \tag{9-2}$$

The probability distributions for these two functions can be written

$$|\Psi_S|^2 = A + B \tag{9-3}$$
$$|\Psi_A|^2 = A - B \tag{9-4}$$

where

$$A = \tfrac{1}{2}[|\psi_a(x_1)\psi_b(x_2)|^2 + |\psi_a(x_2)\psi_b(x_1)|^2] \tag{9-5}$$

and

$$B = \psi_a(x_1)\psi_b(x_1)\psi_a(x_2)\psi_b(x_2) \tag{9-6}$$

If we concentrate for the moment on one of the electrons, we see that for the nonoverlapping wave functions in Figure 9–2b and c, for every value of x_1, either $\psi_a(x_1) = 0$ or $\psi_b(x_1) = 0$; thus $B = 0$ and $|\psi_S|^2$ and $|\psi_A|^2$ give the same probability distribution. This is not the case when the wave functions ψ_a and ψ_b overlap, for then $B \neq 0$. The term B is called the *exchange* or *interference term* and has no classical analog.

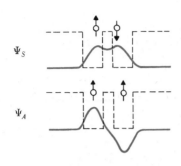

figure 9–3

*Symmetric and antisymmetric space wave
functions for two square wells
close together. The probability
distributions and energies are not the same
for the two wave functions in this case.
The symmetric space wave function
is larger between the wells and
has a lower energy than the
antisymmetric space wave function.*

Figure 9–3 shows the symmetric and antisymmetric wave functions when the wells are very close together. In the limit of no separation, Ψ_S approaches the ground-state function for a well of size $2L$ and thus the energy is lower than the original energy by a factor of 4, whereas Ψ_A approaches the first excited-state wave function for a well of size $2L$, which has about the same energy as the original energy.[1] There are two important results of this discussion:

1. The originally equal energies for Ψ_A and Ψ_S are split into two different energies as the wells become close.
2. The wave function for the symmetric state is large in the region between the wells, whereas that for the antisymmetric state is small.

We can understand the lowering of the kinetic energy of the electrons in the singlet state as the wells are brought together in terms of the uncertainty principle. When the wells are close each electron has more space to move about in; thus it is not so localized and the minimum kinetic energy is reduced.

We now turn to the problem of two hydrogen atoms. In the ground state, the hydrogen-atom wave function is proportional to $e^{-r/a}$. For a one-dimensional model, we shall write this as $e^{-|x|/a}$. Figure 9–4 shows the symmetric and antisymmetric combinations for two separations of the protons. The results are similar to the square-well case; Ψ_S is large in the region between the protons. This concentration of charge between the protons for Ψ_S holds the protons together. It is interesting to compare this situation with our discussion of the He atom in Chapter 8. In the excited state of He, the energy of the space-symmetric state is *higher* because

[1]For infinite wells, $E_n = n^2h^2/8mL^2$; thus, doubling both L and n gives the original energy. For finite wells, the energy of the antisymmetric state increases slightly as the wells are brought together.

the electrons are close together and they repel each other. In H_2, the positive energy of repulsion for the electrons is also greater in the symmetric state because they are close; however, the negative energy of attraction of each electron for the two protons is more important. The potential energy versus separation for two H atoms can be calculated, approximately, by calculating the interaction energy of the two electrons and two protons, using the charge density $e|\Psi_S|^2$ or $e|\Psi_A|^2$, where Ψ_S and Ψ_A are given by Eqs. (9–1) and (9–2), with ψ_a and ψ_b now representing hydrogen-atom wave functions. The results are sketched in Figure 9–5, which also includes a sketch of the calculation when the contribution from the exchange term B is neglected. We see from this sketch that the potential energy for the symmetric state is lower, as expected, and is of similar shape to that for ionic bonding. As the separation approaches zero, all these curves approach $+\infty$. For H_2, this repulsion is due to the repulsion of the protons; for other atoms, it is due to the overlap of the core electrons and to the exclusion principle. The equilibrium separation for H_2 is $r_0 = 0.74$ Å, and the binding energy is 4.48 eV.

We can now see why three H atoms do not bond to form H_3. If a third H atom is brought near an H_2 molecule, the third electron

figure 9–4   *One-dimensional symmetric and antisymmetric electron space wave functions for* (a) *two protons far apart, and* (b) *two protons close together.* (c) *Probability distributions for wave functions in* (b).

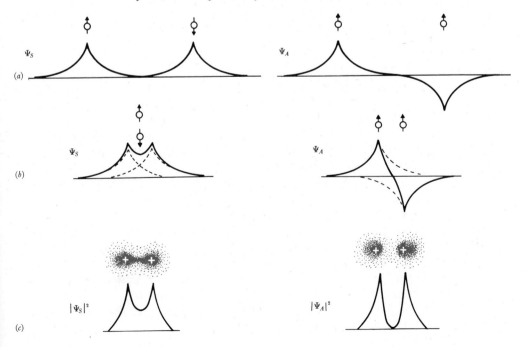

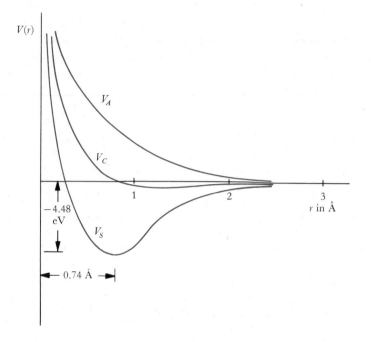

figure 9–5   *Potential energy versus separation for two hydrogen atoms. V_S is for the symmetric space wave function, and V_A is for the antisymmetric space wave function. V_C is the semiclassical result, ignoring the exchange term B in Eqs. (9–3) and (9–4).*

cannot be in a $1s$ state and have its spin antiparallel to both the other electrons. If it is in an antisymmetric state with respect to exchange with one of the electrons, the repulsion of this atom is greater than the attraction of the other. As the three atoms are pushed together, the third electron is essentially forced into a higher quantum state by the exclusion principle. The bond between two H atoms is called a *saturated bond* because there is no room for another electron. The two electrons being shared essentially fill up the $1s$ states of both atoms.

It is found that two identical atoms can bond with what is called a one-electron bond. For example, two protons can share one electron to form the hydrogen molecule ion H_2^+. Because the two protons are identical, the wave function of the electron must be symmetric or antisymmetric in space. The symmetric wave function is concentrated between the protons and thus leads to bonding. This bonding is weaker than the two-electron bond. The equilibrium separation of the protons in H_2^+ is 1.06 Å, and the binding energy is 2.65 eV. If the atoms are not identical, one-electron bonds are usually not formed (unless the atoms are very similar), because the wave function of the electron need not be symmetric in space; thus the electron tends to stay near the atom for which the potential energy is lower, and therefore the electron is not shared.

It should be clear now why He atoms do not bond together to form He_2. There are no valence electrons that can be shared. The electrons in the closed shell are forced into higher energy states when two atoms are brought together. At low temperatures or high pressures, He atoms do bond together, but the bonds are very weak and are due to van der Waals forces, which we shall discuss next. The bonding is so weak that He boils at 4°K at atmospheric pressure and does not form a solid at any temperature unless the pressure is greater than about 20 atmospheres.

VAN DER WAALS BONDING
As mentioned above, atoms and molecules that do not form ionic or covalent bonds can form weak bonds called *van der Waals bonds.* These attractive forces arise because of the electrostatic attraction of electric dipoles. It is not hard to see that molecules with permanent dipole moments — polar molecules such as NaCl or H_2O — will attract other polar molecules, as shown in Figure 9–6. A nonpolar molecule will be polarized by the field of a polar molecule and thus have an induced dipole moment and be attracted to the polar molecule. It is somewhat harder to see why two nonpolar molecules attract each other. Though the average dipole moment $\bar{p}$ of a nonpolar molecule is zero, the average square-dipole moment $\overline{p^2}$ is not, because of fluctuations of the charge. Thus the instantaneous dipole moment of a nonpolar molecule is, in general, not zero. When two nonpolar molecules are nearby, the fluctuations in the instantaneous dipole moments tend to be correlated so as to produce attraction, as illustrated in Figure 9–7. This attractive force between nonpolar molecules is called a *van der Waals force.*

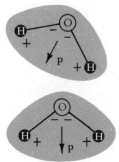

figure 9–6

Bonding of H_2O *molecules because of the attraction of the electric dipoles.*

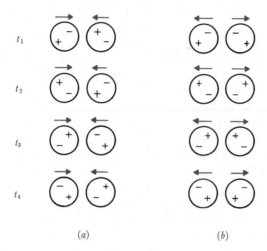

(a) (b)

figure 9–7   Van der Waals attraction of molecules with zero average dipole moments. (a) Possible orientations of instantaneous dipole moments at different times leading to attraction. (b) Possible orientations leading to repulsion. The electric field of the instantaneous dipole moment of one molecule tends to polarize the other molecule; thus the orientations leading to attraction (a) are much more likely than those leading to repulsion (b).

METALLIC BONDING   The nature of the bonding of atoms in a metal is different from the bonding of atoms in a molecule. In a metal, two atoms do not bond together by exchanging or sharing an electron to form a molecule. Instead, each valence electron is shared by many atoms. The bonding is thus distributed throughout the metal rather than being between two atoms. A metal can be thought of as a lattice of positive ions held together by a "gas" of essentially free electrons that roam over the entire solid. The number of free electrons per atom varies from metal to metal but is of the order of one per atom.

9·2
ENERGY LEVELS   As might be expected, the energy levels of molecular systems are
AND SPECTRA   even more complex than those of atoms. For simplicity, we shall
OF MOLECULES   consider only diatomic molecules. The energy of a molecule can be conveniently separated into three parts: energy due to excitation of the electrons in the molecule, energy of vibration of the molecule, and energy of rotation of the molecule. Fortunately, the magnitudes of these energies are sufficiently different that they can be treated separately. The energies of electronic excitations of a molecule are of the order of magnitude of 1 eV, the same as for the excitation of atoms. The energies of vibration and rotation are about 100 to 1,000 times smaller than this.

The energy of rotation is given classically by

$$E = \tfrac{1}{2}I\omega^2 = \frac{(I\omega)^2}{2I} = \frac{L^2}{2I} \tag{9-7}$$

where I is the moment of inertia, ω the angular frequency of rotation, and L the angular momentum. The Schroedinger equation for the rotation of a rigid body of moment of inertia I is

$$\frac{1}{2I} L_{op}{}^2 \Psi(\theta,\phi) = E\Psi(\theta,\phi) \tag{9-8}$$

We solved this equation in Chapter 7 while considering the hydrogen atom. The angular momentum is quantized and has the values $L^2 = l(l+1)\hbar^2$, where $l = 0, 1, 2, 3, \dots$. Thus the energy levels are given by

$$E_l = \frac{l(l+1)\hbar^2}{2I} \tag{9-9}$$

The moment of inertia about an axis through the center of mass of a diatomic molecule is (see Figure 9–8)

$$I = m_1 r_1{}^2 + m_2 r_2{}^2$$

Using the relations $m_1 r_1 = m_2 r_2$ for the distances to the center of mass and $r_0 = r_1 + r_2$ for the separation distance, the moment of inertia can be written (see Problem 9–10)

$$I = \mu r_0{}^2$$

where μ is the reduced mass $\mu = m_1 m_2/(m_1 + m_2)$. If the masses are equal, as in H_2 and O_2, $\mu = \tfrac{1}{2}m$ and

$$I = \tfrac{1}{2}m r_0{}^2$$

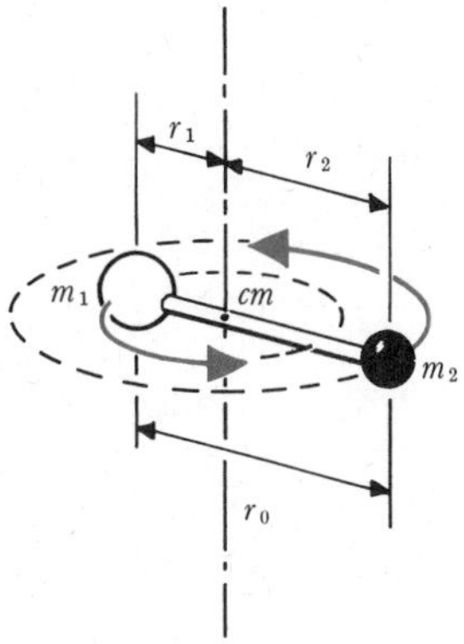

figure 9–8

Diatomic molecule rotating about an axis through the center of mass.

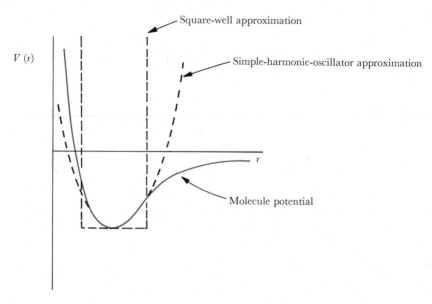

figure 9–9 *Molecular potential. The simple-harmonic-oscillator approximation used to calculate the energy levels and a square-well approximation used to estimate the order of magnitude of the energy levels are indicated by the dashed curves.*

Let us calculate the order of magnitude of the rotational energy levels for H_2. We have

$$E_l = \frac{l(l+1)\hbar^2}{mr_0{}^2} = \frac{l(l+1)(\hbar c)^2}{mc^2 r_0{}^2}$$

Taking for the rest energy of the proton, $mc^2 = 938$ MeV $\approx 10^9$ eV and $r_0 \approx 1$ Å, we obtain, using $\hbar c = 1,970$ eV-Å,

$$E \approx \frac{l(l+1)(1.97)^2 10^6 \, (\text{eV-Å})^2}{10^9 \, \text{eV}(1 \, \text{Å})^2} \approx l(l+1)4 \times 10^{-3} \, \text{eV}$$

Other diatomic molecules have roughly the same separation but larger masses; thus we see that the rotational-energy levels are smaller than those due to electronic excitation by a factor of about 1,000 or more, and transitions between pure rotational-energy levels yield photons in the infrared region.

The vibrational energies are a little harder to estimate. If we approximate the potential-energy curve of Figure 9–1 by a parabola near the equilibrium point, we can use the results of our study of the simple harmonic oscillator in Chapter 6. The energy levels are given by

$$E_n = (n + \tfrac{1}{2})\hbar\omega$$

where ω is the classical frequency of vibration. We could estimate ω by fitting the one-dimensional harmonic potential to the curve of Figure 9–1, but for simplicity, we can get a rough idea of the order of magnitude of the vibrational energies by observing that the energy of an atom of mass m in a square well of length r_0 is

$$E_n = n^2 \frac{h^2}{8mr_0{}^2} = n^2 \frac{4\pi^2\hbar^2}{8mr_0{}^2} = n^2 \frac{\pi^2}{2} \frac{\hbar^2}{mr_0{}^2}$$

Except for the factor $\pi^2/2 \approx 5$ (and n^2), this expression is the same as that for rotation; thus we can expect the vibrational-energy levels to be closer in magnitude to the rotational energies than to the electronic energies. Actually, the vibrational energies are typically greater than the rotational energies by a factor of ten or more. Figure 9–10 is a schematic sketch of some electronic, vibrational, and rotational energy levels of a molecule. The levels are labeled by the quantum numbers n for vibration and l for rotation. The lower vibrational levels are evenly spaced, with $\Delta E_n \approx \hbar\omega$. For higher vibrational levels, the approximation that the potential energy is a simple quadratic is not as good. The actual potential spreads somewhat more rapidly, as can be seen from Figure 9–1, and the spacing of the vibrational levels becomes closer

figure 9–10

Electronic-, vibrational-, and rotational-energy levels of a diatomic molecule. The rotational levels are shown in an enlargement of the $n = 0$ and $n = 1$ vibrational levels.

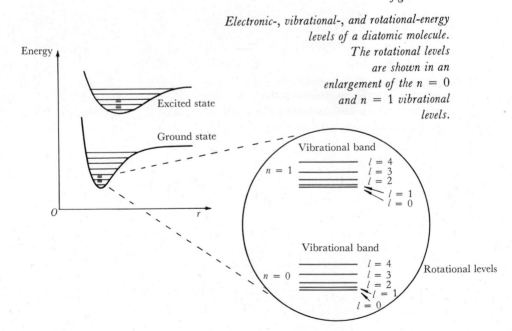

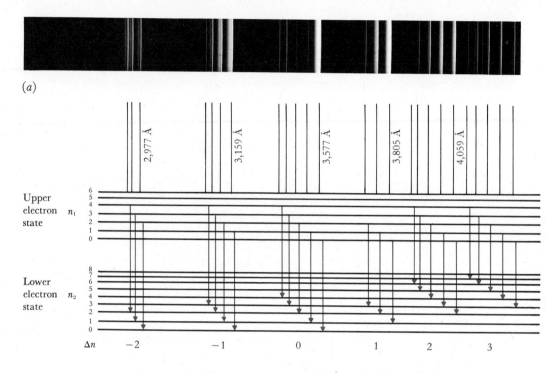

(a)

2,977 Å
3,159 Å
3,577 Å
3,805 Å
4,059 Å

Upper electron state n_1

6
5
4
3
2
1
0

Lower electron state n_2

8
7
6
5
4
3
2
1
0

Δn -2 -1 0 1 2 3

(b)

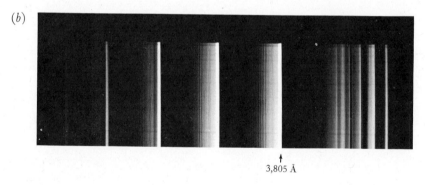

3,805 Å

figure 9–11

Part of the emission spectrum of N_2.
(a) *These components of the band are due to transitions between the vibrational levels of two electronic states as indicated in the diagram.*
(b) *An enlargement of part of* (a) *shows that the apparent lines in* (a) *are in fact band heads with structure due to rotational levels.*
(*Courtesy of Dr. J. A. Marquisee.*)

for large quantum numbers n. The energy difference between the $l + 1$ rotational level and the lth is

$$E_{l+1} - E_l = [(l + 1)(l + 2) - l(l + 1)]\frac{\hbar^2}{2I}$$

$$= 2(l + 1)\frac{\hbar^2}{2I} \tag{9-10}$$

Thus the level spacing increases with l.

Because the energies of vibration or rotation of a molecule are so much smaller than the energies of excitation of an atomic electron, molecular vibration and rotation show up in optical transitions as a fine splitting of the lines. When the structure is not resolved, the spectrum appears as bands. Figure 9–11 shows a typical band spectrum. Much of molecular spectroscopy is done by infrared absorption techniques in which only the vibrational and rotational energy levels are excited. We shall therefore concentrate on what is called the *vibration-rotation spectrum*.

In Section 6·8 we saw that, for the simple harmonic oscillator, only transitions for which $\Delta n = \pm 1$ were allowed for electric dipole radiation. This selection rule is obeyed for transitions involving the lowest vibrational levels but not for the higher levels because of the deviation of the molecular potential from that of a simple harmonic oscillator. For ordinary temperatures ($T \approx 300°K$), the vibrational energies are sufficiently large compared with kT that most of the molecules are in the lowest vibrational state. The transition $n = 0$ to $n = 1$ is predominant in absorption. The rotational energies, however, are sufficiently less than kT that the molecules are distributed among several rotational states. Electric-dipole transitions between rotational states obey the selection rule

$$\Delta l = \pm 1$$

If the original rotational-vibrational energy is

$$E_l = E_e + \tfrac{1}{2}\hbar\omega + l(l + 1)E_{0r} \tag{9-11}$$

where E_e is the electronic energy, $n = 0$, and $E_{0r} = \hbar^2/2I$, the final energy for the transition l to $l + 1$ is

$$E_{l+1} = E_e + \tfrac{3}{2}\hbar\omega + (l + 1)(l + 2)E_{0r} \tag{9-12}$$

For the transition l to $l - 1$, the final energy is

$$E_{l-1} = E_e + \tfrac{3}{2}\hbar\omega + (l - 1)lE_{0r} \tag{9-13}$$

The energy differences are thus

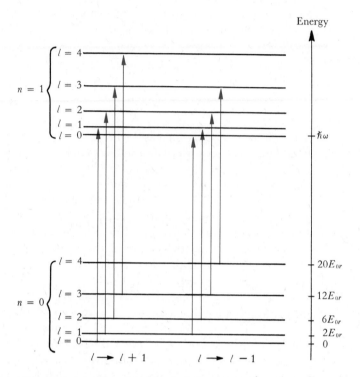

figure 9–12   *Absorptive transitions between the lowest rotational bands $n = 0$ and $n = 1$ in a diatomic molecule. These transitions obey the selection rule $\Delta l = \pm 1$ and fall into two bands. The energies of the $l \to l - 1$ band are $\hbar\omega - 2E_{0r}$, $\hbar\omega - 4E_{0r}$, $\hbar\omega - 6E_{0r}$, . . . , whereas the energies of the $l \to l + 1$ band are $\hbar\omega + 2E_{0r}$, $\hbar\omega + 4E_{0r}$, $\hbar\omega + 6E_{0r}$, . . . , where $E_{0r} = \hbar^2/2I$.*

$$\Delta E_{l \to l+1} = \hbar\omega + 2(l + 1)E_{0r} \qquad\qquad (9\text{–}14)$$

where $l = 0, 1, 2, \ldots$, and

$$\Delta E_{l \to l-1} = \hbar\omega - 2lE_{0r} \qquad\qquad (9\text{–}15)$$

where $l = 1, 2, \ldots$. (l begins at $l = 1$ in the second equation because from $l = 0$, only the transition $l \to l + 1$ is possible.) Figure 9–13 shows the absorption spectrum for HCl. As can be seen from Eqs. (9–14) and (9–15), the absorption spectrum contains frequencies equally spaced by $2E_{0r}/\hbar$ except that there is a gap of $4E_{0r}/\hbar$ at the vibrational frequency ω. A measurement of the position of the gap determines ω, while a measurement of the spacing of the peaks determines E_{0r}, which is inversely proportional to the moment of inertia.

figure 9–13

Absorption spectrum of the diatomic molecule HCl.
The moment of inertia can be determined from the energy spacing between
the large peaks in each band of $2E_{0r} = 2(\hbar^2/2I)$.
The bands are separated by a gap of $4E_{0r}$;
the frequency of the center of this gap is the frequency of vibration.
The double peak structure is because of the two isotopes of chlorine,
Cl^{35} (abundance of 75.5%) and Cl^{37} (abundance of 24.5%).
(This spectrum was taken by T. Faulkner and T. Nestrick
at Oakland University, Rochester, Mich.)

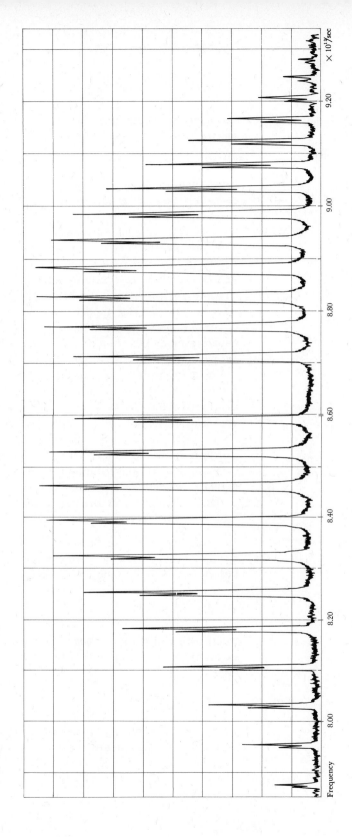

Molecules such as H_2 or O_2 have no electric-dipole moment; thus vibration or rotation of these molecules does not involve a changing dipole moment and there is no vibrational-rotational electric-dipole absorption or radiation for these molecules.

9·3 CLASSICAL FREE-ELECTRON THEORY OF METALS

Since metals conduct electricity so readily, there must be charges in metals that are relatively free to move. The idea that metals contain free electrons that move through a lattice of relatively fixed positive ions was proposed by Drude and Thomson around 1900 and developed by Lorentz. Though this model is quite successful in describing some aspects of the conduction of electricity and heat, it has some serious failures. Ohm's law and the relation between the conductivity of heat and electricity are correctly predicted. However, the model gives the wrong temperature dependence for electrical conductivity, and it predicts that the heat capacity of metals should be greater than that of insulators by $\frac{3}{2}R$ per mole, which is not the case.

We shall outline the classical theory in this section. The main defects of this theory are the use of the classical Maxwell-Boltzmann distribution for electrons in a metal and the treatment of the scattering of electrons by the lattice as a classical particle scattering. In the next section, after showing that the Maxwell-Boltzmann distribution violates the exclusion principle, we shall discuss the quantum statistical distributions. We shall then show, how a modification of the classical free-electron theory of metals leads to a better understanding of the electrical and thermal properties of metals.

ELECTRICAL CONDUCTION

It is well known that the current in a conductor is proportional to the applied voltage over a wide range of voltages. This relation is known as Ohm's law and can be written

$$I = \frac{V}{R}$$

where R is called the *resistance*. The resistance of a wire is proportional to the length and inversely proportional to the cross-sectional area

$$R = \rho \frac{L}{A}$$

where the constant of proportionality ρ, called the *resistivity*, is a property of the conductor. We can thus write Ohm's law

$$I = \frac{A}{\rho} \frac{V}{L}$$

For a constant electric field $\mathcal{E}$, the voltage is just $V = \mathcal{E}L$. In terms of the current density $j = I/A$, Ohm's law is

$$j = \frac{1}{\rho}\,\mathcal{E} = \sigma\mathcal{E} \tag{9–16}$$

where σ is called the *conductivity*. The objective of the classical theory of conductivity is to find an expression for ρ or σ in terms of the properties of metals.

If there are n electrons per unit volume, moving with an average speed u (called the *drift velocity*) parallel to the wire, the current density is

$$j = neu \tag{9–17}$$

We can estimate the drift velocity for a typical case.

Example 9–1   What is the drift velocity for a current of 1 amp in a No. 14 copper wire (diameter of 0.064 in. = 0.163 cm)? Assuming one free electron per atom, n is the same as the number density of copper atoms:

$$n = \frac{(6.02 \times 10^{23}\text{ atoms/mole})\ 8.9\text{ g/cm}^3}{63.5\text{ g/mole}}$$

$$= 8.5 \times 10^{22}\text{ atoms/cm}^3$$

Then

$$u = \frac{I}{Ane} = \frac{1\text{ C/sec}}{(\pi/4)(0.16\text{ cm})^2(8.5 \times 10^{22}/\text{cm}^3)(1.6 \times 10^{-19}\text{ C})}$$

$$\approx 4 \times 10^{-3}\text{ cm/sec}$$

We see that typical drift velocities are quite small.

*

If the electrons are completely free, their acceleration in an electric field $\mathcal{E}$ will be given by

$$m\frac{dv}{dt} = e\mathcal{E}$$

and the speed will increase linearly with time. Thus a steady relation such as Eq. (9–16) would not exist. In our study of the Millikan oil-drop experiment, we found that a steady-state velocity is reached if there is a retarding force proportional to the speed. Let us assume that this is the case for the motion of electrons in a metal. The

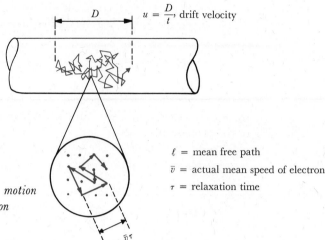

figure 9–14

Electron path in a wire.
Superimposed on the random motion
is a slow drift in the direction
of the electric force qℰ.

ℓ = mean free path
$\bar{v}$ = actual mean speed of electron
τ = relaxation time

equation of motion is then

$$m \frac{dv}{dt} = e\mathcal{E} - bv \tag{9–18}$$

where b is some constant. The solution of this equation is

$$v = v_t(1 - e^{-t/\tau}) \tag{9–19}$$

where $\tau = m/b$ is called the relaxation time and

$$v_t = \frac{e\mathcal{E}}{b} = \frac{e\mathcal{E}\tau}{m} \tag{9–20}$$

is the terminal velocity. The terminal velocity is just that which an electron would attain in a time τ with acceleration $e\mathcal{E}/m$. Using $(e\mathcal{E}\tau/m)$ for the drift velocity in Eq. (9–17), the current density is

$$j = \frac{ne^2\tau}{m} \mathcal{E} \tag{9–21}$$

We thus have Ohm's law with the conductivity given by

$$\sigma = \frac{ne^2\tau}{m} \tag{9–22}$$

If $\bar{v}$ and ℓ are the mean speed and mean free path of the electrons, the relaxation time is

$$\tau = \frac{\ell}{\bar{v}}$$

Then

$$\sigma = \frac{ne^2 \ell}{m\bar{v}} \tag{9-23a}$$

and the resistivity is

$$\rho = \frac{1}{\sigma} = \frac{m\bar{v}}{ne^2 \ell} \tag{9-23b}$$

We can estimate the mean free path from Eq. (2–37) (page 84), replacing d by r, the radius of the copper atom, assuming the size of the electron to be negligible. Using $r = 10^{-8}$ cm, we obtain

$$\ell = \frac{1}{n\pi r^2} = \frac{1}{(8.5 \times 10^{22})\pi(10^{-8})^2} \approx 3.8 \text{ Å} \tag{9-24}$$

Using the Maxwell-Boltzmann speed distribution for the electrons, the mean speed is

$$\bar{v} = \left(\frac{8kT}{\pi m}\right)^{1/2} \approx 10^7 \text{ cm/sec} \tag{9-25}$$

for $T = 300°$K. The relaxation time is then

$$\tau = \frac{\ell}{\bar{v}} \approx 3.8 \times 10^{-15} \text{ sec}$$

Using these results to compute the conductivity for copper at $T = 300°$K, we obtain $\sigma \approx 9 \times 10^6$/ohm-meter. This is about six times smaller than the experimental result. In addition to this discrepancy, the temperature dependence is incorrect because the resistance is proportional to the absolute temperature, whereas from Eq. (9–23b),

$$\rho \propto \bar{v} \propto T^{1/2}$$

Thus the numerical discrepancy is even worse at lower temperatures. We see that, though this classical model does predict Ohm's law, the numerical value and temperature dependence of ρ or σ are not correct.

HEAT CONDUCTION   Good conductors of electricity are also good conductors of heat. The classical theory assumes that this is because the electron gas is mainly responsible for heat conduction in metals. The coefficient of heat conduction of a gas, Eq. (2–48), is

$$K = \frac{1}{3} \frac{n\bar{v} \ell C_v}{N_A} \tag{9-26}$$

The molar heat capacity for an electron gas obeying the Maxwell-Boltzmann distribution is

$$C_v = \tfrac{3}{2}R = \tfrac{3}{2}N_A k$$

Thus the coefficient of heat conduction can be written

$$K = \tfrac{1}{2}n\bar{v}\ell k \qquad (9\text{-}27)$$

Thus K and σ are related by

$$\frac{K}{\sigma} = \frac{\tfrac{1}{2}n\bar{v}\ell k}{ne^2 \ell / m\bar{v}} = \frac{m\bar{v}^2 k}{2e^2} = \frac{4k^2 T}{\pi e^2} \qquad (9\text{-}28)$$

using Eq. (9-25) for $\bar{v}$. The classical theory therefore predicts that the ratio of thermal conductivity to electrical conductivity is proportional to the absolute temperature and the proportionality constant is independent of the metal. This is known as the *Wiedemann-Franz law*. The ratio $K/\sigma T$ is called the *Lorentz number*

$$L = \frac{K}{\sigma T} = \frac{4k^2}{\pi e^2} \approx 1.0 \times 10^{-8}\,\text{watt-ohm/°K}^2 \qquad (9\text{-}29)$$

Table 9-1 shows that $K/\sigma T$ is indeed nearly the same for all metals and is independent of temperature, though the numerical value is somewhat higher than predicted. Because of the simplicity of the model, we can only hope for an order-of-magnitude agreement. The important test of the model is that, though K and σ vary greatly with temperature and from metal to metal, the ratio $K/\sigma T$ does not.

HEAT CAPACITY   If the electron gas has a Maxwellian distribution, it should have a mean kinetic energy of $\tfrac{3}{2}kT$, and the molar heat capacity of a metal should be $\tfrac{3}{2}R$ greater than that of an insulator; that is,

$$C_v = (3R)_{\text{lattice vibrations}} + (\tfrac{3}{2}R)_{\text{electron gas}} = \tfrac{9}{2}R$$

This is not observed. The molar heat capacity of metals is very nearly $3R$. At high temperatures it is slightly greater, but the increase over $3R$ is nowhere near the value of $\tfrac{3}{2}R$ predicted by the classical theory. The increase is, in fact, proportional to temperature, and at $T = 300°$K, it is only about $0.02R$.

9·4

QUANTUM STATISTICS   One of the difficulties of the classical free-electron theory of metals is connected with the assumption that the Maxwell-Boltzmann distribution applies to the electron gas. In this section we shall examine the effects of quantum mechanics on the energy distributable 9–1

Lorentz number
= $(K/\sigma T) \times 10^8$
for several metals
at 0°C and 100°C.
(From Kittel,
Ref. 2)

metal	0°C	100°C	metal	0°C	100°C
Ag	2.31	2.37	Pb	2.47	2.56
Au	2.35	2.40	Pt	2.51	2.60
Cd	2.42	2.43	Sn	2.52	2.49
Cu	2.23	2.33	W	3.04	3.20
Ir	2.49	2.49	Zn	2.31	2.33
Mo	2.61	2.79			

tion of the electrons. Because of the exclusion principle, the energy distribution of electrons in a metal is not even approximately Maxwellian. We shall first consider the energy distribution at $T = 0$. This can be calculated rather easily and is a good approximation to the distribution at other temperatures. Even for temperatures as high as several thousand degrees, the energy distribution of an electron gas does not differ very much from that at $T = 0$.

THE FERMI ENERGY AT $T = 0$

In the classical picture, at $T = 0$, all the electrons have zero kinetic energy. As the conductor is heated, the lattice ions acquire an average kinetic energy of $\frac{3}{2}kT$, which is imparted to the electron gas by interactions of the lattice with the electrons (the interactions we have called *collisions*). The electrons are expected to have a mean kinetic energy of $\frac{3}{2}kT$ in equilibrium; those with larger energies lose energy on the average when colliding with a lattice ion, and those with less energy gain on the average.

Since the electrons are confined to the space occupied by the metal, it is clear from the uncertainty principle that even at $T = 0$, an electron cannot have zero kinetic energy. Furthermore, the exclusion principle prevents more than two electrons (with opposite spins) from being in the lowest energy state. At $T = 0$, we expect the electrons to have the lowest energies consistent with the exclusion principle. It is instructive to consider a one-dimensional model first.

Consider N electrons in a one-dimensional infinite square well of size L. The lowest energy state is

$$E_1 = \frac{h^2}{8mL^2}$$

and the energy levels are given by

$$E_n = n^2 E_1 = n^2 \frac{h^2}{8mL^2} \tag{9-30}$$

We can put two electrons in the state $n = 1$, two in the state $n = 2$, etc. The N electrons will thus fill up $N/2$ states (from $n = 1$ to

$n = N/2$). The energy of the last-filled state (or half-filled if N is odd) is called the *Fermi energy* at $T = 0$. We can calculate this energy for N electrons by setting $n = N/2$ in Eq. (9-30):

$$E_F = E_{N/2} = \left(\frac{N}{2}\right)^2 \frac{h^2}{8mL^2} = \frac{h^2}{32m}\left(\frac{N}{L}\right)^2 \tag{9-31}$$

We see that the Fermi energy is a function of the number of electrons per unit length, the number density in one dimension. The number density of electrons in copper is $8.5 \times 10^{22}/\text{cm}^3$ assuming one free electron per atom. In one dimension, this is

$$\frac{N}{L} = (8.5 \times 10^{22})^{1/3}/\text{cm} = 4.4 \times 10^7/\text{cm} = 0.44/\overset{\circ}{\text{A}}$$

The Fermi energy is then

$$E_F = \frac{(hc)^2}{32mc^2}\left(\frac{N}{L}\right)^2 = \frac{(12{,}400 \text{ eV-}\overset{\circ}{\text{A}})^2(0.44/\overset{\circ}{\text{A}})^2}{(32)(5.1 \times 10^5 \text{ eV})} \approx 1.8 \text{ eV}$$

The average energy is the total energy divided by the number of particles:

$$\bar{E} = \frac{1}{N}\sum_{n=1}^{N/2} 2n^2 E_0$$

Since $N/2 \gg 1$, we can approximate the sum by an integral:

$$\sum_1^{N/2} n^2 \approx \int_0^{N/2} n^2\, dn = \frac{1}{3}\left(\frac{N}{2}\right)^3$$

Thus

$$\bar{E} = \frac{2E_0}{N}\frac{1}{3}\left(\frac{N}{2}\right)^3 = \frac{1}{3}\left(\frac{N}{2}\right)^2 E_0 = \frac{1}{3}E_F \tag{9-32}$$

Our one-dimensional calculation thus gives an average energy of about 0.6 eV at $T = 0$. The temperature at which the average energy would be 0.6 eV for a one-dimensional Maxwell distribution is about 14,000°K, obtained from $\frac{1}{2}kT = 0.6$ eV.

Since the energy states are so close together, we can assume that the energy states are continuous. Let $n(E)\, dE$ be the number of particles with energy between E and $E + dE$. We can write this distribution function as

$$n(E)\, dE = g(E)\, dE\, F \tag{9-33}$$

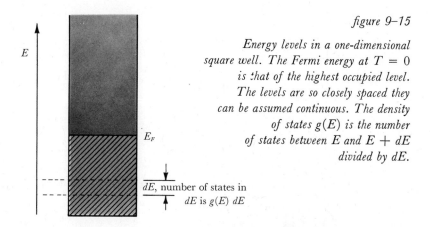

figure 9–15

Energy levels in a one-dimensional square well. The Fermi energy at $T = 0$ is that of the highest occupied level. The levels are so closely spaced they can be assumed continuous. The density of states $g(E)$ is the number of states between E and $E + dE$ divided by dE.

where $g(E)\, dE$ is the number of states in dE and F is the probability that a state will be occupied. At $T = 0$,

$$F = 1 \quad \text{for } E < E_F$$
$$F = 0 \quad \text{for } E > E_F \tag{9-34}$$

The density of states $g(E)$ is given in one dimension by

$$g(E) = 2\frac{dn}{dE}$$

where $E = n^2 E_0$ and the 2 is for the two spin states per space state. Then $dE = 2nE_0\, dn = 2E^{1/2}E_0^{1/2}\, dn$, and

$$g(E) = E_0^{-1/2}E^{-1/2} \tag{9-35}$$

The energy distribution is

$$n(E)\, dE = E_0^{1/2}E^{-1/2}F$$

In three dimensions it is a little more difficult to count the number of states. For simplicity, let us assume the metal to be a cube of side L. We shall take the potential energy to be that of a three-dimensional infinite square well. The Schroedinger equation for this problem is not difficult to solve in rectangular coordinates (see Problem 7–12) because it can be separated into three one-dimensional square-well equations. The allowed energies are

$$E = (n_1^2 + n_2^2 + n_3^2)E_0 \tag{9-36}$$

with $E_0 = h^2/8mL^2$ as before. Each set of values n_1, n_2, and n_3

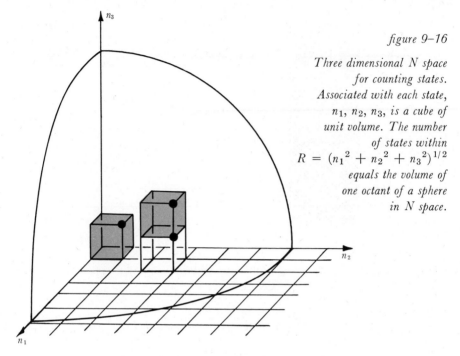

figure 9–16

*Three dimensional N space
for counting states.
Associated with each state,
n_1, n_2, n_3, is a cube of
unit volume. The number
of states within
$R = (n_1{}^2 + n_2{}^2 + n_3{}^2)^{1/2}$
equals the volume of
one octant of a sphere
in N space.*

corresponds to one space state and two quantum states because of the spin. We now wish to count the number of states below a certain energy E. Consider the space formed by the axes n_1, n_2, and n_3. (See Figure 9–16.) We are interested only in the octant for which $n_1 > 0$, $n_2 > 0$, and $n_3 > 0$. Each set n_1, n_2, and n_3 corresponds to a point on a cubical lattice. The number of points in a volume in this space just equals the volume since each cube has a volume of 1. From Eq. (9–36) we see that the total energy is

$$E = R^2 \frac{h^2}{8mL^2} = R^2 E_0$$

where $R = (n_1{}^2 + n_2{}^2 + n_3{}^2)^{1/2}$. The number of states within the radius R is

$$N = 2 \frac{1}{8} \frac{4}{3} \pi R^3 = \frac{1}{3} \pi \left(\frac{E}{E_0} \right)^{3/2} \tag{9–37}$$

The factor 2 is for the two spin states per space state, and the factor $\frac{1}{8}$ is because only $\frac{1}{8}$ of the sphere has positive values of n_1, n_2, and n_3. If we have N particles, they will fill the states up to the Fermi energy given by Eq. (9–37). We thus have in three dimensions at $T = 0$,

$$E_F = \left(\frac{3N}{\pi} \right)^{2/3} E_0 = \frac{h^2}{8m} \left(\frac{3N}{\pi L^3} \right)^{2/3} \tag{9–38}$$

Once again E_F depends only on the number density N/L^3. Taking $N/L^3 = 8.5 \times 10^{22}$ for copper, we find $E_F = 7.04$ eV. The density of states is determined by differentiating Eq. (9–37):

$$dN = \frac{\pi}{2} E_0^{-3/2} E^{1/2} \, dE = \frac{\pi}{2} \left(\frac{8mL^2}{h^2}\right)^{3/2} E^{1/2} \, dE$$

Thus

$$g(E) = \frac{dN}{dE} = \frac{\pi}{2} \left(\frac{8mL^2}{h^2}\right)^{3/2} E^{1/2} \tag{9–39}$$

In terms of the Fermi energy, the density of states is

$$g(E) = \frac{3N}{2} E_F^{-3/2} E^{1/2} \, dE \tag{9–40}$$

using $E_0^{-3/2} = (3N/\pi)E_F^{-3/2}$. The number of electrons in dE is thus

$$n(E) \, dE = g(E) \, dE \, F \tag{9–41}$$

where the Fermi factor is the same as in the one-dimensional model. The average energy at $T = 0$ is

$$\bar{E} = \frac{1}{N} \int En(E) \, dE = \frac{1}{N} \int_0^{E_F} \left(\frac{3N}{2}\right) E_F^{-3/2} E^{3/2} \, dE = \tfrac{3}{5} E_F$$

At higher temperatures, some electrons will gain energy and thus occupy higher energy states. However, electrons cannot move to a higher or lower energy state unless it is unoccupied. Since the kinetic energy of the lattice ions is of the order of kT, we do not expect electrons to gain much more energy than kT; therefore only those with energies within about kT of the Fermi energy can gain energy as the temperature is increased. At $T = 300°$K, kT is only 0.026 eV, so the exclusion principle prevents all but a few electrons from gaining energy by random collisions. Figure 9–17 shows sketches of the density of states (a), the Fermi factor (b), and the product of these, which gives the energy distribution (c).

It is convenient to define the temperature T_F, called the *Fermi temperature*, by

$$kT_F = E_F \tag{9–42}$$

For temperatures much lower than the Fermi temperature, the average energy of the lattice ions will be much less than the Fermi energy; thus we expect that the electron energy distribution will not differ greatly from that at $T = 0$. The Fermi temperature corresponding to $E_F \approx 7$ eV for copper is about 81,000°K.

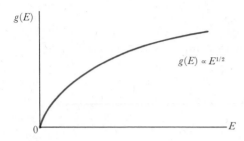

$g(E) \propto E^{1/2}$

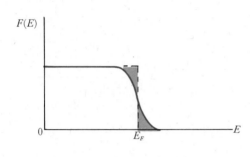

figure 9–17

*The Fermi energy-distribution
function $n(E)$ is the product of
the density of states $g(E)$
and the Fermi factor F.
The dashed curves show the Fermi
factor and energy distribution
at $T = 0$. At higher temperatures,
some electrons with energies
near the Fermi energy are excited,
as indicated by the shaded
regions in (b) and (c).*

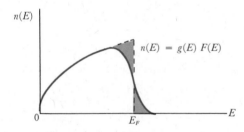

$n(E) = g(E) \, F(E)$

QUANTUM
STATISTICAL
DISTRIBUTION
FUNCTIONS

We shall now present the analytical form of the distribution function
for electron energies at any temperature T. This distribution is
called the *Fermi-Dirac distribution*. We shall compare it with the
classical Maxwell-Boltzmann distribution and with the *Bose-Einstein
distribution*, which governs indistinguishable idential particles that
do not obey the exclusion principle.

In the statistical derivation of the Maxwell-Boltzmann distribution (see appendix C), the following assumptions are made:

1. The equilibrium distribution is the most probable distribution
   consistent with a constant number of particles and constant energy.
2. The particles are identical but distinguishable.
3. There is no restriction on the number of particles in any state.

To compare with the quantum distributions, it is convenient to write the Maxwell-Boltzmann distribution as the number (or density) of states times the probability that a state will be occupied. Let n_i be the number of particles with energy E_i. Then the Maxwell-Boltzmann distribution is

$$n_i = g_i F_{\mathrm{MB}} \qquad (9\text{-}43)$$

where $F_{\mathrm{MB}} = Ae^{-E_i/kt}$ is the probability that a state is occupied. We shall call F_{MB} the Maxwell-Boltzmann factor. The constant A is determined by normalization and is proportional to the total number of particles. For the case of continuous energies, the distribution can be written

$$n(E)\,dE = g(E)\,dE\,F_{\mathrm{MB}} \qquad (9\text{-}44)$$

where $g(E)$ is the density of states.

We have seen that because of the wave nature of all particles, identical particles cannot be distinguished if their wave functions overlap. Thus assumption 2 cannot hold for any type of particle except in the classical limit in which the wave packets are very narrow and do not overlap. This assumption is important because the most probable distribution is defined to be the one that can be realized in the greatest number of ways, and the number of ways a particular distribution can be realized depends on whether the particles are distinguishable. We can illustrate this point by considering a simple probability example.

Example 9-2   Consider the possible arrangements of three objects in two boxes, which we shall label H and T since this problem can be done experimentally by flipping three coins. We wish to find the probability that there will be n_H in box H and n_T in box T. The probability is defined as the number of ways this arrangement can be realized divided by the total number of combinations. Figure 9–18 shows the eight different ways possible if the objects labeled A, B, and C are identical but distinguishable. A ninth way is shown in Figure 9–18i. This is not different from 9–18c if the objects are identical. The probability of two objects in box H and one in box T is $\frac{3}{8}$. The probability of all three being in H is $\frac{1}{8}$. Figure 9–19 shows the situation if the objects are assumed to be indistinguishable. There are now only four different arrangements. The probability that two are in box H and one in T is now $\frac{1}{4}$, and the probability that all three are in box H is also $\frac{1}{4}$.

*

If we keep assumptions 1 and 3 but, instead of assumption 2, assume that the particles in a gas are indistinguishable, we obtain

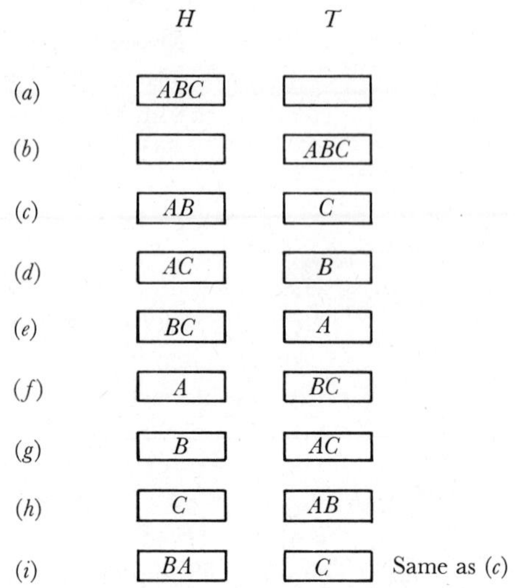

figure 9–18

The eight different ways of arranging three identical but distinguishable objects in two boxes. A ninth way, shown in (i), is the same as (c). Assuming that each object is equally likely to be in either box, the probability of all three objects being in box H is 1/8.

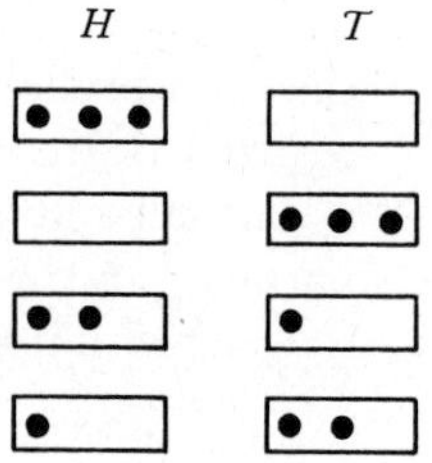

figure 9–19

The four different ways of arranging three identical and indistinguishable objects in two boxes. For this case the probability of all three objects being in box H is 1/4. Compare this with Figure 9–18.

the Bose-Einstein distribution. This describes particles with integral spin that do not obey the exclusion principle, such as α particles ($S = 0$), deuterons ($S = 1$), and photons ($S = 1$). If we also give up assumption 3 and place the restriction that not more than one particle can occupy a quantum state, we obtain the Fermi-Dirac distribution. The derivations of these results will not be given here; they can be found in many kinetic-theory texts, such as Ref. 8 in Chapter 2. Both distributions can be written in the form

$$n(E)\, dE = g(E)\, dE\, F_{\text{FD}} \qquad \text{for Fermi-Dirac}$$
$$= g(E)\, dE\, F_{\text{BE}} \qquad \text{for Bose-Einstein} \tag{9-45}$$

where

$$F_{\text{FD}} = \frac{1}{Be^{+E/kT} + 1} \tag{9-46}$$

and

$$F_{BE} = \frac{1}{Be^{+E/kT} - 1} \tag{9-47}$$

and the constant B is determined by normalization and depends on the number of particles.

Let us now compare these distributions. Both the Bose-Einstein and the Fermi-Dirac distributions are the same as the Maxwell-Boltzmann distribution if

$$Be^{E/kT} \gg 1 \tag{9-48}$$

or $Ae^{-E/kT} \ll 1$, where $A = 1/B$. In the Maxwell-Boltzmann distribution, the quantity $Ae^{-E/kT}$ is the number of particles per state in dE. Thus, if the number of particles per state is much less than 1, the quantum distributions differ little from the classical distribution. For energies of the order of kT, the Maxwell-Boltzmann distribution will be a good approximation of $A \ll 1$. We have already seen that for a metal containing one free electron per atom, the number of states of energy $0 < E < kT$ is much less than the number of electrons unless T is extremely large.

In order to see when we can replace the quantum distributions by the simpler classical distribution, we need only to assume the classical distribution and compute A. The classical distribution will be valid if $Ae^{-E/kT}$ is much less than 1. Let us compute A for N particles in a cube of side L and volume $V = L^3$. If the particles are electrons, the density of states is given by Eq. (9-39), which can be written

$$g_e(E)\, dE = \frac{4\pi V}{h^3} (2m)^{3/2} E^{1/2}\, dE \tag{9-49}$$

If the particles are He atoms, for example, the density of states is the same except that the mass is now the mass of the helium atom and there is no factor of 2 introduced into g_e because of the two electron-spin states. Thus we have for He, which has spin zero and thus should obey BE statistics

$$g_{He}(E)\, dE = \frac{2\pi V}{h^3} (2M)^{3/2} E^{1/2}\, dE \tag{9-50}$$

We can compute A for these two cases from the normalization condition

$$\int n(E)\, dE = N$$

For electrons we have

$$N = \int n(E) \, dE = A_e \frac{4\pi V}{h^3} (2m)^{3/2} \int_0^\infty E^{1/2} e^{-E/kT} \, dE$$

$$= \frac{2V}{h^3} (2\pi m kT)^{3/2} A_e$$

or

$$A_e = \frac{N}{V} \frac{h^3}{2} (2\pi m kT)^{-3/2} \tag{9-51}$$

For the case of He, we obtain

$$A_{\text{He}} = \frac{N}{V} h^3 (2\pi M kT)^{-3/2} \tag{9-52}$$

Let us compute these numbers for an electron gas and He gas. Assuming one electron per atom in copper, we have 6.02×10^{23} electrons in one mole, which has the volume 7.1 cm³. Using $hc = 1.24 \times 10^{-4}$ eV-cm and $mc^2 = 5.1 \times 10^5$ eV, we obtain at $T = 300°K$,

$$A_e \approx 3,500$$

Thus the approximation $A \ll 1$ is not valid. This is just the result we saw before; if electrons followed the MB distribution, there would be many electrons per quantum state, thus violating the exclusion principle.

If we compute A_{He} for He gas at standard conditions, we obtain

$$A_{\text{He}} \approx 3.5 \times 10^{-6}$$

This is much smaller because the mass of He is about 8,000 times that of the electron. Thus $(M/m)^{3/2} \approx 10^6$. Also the density of He is much smaller; one mole occupies 22.4×10^3 cm³, compared with 7.1 cm³ for the electron gas in copper.

We see that, even for the very light gas, He, there is only about 1 out of 10^6 states occupied at $E \approx kT$; thus the BE distribution differs little from the MB distribution. The MB distribution therefore gives an excellent approximation to the BE distribution in practically every case of interest; however, it is not at all a good approximation to the FD distribution in most cases of interest. Let us examine the Fermi-Dirac distribution in more detail.

The constant B in this distribution is determined from

$$\int n(E)\, dE = N = \int_0^\infty \frac{g(E)\, dE}{Be^{E/kT} + 1} \tag{9-53}$$

This integral is difficult to compute. We shall obtain an approximate expression for B which turns out to be quite useful over a wide range of temperatures. Let us write $g(E)$ in terms of the Fermi energy, as in Eq. (9-40):

$$g(E) = \frac{3N}{2} E_F^{-3/2} E^{1/2}$$

Since we have seen that $A \gg 1$ or $B \ll 1$ at not too high temperatures, let us assume that $Be^{E/kT}$ is completely negligible up to the energy for which $Be^{E/kT} = 1$. Above this energy we shall assume that $Be^{E/kT}$ is very large and that the integrand is negligible. This amounts to integrating $g(E)\, dE$ from $E = 0$ to $E = E_1$, defined by $Be^{E_1/kT} = 1$. The result is

$$N \approx \int_0^{E_1} \frac{3N}{2} E_F^{-3/2} E^{1/2}\, dE = \frac{3N}{2} \left(\frac{E_1}{E_F}\right)^{3/2} \left(\frac{2}{3}\right)$$

or $E_1 = E_F$, giving for B the approximate result

$$B \approx e^{-E_F/kT} \tag{9-54}$$

Since E_F is of the order of 1 to 7 eV for metals, $e^{-E_F/kT}$ will be small up to $T_F = E_F/k \approx 81{,}000°$, thus this is a useful approximation. The Fermi factor is then

$$F_{FD} = \frac{1}{e^{(E-E_F)/kT} + 1} \tag{9-55}$$

As $T \to 0$, $e^{(E-E_F)/kT}$ approaches $e^{+\infty}$ for E greater than E_F and $e^{-\infty}$ for E less than E_F. Thus as $T \to 0$, $F_{FD} \to 0$ for $E > E_F$ and $F_{FD} \to 1$ for $E < E_F$ in agreement with our more qualitative discussion at the beginning of this section.

Equation (9-54) is an approximation if E_F is defined as the Fermi energy at $T = 0$. It is customary to define the Fermi energy for any T by taking Eq. (9-54) to be exact. This amounts to merely rewriting the normalization constant B as $B \equiv e^{-E_F/kT}$, which defines E_F. We should then use some other notation such as $E_F(0)$ for the Fermi energy at $T = 0$. Over a wide range of temperatures we can approximate E_F by $E_F(0)$. From Eq. (9-55) we see that the Fermi energy is defined as the energy at which the probability of a state being occupied is $\frac{1}{2}$.

In this section we shall return to the phenomena of electrical conductivity, heat conductivity, and the heat capacity of metals. We shall continue to assume that each atom contributes about one electron, but we shall use the Fermi-Dirac distribution rather than the Maxwell-Boltzmann distribution for the energies of these electrons. We shall also investigate the effect of the wave properties of the electrons on the scattering by the lattice ions.

Consider N electrons in a three-dimensional square well of depth V_0. At $T = 0$, the energy states are filled up to the Fermi energy, which is about 7 eV for copper. The energy needed to remove an electron from the metal is the work function ϕ, which is about 4 eV for copper. Thus the depth of the potential well is about 11 eV for copper and of the same order of magnitude for other metals. Since V_0 is so much greater than the lowest energy E_0 calculated for an infinite well, the energy levels for this finite well will differ by a negligible amount from those of an infinite well.

HEAT CAPACITY
Let us estimate the contribution of the electron gas to the molar heat capacity. At $T = 0$, the average energy of the electrons is $\frac{3}{5}E_F$, so the total energy is $U = \frac{3}{5}NE_F$. At a temperature T, only those electrons near the Fermi level can be excited by random collisions with the lattice ions which have an average energy of the order of kT. The fraction of the electrons that are excited is of the order kT/E_F, and their energy is increased from that at $T = 0$ by an amount of the order of kT. We can thus write for the energy of the N electrons at temperature T,

$$U = \tfrac{3}{5}NE_F + \alpha N \frac{kT}{E_F} kT$$

where α is some constant which we expect to be of the order of 1 if our reasoning is correct. [To calculate α we would need to work with the rather complicated expression (9–49) for the Fermi-Dirac distribution and carry out the normalization integral (9–53) by some approximate method.] A detailed calculation, first done by Sommerfeld, shows that this equation is correct with $\alpha = \pi^2/4$. Using this result, the molar heat capacity is

$$C_v = \frac{dU}{dT} = 2\alpha Nk \frac{kT}{E_F} = \frac{\pi^2}{2} R \frac{T}{T_F} \tag{9–56}$$

where $Nk = R$ for 1 mole and $T_F = E_F/k$ is the Fermi temperature. We see that because of the large value of T_F, the contribution of the electron gas is a small fraction of R at ordinary temperatures. Using $T_F = 81,000°K$ for copper, the molar heat capacity of the electron gas at $T = 300°K$ is $C_v = (\pi^2/2)(300/81,000)R \approx 0.02R$.

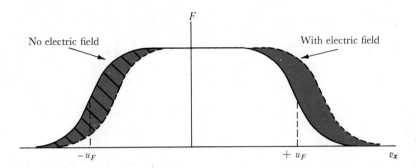

figure 9–20   Occupation probability F versus velocity in one dimension with no electric field and with an electric field. The change is greatly exaggerated.

ELECTRICAL CONDUCTION   We might expect that most of the electrons could not participate in the conduction of electricity because of the exclusion principle, but this is not the case — the electric field accelerates all the electrons together. Figure 9–20 shows the Fermi factor versus velocity for some temperature that is small compared with T_F. The factor is approximately 1 for $-u_F < v_x < +u_F$, where u_F is the speed corresponding to the Fermi energy

$$u_F = \left(\frac{2E_F}{m}\right)^{1/2} \tag{9-57}$$

For copper, $u_F = 1.6 \times 10^8$ cm/sec. The dotted curve shows the factor after the electric field has acted for a time τ. The net effect is equivalent to shifting only the electrons near the Fermi level. We can use the classical equation (9–23) for conduction if we use the Fermi speed u_F for $\bar{v}$:

$$\sigma = \frac{ne^2\ell}{mu_F} = \frac{1}{\rho} \tag{9-58}$$

We now have two problems. Since u_F is independent of temperature (to a very good approximation), the above expressions for σ and ρ are independent of temperature unless the mean free path depends on it. The second problem is in the magnitudes. We saw in Section 9·4 that the expression for σ was too small by about a factor of 6 using $\bar{v}$ calculated from the Maxwell-Boltzmann distribution. Since u_F is about 16 times this value of $\bar{v}$, the magnitude of σ predicted from Eq. (9–58) will be even smaller by another factor of 16.

The resolution of both of these problems lies in the mean-free-path factor. If we use u_F in Eq. (9–58) and the experimental value $\sigma \approx 6 \times 10^7$/ohm-meter, we obtain for the mean free path $\ell \approx 370$ Å, about 100 times the value of 3.8 Å calculated from

$$\ell = \frac{1}{n\pi r^2}$$

where $r \approx 1$ Å is the radius of the copper atom.

It is perhaps not too surprising that the mean free path of electrons in the copper lattice is not given correctly by classical kinetic theory. The wave nature of the electron must be taken into account. The wave phenomenon analogous to the collision of an electron with a lattice ion is the scattering of an electron wave by the ion. If the wavelength is long compared with the crystal spacing, Bragg scattering cannot occur. A detailed calculation of the scatterings of electron waves by a perfectly ordered crystal shows that there is *no scattering* and the mean free path is infinite. Thus the scattering of electron waves must arise from imperfections in the lattice due to impurities or thermal vibrations.

Let us estimate the mean free path of an electron assuming that the lattice ions are *points* which are vibrating due to their thermal energy. We shall take for the scattering cross section $\pi \overline{r^2}$, where $\overline{r^2} = \overline{x^2} + \overline{y^2}$ is the mean square displacement of the point atom in a plane perpendicular to the direction of the electron. We can calculate $\overline{r^2}$ from the equipartition theorem. We have

$$\tfrac{1}{2}K\overline{r^2} = \tfrac{1}{2}M\omega^2\overline{r^2} = kT \tag{9-59}$$

where K is the force constant, M the mass of the ion, and $\omega = (K/M)^{1/2}$ is the angular frequency of vibration. The mean free path is then

$$\ell = \frac{1}{n\pi\overline{r^2}} = \frac{M\omega^2}{2\pi nk}\frac{1}{T} \tag{9-60}$$

We thus see from Eq. (9–58) that this gives the correct temperature dependence for σ and ρ; that is, $\rho \propto T$ rather than $\rho \propto T^{1/2}$, as was obtained from the classical calculation.

We can calculate the magnitude of $\overline{r^2}$, and therefore ℓ, using the Einstein model of a solid, which is fairly accurate except at very low temperatures. In the Einstein model (see Chapter 3, Section 3·6) all the atoms vibrate with the same frequency. The Einstein temperature is defined by

$$kT_E = hf = \hbar\omega$$

Using this for ω, we have

$$\overline{r^2} = \frac{2kT}{M\omega^2} = \frac{2T\hbar^2}{MkT_E^2} = \frac{2(\hbar c)^2}{Mc^2kT_E}\frac{T}{T_E} \tag{9-61}$$

The Einstein temperature for copper is about $200°K$. Using $kT_E \approx 0.17$ eV and $Mc^2 = 63.5 \times 931$ MeV for the mass of the copper ion, the value of $\overline{r^2}$ at $T = 300°K$ is $\overline{r^2} \approx 1.1 \times 10^{-2} \text{Å}^2$. We see that this is a much smaller area than that presented by the copper atom of radius 1 Å. The mean free path is thus about

$$\ell \approx \frac{1}{n\pi\overline{r^2}} = \frac{1}{(8.5 \times 10^{22}/\text{cm}^3)\pi(1.1 \times 10^{-18} \text{ cm}^2)} \approx 340 \text{ Å}$$

which is roughly in agreement with that calculated from Eq. (9–58) using the experimental value of σ. We thus see that the classical mean-free-path method of explaining conductivity works quite well if the mean speed $\bar{v}$ is taken to be that of the electrons at the Fermi level and if collisions are interpreted in terms of the scattering of electron waves, for which only deviations from a perfectly ordered lattice are important.

The presence of impurities in a metal also causes deviations from perfect regularity in the crystal. These are approximately independent of temperature. The resistivity of a metal containing impurities can be written $\rho = \rho_t + \rho_I$, where ρ_t is due to the thermal motion of the lattice and ρ_I is due to impurities. Figure 9–21 shows a typical resistance-versus-temperature curve for a metal with impurities. As the temperature approaches zero, ρ_t approaches zero and the resistivity approaches the constant ρ_I, which is due to impurities.

HEAT CONDUCTION We can use Eq. (9–56) for the heat capacity of the electron gas to calculate the heat conductivity. We have, from Eq. (9–26), replacing $\bar{v}$ by u_F.

$$K = \frac{1}{3}\frac{nu_F\ell C_v}{N_A} = \frac{1}{3}\frac{nu_F\ell}{N_A}\frac{\pi^2}{2}\frac{RkT}{E_F}$$

which can be simplified using $R = N_Ak$ and $E_F = \frac{1}{2}mu_F^2$ to give

$$K = \frac{n\ell\pi^2k^2T}{3mu_F} \tag{9-62}$$

Thus

$$\frac{K}{\sigma T} = \frac{\pi^2}{3}\frac{k^2}{e^2} = 2.45 \times 10^{-8} \text{ watt-ohm/}°K^2 \tag{9-63}$$

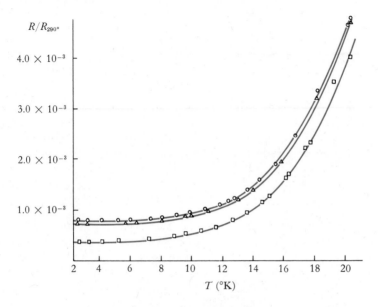

figure 9–21   *Relative resistance versus temperature for three samples of sodium. The three curves have the same temperature dependence but have different magnitudes because of the different amounts of impurities in the samples.* [*MacDonald and Mendelssohn*, Proceedings of the Royal Society, **A202,** *103 (1950).*]

We see that the Wiedemann-Franz law is also predicted by this quantum calculation and that the value of the Lorentz number, $K/\sigma T = 2.45 \times 10^{-8}$, is in good agreement with the experimental values listed in Table 9–1.

9·6
BAND THEORY
OF SOLIDS

We have seen that the free-electron model gives a good account of the thermal and electrical properties of conductors. This simple model, however, gives no indication of why one material is a good conductor and another is an insulator. The conductivity of materials varies enormously from the best insulators to the best conductors.

In order to understand why some materials conduct and others do not, we must refine the free-electron model and consider the effect of the lattice on the electron energy levels. There are two standard approaches to the problem of determining the energy levels of electrons in a crystal. One is to consider the problem of an electron moving in a periodic potential and determine the possible energies by solving the Schroedinger equation. Figure 9–22*a* shows a one-dimensional sketch of the potential-energy function for a lattice of positive ions. The most important feature of this potential is not the shape but the fact that it is periodic. A simpler

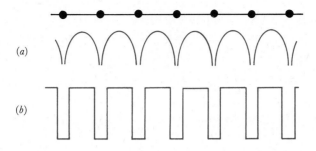

(a)

(b)

figure 9–22 (a) *One-dimensional potential energy of an electron in a crystal. $V(x)$ approaches $-\infty$ at the atom sites.* (b) *Simplified (Kronig-Penney) model of potential energy of an electron in a crystal.*

periodic potential is shown in Figure 9–22*b*. This potential is called the *Kronig-Penney model*. It has the important feature of periodicity and is easier to treat mathematically; however, even for this model the mathematical solution of the Schroedinger equation is fairly complicated, and we shall not present it here. For both potential functions shown in Figure 9–22*a* and *b*, the solutions of the Schroedinger equation have the following characteristic: For certain ranges of energy, there exist traveling-wave-type solutions of the Schroedinger equation. These energy ranges, called *bands*, are separated by an energy gap E_g in which no traveling wave can exist. Figure 9–23*a* shows the energy versus the wave number k for a completely free electron. This is, of course, merely a sketch of

figure 9–23

(a) *Energy versus k for a free electron.*
(b) *Energy versus k for a nearly free electron in the one-dimensional periodic potential of Figure 9–22. Energy gaps occur at the k values, satisfying the Bragg scattering condition.*

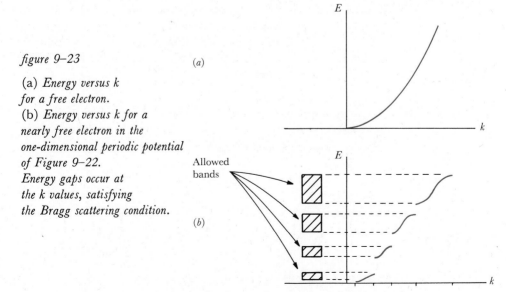

$E = \hbar^2 k^2 / 2m$. Figure 9–23*b* shows E versus k for an electron in the periodic potential (9–22*b*). The energy gaps occur at

$$ka = \pm n\pi \qquad\qquad (9\text{–}64)$$

where a is the lattice spacing. We can understand this result in terms of the Bragg condition

$$n\lambda = 2a \sin \theta$$

In one dimension, $\theta = 90°$ for reflection. Using $k = 2\pi/\lambda$, Eq. (9–64) is just the condition for Bragg reflection. The reason that traveling waves cannot exist for these wave numbers is that the reflection from one atom in the chain is in phase with the reflection from the next atom. Thus standing waves are set up. Figure 9–24 shows a sketch of $|\psi|^2$ for the two types of standing waves for the value $k = \pi/a$,

$$\psi_1 = \sin kx = \sin \frac{\pi x}{a}$$
$$\psi_2 = \cos kx = \cos \frac{\pi x}{a}$$

Since ψ_2 gives a concentration of electron-charge density nearer the ion cores than ψ_1, the potential energy is less for ψ_2 than for ψ_1. The energy difference corresponds to the energy gap. Within the allowed energy bands, the energy has a continuous range if the number of atoms in the chain is infinite; for N atoms, there are N allowed energy levels in each band. Since the number of atoms is so large in a macroscopic solid, the energy bands can be considered continuous. Calculations in three dimensions are more difficult, of course, but the results are similar. The allowed ranges of the wave vector **k** are called *Brillouin zones*.

figure 9–24   *Probability distribution for standing waves of wave number k in a one-dimensional crystal. Dotted curve $|\psi_2|^2$ is maximum at the lattice ion sites, thus it has a lower potential energy than the solid curve $|\psi_1|^2$.*

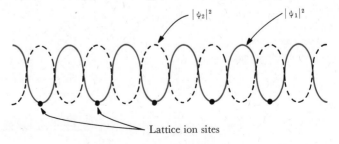

Lattice ion sites

(a)

(b)

figure 9–25

*Wave functions with
different symmetries for
six atoms in one dimension.
The perfectly symmetric
function (a) has the
lowest energy, whereas
the perfectly antisymmetric
function (f) has
the highest energy. (From
Shockley, Ref. 6)*

(c)

(d)

(e)

(f)

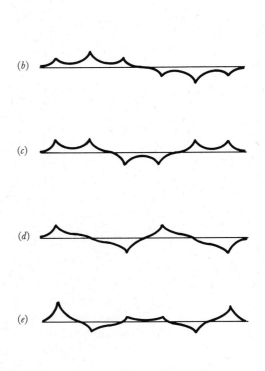

   The second approach to finding the energy levels of electrons in
solids is to trace the energy levels of the individual atoms as they
are brought together to form a solid. In Section 9·1 we saw that
when two H atoms are brought together, the two $1s$ levels (one
for each atom) are split into two molecular levels having different
energies depending on the space symmetry of the wave functions.
   Figure 9–25 shows sketches of one-dimensional s-state wave
functions for six atoms. These might represent, for example, six
sodium atoms each with a $3s$ electron. In Figure 9–25a, the wave
function is symmetric between each pair of atoms. The charge concentration between two atoms is roughly the same as that for the
symmetric state of two atoms. In Figure 9–25f, the wave function
is antisymmetric between any two atoms and is similar to that for
the antisymmetric state of two atoms. The six energy levels (twelve,
counting spin states), which are all the same when the atoms are
far apart, split into six different energies when they are close. The
lowest energy corresponds to Figure 9–25a and the highest to 9–25f.

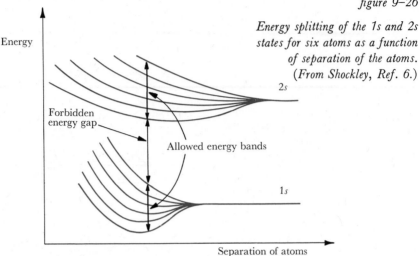

figure 9–26

Energy splitting of the 1s and 2s states for six atoms as a function of separation of the atoms. (From Shockley, Ref. 6.)

Energy

Forbidden energy gap

Allowed energy bands

2s

1s

Separation of atoms

The difference in these two energies depends on the spacing of the atoms but not on the number of atoms, since the concentration of charge for these extreme cases (perfectly symmetric and perfectly antisymmetric) does not change when more atoms are added. Figure 9–26 shows the splitting of the 1s states and 2s states for six atoms as a function of lattice separation. For N atoms, there are N states in a band; thus these bands are nearly continuous in the case of macroscopic solids when $N \approx 10^{23}$. The details of the splitting of the levels, such as are shown in Figure 9–26, depend on the type of atom and the type of bonding and crystal structure.

figure 9–27

Energy-band structure of sodium. The 3p band overlaps the half-filled 3s band. Sodium is a conductor because just above the filled states are many empty states which can receive electrons excited by an electric field.

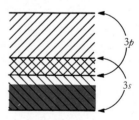

3p

3s

2p

2s

1s

We are now ready to understand why some solids are very good conductors and others very poor. Consider sodium first. There is room for two electrons in the 3s state of each atom, but each separated Na atom has only one 3s electron. When N atoms are thus bound in a solid, the 3s energy band is only half-filled. In addition, the 3p band actually crosses the 3s band. The allowed energy bands of sodium are shown schematically in Figure 9–27. The occupied levels are shaded. We see that there are many allowed empty energy states just above the filled ones, so the valence electrons can easily be raised to a higher energy state by an electric field, and sodium is a good conductor. Magnesium has two 3s electrons; thus the 3s band is filled. However, because the 3p band crosses the 3s band, just as it does for sodium, magnesium is also a conductor.

A solid which has only completely-filled bands is an insulator if the energy gap between the last-filled band (called the *valence band*) and the next allowed band (called the *conduction band*) is large. If

figure 9–28   *Splitting of the 2s and 2p states of carbon, or the 3s and 3p states of silicon, versus separation of the atoms. The energy gap between the four filled states in the valence band and the empty states in the conduction band is 7 eV for the diamond-atom spacing, $R_D = 1.54$ Å, and 1.09 eV for the silicon-atom spacing, $R_{Si} = 2.35$ Å. The splitting is similar for the 4s and 4p levels in germanium, which has an atom spacing of 2.43 Å, giving an energy gap of only 0.7 eV. (From Sproull, Ref. 5.)*

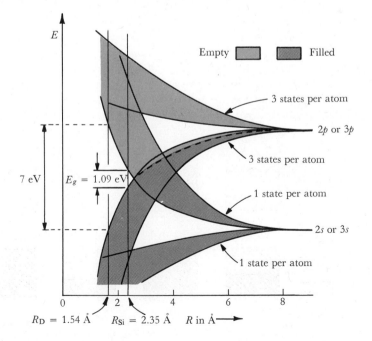

the gap is small, the solid is a semiconductor. Consider carbon, which has two $2s$ electrons and two $2p$ electrons. We might expect carbon to be a conductor because of the four unfilled $2p$ states. However, when carbon atoms are brought close together, the $2s$ and $2p$ levels split, as shown in Figure 9–28. This splitting is due to the nature of the covalent bond and is similar to the splitting of the $1s$ levels of hydrogen discussed in Section 9·1. The energy of the levels corresponding to space-symmetric wave functions — one of the $2s$ levels and three of the $2p$ levels — is lowered, while the energy of the other four levels (one $2s$ and three $2p$), corresponding to space-antisymmetric wave functions, is raised. Thus the valence band contains four levels per atom which are filled, and the conduction band is empty. At the diamond-lattice spacing of about 1.54 Å, the energy gap between the valence band and conduction band is about 7 eV, so diamond is an insulator.

The band structure is similar for silicon, which has two $3s$ and two $3p$ electrons, and also for germanium, which has two $4s$ and two $4p$ electrons. At the silicon-lattice spacing of 2.35 Å, the energy gap is about 1 eV, whereas, at the germanium-lattice spacing of 2.88 Å, the energy gap is only about 0.7 eV. These solids are called *intrinsic semiconductors*. Even at room temperature there are a few electrons in the conduction band because of thermal excitation. This leaves the same number of unoccupied states, or holes, in the nearly filled valence band. In the presence of an electric field,

figure 9–29   *Four possible band structures for a solid. In (a), the allowed band is only partially full; thus electrons can be excited to nearby energy states and (a) is a conductor. In (b), there is a forbidden band with a large energy gap between the filled band and the next allowed band; thus (b) is an insulator. (c) is a conductor because the allowed bands overlap. In (d), the energy gap between the filled band and the next allowed band is very small; thus some electrons are excited to the conduction band at normal temperatures, leaving holes in the valence band. (d) is a semiconductor.*

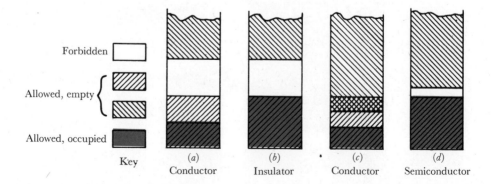

Forbidden

Allowed, empty

Allowed, occupied

Key

(a)	(b)	(c)	(d)
Conductor	Insulator	Conductor	Semiconductor

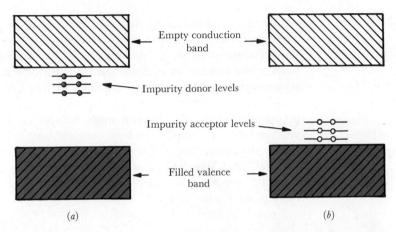

figure 9–30 (a) *Energy bands of an n-type semiconductor. Impurity atoms provide filled energy levels just below the empty conduction band and donate electrons to the conduction band.* (b) *Energy bands of a p-type semiconductor. Impurity atoms provide empty energy levels just above the filled valence band and accept electrons from it.*

in addition to the motion of electrons in the conduction band, electrons in the valence band can move into the holes, thus creating other holes. For the valence band, it is easier to speak of the motion of the holes than of the electrons. The holes act like positive charges. The conductivity of germanium at room temperature is about 2/ohm-meter. As the temperature is increased, the conductivity increases because the effect of increasing the number of carriers (electrons and holes) outweighs the increase in the scattering by the lattice.

We can now see why ionic crystals are insulators. The energy bands of interest in NaCl are those from the energy levels in the Na^+ ion and the Cl^- ion. Both these ions have closed-shell structures; therefore the highest occupied band in NaCl is completely full and there is a large energy gap between it and the empty conduction band.

The properties of a material can be greatly changed by adding impurities. Consider the effect of replacing one germanium atom with an arsenic atom. The arsenic atom has five electrons in the $n = 4$ shell, rather than four as in germanium. Thus arsenic has one extra electron in addition to the four bonding electrons. (Germanium has the four-covalent-bond diamond structure.) The "Bohr orbit" for this electron is large compared with the lattice spacing, so the electron is very weakly bound to the arsenic atom. The effect on the band structure of doping a germanium crystal with arsenic is shown in Figure 9–30a. The levels just below the conduction band are due to the extra electrons of the arsenic atoms. These levels are called *donor levels* because the arsenic atoms essentially donate electrons to the conduction band without creating holes in the valence band. Such a semiconductor is called an *n-type* semiconductor because the carriers are *n*egative electrons.

If gallium, with three $n = 4$ electrons, is used to replace a germanium atom, the gallium atom accepts electrons from the valence band to complete its four covalent bonds, thus creating a hole in the valence band. The effect on the band structure of doping with gallium is shown in Figure 9–30*b*. A semiconductor doped with acceptor impurities is called a *p-type* semiconductor because the carriers are *p*ositive holes.

9·7
SUPER-
CONDUCTIVITY

In 1911, H. Kamerlingh Onnes found that the resistance of mercury dropped suddenly to zero at a temperature of about 4.2°K. Figure 9–31 shows a sketch of his data. Since then this behavior, called *superconductivity*, has been observed in many materials. The critical temperature varies from material to material, but below the critical temperature, the resistance is apparently zero. Steady currents have been observed to persist in superconducting rings for several years with no apparent loss. Table 9–2 lists some superconducting materials with their critical temperatures. In the presence of a magnetic field, the critical temperature is lower than with no field. As the magnetic field increases, the critical temperature decreases. If the magnetic field is greater than a critical field H_c superconductivity does not exist at any temperature.

table 9–2

Critical temperatures for some superconducting elements.

element	$T_c(°K)$
Al	1.2
Hg	4.2
In	3.4
Nb	9.2
Pb	7.2
Sn	3.7
Ta	4.4

Another property of superconduction is called the *Meissner effect;* when a superconductor in a magnetic field is cooled below the critical temperature, the magnetic-field lines are expelled from the superconductor. A magnetic field cannot exist inside a superconductor.

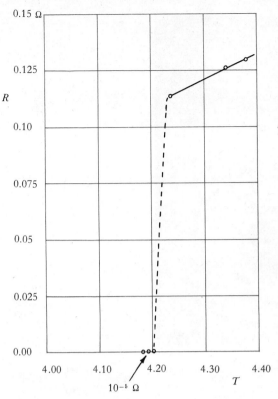

0.15 Ω

R

0.125

0.10

0.075

0.05

0.025

0.00

4.00   4.10   4.20   4.30   4.40

10^{-5} Ω

T

figure 9–31

*Resistance in ohms
of a specimen of mercury
versus absolute temperature.
This plot by Kamerlingh Onnes
marked the discovery of
superconductivity.
(From Kittel, Ref. 3.)*

figure 9–32

*Demonstration of persistent currents.
Currents are first induced in
the superconducting rings. When the
lead ball is dropped into the
rings, a persistent current is induced
on the surface of the ball as it
approaches the rings. The current is
in the opposite direction of that in
the rings so that the ball is repelled.
The ball thus floats at the
height at which the weight of the
ball is balanced by the magnetic
force of repulsion due to the currents.
(Courtesy of 500, Incorporated.)*

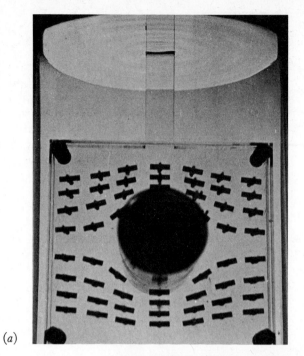

(a)

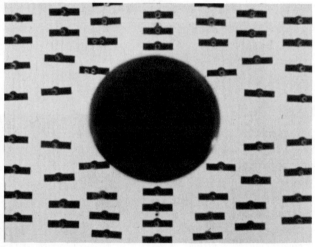

(b)

figure 9–33   Demonstration of the Meissner effect. (a) A superconducting tin cylinder is
situated with its axis perpendicular to a horizontal magnetic field of 80 gauss.
The direction of the field lines near the cylinder is indicated by the weakly
magnetized compass needles mounted in a Lucite sandwich so that they are
free to turn. (The ellipse at the top is the liquid helium surface as seen from
below.) (b) The same as (a) except that the temperature is such that the tin
cylinder is normally conducting. The compass needles now point in the direction
of the horizontal field except for small fluctuations due to their mutual interactions. (Courtesy of Dr. A. Leitner and Michigan State University.)

It has been recognized for some time that superconducitvity is due to a collective action of the conducting electrons. In 1957, Bardeen, Cooper, and Schrieffer published a successful theory of superconductivity which is now known as the *BCS theory*. In this theory, the electrons are coupled in pairs at low temperatures. One electron interacts with the lattice and perturbs it. The perturbed lattice interacts with another electron in such a way that there is an attraction between the two electrons which, at low temperatures, can overcome the Coulomb repulsion between them. The electron-lattice-electron interaction produces an energy gap between the superconducting state, in which the electrons act collectively, and the normal states, in which the electrons act individually. Energy from an electric field can be absorbed by the electrons in this collective state to produce a superconducting current. However, energy cannot be dissipated by individual collisions of electron and lattice unless the temperature is high enough so that the electron bonds are broken. Materials, such as copper or gold that are very good conductors at normal temperatures have weak electron-lattice interactions; thus the electron-lattice-electron interaction is very weak, and these materials do not superconduct. At temperatures as low as 0.05°K, these materials are still normal conductors. In the superconducting state, the conduction of heat is *less* than normal because heat conduction by the electrons is an individual energy exchange process. This collective behavior of the electrons in a superconductor is somewhat similar to, but not the same as, the collective behavior of helium atoms in liquid helium II, which occurs below 2.17°K and will be discussed next. The superconducting electron gas and liquid helium II are sometimes called *superfluids*.

9·8
LIQUID HELIUM II

We saw in Section 9·4 that for most ordinary gases, the Bose-Einstein distribution differs very little from the Maxwell-Boltzmann distribution because there are many quantum states per particle due to the low density of gases and the large mass of molecules compared with that of electrons. There are two interesting applications of the Bose-Einstein distribution. One is blackbody radiation. The Planck formula for the spectral distribution of blackbody radiation can be derived by considering the radiation to be a gas of photons obeying the Bose-Einstein distribution. This was the first done by Bose in 1924. This calculation will not be presented here, but it is outlined in Problem 9–16. The other interesting application of the Bose-Einstein distribution is liquid helium. The somewhat daring idea that liquid helium can be treated as an ideal gas obeying the Bose-Einstein distribution was suggested in 1938

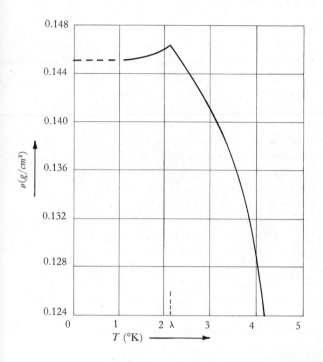

figure 9–34

*Plot of density of liquid
helium versus temperature,
by Kamerlingh Onnes,
and Boks.*
(*From London:* Superfluids, *Dover
Publications, Inc., New York, 1964.
Reprinted by permission of
the publisher.*)

figure 9–35

*H. Kamerlingh Onnes and
J. D. van der Waals by the
helium liquefier in the
Kamerlingh Onnes Laboratory
in Leiden in 1911.*
(*Courtesy of the Kamerlingh
Onnes Laboratory.*)

by F. London in an attempt to understand the amazing properties of helium at low temperatures.

We shall describe some of the properties of liquid helium at low temperatures and give a brief outline of the London theory.

When liquid helium is cooled, a remarkable change takes place at a temperature of about 2.2°K (actually, at 2.17°K). In 1924, H. Kamerlingh Onnes and J. Boks measured the density of liquid helium as a function of temperature and obtained the curve shown in Figure 9–34. In 1928, Keesom and Wolfke suggested that this discontinuity in the slope of the curve was an indication of a phase transition. They used the terms "helium I" for the liquid above 2.2°K and "helium II" for the liquid below that temperature. Keesom and Clusius in 1932 measured the specific heat as a function of temperature and obtained the curve shown in Figure 9–36. Because of the similarity of this curve to the Greek letter λ, the transition is called the *lambda point*. Just above the lambda point, He boils vigorously as it evaporates. The bubbling immediately ceases at the lambda point, although the evaporation continues. This effect is due to the sudden increase in the thermal conductivity at the lambda point.

Measurements of thermal conductivity show that helium II conducts heat better than helium I by a factor of more than a

figure 9–36   *Specific heat of liquid helium versus temperature. Because of the resemblance of this curve to the Greek letter λ, the transition point is called the lambda point. (From London:* Superfluids, Dover Publications, Inc., *New York, 1964. Reprinted by permission of the publisher.)*

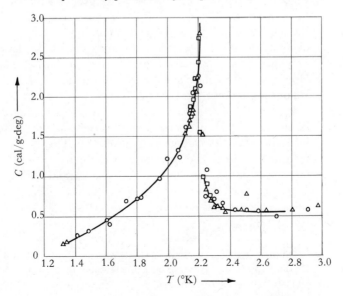

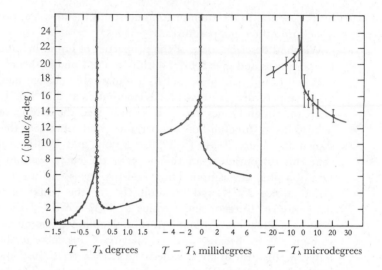

figure 9-37 *The lambda point with high resolution. The specific heat curve maintains its geometric shape as the scale is expanded. Near the λ point, the data fall on the curves given by* $C = 4.55 - 3.00 \log_{10}|T - T_\lambda| - 5.20\Delta$, *where* $\Delta = 0$ *for* $T < T_\lambda$ *and* $\Delta = 1$ *for* $T > T_\lambda$. (*From M. J. Buckingham and W. M. Fairbank, "The Nature of the λ-Transition,"* Progress in Low Temperature Physics, *edited by C. J. Gorter, Vol. III, p. 80, North-Holland Publishing Company, Amsterdam, 1961.*)

million; in fact, helium II is a better heat conductor than any metal. The conduction process is quite different from the usual process, for the heat conducted is not proportional to the temperature difference. If the viscosity of liquid helium II is measured by the method of passing the liquid through a fine capillary, the result depends on the size of the capillary; the measured viscosity approaches zero as the diameter of the capillary is made smaller. However, if the rotating-disk method is used, the measured viscosity is not too different from that of helium I.

Rather than mention the many other interesting properties of liquid helium II, we shall discuss briefly a theory suggested by F. London in 1938 and elaborated by Tisza.[2] In this theory, helium II is imagined to consist of two parts, a normal fluid with properties similar to helium I and a superfluid with quite different properties. The density of liquid helium II is the sum of the densities of the normal fluid and the superfluid:

$$\rho = \rho_s + \rho_n \qquad (9\text{-}65)$$

[2]Many of the properties are elegantly displayed in the film "Liquid Helium II, the Superfluid," available from the Audio Visual Center, Michigan State University, East Lansing, Michigan.

As the temperature is lowered from the lambda point, the density of the superfluid increases and that of the normal fluid decreases until, at absolute zero, only the superfluid remains. The superfluid is supposed to correspond to the helium molecules being in the lowest possible quantum state, the ground state. These molecules are not excited to higher states, so the superfluid cannot contribute to viscosity. When the viscosity of helium II is measured by the rotating-disk method, only the normal-fluid component exerts a viscous force on the disk. As the temperature is lowered, the fraction of helium in the normal component decreases from 100 percent at the lambda point to zero percent at $T = 0°K$; thus the viscosity decreases rapidly with temperature in agreement with experiment. On the other hand, when the viscosity is measured by passing the liquid through a fine capillary, the superfluid shows no resistance to flow. As the diameter of the capillary is reduced, the amount of normal fluid getting through the capillary is reduced

figure 9–38   (a) *Liquid helium being cooled by evaporation just above the lambda point boils vigorously.* (b) *Below the lambda point the boiling ceases and the superfluid runs out through the fine pores in the bottom of the vessel suspended above the helium bath.* (*Courtesy of Clarendon Laboratory. From* The Quest for Absolute Zero: The Meaning of Low Temperature Physics, *by K. Mendelssohn, World University Library, McGraw-Hill Book Company, New York, 1966.*)

(a)   (b)

(a)

(b)

(c)

figure 9–39   *Some remarkable properties of liquid helium II. (a) The Rollin creeping film. The liquid helium in the dish is at a temperature of about 1.6°K. A thin film creeps up the sides of the dish, over the edge, and down the outside to form the drop shown. (b) The thermo-mechanical effect. The bulb is in a cold bath of liquid helium II at 1.6°K. When light containing infrared radiation is focused on the bulb, liquid helium rises above the ambient level. The height of the level depends on the narrowness of the tube. If the tube is packed with powder and the top drawn out into a fine capillary, the super-fluid spurts out in a jet as shown in (c), hence the name "fountain effect."* [(a) and (b) Courtesy of Dr. A. Leitner and Michigan State University. (c) Courtesy of 500, Incorporated.]

until, in the limit of very small diameter, only the superfluid gets through and there is no viscosity.

It is not obvious that liquid helium should behave at all like an ideal gas. The atoms do exert forces on each other; however, because they are reasonably far apart, as evidenced by the very low density, these forces are quite weak. The ideal-gas model is used because it is relatively simple and because it yields insight into the behavior of this interesting fluid.

In Section 9·4 we calculated the normalization constant A_{He} to be about 3.5×10^{-6} for helium gas at 300°K, indicating that there were few particles per quantum state and therefore the Maxwell-Boltzmann distribution could be used. Since the density of liquid helium is about 0.145 g/cm³, the volume of 1 mole is

$$V = \frac{4 \text{ g/mole}}{0.145 \text{ g/cm}^3} = 27.6 \text{ cm}^3/\text{mole}$$

Using this volume in Eq. (9–52), rather than 22.4×10^3 cm³, we can calculate A_{He} for liquid helium. At $T \approx 2°K$, the result is $A_{He} \approx 5$. Thus the Maxwell-Boltzmann distribution would not be a good approximation for this "gas."

Let us see how Bose-Einstein statistics are related to the two-fluid model. We shall assume liquid helium to be an ideal gas of N atoms, following the BE distribution, for which the number of molecules in state i is

$$n_i = \frac{g_i}{Be^{E_i/kT} - 1} = \frac{g_i}{e^{\alpha}e^{E_i/kT} - 1} \tag{9–66}$$

where we have written $B = e^{\alpha}$ for convenience. The constant α cannot be negative, for if it were, n_i would be negative for values of $E_i/kT < |\alpha|$. We shall choose our energy scale such that the lowest energy state is labeled $E_0 = 0$. We have already seen that for a gas of N particles in a macroscopic box (the container), the energy states are numerous and close together. It is thus convenient to treat these states as a continuum and replace g_i (the number of states with energy E_i) with the density of states $g(E) \, dE$ (the number of states in the energy interval dE). The density of states for this problem was found in Section 9·4 [Eq. (9–50)]:

$$g(E) \, dE = \frac{2\pi V}{h^3} (2M)^{3/2} E^{1/2} \, dE$$

We should note, however, that replacing the discrete distribution of energy states by a continuous distribution ignores the ground state. Since there is only one such state, this is usually of little consequence. For the moment, we shall ignore this one state, but we shall see that this leads to difficulties, and we shall need to include this state explicitly later. The constant α is determined by the normalization condition,

$$N = \int n(E)\, dE = \frac{2\pi V}{h^3} (2M)^{3/2} \int_0^\infty \frac{E^{1/2}\, dE}{e^\alpha e^{E/kT} - 1}$$

$$= \frac{2\pi V}{h^3} (2M)^{3/2} (kT)^{3/2} \int_0^\infty \frac{x^{1/2}\, dx}{e^{\alpha+x} - 1} \tag{9-67}$$

where $x = E/kT$. The integral in Eq. (9-67) is a function of α which can be tabulated. It is customary to write Eq. 9-67 in the form

$$N = V \left(\frac{2\pi MkT}{h^2} \right)^{3/2} F(\alpha) \tag{9-68}$$

where

$$F(\alpha) = \frac{2}{\sqrt{\pi}} \int_0^\infty \frac{x^{1/2}\, dx}{e^{\alpha+x} - 1} \tag{9-69}$$

The function $F(\alpha)$ is sketched in Figure 9-40. It is a monotonically decreasing function for positive α which has a maximum value at $\alpha = 0$ of $F(0) = 2.612$. Equation (9-68) thus implies that

$$\frac{N}{V} \le 2.612 \left(\frac{2\pi MkT}{h^2} \right)^{3/2}$$

In terms of the temperature, Eq. (9-68) implies that

$$T \ge \frac{h^2}{2\pi Mk} \left(\frac{N}{2.612V} \right)^{2/3} = T_c \tag{9-70}$$

Using $V = 27.6$ cm^3 for the molar volume corresponding to the maximum density of 0.145 g/cm^3 (as can be seen from Figure 9-34, the density of helium does not vary greatly with temperature) we find for the critical temperature from Eq. (9-70)

$$T_c \approx 3.1°\text{K}$$

For temperatures below this critical point, the normalization equation (9-68) cannot be satisfied. We now see why we cannot ignore the ground state. Evidently a significant number of molecules must be in this state at low temperatures; this number is

$$N_0 = \frac{g_0}{e^\alpha e^{E_0/kT} - 1} = \frac{1}{e^\alpha - 1} \tag{9-71}$$

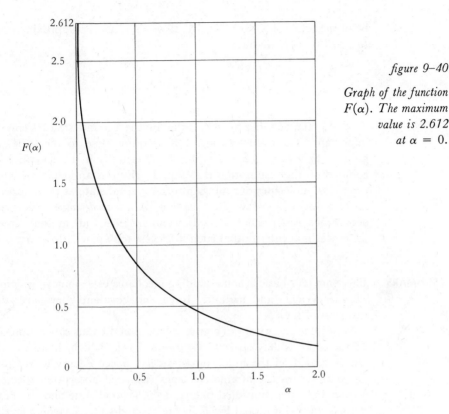

figure 9–40

Graph of the function
F(α). The maximum
value is 2.612
at α = 0.

since $g_0 = 1$ for this single state and $E_0 = 0$. The number becomes very large as α becomes small. We thus write for the normalization condition

$$N = N_0 + V\left(\frac{2\pi MkT}{h^2}\right)^{3/2} F(\alpha)$$

$$= \frac{1}{e^\alpha - 1} + V\left(\frac{2\pi kT}{h^2}\right)^{3/2} F(\alpha) \qquad (9\text{–}72)$$

This equation can be satisfied by the appropriate value of α for any temperature and density. Approximate methods can be used to find the relative number of molecules in the ground state. For example, using the definition of T_c, Eq. (9–72) can be written

$$N = N_0 + N\left(\frac{T}{T_c}\right)^{3/2} \frac{F(\alpha)}{F(0)}$$

For $T < T_c$, the solution of this equation for α can be shown to be of the order of $\alpha \approx N^{-1} \ll 1$. If we then use the approximation $F(\alpha)/F(0) \approx 1$, we have

$$\frac{N_0}{N} \approx 1 - \left(\frac{T}{T_c}\right)^{3/2}$$

We shall not pursue this theory further. We can see that for $T < T_c$, the number of molecules in the ground state becomes important. The value $T_c \approx 3.1°K$ is quite close to the lambda point temperature $T_\lambda = 2.17°K$, considering that this calculation is based on the assumption that liquid helium is an ideal gas. The process of molecules dropping into the ground state as the temperature is lowered below T_c is called *Einstein condensation*. Such an occurrence was predicted by Einstein in 1924, but at that time, there was no evidence that such a process took place in nature.

SUMMARY There are four basic atomic bonding mechanisms — ionic, covalent, van der Waals, and metallic. Ionic and covalent bonds are the strongest of these.

Molecular energy states consist of rotational bands superimposed on the more widely spaced vibrational levels, which, in turn, are superimposed on the much more widely spaced energy levels due to excitation of the atomic electrons. Infrared absorption spectra involve only the rotational bands of the ground state and the first excited-state vibrational levels in the ground-state electronic level; this is because the molecules are all initially in the lowest vibrational state $n = 0$, and Δn must be ± 1. The absorption spectrum for diatomic molecules consists of equally spaced maxima separated by $\Delta E = 2(\hbar^2/2I)$, with a gap of twice this separation at the energy of vibration $\hbar\omega$.

In the classical free-electron theory of metals, the electrical conductivity is given by $\sigma = ne^2\ell/m\bar{v}$, where $\bar{v}$ is the mean speed of the electrons in the electron gas given by the Maxwell distribution and ℓ is the mean free path of the electrons, which is inversely proportional to the area of the lattice atoms. The ratio of the electrical conductivity to the coefficient of heat conduction is a constant times the absolute temperature, and the contribution of the electron gas to the heat capacity should be $\frac{3}{2}R$. This theory accounts for Ohm's law, but it gives the wrong temperature dependence for the conductivity and gives numerical values of σ which are too low. The prediction that the heat capacity for metals should be $\frac{3}{2}R$ higher than that for other solids is not observed.

In the quantum-mechanical, free-electron theory of metals, the electrons have a Fermi-Dirac energy distribution. The above expression for σ holds if $\bar{v}$ is replaced by u_F — the Fermi speed, which is essentially independent of temperature — and ℓ is interpreted as the mean free path for electrons in a lattice of point atoms which are vibrating. At $T = 0$, the mean free path is infinite for a perfectly ordered lattice. The ratio of the coefficient of heat conduction to electrical conductivity is still a constant times the temperature. However, the contribution of the electron gas to the heat capacity is very small because there are few unoccupied energy states to which the electrons can be randomly excited.

The energy-distribution function for identical particles can be written

$$n(E) \, dE = g(E) \, dE \, F_{\text{FD}} \qquad \text{(Fermi-Dirac)}$$

or

$$n(E) \, dE = g(E) \, dE \, F_{\text{BE}} \qquad \text{(Bose-Einstein)}$$

where $g(E)$ is the density of states and the factors F_{FD} and F_{BE} are given by

$$F_{\text{FD}} = \frac{1}{B e^{E/kT} + 1}$$

$$F_{\text{BE}} = \frac{1}{B e^{E/kT} - 1}$$

Both F_{FD} and F_{BE} approach the Maxwell-Boltzmann factor

$$F_{\text{MB}} = \frac{1}{B e^{E/kT}}$$

when $E \gg kT$. The Maxwell-Boltzmann distribution is a good approximation for either quantum distribution if the normalization constant $A = 1/B$, computed from the Maxwell-Boltzmann distribution, satisfies $A \ll 1$. This condition is equivalent to the condition that the number of particles is much lower than the number of available energy states. This condition is always met for ordinary gases because of the large atomic masses and low densities. It is almost never met for electron gases. The constant B in the Fermi-Dirac distribution is usually written $B = e^{-E_F/kT}$, which defines the Fermi energy E_F. The Fermi energy is that for which the occupation probability is $\frac{1}{2}$, as can be seen from

$$F_{\text{FD}} = \frac{1}{e^{(E - E_F)/kT} + 1}$$

At $T = 0$, the Fermi energy $E_F(0)$ is that of the highest-filled energy level. For N particles in volume V, this is

$$E_F(0) = \frac{h^2}{8m} \left(\frac{3N}{\pi V} \right)^{2/3}$$

which, for copper, is about 7 eV. For low temperatures, $E_F \approx E_F(0)$ is a very good approximation.

When many atoms are brought together, the individual energy levels are split into bands of allowed energies separated by gaps of forbidden energies. The splitting depends on the type of bonding and the lattice separation. A material for which the highest occupied band is not full is a conductor. If this band is full, the material is an insulator if there is a gap that is large, compared with kT, between the filled band and the next allowed band. If the gap is small, such as in germanium, for which it is about 0.7 eV, the material is an intrinsic semiconductor because there are some electrons in the conduction band due to thermal energy. Impurity semiconductors can be made by doping with an impurity which contributes either filled energy levels just below the conduction band (donor, or n-type) or empty energy levels just above the filled valence band (acceptor, or p-type).

In many materials called *superconductors*, the resistance drops suddenly to zero below a critical temperature T_c, which is typically a few degrees above 0°K. Superconductivity is due to a collective action of the electrons.

The unusual properties of liquid helium at low temperatures can be understood qualitatively by assuming that liquid helium is an ideal gas that obeys the Bose-Einstein distribution.

REFERENCES

1. Enrico Fermi, *Molecules, Crystals, and Quantum Statistics*, translated by M. Ferro-Luzzi, W. A. Benjamin, Inc., New York, 1966.
2. Alan Holden, *The Nature of Solids*, The Columbia University Press, New York, 1965. This is an excellent nonmathematical treatment of the properties of solids.
3. C. Kittel, *Introduction to Solid State Physics*, 3rd ed., John Wiley & Sons, Inc., New York, 1966.
4. A. Dekker, *Solid State Physics*, Prentice-Hall, Inc., Englewood Cliffs, N.J., 1957.
5. R. Sproull, *Modern Physics*, John Wiley & Sons, Inc., New York, 1963.
6. W. Shockley, *Electrons and Holes in Semiconductors*, D. Van Nostrand Company, Inc., Princeton, N.J., 1950.
7. F. London, *Superfluids*, vol. II, *Macroscopic Theory of Superfluid Helium*, Dover Publications, Inc., New York, 1954.
8. C. Lane, *Superfluid Physics*, McGraw-Hill Book Company, New York, 1962.
9. K. Mendelssohn, *The Quest for Absolute Zero; The Meaning of Low Temperature Physics*, World University Library, McGraw-Hill Book Company, New York, 1966.

10. A. Leitner, *Introduction to Superconductivity*, (1965) and *Liquid Helium II, the Superfluid*, (1963), Michigan State University, East Lansing, Michigan. These two excellent films, the first running 48 minutes and the second, 39 minutes, are probably the best available introduction to these subjects.

A good discussion of quantum statistics can be found in *Statistical Thermodynamics*, by Sears et al., Ref. 8 in Chapter 2.

PROBLEMS

SET A

9-1. The equilibrium separation of the K^+ and Cl^- ions in KCl is about 2.79 Å. (*a*) Calculate the potential energy of attraction of the ions assuming them to be point charges. (*b*) The ionization potential of potassium is 4.34 eV, and the electron affinity of Cl is 3.8 eV. Find the dissociation energy, neglecting the energy of repulsion. (*c*) The measured dissociation energy is 4.42 eV. What is the energy due to repulsion of the ions?

9-2. Indicate the mean value of r for two vibration levels in the potential-energy curve of Figure 9-1, and show that because of the assymmetry in the curve, $\bar{r}$ increases with increasing temperature and thus solids expand when heated.

9-3. (*a*) Explain why the moment of inertia of a diatomic molecule increases with increasing angular momentum for the same vibrational level.

(*b*) Explain why the moment of inertia of a diatomic molecule increases with increasing vibration energy.

9-4. There are about 2.5×10^{22} free electrons per cm^3 in sodium. (*a*) Calculate the Fermi energy at $T = 0$. (*b*) Calculate the Fermi velocity u_F at $T = 0$. (*c*) Calculate the Fermi temperature T_F. (*d*) Using $\rho = 1$ g/cm^3 for the density and $M = 23$ g/mole for the atomic weight, calculate the number of free electrons per atom for sodium.

9-5. Do Problem 9-4 for gold, which has 5.9×10^{22} free electrons per cm^3; $\rho = 19.3$ g/cm^3 and $M = 197$ g/mole.

9-6. Compare the kinetic energy of the outer electron in a lithium atom, obtained from the ionization potential, with the mean energy of the valence electrons in lithium metal, which has a Fermi energy of 4.7 eV. (Assume that the kinetic energy of the outer electron in the atom equals the magnitude of the total energy, as it does in the Bohr theory.)

9-7. At what temperature is the heat capacity due to the electron gas in a metal equal to 10 percent of that due to the lattice vibrations for copper?

9-8. Why should the work function of a metal be approximately independent of temperature?

SET B

9-9. (a) Calculate the electrostatic potential energy of Na^+ and Cl^- ions at their equilibrium separation distance of 2.4 Å, assuming the ions to be point charges.

(b) What is the energy of repulsion at this separation?

(c) Assume that the energy of repulsion varies as C/r^n. From Figure 9-1, this energy equals Ke^2/r at about $r = 1.4$ Å. Use this and your answer to part b to calculate n and C. (Though this calculation is not very accurate, the energy of repulsion does vary much more rapidly with r than does the energy of attraction.)

9-10. Derive the following expression for the moment of inertia of a diatomic molecule: $I = \mu r_0^2$ where r_0 is the distance between the masses, and μ is the reduced mass $\mu = \dfrac{m_1 m_2}{m_1 + m_2}$.

9-11. The central frequency for the absorption band of HCl, shown in Figure 9-13, is $f_0 = 8.66 \times 10^{13}$ sec^{-1}, and the absorption peaks are separated by about $\Delta f = 6 \times 10^{11}$ sec^{-1}.

(a) What is the magnitude of the zero-point vibration energy for HCl?

(b) What is the moment of inertia of HCl?

(c) Calculate the reduced mass of HCl, and from part b, find the equilibrium separation of the atoms.

9-12. What is the ratio of the number of H_2 molecules in states $l = 2$ and $l = 1$ to those in the $l = 0$ rotational state at $T = 300°K$? The statistical weights are $g_l = 2l + 1$.

9-13. Calculate the Fermi energy at $T = 0$ for neutrons in a three-dimensional well. The density of neutrons in a nucleus is approximately $10^{44}/m^3$.

9-14. Electrons that escape from a metal in thermionic emission must have energy as least as great as $E = E_F + \phi$, where E_F is the Fermi energy and ϕ is the work function. Show that the electrons likely to escape have the Maxwell-Boltzmann energy distribution. (Assume that $kT \ll \phi$. Is this a good assumption?)

9-15. (a) Sketch the function $n(E)$ versus E for the Fermi distribution at $T = 0$ and at $T = 0.1T_F$.

(b) At $T = 0$, what fraction of the electrons have less than the mean energy?

9-16. If the assumptions leading to the Bose-Einstein distributions are modified such that the number of particles is not assumed constant, the resulting distribution has $B = 1$. This distribution can be applied to a gas of photons. Consider the photons to be in a cubic box of side L. The momentum components of a photon are quantized by the standing wave conditions $k_x = n_1\pi/L$, $k_y = n_2\pi/L$, $k_z = n_3\pi/L$, where $p = \hbar(k_x^2 + k_y^2 + k_z^2)^{1/2}$ is the magnitude of the momentum.

(a) Show that the energy of a photon can be written $E = N(\hbar c\pi/L)$, where $N^2 = n_1^2 + n_2^2 + n_3^2$.

(b) Assuming two photons per space state because of the two possible polarizations, show that the number of states between N and $N + dN$ is $\pi N^2\, dN$.

(c) Find the density of states and show that the number of photons in the energy interval dE is

$$n(E)\, dE = \frac{(8\pi L^3/h^3 c^3)\, E^2\, dE}{e^{E/kT} - 1}$$

(d) The energy density in dE is given by $u(E)\, dE = En(E) \times dE/L^3$. Use this to obtain the Planck blackbody-radiation formula for energy density in $d\lambda$, where λ is the wavelength

$$f(\lambda)\, d\lambda = \frac{8\pi\lambda^{-5}\, d\lambda}{e^{hc/\lambda kT} - 1}$$

TEN
NUCLEAR
PHYSICS

In this chapter we shall study some of the properties of the atomic nucleus. The first information about the nucleus came from the discovery of radioactivity by Becquerel in 1896, and this subject was studied by many physicists in the first decades of the twentieth century. The rays emitted by radioactive nuclei were classified as α, β, and γ rays according to their ability to penetrate matter and ionize air; the α radiation has the least penetration and produces the most ionization, and the γ has the most penetration with the least ionization. It was later found that α rays are He nuclei, β rays are electrons, and γ rays are very short-wavelength electromagnetic radiation. Rutherford's α-particle-scattering experiments in 1911 showed that the radius of the atomic nucleus (assuming a spherical shape) is about 10^{-4} or 10^{-5} times that of the atom, for Coulomb's law correctly predicted the experimental results as long as the α particle did not come within about 10^{-12} cm $= 10$ fermis of the center of the nucleus. In 1919, Rutherford bombarded nitrogen with α particles and observed scintillations on a zinc sulphide screen due to protons, which have a much longer range in air than

α particles. This was the first observation of artificial nuclear disintegration. Such experiments were extended to many other elements in the next few years.

In 1928, the correct theory of α radioactivity as a quantum-mechanical, barrier-penetration phenomenon was given by Gamow, Gurney, and Condon. In 1932, the neutron was discovered by Chadwick, and the first nuclear reaction using artificially accelerated particles was observed by Cockcroft and Walton. It is quite reasonable to mark the year 1932 as the beginning of modern nuclear physics. With the discovery of the neutron, it became possible to understand some of the properties of nuclear structure; also, the advent of nuclear accelerators made possible many experimental studies without the severe limitations of the availability and energy of naturally radioactive sources.

The study of nuclear physics is quite different from that of atomic physics. The simplest atom, the hydrogen atom, can be completely understood by solving the Schroedinger equation using the known potential energy of interaction between the electron and proton, $V(r) = -Ke^2/r$, though as we have seen, the mathematics needed is fairly complicated. The analogous problem in nuclear physics is the simplest nucleus (other than a single proton), the deuteron, consisting of a proton and a neutron. We cannot simply solve the Schroedinger equation for this problem and then compare with experiment, because the potential energy of interaction V is not known. There is no macroscopic way to measure the force between a neutron and a proton. It is clear from the stability of He^4 that there are other forces much stronger than electromagnetic or gravitational forces between nucleons. (The word "nucleon" refers to either a proton or a neutron.) The electrostatic potential energy of two protons separated by one fermi is

$$V = \frac{Ke^2}{r} = \frac{1.44 \text{ MeV-F}}{1 \text{ F}} = 1.44 \text{ MeV}$$

and the gravitational potential energy is smaller than this by a factor of 10^{-35}. The energy needed to remove a proton or neutron from He^4 is about 20 MeV. The force responsible for this large binding energy is called the *nuclear force*. The determination of the characteristics of the nuclear force is one of the central problems of nuclear physics. Information about this force can be obtained from scattering experiments involving protons and neutrons. Although the results of a scattering experiment can be predicted unambiguously from a knowledge of the force law, the force law cannot be completely determined from the results of such an experiment. The results of many scattering experiments do indicate that the nuclear force is the same between any two nucleons —

that is, n-n, p-p, and n-p — and that the force is strong when the particles are close and drops rapidly to zero when the particles are separated by a few fermis. The potential energy of the interaction can be roughly represented by a square well of about 40 MeV depth and a few fermis width.

It is not possible to give an adequate discussion of the many facets of nuclear physics in a short space. In the next two sections we describe the discovery of the neutron and discuss some of the properties of the ground states of nuclei. We then consider an important model for the description of nuclei, the shell model. In Sections 10·4 and 10·5 we shall discuss some aspects of radioactivity and some typical nuclear reactions used to determine nuclear properties. Section 10·6 is a brief introduction to the subject of elementary particles. The chapter concludes with a discussion of the interactions of nuclear particles with matter, a subject that is important for the understanding of the detection of nuclear particles. The important subject of nuclear technology — particle accelerators and particle detectors — has been completely omitted in order to concentrate on nuclear structure.

10·1
THE DISCOVERY OF THE NEUTRON

The experiments of Moseley (see Chap. 4, Section 4·4) showed that the nuclear charge is Z times the proton charge, where Z is the atomic number, which is about half the atomic weight A (except for hydrogen, for which $Z = A$). Thus the nucleus has a mass about equal to that of A protons but charge of only $Z = \frac{1}{2}A$ protons. Before the discovery of the neutron, it was difficult to understand this unless there were $A - Z$ electrons in the nucleus to balance the charge without changing the mass very much. The idea that the nucleus contained electrons was supported by the observation of β decay, in which electrons are ejected. However, there were serious difficulties with this model. A relatively simple calculation from the uncertainty principle shows that an electron has a minimum kinetic energy of about 50 to 100 MeV if it is confined in a region of $r < 10^{-12}$ cm. The energies of the electrons in β decay are only of the order of 1 or 2 MeV. There is no evidence for such a strong attractive force between nuclei and electrons, which would be implied by a negative potential energy of 50 to 100 MeV inside the nucleus. Since the electrostatic potential energy of the electron and nucleus is negative, there is no barrier, as there is in α decay. Thus if the electron's total energy is positive, as required for β decay, the electron should leak out immediately. A further difficulty is the observation that the magnetic moments of nuclei are of the order of nuclear magnetons, $e\hbar/2m_p$, about 2,000 times smaller than a Bohr magneton $e\hbar/2m_e$, which would be expected if there were electrons inside the nucleus.

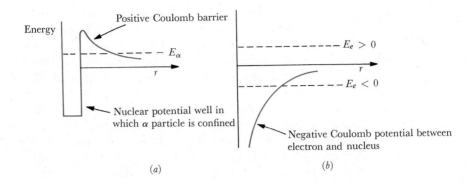

figure 10–1   (a) *Potential barrier for an α particle compared with* (b), *potential for a negative electron. Because there is no barrier for the electron, it will not be bound at all unless the total energy is negative, in which case it can never escape.*

The most convincing argument against electrons in the nucleus concerns angular momentum. The angular momentum of the nitrogen nucleus has a quantum number 1, which can be inferred from a very small splitting of atomic spectra called *hyperfine structure* (see Section 10·2). It is also known (from molecular spectra) that the nitrogen nucleus obeys Bose-Einstein rather than Fermi-Dirac statistics. If N^{14} contained 14 protons each with spin $\frac{1}{2}$ and 7 electrons each with spin $\frac{1}{2}$, the resultant angular momentum would have to be $\frac{1}{2}$, $\frac{3}{2}$, $\frac{5}{2}$, etc., and the nucleus would obey Fermi-Dirac statistics.

In 1920 Rutherford suggested that there might be a neutral particle, possibly a proton and an electron tightly bound together, which he called a *neutron*. When such a particle was found by Chadwick in 1932, the idea that electrons were permanent constituents of nuclei was abandoned. Instead, the nucleus was assumed to contain N neutrons and Z protons, a total of $A = N + Z$ particles. The picture of the neutron being a proton and electron bound together has also been abandoned, since the spin of the neutron is $\frac{1}{2}$.

In 1930, Bothe and Becker found that many nuclei became radioactive and emitted what was then thought to be γ rays when bombarded by α particles from radioactive polonium (see Figure 10–2). Using a much stronger polonium α source, Curie and Joliot repeated these experiments in 1932 and measured the penetration of the unknown γ rays in lead. For the most penetrating radiation, that from beryllium, they found that it took 4.7 cm of lead to reduce the intensity by $\frac{1}{2}$. Calculating the absorption expected by the Compton scattering process, they found the energy of the γ rays from Be to be about 15 MeV. This was much higher than the energy of γ rays emitted by naturally radioactive substances. They also found that sheets of lead, carbon, aluminum, etc., placed between the γ rays and their ionization-chamber detector, had little effect, but thin sheets of material such as paraffin, which contained hydrogen, produced a secondary radiation that greatly increased the ionization in their detector. They correctly surmised that this secondary radiation consisted of protons. By measuring the range of these protons in air, they found the energy of the protons to be about 5.7 MeV. This result was quite startling. The ejection of a proton from a substance by a γ ray is analogous to Compton scattering of x rays by electrons. The maximum change in wavelength in Compton scattering by protons is $2h/m_pc$, obtained from Eq. (3–33) with $\theta = 180°$. It is easy to calculate that the energy of the γ ray must be at least 50 MeV in order to give the proton 5.7 MeV (see Problem 10–10). Curie and Joliot found similar results using α particles on boron, though the radiation from boron was weaker.

Chadwick thought it unlikely that the protons were ejected by the Compton scattering process. Not only were rays of very high energy needed, but the number of protons observed was several thousand times greater than predicted for this scattering process. He extended the experiment by exposing many materials, including the gases hydrogen, helium, oxygen, nitrogen, and argon, to the beryllium and boron radiation produced by bombardment with polonium α particles. He found that the beryllium radiation produced recoil atoms of about the same number for all the gases. By measuring the energy of recoil, he could compute the energy of the incident γ rays just as did Curie and Joliot. He found that the result depended on which gas was used. For example, it required about 50-MeV γ rays to produce recoil hydrogen atoms, but 90-MeV γ rays were needed to produce the recoil nitrogen atoms observed. He then computed the results to be expected if the beryllium radiation consisted of neutral particles of mass approximately equal to the proton mass. The maximum energy occurs when the neutral particle (which Chadwick called the neutron, after Rutherford) makes a head-on collision with the gas atom. For the case of recoil protons, the neutron will transfer all its kinetic energy in a head-on collision because the two particles have the same mass. Since the maximum energy of the recoil protons was measured to be 5.7 MeV, this is the energy of the neutrons emitted from beryllium. Using these results, it was easy to calculate the maximum recoil energy of other atoms such as nitrogen. These calculated energies agreed with Chadwick's experimental results. It was not possible to determine the mass of the neutron accurately from the calculations, but it could be determined in principle from the reaction $He^4 + Be^9 \rightarrow C^{12} + n$ if the masses were

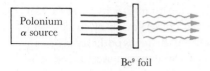

(a) An alpha particle hitting Be⁹ foil produces unknown radiation.

Be⁹ foil

(b) The intensity of the unknown radiation is reduced to ½ by 4.7 cm of lead. If the radiation is gamma radiation, its energy must be about 15 MeV.

4.7 cm of lead

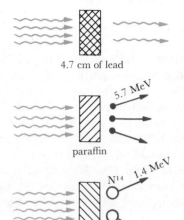

5.7 MeV

paraffin

(c) Many protons are produced by the unknown radiation incident on paraffin. If the radiation is gamma radiation, the energy must be about 50 MeV to produce 5.7 MeV protons by Compton scattering. If the radiation consists of uncharged particles with the same mass of the proton (neutrons), the energy of the neutron need be only 5.7 MeV to produce 5.7 MeV protons by collisions.

N¹⁴ 1.4 MeV

N¹⁴

(d) The unknown radiation incident on nitrogen gas produces recoil N¹⁴ atoms with energy of 1.4 MeV which requires 90 MeV gamma rays or 5.7 MeV neutrons.

figure 10–2 *Schematic description of experiments of Bothe and Becker, Currie and Joliot, and Chadwick leading to the discovery of the neutron.*

known. The mass of Be^9 had not been measured accurately at that time, but that of boron and nitrogen had. Using the reaction He^4 + B^{11} → N^{14} + n, Chadwick determined the mass of the neutron from

$$(Mc^2)_{\text{He}^4} + (Mc^2)_{\text{B}^{11}} + KE(\text{He}^4)$$
$$= (Mc^2)_{\text{N}^{14}} + (Mc^2)_n + KE(n) \qquad (10\text{--}1)$$

with the result: $1.005 < m(n) < 1.008$ atomic mass units.

Chadwick's paper "The Existence of the Neutron," makes an excellent introduction to the study of nuclear physics.[1] We quote from the last two paragraphs:

"In conclusion, I may restate briefly the case for supposing that the radiation, the effects of which have been examined in this paper, consists of neutral particles rather than of radiation quanta. Firstly, there is no evidence from electron collisions of the presence of a radiation of such a quantum energy as is necessary to account

[1]*Proceedings of the Royal Society,* **A136,** 692 (1932). This paper is reprinted in Ref. 1, and in Ref. 2 of Chapters 2 and 3.

for the nuclear collisions. Secondly, the quantum hypothesis can be sustained only by relinquishing the conservation of energy and momentum. On the other hand, the neutron hypothesis gives an immediate and simple explanation of the experimental facts; it is consistent in itself and it throws new light on the problem of nuclear structure.

"Summary:

"The properties of the penetrating radiation emitted from beryllium (and boron) when bombarded by the α-particles of polonium have been examined. It is concluded that the radiation consists, not of quanta as hitherto supposed, but of neutrons, particles of mass 1 and charge 0. Evidence is given to show that the mass of the neutron is probably between 1.005 and 1.008. This suggests that the neutron consists of a proton and an electron in close combination, the binding energy being about 1 to 2×10^6 electron-volts. From experiments on the passage of the neutrons through matter, the frequency of their collisions with atomic nuclei and with electrons is discussed."

**10·2
GROUND-STATE
PROPERTIES
OF NUCLEI**

In this section we discuss some of the properties of nuclei in the ground state. We shall mention just a few methods of determining some of these properties.[2] We shall use the following standard symbols and terminology: The letter N stands for the number of neutrons in a nucleus, and Z for the number of protons (Z is also the atomic number); $A = N + Z$ is the total number of nucleons, sometimes called the *mass number* or the *atomic weight*. Nuclei are often referred to by the chemical symbol with a superscript giving the value of A, such as O^{16} or O^{15}. Sometimes N is given as a subscript and Z as a presubscript, such as $_8O_7^{15}$, though this is not necessary because each element (Z number) has a unique chemical symbol. Nuclei with the same Z, such as O^{15} and O^{16}, are called *isotopes*. Nuclei with the same N, such as $_6C_7^{13}$ and $_7N_7^{14}$, are called *isotones*, while nuclei with the same A, such as C^{14} and N^{14}, are called *isobars*. A nucleus in an excited state with a particularly long decay time is called an *isomer*, and the state is called an *isomeric state*. For example, Ba^{137} has an isomeric state of energy 0.66 MeV above the ground state with a mean life of about 1.8 minutes.

SIZE AND SHAPE
OF NUCLEI

With a few exceptions, nuclei are nearly spherical. Almost all the exceptions occur in the rare-earth region (the transition period in

[2]Reference 2 contains a particularly good discussion of the experimental methods used in measuring nuclear properties.

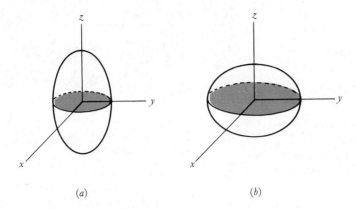

figure 10–3   *Nonspherical nuclear shapes. Nuclei with positive quadrupole moments have $(z^2)_{\text{ave}}$ greater than $(x^2)_{\text{ave}}$ or $(y^2)_{\text{ave}}$ and are of watermelon shape, as in (a). Nuclei with negative quadrupole moments have $(z^2)_{\text{ave}}$ less than $(x^2)_{\text{ave}}$ or $(y^2)_{\text{ave}}$ and are shaped like flattened pumpkins, as in (b).*

the periodic table, $Z = 58$ to $Z = 70$), in which the shape is el-lipsoidal, with the major axis differing from the minor axis by only about 20 percent or less. For these heavy nuclei, the atomic elec-tron wave functions penetrate the nucleus, and deviations from spherical shape show up as small changes in the atomic energy levels. If the nucleus is shaped like a watermelon (Figure 10–3), with the z axis larger than the x and y axes, the average value of z^2, defined by

$$(z^2)_{\text{ave}} \equiv \frac{1}{q} \int z^2 \rho \, dV \qquad (10\text{-}2)$$

is larger than the average value of x^2 and y^2 (q is the total nuclear charge). For this case the quadrupole moment, which is propor-tional to $3(z^2)_{\text{ave}} - (x^2 + y^2 + z^2)_{\text{ave}}$, is positive. This is the most common case for nonspherical nuclei. Nuclei with negative quadrupole moments are shaped more like flattened pumpkins, with the two equal axes longer than the third axis.

The nuclear radius can be determined by scattering experiments similar to the first ones of Rutherford, or in some cases from meas-urements of radioactivity. An interesting, nearly classical method of determining the nuclear radius involves the measurement of the energy of positron β decay between *mirror nuclei*, two nuclei that can be made from each other by exchanging the Z and N numbers (Figure 10–4). An example is O^{15}, with 8 protons and 7 neutrons, and N^{15}, with 8 neutrons and 7 protons. Assuming that the nuclear force between nucleons is independent of the kind of nucleons, the

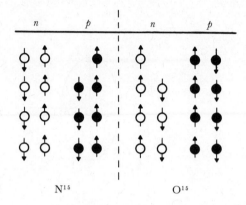

figure 10–4

*Mirror nuclei. If all the neutrons
are changed to protons and
all the protons are changed
to neutrons, N^{15} becomes
its mirror, O^{15}. The ground-state
energy of mirror nuclei pairs
differs only in the electrostatic energy.*

only difference in energy between O^{15} and N^{15} is electrostatic.
The electrostatic energy of a ball of uniform charge is

$$W = \frac{3}{5} \frac{Kq^2}{R} \tag{10–3}$$

where q is the charge and R is the radius. The energy difference
between O^{15} and N^{15} is then

$$W = \frac{3}{5} \frac{Ke^2}{R} [Z^2 - (Z-1)^2]$$

with $Z = 8$. A measurement of the energy of the decay, $O^{15} \rightarrow$
$N^{15} + \beta^+$ (positron) $+ \nu$ (neutrino), thus gives a measurement
of R. Assuming a uniform charge distribution, measurements of
the positron decay energies for 18 pairs of mirror nuclei give for
the nuclear radius

$$R = R_0 A^{1/3} \quad \text{with } R_0 = 1.5 \times 10^{-13} \text{ cm} \tag{10–4}$$

where A is the atomic number. A quantum-mechanical correction
using a charge distribution calculated from the nuclear shell model
changes the value of R_0 to 1.2×10^{-13} cm. The consistency of
these results with others is a strong indication that the nuclear
energy is the same for these nuclei. The most extensive measurements of the nuclear radius have been done by Robert Hofstadter
et al. in a series of experiments begun in 1953. In these experiments, nuclei were bombarded with electrons having energies of
about 200 to 500 MeV from the Stanford linear accelerator. The
wavelength of a 500-MeV electron is about 2.5 F, which is smaller
than the radius of heavy nuclei. Thus it is possible to learn something about the detailed structure of the charge distribution of

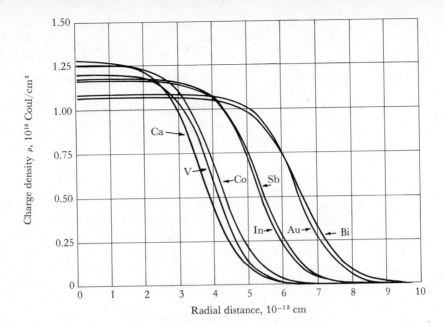

(a)

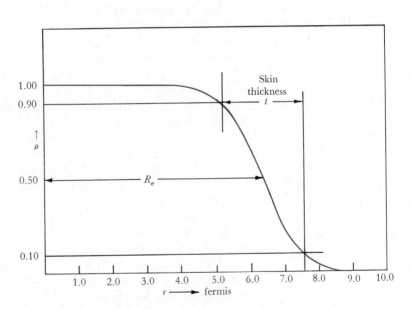

(b)

figure 10–5

(a) *Charge density versus distance for several nuclei as determined by electron-scattering experiments.*
(b) *Definitions of parameters R_e and t used to describe nuclear charge density.*
[*From Hofstadter,* Annual Review of Nuclear Science, **7,** *231 (1957).*]

nuclei by analyzing the scattering of these electrons.[3] The analysis is fairly complicated because the electrons are relativistic. Figure 10–5a shows some charge distributions obtained from these experiments. The mean electromagnetic radius R_e and the surface thickness t, indicated in Figure 10–5b, are given by

$$t = 2.4 \pm 0.3 \text{ F}$$
$$R_e = (1.07 \pm 0.02)A^{1/3} \text{ F}$$

(10-5)

[3]Hofstadter was awarded the Nobel Prize for physics jointly with R. L. Mössbauer in 1961.

These results are not too different from those obtained from positron decay.

A different type of nuclear radius can be determined by measuring the attenuation of a beam of fast neutrons. The total cross section for attenuation can be written

$$\sigma = 2\pi(R + \lambda)^2 \tag{10-6}$$

where λ is the de Broglie wavelength divided by 2π and R is the nuclear radius. Thus the neutrons must be fast enough so that $\lambda < R$ in order to gain information about R from the measurement of σ. These experiments do not measure the charge distribution but, instead, measure the "radius" of the nuclear force between a neutron and the nucleus. The results of these measurements are

$$R = R_0 A^{1/3} \qquad \text{with } R_0 = 1.4 \text{ F} \tag{10-7}$$

These different types of experiments thus give compatible but not identical results. The fact that the radius is proportional to $A^{1/3}$ means that the volume is proportional to A, the number of nucleons. This means that the density is the same for all nuclei. The numerical value is easily computed to be about 10^{14} g/cm^3. This fantastically high density, compared with 1 g/cm^3 for atoms, is, of course, a consequence of the fact that nearly all the mass of the atom is concentrated in a region of radius about 10^{-5} that of the atom.

SYSTEMATICS OF N AND Z NUMBERS

There are about 260 stable nuclei. Figure 10–6 shows a plot of the neutron number N versus the proton number Z for stable nuclei. The straight line is $N = Z$. This result can be understood in terms of the exclusion principle and electrostatic energy of the protons. (See Examples 8–2 and 8–3.) If we consider the kinetic energy of A particles in a one-dimensional square well, the energy is least if $\frac{1}{2}A$ are neutrons and $\frac{1}{2}A$ are protons and greatest if all the particles are of one type. There is therefore a tendency for N and Z to be equal. If we include the electrostatic energy of repulsion of the protons, the result is changed somewhat. This potential energy is proportional to Z^2. At large enough A, the energy is increased less by adding two neutrons than by adding one neutron and one proton; thus the difference $N - Z$ increases with increasing Z.

There is also a tendency for nucleons to pair. Of the 264 nuclei that are stable, 158 have even Z and even N, 49 have odd Z and even N, 53 have even Z and odd N, and only 4 have both N and Z odd.

Since there are about 100 different elements and about 260 stable nuclei, there is an average of about $2\frac{1}{2}$ isotopes per element.

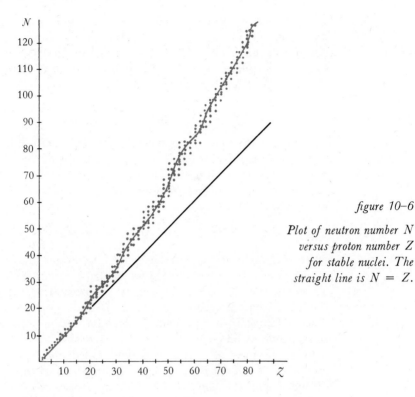

figure 10–6

Plot of neutron number N versus proton number Z for stable nuclei. The straight line is N = Z.

There is an unusually large number of isotopes for nuclei with Z equal to 20, 28, 50, and 82. For example, tin, with $Z = 50$, has 10 stable isotopes. Nuclei with these same numbers of neutrons have a larger-than-average number of isotones. These numbers are called *magic numbers* and are a manifestation of shell structure in very much the same way that the atomic magic numbers 2, 10, 18, and 36 correspond to closed-electron shell structure.

Nuclei that do not fall on the N-versus-Z stability curve are radioactive. We shall discuss radioactivity in Section 10·4.

MASSES AND
BINDING ENERGY

The mass of an atom can be accurately measured in a mass spectrometer, which measures q/M for ions by bending them in a magnetic field. The mass of an atom is not quite equal to the mass of the nucleus plus the mass of the electrons because of the binding energy of the electrons (see Section 1·10 for the definitions of mass and energy units and for examples of the calculation of binding energies). The binding energy of the electrons is defined by

$$B_{\text{atomic}} = M_N c^2 + Z m_e c^2 - M_a c^2 \qquad (10\text{–}8)$$

where M_N is the mass of the nucleus, M_a is the mass of the atom, and m_e is the mass of an electron. Because the binding energies of atoms are only of the order of keV, compared with nuclear binding energies of the order of MeV, atomic binding energies are usually neglected in nuclear physics. The binding energy of a nucleus with Z protons and N neutrons is defined by

$$B_{\text{nuclear}} \equiv Zm_pc^2 + Nm_nc^2 - M_Nc^2 \tag{10-9}$$

where m_p is the mass of a proton and m_n the mass of a neutron. Since the mass of an atom is very nearly equal to the mass of the nucleus plus the mass of the electrons (neglecting the atomic binding energy), the nuclear binding energy can be accurately computed from

$$B_{\text{nuclear}} = ZM_{\text{H}}c^2 + Nm_nc^2 - M_ac^2 \tag{10-10}$$

where M_{H} is the mass of the hydrogen atom and M_a is the mass of the atom. Note that the masses of the Z electrons cancel out. This expression is more convenient to use because it is the mass of the atom that is usually measured in mass spectrometers. The masses of all stable isotopes and of some unstable isotopes are listed in Appendix A on page 493.

Once the mass of a nucleus is determined, the binding energy can be computed; it is approximately proportional to the number of nucleons in the nucleus. The binding energy per nucleon B/A is sketched versus A in Figure 10-7. The mean value is about 8.3 MeV. The fact that this curve is approximately constant (for $A > 16$) indicates that there is saturation of nuclear forces. If each nucleon bonded to every other nucleon, there would be $A - 1$ bonds for each nucleon, or $\frac{1}{2}A(A - 1)$ total bonds, and the binding energy per nucleon would be proportional to $A - 1$ rather than constant. Figure 10-7 indicates that, instead, there is a fixed number of bonds per nucleon, such as would be the case if each nucleon were attracted only to its nearest neighbors. Such a situation also leads to a constant density, consistent with the measurements of radius. If the binding energy per nucleon were proportional to the number of nucleons, the radius would be approximately constant, as is the case for atoms.

The fact that the density and the binding energy per nucleon are approximately the same for all nuclei was noticed in the early 1930s after a sufficient number of atomic masses had been measured; this led to the comparison of a nucleus to a liquid drop, which also has a constant density, independent of the number of molecules. The energy required to remove molecules from a liquid is the heat of vaporization. This is proportional to the mass or number of molecules in the liquid, just as the binding energy is proportional to the number of nucleons. Using this analogy, Weizsacker in 1935

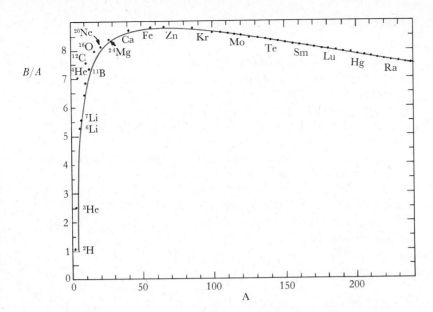

figure 10–7 *The binding energy per particle versus mass number A. The solid curve represents a semiempirical binding-energy formula, Eq. (10–12). (From* Principles of Modern Physics, *by Leighton, copyright 1959. Used by permission of McGraw-Hill Book Company, New York.)*

developed a formula for the mass of a nucleus — or the binding energy, since the two are related by Eq. (10–9) — as a function of A and Z which is called the *Weizsacker semiempirical mass formula.* We shall write down one version of this formula and discuss the origin of the terms:

$$M_N(A,Z) = \overset{0}{[Zm_p + (A - Z)m_n]} - \overset{1}{a_1 A} + \overset{2}{a_2 A^{2/3}}$$

$$+ \overset{3}{a_3 Z^2 A^{-1/3}} \qquad\qquad (10\text{--}11)$$

$$+ \overset{4}{a_4 (A - 2Z)^2 A^{-1}} \pm \overset{5}{a_5 A^{-1}}$$

0. In the first approximation, the mass is just equal to the sum of the masses of the Z protons and the $(A - Z)$ neutrons. This, of course, neglects the binding energy completely. The remaining terms are due to the binding energy.

1. It is important to understand the reason for the sign of this and the remaining terms. It is not difficult if we remember that attractive forces correspond to a negative potential energy and thus a negative contribution to the mass. Term 1 accounts for

the fact that the number of bonds is proportional to A, the number of particles. This gives a constant term to the binding energy per nucleon.

2. This is a correction to term 1. The nucleons on the surface of the nucleus do not have as many bonds as those in the interior of the nucleus. This is analogous to the surface tension in a liquid drop. Since the surface area is proportional to R^2, which is proportional to $A^{2/3}$, we add this term.

3. This term accounts for the positive electrostatic energy of a charged drop which is proportional to $Z^2/R \propto Z^2 A^{-1/3}$. Using the classical expression for the energy of a uniformly charged drop,

$$W = \frac{3}{5} \frac{K Z^2 e^2}{R}$$

the constant a_3 is equal to

$$\frac{0.6 K e^2}{R_0 c^2}$$

4. This term is not analogous to a liquid drop. It is a quantum-mechanical term that accounts for the fact that the energy is increased because of the exclusion principle if $N \neq Z$. The quantity $A - 2Z = N + Z - 2Z = N - Z$ is the number of neutrons in excess of the number of protons. The expression $(A - 2Z)^2/A = (N - Z)^2/A$ is an empirical term which is zero if $N = Z$ and is independent of the sign of $N - Z$.

5. This last term is an empirical one to account for the pairing tendency of the nucleons. The plus sign is used if Z and N are both odd, the negative sign for both Z and N even. For the case Z or N even and the other odd, the term is taken to be zero.

Using Eq. (10–9), the binding energy is

$$B = [+a_1 A - a_2 A^{2/3} - a_3 Z^2 A^{-1/3} \\ - a_4 (A - 2Z)^2 A^{-1} \pm a_5 A^{-1}] c^2 \qquad (10\text{–}12)$$

There have been various attempts to fit this expression, or refinements of it, to the binding energies calculated from the measured masses. The solid curve in Figure 10–7 is one such fit, with the following parameters [from Green, *Physical Review*, **95**, 1006 (1954)]:

$$a_1 c^2 = 15.7 \text{ MeV}$$
$$a_2 c^2 = 17.8 \text{ MeV}$$
$$a_3 c^2 = 0.712 \text{ MeV}$$
$$a_4 c^2 = 23.6 \text{ MeV}$$
$$a_5 c^2 = 132 \text{ MeV or } 0$$

Although Eq. (10–12) could be used for calculating unknown masses of nuclei, the results would not be particularly accurate. The expression is useful in discussing stability and radioactivity. It is also useful in discussing fluctuations from the average behavior due to shell effects. We shall make use of this in Section 10·4.

NUCLEAR ANGULAR MOMENTUM AND MAGNETIC MOMENTS

The spin quantum number of the neutron and the proton is $\frac{1}{2}$. The angular momentum of the nucleus is a combination of the spin angular momenta of the nucleons plus any orbital angular momentum due to the motion of the nucleons. This resultant angular momentum is usually called *nuclear spin* and designated by the symbol **I**. Evidence for nuclear spin was first found in atomic spectra. The nuclear spin can add to the angular momentum **J** of the electrons to form a total angular momentum **F**:

$$\mathbf{F} = \mathbf{I} + \mathbf{J} \tag{10–13}$$

The possible quantum numbers for F are $I + J$, $I + J - 1 \ldots |I - J|$, using the usual rules for combining angular momenta. The number of values of F is $2J + 1$ or $2I + 1$, whichever is the smaller. Because of the energy of interaction of the electronic magnetic moment and the nuclear magnetic moment associated with I, each spectral line is split into $2J + 1$ or $2I + 1$ components. This splitting, called *hyperfine structure*, is very small, of the order of 10^{-6} eV. It can be observed only with extremely high resolution. For the cases $I < J$, the nuclear spin can be determined by counting the number of lines in the hyperfine splitting. The spin of all even-even nuclei (those with even Z and even N) is zero in the ground state. Evidently the nucleons couple together in such a way that their angular momenta add to zero in pairs, such as is often the case for electrons in atoms. There is no such simple rule for other nuclei with either odd N or odd Z or both. One of the successes of the shell model to be discussed in Section 10·3 is the correct prediction of nuclear spins for many nuclei.

The magnetic moment of the nucleus is of the order of the nuclear magneton.

$$\mu_N = \frac{e\hbar}{2m_p}$$

where m_p is the mass of the proton. The exact value is difficult to predict because it depends on the detailed motion of the nucleons. If the proton and neutron obeyed the Dirac relativistic wave equation, as does the electron, the magnetic moment due to spin would be 1 nuclear magneton for the proton and zero for the neutron because it has no charge. The experimentally determined moments of the nucleons are

$$(u_p)_z = +2.79\mu_N$$

$$(u_n)_z = -1.91\mu_N$$

Thus the proton and neutron are more complicated particles than the electron. It is interesting that the deviations of these moments from those predicted by the Dirac equation are about the same magnitude, 1.91 for the neutron and 1.79 for the proton. The reason for the values of the magnetic moments of the nucleons is not yet understood.

GROUND-STATE PROPERTIES OF THE DEUTERON   We shall discuss briefly some of the properties of the deuteron to indicate several of the complexities of the nuclear force. We have already mentioned that the binding energy is 2.22 MeV. The binding energy of 1.11 MeV per nucleon is the lowest found in nuclei and is much lower than the average of 8 MeV per nucleon. This indicates that saturation has not been reached with just two particles. The angular-momentum quantum number is found to be 1, and the magnetic moment is $0.857\mu_N$, which is just about $2\frac{1}{2}$ percent smaller than the sum of the moments of the proton and neutron, $2.79 - 1.91 = 0.88\mu_N$. This near agreement is consistent with a ground-state orbital angular momentum of 0 and parallel spins. There are no bound excited states of the deuteron. Neutron-proton scattering experiments indicate that the force between n and p in the singlet state (antiparallel spins) is just sufficiently less strong than the triplet state to make the deuteron unstable if the spins are antiparallel. The quadrupole moment of the deuteron should be zero if the particles are in the spherically symmetric $l = 0$ state. However, there is a small, measurable quadrupole moment. If it is assumed that the orbital quantum number is other than $l = 0$, neither the calculated magnetic moment nor the quadrupole moment is in agreement with experiment. If the force between the neutron and proton is not assumed to be central (along the line joining the particles), orbital angular momentum is not conserved and the ground-state wave function can be a mixture of different l states. The assumption of 96 percent $l = 0$ state and 4 percent $l = 2$ state, with the spins parallel, gives the correct quadrupole moment and the correct magnetic moment. Thus the ground-state properties of the deuteron indicate that the nuclear force depends on the orientation of the spins of the particles and has a small noncentral part.

10·3
THE SHELL MODEL

Although the gross features of the binding energy of nuclei are well accounted for by the semiempirical mass formula, the binding energy and the other properties do not vary with perfect smoothness from nucleus to nucleus. It is not surprising that the smooth curve predicted by Eq. (10–12) does not fit the data for very small A, for which the addition of a proton or a neutron makes a drastic difference. However, even for large A there are some wide fluctuations in nuclear properties in neighboring nuclei. Consider the binding energy of the last neutron in a nucleus. (Note that this is not the same as the average binding energy per nucleon.) We can calculate this from the semiempirical mass formula by computing the difference in mass $M(A - 1, Z) + m_n - M(A,Z)$. Figure 10–8 shows a plot of the difference between the experimentally measured binding energy of the last neutron and that calculated from Eq. (10–12) as a function of the neutron number N. There are large fluctuations in the regions of $N = 20$, 28, 50, 82, and 126. These are also the neutron numbers of the nuclei that have an unusually large number of isotones and the proton numbers (except that there is no element with $Z = 126$) of nuclei that have an unusually large number of isotopes — the so-called "magic numbers." In the region between these magic numbers, the binding energy of the last neutron is predicted quite accurately by the semiempirical mass formula. Figure 10–8 should be compared with Figure 8–6, which shows the binding energy of the last electron in an atom as a function of atomic number Z. The similarity of these two figures suggests a shell structure for the nucleus analogous to the shell structure of atoms. (There is other evidence for these magic num-

figure 10–8 *Difference in the measured binding energy of the last neutron and that calculated from mass formula versus neutron number. Note the similarity of this curve and the ionization potential of atoms versus Z (Figure 8–6). The neutron numbers 50, 82, and 126 correspond to closed shells. [From J. Harvey, Physical Review,* **81***, 353 (1951).]*

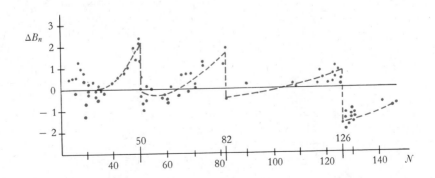

bers, such as neutron capture and cross sections, which we shall not describe here. See Ref. 3 for a more detailed discussion of the evidence for shell structure.)

Although the unusual stability of the nuclei with N or Z equal to one of the magic numbers was noticed in the 1930s, there was no successful explanation in terms of shell structure until 1949. In the discussion of atoms in Chapter 8, we started with a fixed positive charge $+Ze$ and computed the energies of individual electrons, assuming at first that each electron was independent of the others as long as the exclusion principle was not violated. The interaction of the outer electrons with the inner core could be taken care of by assuming an effective nuclear charge less than Z because of the screening of the inner electrons. This works quite well since the electrons are fairly far from each other in an atom. Thus we used the individual electron quantum states of the hydrogen atom, nlm_l, and m_s for the electrons in complex atoms as a first approximation. The atomic magic numbers come about naturally due to the large energy difference between one shell or subshell and the next. The actual calculations of atomic wave functions and atomic energies require powerful approximation or numerical techniques, but they can be done quite reliably because the forces involved are well known.

The situation is not the same for the nuclear shell model. In the first place, there is no originally given central potential analogous to the fixed positive charge of the atom. The interaction of the nucleons with each other is the only interaction present. The situation is complicated by the fact that we know little about the force law between nucleons except that it is strong and has a short range. At first sight, it is difficult to imagine a neutron or proton moving almost freely in a well-defined orbit when there are $A - 1$ particles nearby exerting very strong forces on it. Despite these difficulties, the observed properties, such as are illustrated in Figure 10–8, give a strong motivation to try a model in which each nucleon moves about more or less freely in an average potential field produced by the other nucleons. The assumption that the nucleon can move in an orbit without making many collisions can be rationalized by using the exclusion principle. Consider N neutrons in some potential well. In the ground state, the N lowest-energy levels will be filled. A collision between two neutrons which does not result in their merely exchanging states is forbidden by the exclusion principle if there are no unfilled states. A collision involving the exchange of identical particles has no effect. Thus only those nucleons near the top of the Fermi level can make collisions with each other. This is analogous to the result that most of the free electrons in a metal cannot absorb energy in random collisions with the lattice because all the nearby energy levels are full.

The first shell-model calculations failed to produce the correct magic numbers. In 1949, Mayer and Jensen independently showed that, with a modification in these calculations, the magic numbers did follow directly from a relatively simple shell model. We shall consider only some of the qualitative aspects of the nuclear shell model. Detailed calculations of energies and wave functions require many approximations, the understanding of which is a major current problem in nuclear physics.

Let us consider one nucleon of mass m moving in a spherically symmetric potential, $V(r)$. The Schroedinger equation for this problem in three dimensions is the same as Eq. (7–4). Since we are assuming $V(r)$ to be independent of θ and ϕ, the angular part of the equation can be separated and solved, as discussed in Chapter 7. The result is that the square of the angular momentum is quantized to the values $l(l+1)\hbar^2$, and the z component to the values $m_l\hbar$. The radial equation is (see also Eq. 7–28):

$$-\frac{\hbar^2}{2mr^2}\frac{d}{dr}(r^2R') + \frac{l(l+1)\hbar^2}{2mr^2} + V(r)R = ER \qquad (10\text{–}14)$$

The solution of this equation, of course, depends on the form of the potential energy $V(r)$. Though $V(r)$ is not known, we certainly expect it to be quite different from the $1/r$ potential used in Chapter 7 for atoms. Because the nuclear force is so strong and is negligible within a few fermis of the nuclear surface, it does not matter too much what the exact form of $V(r)$ is. Various guesses have been made. The simplest is the finite square well

$$\begin{aligned} V(r) &= -V_0 \qquad \text{for } r < R \\ &= 0 \qquad \text{for } r > R \end{aligned}$$

where R is the nuclear radius. This corresponds to an infinite attractive force at $r = R$ [the force is related to $V(r)$ by $F_r = -dV/dr$] and no force for other r. A more reasonable potential is obtained by rounding the corners of the square well shown in Figure 10–9. This makes the problem more difficult to solve analytically. Another form of $V(r)$, for which Eq. (10–14) can be solved exactly, is the three-dimensional harmonic oscillator

$$V(r) = -V_0 + \tfrac{1}{2}m\omega^2 r^2 \qquad (10\text{–}15)$$

Since the exact shape of the potential energy is not too important, we shall consider only those forms which are the simplest mathematically. Even for these cases, the detailed solutions of the three-dimensional Schroedinger equations are difficult and not particularly illuminating, so we shall discuss the results qualitatively.

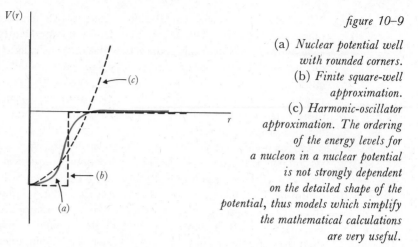

figure 10-9

(a) *Nuclear potential well with rounded corners.*
(b) *Finite square-well approximation.*
(c) *Harmonic-oscillator approximation. The ordering of the energy levels for a nucleon in a nuclear potential is not strongly dependent on the detailed shape of the potential, thus models which simplify the mathematical calculations are very useful.*

The allowed energies for a particle in the three-dimensional harmonic-oscillator potential, Eq. (10–15), are given by

$$E = [2(n - 1) + l]\hbar\omega + \tfrac{3}{2}\hbar\omega \qquad (10\text{–}16)$$

where l is the orbital-angular-momentum quantum number, which can have any of the values 0, 1, 2, . . . , and n can have any of the values $n = 1, 2, 3, ...$ (This n is *not* the same as the n defined in the hydrogen-atom solutions. There is no restriction that l be less than n for this problem.) The zero-point energy $\tfrac{3}{2}\hbar\omega$ is analogous to the one-dimensional zero-point energy $\tfrac{1}{2}\hbar\omega$. It is customary to neglect this energy when listing the allowed energies. We have, then,

$$E = n_0\hbar\omega \qquad (10\text{–}17)$$

where $n_0 = 2(n - 1) + l$. The lowest energy is then $E = 0$ (neglecting the zero-point energy) for $l = 0$ and $n = 1$. This is called the $1s$ state. The next level is the $1p$ level, with energy $E = \hbar\omega$. There are two states, the $2s$ state and the $1d$ state, with energy $2\hbar\omega$. These energy levels are plotted in Figure 10–10a. As can be seen from Eq. (10–17), states with the same energy have either even l or odd l. In Figure 10–10c, the results of a calculation of the allowed energies in an infinite three-dimensional square well are plotted. For this problem there is no degeneracy of states with different values of n and l. We can understand the ordering qualitatively if we think of deforming the oscillator potential into the square-well potential. Since the particle in the $1d$ state has larger angular momentum than one in the $2s$ state, it is farther from the origin on the average, and its energy is lower in the square well where the potential energy is lower at larger r. The center plot in Figure 10–10b shows the expected results for an intermediate case between the square well and the oscillator well. The number in parentheses in this figure is the number of neutrons that can be put into each state consistant with the exclusion principle. The total number, counting from the lowest-energy state, is also indicated.

We would expect from this theory that the magic numbers would be 2, 8, 20, 40, 70 or 92, and 138 since, after these numbers, there are relatively large energy differences. Though the first three numbers — 2, 8, and 20 — do agree with the observed stability of He^4 ($N = 2$, $Z = 2$), O^{16} ($Z = N = 8$), and Ca^{40} ($Z = N = 20$), the rest of the numbers are not the magic numbers. For example, there is no evidence from Figure 10–10 for the magic number 50. Calculations for various other potential wells give about the same ordering and spacing of the energy levels as are shown in Figure 10–10. In 1949, Maria G. Mayer and J. Hans Jensen independently pointed out that if the nuclear force was strongly dependent on the orientation of the spin of the nucleon relative to the orbital angular momentum, the magic numbers could be obtained

figure 10–10   *Energy levels for a single particle in* (a) *oscillator potential,* (b) *potential well of intermediate shape, and* (c) *square well.* (*From Mayer and Jensen, Ref. 3.*)

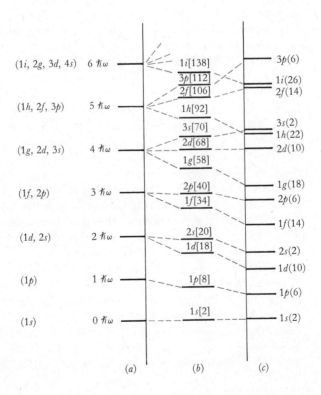

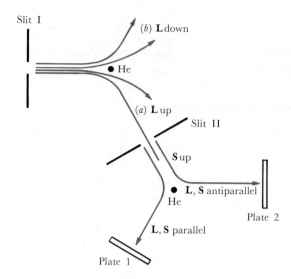

Slit I

(b) **L** down

● He

(a) **L** up

Slit II

S up

● **L, S** antiparallel
He

Plate 2

L, S parallel

Plate 1

figure 10–11   *Double scattering experiment of protons on helium nuclei showing spin-orbit force. Protons scattered down* (a) *have orbital angular momentum relative to the first He nucleus up. Assuming that the force is stronger for* **S** *parallel to* **L**, *particles accepted by slit II are likely to have spin up. Particles scattered toward plate 1 have* **L** *up (relative to second He nucleus), thus most of these have spin and orbital angular momenta parallel. In this experiment, more particles arrive at plate 1 than at plate 2, confirming the assumption that the nuclear force is stronger if the spin is parallel to the orbital angular momentum. (From Mayer and Jensen, Ref. 3.)*

from a shell model. We have seen that there is such a "spin-orbit" force in atomic physics, for the energy of an atom does depend on whether $j = l + \frac{1}{2}$ or $j = l - \frac{1}{2}$. This fine-structure splitting in atoms is very much smaller than the energy difference between shells or subshells in the atom and can be neglected in the first approximation to atomic energies. Before we see how the assumption of a strong nuclear spin-orbit force produces the magic numbers, we shall describe an experiment that shows the existence of such a force, which depends on the relative orientation of the spin of a nucleon and its orbital angular momentum.

Figure 10–11 is a schematic drawing of a scattering experiment of protons and helium nuclei. The He^4 nucleus is a convenient target because it has zero spin. In the figure, it is assumed that the protons are repelled by the He nucleus; however, the analysis does not depend on the sign of the force. The classical orbital angular momentum of the protons marked a, relative to the first He^4 nucleus, is in the direction $\mathbf{r}_a \times m\mathbf{v}$, which we shall call "up," whereas those protons marked b have orbital angular momentum "down." If we assume that the force is stronger when **L** and **S** are parallel and if we concentrate only on the protons selected by slit II, there will be more with spin up in this beam than with spin down. Thus the beam is polarized. In order to analyze the polarization, another scattering is necessary. If our assumption that the force is stronger for **L** and **S** parallel is correct, there should be more protons detected on plate 1 than on plate 2. If the force were stronger for antiparallel alignment, slit II would preferentially select protons with spin down and more protons would arrive at plate 2 than at plate 1. If the force were independent of the relative orientation, there would be equal numbers at the plates. When this experiment was first performed in 1952 by M. Heusinkveld and G. Freier, using relatively crude geometry (wide slits, etc.), there were about twice as many protons at plate 1 as at plate 2, indicating that the force was indeed stronger for the case of parallel spin and orbital angular momentum.

Figure 10–12 shows the energy levels with the assumption of a strong spin force. (A stronger force implies a deeper potential well and thus a lower energy.) The levels with **L** parallel to **S** have a lower energy than those with **L** antiparallel to **S**; thus the higher j values have lower energies. The splitting is larger for larger l values. The splitting of the $1g$ level is so great that a large energy difference occurs between the $1g_{9/2}$ ($n = 1, l = 4, j = l + s = 4\frac{1}{2}$) and the $1g_{7/2}$ ($n = 1, l = 4, j = l - s = 3\frac{1}{2}$) levels. Since there are $2j + 1$ values of m_j, there can be 10 neutrons in the $1g_{9/2}$ level, making a total of 50 up through this level. The next large energy difference occurs because of the splitting of the $1h$ level, and this accounts for the magic number 82.

From qualitative considerations alone it is not possible to decide the exact order of the energy levels, for example, whether the $2s_{1/2}$ is higher or lower than the $1d_{3/2}$ level. Questions of this nature can usually be answered from empirical evidence. As an example of the predictions of the shell model, we shall consider the nucleus with one neutron or one proton outside a closed shell. These are the simplest nuclei (except for those with closed shells of both neutrons and protons) and are somewhat analogous to the alkali atoms with one outer electron. Many of the energy levels of these nuclei can be understood in terms of the excitation of one odd nucleon. Table 10–1 lists several nuclei with ± 1 nucleon outside a closed shell, with the predicted state of this nucleon and the measured spin of the nucleus. (The neutron number is given as a subscript.) In all these cases, the spin prediction is correct. This simple shell model is also quite successful in predicting the magnetic moments for these nuclei. For example, the magnetic moment of O^{17} is observed to be -1.89, which is quite close to that of a single neutron, which is predicted by the shell model for this nucleus since the other eight neutrons and the eight protons form a closed shell. For a more complete discussion of the success of this shell model, the reader is referred to Mayer and Jensen's excellent book, Ref. 3. (This model is sometimes called the *extreme individual-particle model* to distinguish it from various more sophisticated extensions in which the nucleon interactions are taken into account.)

figure 10–12   *Energy levels for a single particle in a nuclear well, including spin-orbit split-ting. The number of particles in each level is given at the right, followed by the total number through that level [in brackets]. The total numbers just before the large energy gaps are the magic numbers. [The spacing shown here is for protons; taken from P. F. A. Klinkenberg,* Review of Modern Physics, **24,** *63 (1952). The spacing for neutrons is slightly different.]*

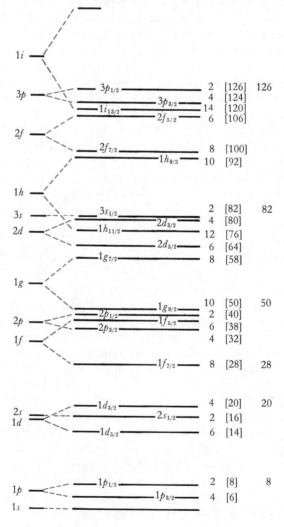

table 10–1

Angular momenta
of nuclei with
closed shells ±1
nucleon
(From Mayer and
Jensen, Ref. 3.)

element	number of odd particles	predicted	measured nucleon spin
$_5B_6^{11}$	5	$p_{3/2}$	3/2
$_6C_7^{13}$	7	$p_{1/2}$	1/2
$_7N_8^{15}$	7	$p_{1/2}$	1/2
$_8O_9^{17}$	9	$d_{5/2}$	5/2
$_{13}Al_{14}^{27}$	13	$d_{5/2}$	5/2
$_{19}K_{20}^{39}$	19	$d_{3/2}$	3/2
$_{82}Pb_{125}^{207}$	125	$p_{1/2}$	1/2
$_{83}Bi_{126}^{209}$	83	$h_{9/2}$	9/2

Perhaps the most serious deficiency of the simple shell model is in the region of the rare-earth nuclei. The quadrupole moments predicted from the orbital motion of the individual protons are much smaller than those observed. Many of the excited states of these nuclei can be most simply understood as being due to the rotation or vibration of the nucleus as a whole, considering it to be a deformed liquid drop. From the shell-model point of view, the rare-earth nuclei lie about midway between the neutron magic numbers 82 and 126. This is just the region for which shell-model calculations are the most difficult since there are many particles outside a closed shell. There are several extensions of the shell model that have been fairly successful in the understanding of these nonspherical nuclei. In one of these, called the *collective model*, the closed-shell core nucleons are treated as a liquid drop deformed by interaction with the outer nucleons which orbit about the core and drag it with them. In another model, called the *unified model*, the Schroedinger equation is solved for individual particles in a nonspherically symmetric potential corresponding to an ellipsoidal nucleus. Much of the work with these models was done by J. Rainwater, A. Bohr (son of Niels Bohr), B. Mottleson, S. Nilsson, et al. in the years 1950 to 1960. A discussion of their work is beyond the scope of this book.

10·4
RADIOACTIVITY

The discovery of natural radioactivity by Becquerel in 1896 marked the beginning of the study of the atomic nucleus. In 1900, Rutherford discovered that the rate of emission of radioactive particles from a substance was not constant but decreased exponentially with time. It so happens this exponential time dependence is characteristic of all radioactivity and indicates that it is a statistical

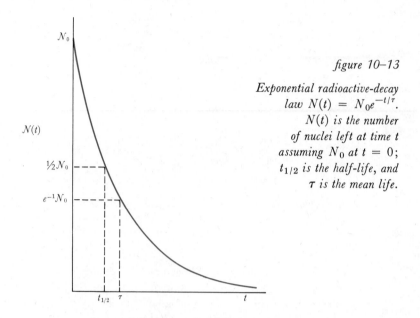

figure 10–13

Exponential radioactive-decay law $N(t) = N_0 e^{-t/\tau}$. $N(t)$ is the number of nuclei left at time t assuming N_0 at $t = 0$; $t_{1/2}$ is the half-life, and τ is the mean life.

process. Because each nucleus is well shielded from others by the atomic electrons, pressure and temperature changes have no effect on nuclear properties. For a statistical decay, the number of nuclei decaying in time dt is just proportional to the time interval dt and the number of nuclei. If $N(t)$ is the number of radioactive nuclei at time t and $-dN$ is the number that decay in dt (the minus sign is necessary because N decreases), we have

$$-dN = \lambda N \, dt \qquad (10\text{–}18)$$

where λ, the constant of proportionality, is the decay rate per nucleus. The solution of this equation is

$$N = N_0 e^{-\lambda t} \qquad (10\text{–}19)$$

where N_0 is the number at $t = 0$. The rate of decay is

$$R = -\frac{dN}{dt} = \lambda N_0 e^{-\lambda t} = R_0 e^{-\lambda t}$$

where $R_0 = \lambda N_0$ is the rate at time $t = 0$.

We can calculate the mean lifetime from Eq. (10–19). The number of nuclei with lifetimes between t and $t + dt$ is just the number that decay in dt, which is $\lambda N \, dt$; thus the fraction of lifetimes in dt is

$$f(t) \, dt = \frac{\lambda N \, dt}{N_0} = \lambda e^{-\lambda t} \, dt \qquad (10\text{–}20)$$

Using this distribution function, the mean lifetime is

$$\tau = \int_0^\infty t f(t) \, dt$$

$$= \int_0^\infty t \lambda e^{-\lambda t} \, dt = \frac{1}{\lambda}$$

(10–21)

Thus the mean lifetime is the reciprocal of the decay constant λ. The half-life $t_{1/2}$ is defined as the time after which the number of radioactive nuclei has decreased to half its original value. From Eq. (10–19),

$$\tfrac{1}{2} N_0 = N_0 e^{-\lambda t_{1/2}}$$

$$\ln \tfrac{1}{2} = -\lambda t_{1/2}$$

$$t_{1/2} = \frac{\ln 2}{\lambda} = (\ln 2)\tau$$

or, using $\ln 2 = 0.693$,

$$t_{1/2} = \frac{0.693}{\lambda} = (0.693)\tau$$

(10–22)

We often have nucleus A decaying into nucleus B, which, in turn, decays into C. For this case, the equation for nucleus B is not as simple as Eq. (10–18) because there is another term describing the production of B. Let us first consider a somewhat different situation, that of a constant rate of production of a radioactive nucleus. If this rate is R_0, the equation for $N(t)$ is

$$\frac{dN}{dt} = R_0 - \lambda N$$

(10–23)

If we start with $N = 0$ at $t = 0$, the solution is

$$N = \frac{R_0}{\lambda} (1 - e^{-\lambda t})$$

(10–24)

This familiar function is sketched in Figure 10–14. After a time of several half-lives, the slope of this curve becomes negligible and the number is nearly equal to its terminal value

$$N \approx \frac{R_0}{\lambda}$$

(10–25)

Example 10–1   In a laboratory experiment, silver-foil strips are placed near a neutron source. The capture of neutrons by Ag^{107} produces Ag^{108},

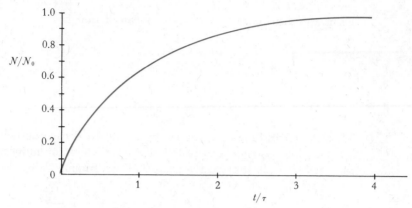

figure 10–14   Function $N/N_0 = 1 - e^{-t/\tau}$.

which is radioactive and decays by β decay with a half-life of 2.4 minutes (thus a mean lifetime of about 3.5 minutes). How long should the foil be left by the neutron source? From Figure 10–14, the number of radioactive Ag^{108} nuclei will be about 95 percent of the maximum number after three mean lifetimes; thus there is not much point in irradiating the silver foil longer than 10 minutes.

*

If the production of the radioactive nucleus is due to the decay of another nucleus, the rate of production is not constant and the situation is more complex. If λ_A is the decay constant of A, which decays into B, and λ_B is the decay constant of B, the differential equation for B is

$$\frac{dN_B}{dt} = -\lambda_B N_B + \lambda_A N_A = -\lambda_B N_B + \lambda_A N_{0A} e^{-\lambda_A t}$$

$$(10\text{–}26)$$

The solution of this equation is not too difficult. However, we shall consider only the special case in which nucleus A (called the *parent nucleus*) has a much longer half-life than nucleus B (called the *daughter nucleus*). For this case, $\lambda_A \ll \lambda_B$. For times much less than the half-life of A, the number of A nuclei is approximately constant. For this case, the rate $\lambda_A N_A \approx \lambda_A N_{0A} = R_0$, and Eq. (10–26) is the same as the constant-rate problem discussed above. If we start with $N_B = 0$ at $t = 0$, the equation for N_B is Eq. (10–24), with $R_0 = \lambda_A N_{0A}$. Thus, for times satisfying

$$\tau_B \ll t \ll \tau_A$$

the number of B nuclei is approximately constant and equal to the maximum value

$$N_B \approx \frac{\lambda_A}{\lambda_B} N_{0A} \qquad (10\text{--}27)$$

An example of this is Ra^{226}, which decays by α decay into Rn^{222}, which also decays by α decay into Po^{218}. The half-life of Ra^{226} is about 1,620 years, and the half-life of Rn^{222} is about 3.83 days. For times greater than about 10 days but less than 1,620 years, the number of Rn^{222} nuclei remains constant. This equilibrium situation is called *secular equilibrium*.

In order for a radioactive substance to be found in nature, either it must have a half-life that is not much smaller than the age of the earth (about 4.5×10^9 years) or it must be continually produced by the decay of another radioactive substance. For a nucleus to be radioactive at all, its mass must be greater than the sum of the masses of the decay products. Because the binding energy of the He^4 nucleus is unusually large, corresponding to an unusually small mass, many heavy nuclei are unstable to α decay. Because the Coulomb barrier inhibits the decay process (the α particle must tunnel through a region in which its energy is less than the potential energy as shown in Figure 6–26), the half-life for α decay can be very long if the decay energy is small. When a nucleus emits an α particle, both N and Z decrease by 2 and A decreases by 4; thus there are four possible α-decay chains, depending on whether A equals $4n$, $4n + 1$, $4n + 2$, or $4n + 3$, where n is an integer. All but the $4n + 1$ series are found in nature. The $4n + 1$ series is not found in nature because its longest-lived member (other than the stable end product Bi^{209}), Np^{237}, has a half-life of only 2×10^6 years, which is much smaller than the age of the earth.

The half-lives for β decay and γ decay are generally much less than the age of the earth. These decays are observed in nature if the radioactive nucleus is continually being produced, as in one of the α-decay chains. For example, the half-life for β decay of Th^{234} is only 24.5 days, but this decay is observed in nature because Th^{234} is produced by the α decay of U^{238}, which has a half-life of 4.5×10^9 years. Radioactive nuclei can also be produced by the bombardment of stable nuclei by various particles from nuclear accelerators or by the natural bombardment by cosmic rays.

We shall not consider the details of the general characteristics of α, β, and γ decay here. Instead, we shall discuss briefly just two important features — the nonconservation of parity in β decay and the Mössbauer effect in γ decay.

NONCONSERVATION
OF PARITY

Parity is defined for a nucleus in the same way as for an atom. If the nuclear wave function changes sign upon reflection of the co-ordinates, the parity is said to be odd, or -1. If the wave function does not change sign, the parity is even, or $+1$:

$$\text{Odd parity, } P = -1: \quad \psi(-x,-y,-z) = -1\psi(x,y,z)$$
$$\text{Even parity, } P = +1: \quad \psi(-x,-y,-z) = +1\psi(x,y,z)$$

The parity of atomic wave functions is related to the orbital angular momentum by $P = (-1)^l$. If l is odd, the parity is odd; if l is even, the parity is even. We have seen in our discussion of radiation from atoms that the parity of an atom can change just as the angular momentum of the atom changes when the atom emits light. In fact, for electric-dipole transitions, $\Delta l = \pm 1$; thus both the parity and angular-momentum quantum numbers change by ± 1. However, if the complete system including the photon is con-sidered, the total angular momentum and the total parity do not change in atomic transitions. In nuclear reactions involving nu-clear forces, the total parity is conserved, as is energy, linear momentum, and angular momentum.

figure 10–15

The mirror image of a right-handed
coordinate system (**x** × **y** in the **z**
direction) is a left-handed coordinate system
(**x** × **y** in the −**z** direction).
No combination of translation and
rotation can change a right-handed
coordinate system into a left-handed
coordinate system.

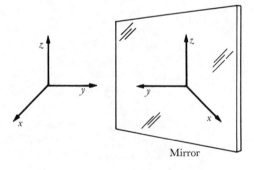

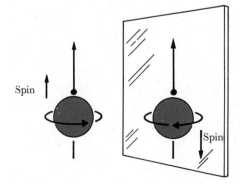

figure 10–16

Spinning nucleus emitting particles
in the direction of its spin.
In the mirror, the image nucleus
is emitting particles in the direction
opposite to the spin.

figure 10–17   *T. D. Lee (left) and C. N. Yang, co-winners of the Nobel Prize (1957) for their suggestion of the nonconservation of parity and their work in elementary particle theory. (Courtesy of Mr. H. Schrader, Princeton University.)*

Until 1956, it was assumed that parity was conserved in all nuclear reactions and nuclear radioactivity. In the summer of 1956, Tsung Dao Lee of Columbia University and Chen Ning Yang of the Institute for Advanced Study suggested that parity might not be conserved in β decay. This suggestion grew out of attempts to understand the peculiar behavior of elementary particles called τ and θ *mesons*. These particles are identical in every way except that the θ meson decays into two mesons with positive parity, whereas the τ decays into three mesons with negative parity. If parity were conserved, these could not be merely two different modes of decay of the same particle. Lee and Yang suggested that the nonconservation of parity could be observed experimentally by the measurement of the angular distribution of electrons emitted in β decay of nuclei which have their spins aligned in some direction. Such an experiment was performed in December, 1956, by a group led by Chien Shiung Wu of Columbia University and Ernest Ambler of the National Bureau of Standards, confirming the predictions of Lee and Yang.[4]

[4]See "The Overthrow of Parity" by Philip Morrison. *Scientific American*, April 1957, reprint #231, W. H. Freeman & Co.

The conservation of parity essentially means that a process described by the coordinates x, y, z appears the same if described by the coordinates $x' = -x$, $y' = -y$, and $z' = -z$. The system x, y, z is called a *right-handed coordinate system* because $\mathbf{x} \times \mathbf{y}$ is in the $+z$ direction. Similarly, the system x', y', z' is called a *left-handed coordinate system* because $\mathbf{x}' \times \mathbf{y}'$ is in the negative z' direction. No rotation can change a right-handed coordinate system into a left-handed one, but reflection in a mirror does, as is shown in Figure 10–15. We can state the law of conservation of parity in more physical terms: if parity is conserved, the mirror image of a process cannot be distinguished from the process itself. Figure 10–16 shows a spinning nucleus emitting electrons in the direction of its spin. In the mirror, the nucleus appears to be emitting electrons in the direction opposite to that of its spin. If parity is conserved in β decay, the chance of emission in the direction of the nuclear spin must equal the chance of emission in the opposite direction, i.e., there can be no preferred direction. Whether or not there is actually a preferred direction in β decay is usually not observable because the nuclear spins are randomly oriented. Wu et al. aligned the nuclei in Co^{60} by placing their sample in a magnetic field at a very low temperature (about $0.01°K$). They found that more particles were emitted opposite to the spin of the nucleus than in the direction of the spin; thus parity is not conserved in the β-decay process.

THE MÖSSBAUER EFFECT

A nucleus in an excited state can decay to a lower-energy state by emitting photons just as an atom decays by emitting light. The photons emitted in the decay to the ground state are not monoenergetic but have a distribution of energies because of the uncertainty in the energy of the excited state. The natural width of the energy distribution of photons, Γ, is related to the mean lifetime of the excited state by $\Gamma = \hbar/\tau$ consistent with the uncertainty principle. The width and thus the lifetime can, in principle, be determined by the technique of resonance fluorescence, the absorption and reemission of a photon emitted by a nucleus of the same type. If the excited state has energy centered at E_0 with width Γ, the cross section for the absorption of photons has a sharp maximum at excitation energy E_0 and drops to half maximum at $E_0 \pm \frac{1}{2}\Gamma$. The integral of the cross section over energy is proportional to Γ; thus a measurement of the cross section for absorption versus energy can determine the width Γ and the lifetime τ. Resonance fluorescence is observed for atomic transitions but not generally for nuclear transitions. The nuclear recoil, which is negligible for atomic transitions because of the low energy, shifts the energy of the emitted photon completely off resonance in nuclear transitions. A nucleus or atom emitting a photon of energy E will recoil with momentum approximately equal to E/c. The energy of the photon will be reduced by the nuclear recoil energy $E_R = p^2/2M \approx E^2/2Mc^2$. If the energy of the excited state is E_0, the energy of the photon will thus be

$$E_\gamma = E_0 - E_R \approx E_0 - \frac{E^2}{2Mc^2} \approx E_0 - \frac{E_0{}^2}{2Mc^2}.$$

Similarly, if the nucleus is to absorb a photon and make a transition of energy E_0, the energy of the photon must be $E_0 + E_0{}^2/2Mc^2$. Thus the center of the emitted photon distribution will be displaced from that of the absorbed distribution by the amount $2E_R = E_0{}^2/Mc^2$. If the width of the excited state is less than this amount, there will be no photons emitted by a nucleus that have energy great enough to be absorbed by another nucleus of the same kind; therefore resonance fluorescence cannot take place.

For a typical mean lifetime of 10^{-8} sec, the width is about $\Gamma = \hbar/\tau \approx 10^{-7}$ eV. A typical atomic transition energy in the visible region is about $E_0 = 1$ eV. Taking an atom of atomic number $A = 100$, $Mc^2 \approx 10^5$ MeV $= 10^{11}$ eV. Then $2E_R \approx 1^2/10^{11} = 10^{-11}$ eV, which is much less than Γ, and the recoil shift is negligible. On the other hand, for a typical nuclear decay energy of 100 keV $= 10^5$ eV, $2E_R \approx (10^5)^2/10^{11} = 10^{-1}$ eV, which is much greater than Γ. For such a nuclear decay, there is no overlap and resonance fluorescence does not occur unless the lines

figure 10–18   (a) *Nuclear energy level has a half-width* Γ. (b) *Shift in energy of emitted photon due to recoil of nucleus.* (c) *Shift in energy of absorptive transition because of the need of the absorbing nucleus to recoil. If the shifted levels* (b) *and* (c) *overlap, resonance fluorescence can occur.*

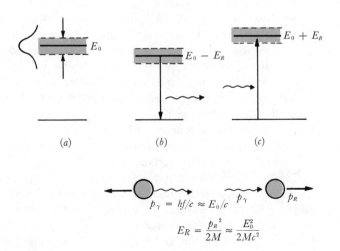

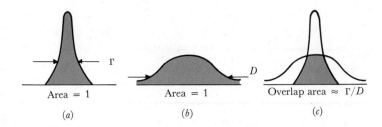

Area = 1   Area = 1   Overlap area $\approx \Gamma/D$

(a)   (b)   (c)

figure 10-19   (a) *Unbroadened line with natural width* Γ. (b) *Doppler-broadened line with the same area as in* (a). (c) *Absorption in resonance fluorescence is proportional to the overlap area, which is approximately* Γ/D.

are broadened greatly by the Doppler effect. The thermal motion of the atoms gives a Doppler broadening of the lines but does not shift the central energy because the motion is random and the chances of increase or decrease of energy are equal. The Doppler energy width is $D = h\,\Delta f$, where Δf is the Doppler frequency shift, which, to first order, is $\pm(v/c)f$. Taking $v/c \approx 10^{-6}$ for a typical value at room temperature, the Doppler width is $D \approx 10^{-6}hf = 10^{-6}E_0$. Thus, for atomic transitions, D is of the order of 10^{-6} eV, about 10 times the natural width. The effect of the Doppler broadening on atomic transitions is to decrease the absorption cross section by a factor of about Γ/D. For nuclear transitions, D is much larger than the natural width and is of the order of the nuclear recoil shift; thus the emission and absorption lines may have some overlap, and some resonance fluorescence may be possible.

In 1950, Moon successfully observed nuclear resonance fluorescence by placing a source on the rim of an ultracentrifuge rotor which revolved such that the tip had a speed of about 800 m/sec, thus introducing an external Doppler shift compensating for the recoil loss. By varying the speed, he was able to measure the absorption cross section as a function of energy and determine a mean life of the order of 10^{-11} sec for his source.

In 1958, Mössbauer used an Ir^{191} source of 129-keV photons, for which the Doppler broadening at room temperature is about twice the recoil shift, so that resonance fluorescence could be observed. When he cooled the source and absorber, he expected to see the absorption decrease because of the decrease in the Doppler width and thus in the overlap. Instead, however, he observed an increase in the absorption. The absorption, in fact, was as much as was to be expected if there had been no recoil and no Doppler broadening. The explanation of this effect is, qualitatively, that at sufficiently low temperatures, an atom in a solid cannot recoil individually because of the quantization of energy states in the lattice. The recoil momentum is absorbed by the crystal as a whole. The effective mass is thus the mass of the crystal, which is so much larger than that of the atom that the recoil energy is completely negligible. Thus the emitted photon has energy E_0 which can be absorbed by another nucleus without recoil. Mössbauer was able to destroy the resonance by moving the source or absorber and so introducing an external Doppler shift. However, this shift need be only of the order of Γ, which is 4.6×10^{-6} eV for Ir^{191}. The velocity needed to obtain a Doppler shift of this energy is only a few centimeters per second. In 1961, Mössbauer received the Nobel Prize for this experiment and his theoretical explanation of the results.

In 1959, it was discovered that the Mössbauer effect could be observed for the 14.4-keV gamma decay of Fe^{57} at room temperatures, thus opening the way for many experimental possibilities without the need for low-temperature apparatus. The natural width of this line is $\Gamma = 10^{-7}$ eV $\approx 10^{-11} E_0$. A relative velocity of only 10^{-3} cm/sec shifts the line by one natural width, and it is thus easily detected. We shall mention only one of the many ap-

figure 10–20

Rudolf L. Mössbauer winner of the Nobel prize (1961) for his discovery of recoilless resonance absorption of gamma rays — the Mössbauer effect. (Courtesy of Wide World Photos.)

figure 10–21   *Equipment for measuring the resonance absorption of gamma rays in Mössbauer effect experiments. An iron-57 source and absorber are maintained at low
temperatures in the vertical cylinders. The source (left cylinder) is mounted
on the carriage of a lathe to control its velocity. The absorber (right cylinder)
is fixed. The horizontal cylinder is a sodium iodide detector for gamma rays.
At the far right is a 256-channel analyzer used to read the gamma spectrum
from the detector. (A magnet used in other experiments to measure hyperfine
splitting of the absorption line is shown at right center.) (Courtesy of Argonne
National Laboratory.)*

plications of the Mössbauer effect. (For more details, see Refs. 4
and 5.)

The theory of general relativity predicts that the frequency of a
light source will change by an amount $\Delta f/f = -\Delta\phi/c^2$ if the gravitational potential is changed by $\Delta\phi$. This is called the *gravitational
red shift*. Before the discovery of the Mössbauer effect, the only
possible observation of this shift was for light from the sun, for
which $\Delta\phi$ was large enough to produce a large $\Delta f/f$. However,
since a shift of 1 percent of Γ can be detected in the Mössbauer
effect, a frequency shift between source and absorber of $\Delta f/f \approx$
10^{-13} can be observed with Fe^{57}. In 1959, R. Pound and G.
Rebka detected the gravitational red shift for an Fe^{57} source and

absorber mounted at a difference in height of 74 ft. A complete description of this experiment can be found in Ref. 4.

10·5
NUCLEAR
REACTIONS

Most of the information about nuclei is obtained by bombarding them with various particles and observing the results. Although the first experiments were limited by the radiations from naturally occurring sources, they produced many important discoveries. In 1932, Cockcroft and Walton succeeded in producing the reaction $p + Li^7 \rightarrow Be^8 \rightarrow He^4 + He^4$, using artifically accelerated protons. About the same time, the Van de Graaff electrostatic generator was built (by R. Van de Graaff in 1931), as was the first cyclotron (by E. O. Lawrence and M. S. Livingston in 1932). Since then, an enormous technology has been developed for accelerating and detecting particles, and many various nuclear reactions have been studied.

When a particle is incident on a nucleus, several different things can happen. The same particle may come out with the same energy (elastic scattering), the same particle may come out with less energy (inelastic scattering), in which case the nucleus is left in an excited state and decays by emitting photons or other particles, or the original particle may be absorbed and another particle or particles emitted.

figure 10–22

The Cockcroft-Walton accelerator. Walton is sitting in the foreground of this picture.
J. D. Cockcroft and E. T. S. Walton produced the first transmutation of nuclei with artificially accelerated particles in 1932, for which they received the Nobel prize (1951). (Courtesy of Cavendish Laboratory.)

(a)

(b)

figure 10–23   (a) *M. S. Livingston and E. O. Lawrence standing in front of their 27-inch cyclotron in 1934. Lawrence won the Nobel Prize (1939) for the invention of the cyclotron.* (b) *A modern 83-inch cyclotron at the University of Michigan. (A deflecting magnet is shown in the foreground.)* [(a) *Courtesy of Lawrence Radiation Laboratory, University of California, Berkeley.* (b) *Courtesy of University of Michigan.*]

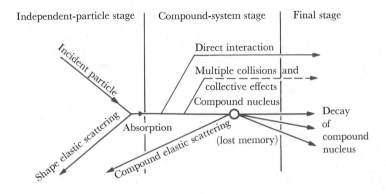

figure 10–24   *Stages in a nuclear reaction according to Weisskopf. [From Weisskopf, Review of Modern Physics, **29**, 174 (1951).]*

Figure 10–24 illustrates the several possible stages of a nuclear reaction according to the theory of V. Weisskopf and H. Feshbach. *Shape elastic scattering* refers to the reflection of the incident wave at the edge of the nuclear potential well. If the incident particle interacts with a single nucleon in the nucleus so that the nucleon leaves the nucleus, the reaction is called a *direct reaction*. Direct reactions are more probable at high energies. If the nucleon does not leave the nucleus but interacts with several other nucleons, complicated excited states can be formed in the nucleus. If the energy is shared by many particles, the excited nucleus is called a *compound nucleus*. The compound nucleus can decay by emission of one or more particles (including photons). The decay of the compound nucleus can be treated as a statistical process independent of the detailed manner of formation.

In this section we shall study some of the systematics of nuclear reactions and some typical reactions produced by incident neutrons, protons, photons, or deuterons. We shall limit the discussion to energies of less than 140 MeV. (At higher energies, mesons and other particles can be created. The study of high-energy reactions is generally used to reveal the properties of elementary particles and of the nuclear force rather than the structure of the nucleus.)

ENERGETICS   Consider a general reaction of particle x on nucleus X resulting in nucleus Y and particle y. The reaction is usually written

$$x + X \rightarrow Y + y + Q \tag{10–28}$$

or, for short, $X(x,y)Y$. The quantity Q is defined by

$$Q = (m_x + m_X - m_y - m_Y)c^2 \tag{10–29}$$

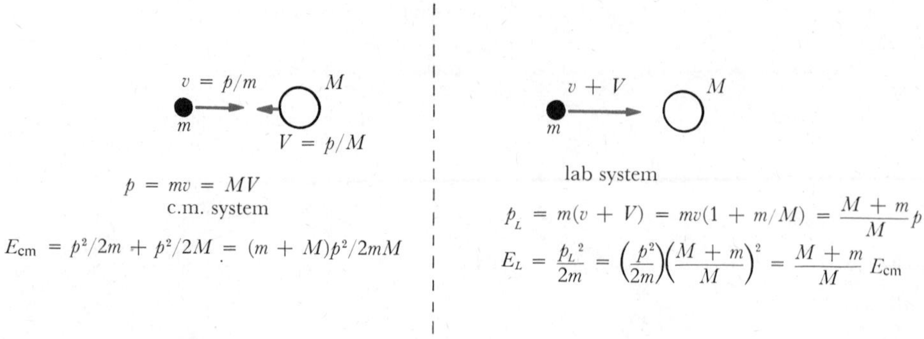

$v = p/m$ M

m $V = p/M$

$p = mv = MV$

c.m. system

$E_{cm} = p^2/2m + p^2/2M \doteq (m + M)p^2/2mM$

$v + V$ M

m

lab system

$p_{L} = m(v + V) = mv(1 + m/M) = \dfrac{M + m}{M}p$

$E_L = \dfrac{p_L{}^2}{2m} = \left(\dfrac{p^2}{2m}\right)\left(\dfrac{M + m}{M}\right)^2 = \dfrac{M + m}{M}E_{cm}$

figure 10–25   *Energetics of nuclear reaction in center-of-mass system and laboratory system. The energies are related by* $E_{\text{lab}} = [(M + m)/M]E_{\text{cm}}.$

The Q value of the reaction is the energy available for the reaction. The Q value for the reaction $n + H^1 \to H^2 + \gamma + Q$ is $Q = 2.22$ MeV; whereas, for the inverse reaction $\gamma + H^2 \to n + H^1 + Q$, $Q = -2.22$ MeV. If Q is positive, the reaction is said to be exothermic. It is energetically possible even if the particles are at rest. If Q is negative, the reaction is endothermic and cannot occur below a threshold energy. In the reference frame in which the total momentum is zero (the center-of-momentum frame), the threshold energy for the two particles is just $|Q|$. However, most reactions occur with one particle X at rest. In this frame, called the *lab frame*, the incident particle must have energy greater than $|Q|$ because, by conservation of momentum, the kinetic energy of y and Y cannot be zero. Consider the nonrelativistic case of x having mass m incident on X having mass M. In the center-of-momentum frame, both particles have the same magnitude of momentum, and the total kinetic energy is

$$E_{cm} = \frac{p^2}{2m} + \frac{p^2}{2M} = \frac{1}{2}p^2\frac{m + M}{mM} \qquad (10\text{–}30)$$

where $p = mv = MV$. We transform to the lab frame by adding V to each velocity so that M is at rest and m has the velocity $v + V$. The momentum of m in the lab frame is then

$$p_L = m(v + V) = mv\left(1 + \frac{m}{M}\right) = p\frac{m + M}{M}$$

and the energy is

$$E_L = \frac{p_L{}^2}{2m} = \frac{p^2}{2m}\left(\frac{m + M}{M}\right)^2 = \frac{m + M}{M}E_{cm} \qquad (10\text{–}31)$$

The threshold for an endothermic reaction in the lab frame is thus

$$E_{th} = \frac{m + M}{M} |Q| \tag{10-32}$$

[If the incident particle is a photon, the Lorentz transformation must be used. For low energies, the momentum of a photon is small and approximate methods can be used. For a photon, $pc = E$, whereas for a proton or neutron, $pc = (2mc^2E)^{1/2} \gg E$ for $E \ll 940$ MeV.]

CROSS SECTION In Chapter 4 we defined the differential-scattering cross section as the ratio of the number of particles scattered into a unit solid angle in some direction divided by the incident intensity. If we sum over all angles, we obtain the total scattering cross section

$$\sigma = \iint \left(\frac{d\sigma}{d\Omega}\right) d\Omega$$

$$\sigma = \frac{\text{number scattered per sec per nucleus}}{\text{number incident per sec per area}} \tag{10-33}$$

In a similar way, we define the cross section for a particular reaction as the number of reactions per second per nucleus divided by the incident intensity. Consider, for example, the bombardment of C^{13} by protons. A number of reactions might occur. Elastic scattering is written $C^{13}(p,p)C^{13}$; the first p indicates an incident proton, the second indicates that the particle that leaves is also a proton. If the scattering is inelastic, the outgoing proton is indicated by p' and the nucleus in an excited state by C^{13*}. Some other possible reactions are

p, n	$C^{13}(p,n)N^{13}$
Capture	$C^{13}(p,\gamma)N^{14}$
p, α	$C^{13}(p,\alpha)B^{10}$

The total cross section is the sum of the partial cross sections:

$$\sigma = \sigma_{p,p} + \sigma_{p,p'} + \sigma_{p,n} + \sigma_{p,\gamma} + \sigma_{p,\alpha} + \cdots$$

Cross sections have the dimensions of area. Since nuclear cross sections are of the order of the square of the nuclear radius, a convenient unit for them is the *barn*, defined by

$$1 \text{ barn} = 10^{-24} \text{ cm}^2 \tag{10-34}$$

The cross section for a particular reaction is a function of energy. For an endothermic reaction, it is zero for energies below the threshold.

THE COMPOUND
NUCLEUS

In 1936, Niels Bohr pointed out that many low-energy reactions could each be described as a two-stage process — the formation of a compound nucleus and the decay of that nucleus. In this description, the incident particle is absorbed by the target nucleus and the energy is shared by all the nucleons of the compound nucleus. After a time that is long compared with the time necessary for the incident particle to cross the nucleus, enough of the excitation energy of the compound nucleus becomes concentrated in one particle and that particle escapes. The emission of a particle is a statistical process and depends only on the excited state of the compound nucleus and not on how it was produced. An incident 1–MeV proton has a speed of about 10^9 cm/sec; thus it takes a time $R/v \approx 10^{-13}/10^9 = 10^{-22}$ sec to cross a nuclear distance. The lifetime of a compound nucleus can be inferred to be about 10^{-16} sec. This is too short to be measured directly, but it is very long compared with 10^{-22} sec (see Figure 10–29). Because the lifetime of the compound state is long compared with the transit time of the incident particle, it is reasonable to assume that the decay is independent of the formation.

The compound nucleus for the reactions listed above is N^{14*}. This nucleus can be formed by many other reactions, such as

$$
\begin{array}{ll}
B^{10} + \alpha & \qquad C^{12} + d \\
N^{13} + n & \qquad B^{10} + \alpha \\
N^{14} + \gamma & \searrow N^{14*} \nearrow \quad N^{14} + \gamma \\
C^{12} + d & \qquad N^{13} + n
\end{array}
\qquad (10\text{--}35)
$$

Since the formation of N^{14*} is independent of the decay, we can write the cross section for a particular reaction such as $C^{13}(p,n)N^{13}$ as the product of the cross section for the formation of the compound nucleus, σ_c, and the relative probability of decay by neutron emission, P_n:

$$
\sigma_{p,n} = \sigma_c P_n \qquad (10\text{--}36)
$$

An illustration of the statistical decay of the compound nucleus is afforded by the energy distributions of neutrons from the reaction (Figure 10–26)

$$
\gamma + Bi^{209} \rightarrow Bi^{208} + n
$$

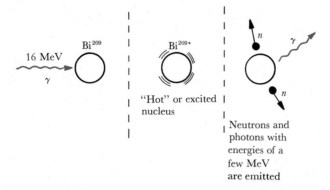

16 MeV → γ

Bi^{209}

Bi^{209*}
"Hot" or excited nucleus

n γ n
Neutrons and photons with energies of a few MeV are emitted

figure 10–26   *Nuclear reaction via formation of compound nucleus. The 16-MeV photon is absorbed by the Bi^{209} nucleus, producing an excited nucleus which lives so long that the excitation energy is shared by many nucleons. The excited nucleus then decays by emitting neutrons and photons of energy of the order of a few MeV.*

The cross section for this reaction and other photonuclear reactions, such as (γ,γ) or (γ,p), shows a broad resonance of width of several MeV and maximum at $E_m \approx 14$ MeV (for Bi and other heavy elements) to 20 MeV (for light elements such as carbon). Consider an incident photon of 16 MeV. The maximum energy of an emitted neutron is $16 - 7.4 = 8.6$ MeV since the binding energy of the last neutron is about 7.4 MeV. Some neutrons are observed to have this energy corresponding to a direct reaction, leaving Bi^{208} in the ground state, and some have about 7.1 MeV, leaving Bi^{208} in an excited state. About 90 percent of the neutron yield from this reaction has a Maxwell distribution in energy with a peak of about 2 MeV; this is to be expected if the compound nucleus Bi^{209*} has a long lifetime (long compared with 10^{-22} sec), and the neutrons "evaporate," just as molecules evaporate from a liquid that is heated. After emitting a neutron of about 2 MeV, the Bi^{209*} nucleus is still in an excited state and emits more neutrons or photons as it decays to the ground state.

DETERMINATION OF EXCITED STATES FROM NUCLEAR REACTIONS

The excited states of a nucleus can be determined in two ways from nuclear reactions. A peak in the cross section $\sigma(E)$ as a function of energy indicates an excited state of the compound nucleus. Information about the lifetime of the excited states of the compound nucleus is obtained by measuring the width of the resonances. Figure 10–27 shows the cross section for formation of N^{14*} by the reaction $B^{10} + \alpha \rightarrow N^{14*}$ as a function of the α-particle energy. The peaks in this curve indicate energy levels in the N^{14} nucleus. The Q value for this reaction is $M(B^{10})c^2 + M(\alpha)c^2 - M(N^{14})c^2 =$ 11.61 MeV.

The kinetic energy in the center-of-momentum frame is related to the lab energy of the α particle by

$$E_{cm} = \frac{M}{M + m} E_L = \frac{10}{14} E_L$$

The peak in Figure 10–27 at $E_L = 1.63$ MeV corresponds to an excited state in N^{14} of energy $E = 11.61 + (10/14)(1.63) = 12.77$ MeV. The same level can be excited by the reaction $C^{12} + H^2 \rightarrow N^{14*}$. For this case, the Q value is 10.26 MeV. Thus the deuteron energy in the lab must be

$$E_{H^2} = (14/12)(12.77 - 10.26) = 2.93 \text{ MeV}$$

Another way to determine the energy levels in a nucleus is to observe the energies of particles scattered inelastically. In this case, the energy levels of the product nucleus are determined. Figure 10–28 shows the energy spectrum of protons from the reaction $p + N^{14} \rightarrow N^{14*} + p'$ using 6.92-MeV protons. (The horizontal scale in this figure is proportional to the momentum of the protons since this is what is measured experimentally.) The two peaks in the curve correspond to losses of energy of 2.31 MeV and 3.75 MeV, which indicate energy levels in N^{14} of 2.31 MeV and 3.75 MeV. The excited product nucleus decays from these states by gamma emission. A measurement of the γ-ray spectrum is an alternative method of determining these energy levels in N^{14}. (Note

figure 10–27   *Cross section for the reaction* $B^{10} + \alpha \rightarrow N^{14*}$ *versus energy. The resonances indicate energy levels in the compound nucleus* N^{14*}. *[From Talbott and Heydenburg,* Physical Review, **90**, *186 (1953).]*

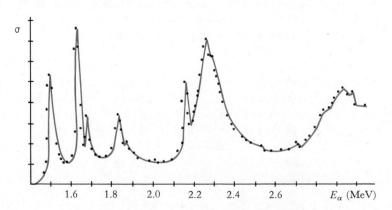

σ

1.6   1.8   2.0   2.2   2.4   2.6 E_α (MeV)

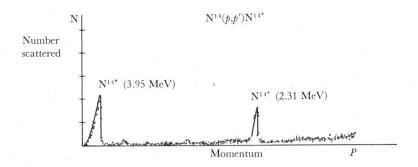

figure 10–28   *Spectrum of protons scattered from* N^{14}, *indicating energy levels in* N^{14}. [*From Bockelman et al.*, Physical Review, **92**, 665 (1953).]

that the compound nucleus for this reaction is O^{15}, not N^{14}.) The method of inelastic scattering can determine energy levels lying just above the ground state, whereas the levels excited in the compound nucleus must be much higher because of the Q values for formation of the compound nucleus. The Q value is the binding energy of the incident particle in the compound nucleus, which is always of the order of 6 to 10 MeV; thus levels of energy less than about 6 MeV cannot be reached in the compound nucleus.

NEUTRON CAPTURE AND FISSION   The most likely reaction with a nucleus for a neutron of energy of more than about 1 MeV is scattering. However, even if the scattering is elastic, the neutron loses some energy to the nucleus. Thus, if a neutron is scattered many times in a material, the energy of the neutron decreases until it is of the order of kT. It is then equally likely to gain energy from a nucleus when it is elastically scattered. A neutron with energy of the order of kT is called a *thermal neutron*. At low energies, a neutron is likely to be captured with the emission of a gamma ray from the excited nucleus:

$$n + {}_ZM^A \rightarrow {}_ZM^{A+1} + \gamma$$

Since the binding energy of a neutron is of the order of 6 to 10 MeV and the kinetic energy of the neutron is negligible compared with this, the excitation energy of the compound nucleus is from 6 to 10 MeV, and gamma rays of this energy are emitted. If there are no resonances, the cross section $\sigma(n,\gamma)$ varies smoothly with energy, decreasing with increasing energy roughly as $E^{-1/2} \propto 1/v$, where v is the speed of the neutron. This energy dependence is easily understood because the time spent by a neutron near a nucleus is inversely proportional to the speed of the neutron; thus the capture cross section is just proportional to this time. Superimposed on the $1/v$ dependence are large fluctuations in the capture cross section due to resonances. Figure 10–29 shows the neutron-capture cross section for silver as a function of energy. The dotted line indicates the $1/v$ dependence. At the maximum of the resonance, the value of the cross section is very large — greater than 5,000 barns — compared with the value of about 10 barns just past the resonance. The fact that this resonance has a width of only a few eV shows that the compound nucleus has a state with a lifetime of the order of $\hbar/1$ eV $\approx 10^{-16}$ sec. Many elements show similar resonances in the neutron-capture cross section. The maximum cross section for Cd^{113} is about 57,000 barns, so this material is useful for shielding against low-energy neutrons.

Some very heavy nuclei with excitation energy of 6 to 10 MeV are unstable to fission — the breaking apart into two nuclei of about half the mass of the original nucleus. When U^{235} captures a neutron, the nucleus emits a gamma ray as it deexcites to the ground state about 15 percent of the time and fissions about 85 percent of the time. The fission process is analogous to the oscillations of a liquid drop. If the oscillations are violent enough, the drop splits into two drops. The energy released in fission can be computed from the known masses of the initial nucleus and final products.

figure 10–29　*Neutron capture cross section for Ag versus energy. The dotted line extension is expected if there were no resonances and the cross section were merely proportional to the time spent near the nucleus, i.e., proportional to $1/v$. The width of the resonance of a few eV indicates a state with a lifetime of the order of $h/\Gamma \approx 10^{-16}$ sec. [From* The Atomic Nucleus *by R. Evans, 1955, by permission of McGraw-Hill Book Company.]*

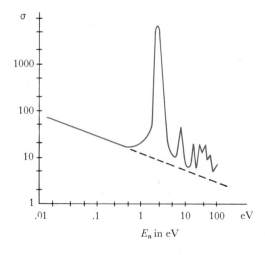

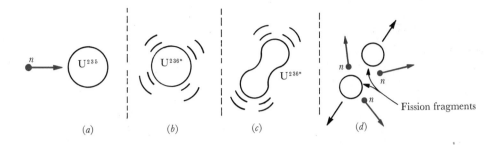

figure 10–30 *Schematic description of nuclear fission. (a) Absorption of a neutron by U^{235} leads to U^{236*} in excited state (b). In (c), the oscillation of U^{236*} has become unstable. (d) The nucleus splits apart, emitting several neutrons which can produce fission in other nuclei.*

We can estimate the energy released by noting from the binding-energy curve (Figure 10–7) that the binding energy per nucleon is about 1 MeV greater for nuclei of mass 100 than for nuclei of mass 200; thus about 200 MeV is released in the fission of one nucleus. This is much greater than any energy release in atomic reactions or even in other nuclear reactions (except the fusion of two low-mass nuclei to form a nucleus of larger mass). If we take a nucleus such as U^{236*} and divide the N and Z numbers by 2, we see that the product nuclei lie on the high neutron side of the stability curve of Figure 10–6. (Actually, in the majority of cases, the masses of the product nuclei are not equal. However, they still lie on the high neutron side of the N-versus-Z stability curve.) Thus, when a nuclear fission takes place, neutrons are often emitted. Since about two neutrons per fission are released on the average, a chain reaction is possible. The neutrons emitted have energies of about 1 MeV, whereas the cross section for capture leading to fission is large at small energies. In order to reduce the energy of the neutrons before they escape from the region containing fissionable material, a moderator is used in a nuclear reactor. Neutrons slow down by transferring their energy to nuclei by elastic collisions (see the discussion in Section 10·7). Thus material, such as carbon or water, containing light nuclei make efficient moderators.

Very heavy nuclei are unstable to spontaneous fission. The half-life varies from about 10^{20} years for Th^{232} to about 2.7 hours for Fm^{256}.

**10·6
ELEMENTARY
PARTICLES**
In 1930 there were only three known particles — the electron, the proton, and the photon. We have described in some detail the discovery of the neutron in 1932. In that same year, the positron was

figure 10–31

First cloud chamber photograph of a positron track. The particle came in from the bottom and followed a circular path in the magnetic field (directed into the paper). It was slowed down in traversing the 6-mm lead plate. The direction of the particle is known because of the greater curvature of the track above the plate. (Courtesy of Dr. C. D. Anderson.)

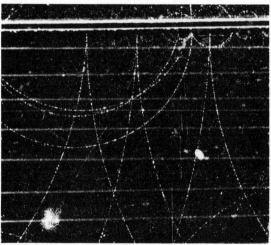

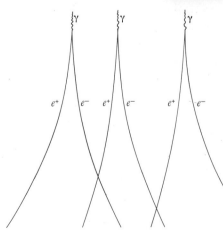

figure 10–32

Tracks of electron-positron pairs produced by 330 MeV synchrotron x rays. (Courtesy of Lawrence Radiation Laboratory, University of California, Berkeley.)

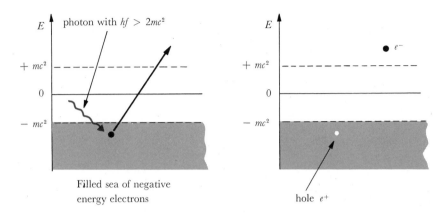

figure 10–33 *Pair production resulting from the collision of a photon with a negative-energy electron. The electron is excited to a positive energy state, leaving a hole which appears as a positron.*

discovered by Carl Anderson. The positron was actually predicted by the Dirac relativistic wave equation, though there was difficulty about the interpretation of this prediction. The energy of a relativistic particle is related to its rest mass and momentum by $E^2 = p^2c^2 + (mc^2)^2$, or $E = \pm(p^2c^2 + m^2c^4)^{1/2}$.

Though we can usually choose the plus sign and ignore the negative-energy solution with a "physical argument," the mathematics of the Dirac relativistic wave equation require the existence of wave functions corresponding to these negative-energy states. Dirac got around this difficulty by postulating that all the negative-energy states were filled and thus would not be observable. Only holes in this "infinite sea" of negative-energy states would be observable. The discovery of a particle with mass identical to that of the electron but with positive charge indicated that the interpretation was reasonable. Figure 10–31 shows Anderson's original cloud-chamber track and Figure 10–32 shows tracks of electron-positron pairs created by high-energy photons in a lead plate.

The process of pair production can be thought of as the interaction of a photon with a negative-energy electron, raising the electron to a positive-energy state (where it appears as a normal electron) and leaving a hole, which appears as a positron. If the Dirac equation can be applied to other spin-$\frac{1}{2}$ particles, such as the proton or neutron, these particles should also have antiparticles. It is not obvious that this is the case because of the anomalous magnetic moments of these particles. The creation of a proton-antiproton pair requires $2Mc^2 = 1,876$ MeV. This much energy was not readily available until recently except in cosmic rays. The antiproton was discovered in 1955, and the antineutron (a particle with

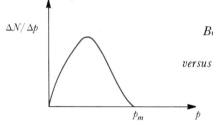

$\Delta N/\Delta p$

p_m

p

figure 10–34

*Beta decay spectrum. The number of emitted
electrons per momentum interval is plotted
versus momentum. The fact that all the electrons
do not have the energy corresponding
to momentum p_m suggests that there
is another particle emitted which shares
the energy of decay.*

the same mass as the neutron but with a positive magnetic moment)
was discovered in 1956.

In 1935 a Japanese physicist, Yukawa, developed a theory of
nuclear forces that required the existence of a particle of mass equal
to about 135 MeV/c^2 which was called a *meson*. Such a particle, the
muon with mass of 105 MeV/c^2, was discovered in 1937 and thought
to be Yukawa's meson. However, in 1946 it was shown that the
muon did not interact with nucleons except through weak and electromagnetic interactions. Thus the muon could not be connected
with nuclear forces. Shortly after this, the pi-meson was discovered.
The pi-meson does interact strongly with nucleons and appears to
be the particle predicted by Yukawa.

The "discovery" of the neutrino has an interesting history. This
particle was postulated to account for the apparent loss of energy
in β decay. Consider the simplest example of β decay, that of the
free neutron. If the neutron decays into just two particles, a proton
plus an electron, $n \rightarrow p^+ + e^-$, the energy of the electron is uniquely
determined by conservation of energy and momentum. This is true
for any decay into just two particles. Since the rest energy of the
neutron is about 0.78 MeV greater than the sum of the rest energies
of the proton and electron, the energy of the electron would be
about 0.78 MeV, neglecting the small recoil energy of the proton.
The measured energy is not unique. There is a spectrum of electron
energies from 0 to about 0.78 MeV (Figure 10–34). In order to
explain the apparent nonconservation of energy in β decay, Pauli
in 1930 suggested that a third particle might be emitted; this particle was called the neutrino. The neutron decay should then be
written

$$n \rightarrow p^+ + e^- + \nu \qquad (10\text{–}37)$$

The mass of the neutrino was assumed to be very much less than
that of the electron because the maximum energy of the electrons
was measured to be equal to the energy available for the decay as
calculated from the mass decrease (within experimental error).
The neutrino is now assumed to be massless. We can see from
Eq. (10–37) that the neutrino is also needed for conservation of

angular momentum, for the electron, proton, and neutron are all spin-$\frac{1}{2}$ particles. The neutrino also has spin $\frac{1}{2}$.

There were many attempts to observe the neutrino directly, but these were not successful until 1956. The force between a neutrino and a nucleus is not nuclear, electromagnetic, or gravitational but is a fourth kind of force. The interaction is called a *weak interaction*. In 1948, C. Sherwin showed that linear momentum was not conserved in β decay unless a neutrino was emitted. He measured the momentum of the β rays from P^{32} and simultaneously measured the recoil of the daughter nucleus S^{32}. The magnitude of the momentum needed for conservation of momentum was just E/c, where E is the energy needed for conservation of energy. In 1956, Reines and Cowen observed the neutrino "directly" by observing the inverse of β decay, $\nu + H^1 \to n + e^+$, using an intense flux of neutrinos from the decay of neutrons from a reactor.

Today there are many known "elementary particles" and many ways of classifying them. The most important is in terms of spin and type of interaction:

1. Integral spin, electromagnetic interaction: photon.
2. $\frac{1}{2}$ integral spin, weak and electromagnetic interaction: leptons.
3. Integral spin, strong and other interactions: mesons.
4. $\frac{1}{2}$ integral spin, strong and other interactions: baryons.

These groups of particles also group according to mass. The heavy particles with mass greater than or equal to the nucleons are called baryons. These interact strongly (via the nuclear force) with each other and with those of intermediate mass, called mesons. The lighter particles — electrons, positrons, neutrinos, and muons — interact with the others only through electromagnetic and weak interactions. The muon might seem to be a meson because of its mass, but it has all the characteristics of a heavy electron and none of the characteristics of mesons. The photon does not fit into this classification.

Table 10–2 lists the elementary particles. It does not include the short-lived resonances, although these are thought to be on an equal footing with the essentially stable particles listed. The "stability" criterion here is that the lifetime is long compared with the natural time $\tau = R/c$, where R is a typical particle radius of 10^{-13} cm. The lifetimes of the essentially stable particles shown are 10^{-16} sec and longer. It should be noted that this table can by no means be assumed to be complete since some members were discovered in this decade. Note that each particle in the table, except the γ, π^0, and η^0 particles, has an antiparticle with identical mass and opposite charge. (The γ, π^0, and η^0 particles are said to be their own antiparticles.)

table 10–2   *Chart of the particles stable against strong nuclear decay* [a]

CLASS	NAME	PARTICLES	ANTIPARTICLES

BARYONS
Strongly Interacting
Fermions
(Spin = half-integral)

		PARTICLES ($S=-3$)	ANTIPARTICLES ($S=+3$)
	Omega Hyperon $I=0$ Spin $=3/2\,\hbar$	Ω^- ($S=-2$)	$\bar{\Omega}^+$ ($S=+2$)
	Cascade Hyperon $I=1/2$ Spin $=1/2\,\hbar$	Ξ^0 Ξ^- $I_3=+\tfrac{1}{2}$ $I_3=-\tfrac{1}{2}$	$\bar{\Xi}^+$ $\bar{\Xi}^0$ $I_3=+\tfrac{1}{2}$ $I_3=-\tfrac{1}{2}$
		$S=-1$	$S=+1$
	Sigma Hyperon $I=1$ Spin $=1/2\,\hbar$	Σ^+ Σ^0 Σ^- $I_3=+1$ $I_3=0$ $I_3=-1$ $S=-1$	$\bar{\Sigma}^+$ $\bar{\Sigma}^0$ $\bar{\Sigma}^-$ $I_3=+1$ $I_3=0$ $I_3=-1$ $S=+1$
	Lambda Hyperon $I=0$ Spin $=1/2\,\hbar$	Λ^0	$\bar{\Lambda}^0$
		Baryon charge center	Anti baryon charge center
	Nucleon (Proton-Neutron) $I=1/2$ Spin $=1/2\,\hbar$	p^+ n^0 $I_3=+1/2$ $I_3=-1/2$	$\bar{n}^0$ $\bar{p}^-$ $I_3=+1/2$ $I_3=-1/2$

MESONS
Strongly Interacting
Bosons
(Spin = 0)

	NAME		
	η-Meson $I=0$	η^0	
	K-Meson $I=1/2$	K^+ K^0 $I_3=+1/2$ $I_3=-1/2$ $S=+1$	$\bar{K}^0$ $\bar{K}^-$ $I_3=+1/2$ $I_3=-1/2$ $S=-1$
	Pi-Meson $I=1$	π^+ π^0 π^- $I_3=+1$ $I_3=0$ $I_3=-1$	

LEPTONS
Weakly Interacting
Fermions
(Spin $=1/2\,\hbar$)

	NAME	PARTICLES	ANTIPARTICLES
	Muon	μ^-	μ^+
	Electron	e^-	e^+ (Positron)
	Neutrino-muon	ν_μ	$\bar{\nu}_\mu$
	Neutrino-electron	ν_e	$\bar{\nu}_e$

MASSLESS (Spin $=1\hbar$)
BOSONS (Spin $=2\hbar$)

	NAME		
	Photon	γ	
	Graviton?		

[a]From C. E. Swartz, *The Fundamental Particles*, 1965, Addison-Wesley, Reading, Mass. Reproduced by permission of the publishers.

Chart of the particles (continued) [a]

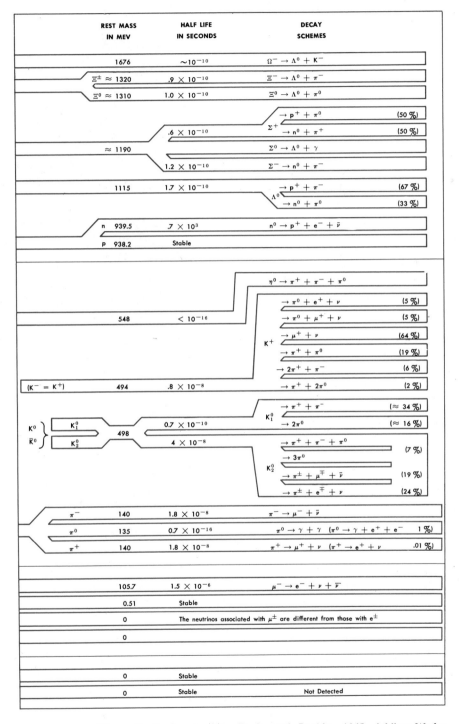

[a]From C. E. Swartz, *The Fundamental Particles*, 1965, Addison-Wesley, Reading, Mass. Reproduced by permission of the publishers.

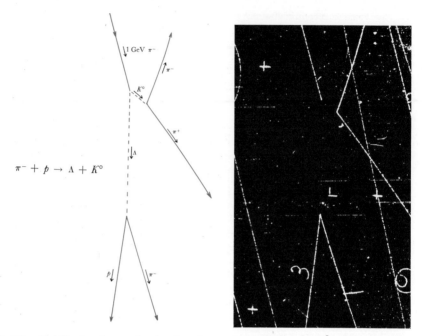

$$\pi^- + p \rightarrow \Lambda + K^\circ$$

figure 10–35 *Bubble chamber tracks showing the creation and decay of K^0 and Λ particles. These neutral particles are identified by the tracks of their decay products. The lambda particle is so named because of the similarity of the tracks of its decay products and the greek letter Λ. (Courtesy Lawrence Radiation Laboratory, University of California, Berkeley.)*

There are two general properties of elementary particles which have been extensively investigated in recent years with some success. The first is detailed classification of the particles (this classification is in terms of conservation laws); the second is the structures of mesons and baryons (in particular assuming that, in some sense, these particles are made up of each other and not of more elementary particles).

CONSERVATION LAWS — When a reaction or decay that is conceivable does not occur, we can usually describe this condition in terms of a conservation law. We do not expect to observe the decay $n \rightarrow p + e^+ + \nu$ because this decay does not conserve charge. The "law of charge conservation" was formulated because such decays are never observed. The total charge before a decay or reaction is always observed to equal the total charge after the decay or reaction. Similarly, the decay of a free proton into a neutron plus electron plus neutrino would violate the conservation of energy and does not occur. In addition to the familiar conservation laws of energy, charge, linear momentum, and angular momentum, there are two other conservation laws that are always obeyed. These are the conservation of leptons and the conservation of baryons (if we count the antiparticles as having -1 lepton or baryon number). Consider the possible decay $p \to \pi^0 + e^+$. This decay would conserve charge, angular momentum, and energy but neither baryons nor leptons. The conservation of leptons and baryons means that whenever a lepton particle or baryon particle is created, an antiparticle of the same type is also created. For example, if we assign $+1$ lepton numbers to the electron and neutrino, the positron and antineutrino have -1 lepton numbers, and the total lepton number on each side of a reaction is the same. The decay of the neutron, Eq. (10–37), should then be written

$$n \to p + e^- + \bar{\nu} \qquad\qquad (10\text{–}38)$$

where $\bar{\nu}$ represents an antineutrino. The fact that neutrinos and antineutrinos are different is illustrated by an experiment sensitive to the detection of the reaction

$$\mathrm{Cl}^{37} + \bar{\nu}_e \to \mathrm{A}^{37} + e^-$$

using an intense (anti) neutrino beam from the decay of reactor neutrons. This reaction is not observed, though the following reaction is:

$$p + \bar{\nu}_e \to n + e^+$$

The neutrinos emitted with muons in pi-meson decay such as

$$\pi^- \to \mu^- + \bar{\nu}_\mu$$

are apparently different from those associated with electrons, for those neutrinos do not produce such reactions as $\nu_\mu + n \to p + e^-$ or $\bar{\nu}_\mu + p \to n + e^+$. A reaction such as $p + p \to p + \bar{p}$ is forbidden by the conservation of baryon number. As mentioned in Chapter 1, the antiproton was first observed in the reaction $p + p \to p + p + p + \bar{p}$. There is no such conservation law for mesons.

There are other conservation laws which are not as universal as those just discussed. Parity is conserved in all but weak interactions. There is a quantity called *isotopic spin* which is conserved only in strong interactions. It can be seen from Table 10–2 that the baryons occur in groups or multiplets of one, two, or three particles of nearly identical mass. If it were not for the electromagnetic field, the particles within a multiplet would be the same. The nuclear forces between protons and protons, protons and neutrons, or neutrons and neutrons, are the same. The "splitting" of particle states because of the electromagnetic field is analogous to the splitting of atomic energy states in a magnetic field. Because of the analogy with isotopes (similar atoms with slightly different masses) and with the splitting of different spin states, the term "isotopic spin" is used to describe the multiplicity. The isotopic spin I of the nucleons is $\frac{1}{2}$, with the two components $I_3 = +\frac{1}{2}$ for the proton and $I_3 = -\frac{1}{2}$ for the neutron. $I = \frac{1}{2}$ for the Xi particles, $I = 0$ for the lambda and omega hyperons, and $I = 1$ for the sigma hyperons. For the mesons, I is taken to be 1 for the pions, $\frac{1}{2}$ for the kaons, and 0 for the eta particle. Decays and reactions in which the total isotopic spin is not conserved do not proceed via strong interactions.

Another quantity that has been defined to explain the nonoccurrence, or unusually long half-lives, of certain seemingly possible reactions and decays is called *strangeness*. For example, the decay $\Xi^- \rightarrow \pi^- + p^+ + \pi^-$ would be expected to have a half-life of the order of 10^{-23} sec (and thus the Ξ would not be observed) if the decay were due to the strong nuclear force. This decay occurs as a two-step process:

$$\Xi^- \rightarrow \Lambda^0 + \pi^-$$
$$ \mathrel{\rule[-1ex]{0.5pt}{2.5ex}\!\!\rule{1.5ex}{0.5pt}}\!\!\rightarrow \pi^- + p^+$$

Each step has a half-life of the order of 10^{-10} sec. A single "strange" particle is never produced in a strong interaction even though all the other conservation conditions are met. This observation prompted the definition of the strangeness number, which is related to the position of the center of charge of a multiplet. Since the proton has a charge of $+1$ and the neutron has 0 charge, the center of charge of this multiplet is at $+\frac{1}{2}$. The strangeness of the nucleons is arbitrarily defined to be 0. If the center of charge of a multiplet is one place to the right of $+\frac{1}{2}$, as is the case for the singlet uncharged lambda particle and the triplet sigma particle, the strangeness is -1. The Xi-particle doublet has its center of charge at $-\frac{1}{2}$, two places to the right of $+\frac{1}{2}$; thus it has strangeness of -2, whereas the omega has strangeness of -3. In strong interaction the strangeness number must be conserved, whereas in weak interactions it can change by ±1. Thus the above decay cannot proceed by strong interactions because the strangeness of the Ξ^- is -2 and that of $p^+ + \pi^- + \pi^-$ is 0 (the strangeness of the π-mesons is taken to be 0 and that of the kaons to be $+1$). The reaction must proceed in two steps by weak interactions.

These conservation laws are summarized in Table 10–3.

COMPOSITE
STRUCTURE   The characteristic fact about our understanding of elementary particles is that we do not understand very much. We have many experimental results, but the most important fact is that there is no detailed theoretical framework which describes these results.

table 10–3

quantity	when conserved
Charge	Always
Energy	Always
Linear momentum	Always
Angular momentum	Always
Baryons	Always
Leptons	Always
Parity	In strong and electromagnetic interactions but not in weak interactions
Isotopic spin	In strong interactions
Strangeness	In strong interactions; changes by ± 1 in weak interactions

Schroedinger quantum mechanics is not sufficient because it is non-relativistic. In addition, it does *not* seem possible to deal with the strongly interacting particles as though they were composites of more elementary particles, although an attempt in this direction has been made by Gell-Mann and Zweig, who postulated basic particles named "quarks." These particles have not been found.

Among some possibilities that particle physicists are studying at present are the following: (1) A theory based on the energy dependence of scattering amplitudes (known as the *S-matrix approach*). The essential assumption here can be phrased such that energy momentum is a more basic quantity than position, so that the scattering amplitudes (whose squares are the scattering cross sections) are the basic elements of any description, as opposed to description in terms of wave functions or fields as functions of position. (2) That spin angular momentum of particles is not quantized during interaction. This is not a return to classical ideas about spin, but it is a recognition that systems of particles during the short time of interaction do not need to have the properties of a set of isolated particles (see Barger and Cline, *Scientific American*, December, 1967). (3) That currents similar to the electromagnetic current can be defined for conserved, or approximately conserved, quantities other than electric charge and that these currents are the basic elements of a theory (i.e., they satisfy very simple rules).

Aside from the fact that these possibilities are of interest, our main purpose in mentioning them is to indicate that this entire subject is in a state of flux. Attempts are being made to discover new approaches in order to understand the results of experiments on high-energy accelerating machines. These attempts may be compared with the efforts of Bohr or, more likely, of his predecessors to develop an understanding of atomic physics.

10·7
THE INTERACTION
OF PARTICLES
WITH MATTER

In this section we shall discuss briefly the main interactions of charged particles, neutrons, and photons with matter. An understanding of these interactions is important for the study of nuclear detectors and shielding. We shall not attempt to give a detailed theory, but instead, we shall indicate the principal factors involved in stopping or attenuating a beam of particles.

CHARGED PARTICLES

When a charged particle traverses matter, it loses energy mainly by excitation and ionization of electrons in the matter. If the particle has energy that is large compared with the ionization energies of the atoms, the energy loss in each encounter with an electron will be only a small fraction of the particle energy. (A heavy particle cannot lose a large fraction of its energy to a free electron because of conservation of momentum, as discussed in Chapter 4 for α particles.) Since the number of electrons in matter is so great, we can treat the problem as a continuous loss of energy. After a fairly well-defined distance, called the *range*, the particle has lost all its kinetic energy and stops. Near the end of the range, the continuous picture of energy loss is not valid, because individual encounters are important. The statistical variation of the path length for monoenergetic particles is called *straggling*. For electrons, this can be quite important; however, for heavy particles of several MeV or more, the path lengths vary by only a few percent or less.

We can get an idea of the important factors in the stopping of a heavy charged particle by considering a simple model. Let ze be the charge and M the mass of the particle moving with speed V past an electron of mass m and charge e. Let b be the impact parameter. We can estimate the momentum imparted to the electron by assuming that the force has the constant value $F = Kze^2/b^2$ for the time it takes the particle to pass the electron, which is of the order of $t \approx 2b/V$ (Figure 10–36). The momentum given to the

figure 10–36   *Model for calculating the energy lost by a charged particle in a collision with an electron. The impulse given to the electron is of the order Ft, where $F = Kze^2/b^2$ is the maximum force and $t \approx 2b/V$ is the time for the particle to pass the electron.*

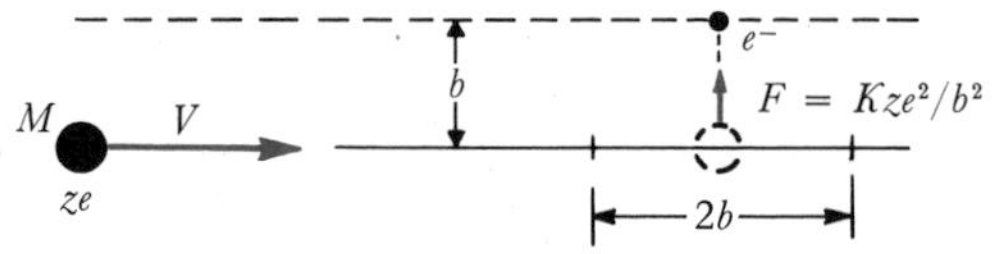

$$\text{Impulse} \approx Ft = \frac{Kze^2}{b^2} \frac{2b}{V}$$

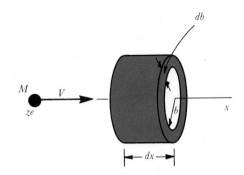

figure 10–37

*In path length dx, the charged particle
collides with $n2\pi b\, db\, dx$ electrons
with impact parameters in db,
where $n = Z(N_A/A)\rho$ is the number
of electrons per unit volume
in the material.*

Volume of shell is $2\pi b\, db\, dx$
Number in shell is $n2\pi b\, db\, dx$

electron is equal to the impulse, which is of the order of magnitude

$$p \approx Ft = \frac{Kze^2}{b^2}\frac{2b}{V} = \frac{2Kze^2}{bV}$$

(The same result is obtained by integration of the variable impulse,
assuming the particle moves in a straight line and the electron
remains at rest.) The energy given to the electron is then

$$E_e = \frac{p^2}{2m} = \frac{2K^2z^2e^4}{mV^2b^2} \tag{10–39}$$

This is thus the energy lost by the particle in one encounter.

In a cylindrical shell of thickness db and length dx (see Figure 10–37), there are $Z(N_A/A)\rho2\pi b\, db\, dx$ electrons, where Z is
the atomic number, A the atomic weight, N_A Avogadro's number,
and ρ the density in grams per cubic centimeter. The energy lost
to these electrons is then

$$-dE = \frac{2K^2z^2e^4}{mV^2b^2}\, Z\frac{N_A}{A}\,\rho2\pi b\, db\, dx \tag{10–40}$$

If we integrate from some minimum b to some maximum b, we
obtain

$$-\frac{dE}{dx} = \frac{4\pi K^2z^2e^4(Z/A)N_A\rho}{mV^2}\, L \tag{10–41}$$

where

$$L = \ln\frac{b_{\max}}{b_{\min}} \tag{10–42}$$

The maximum and minimum values of b can be estimated from
general considerations. For example, this model is certainly not

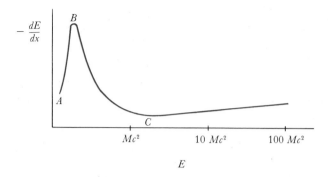

figure 10–38   *Energy loss −dE/dx versus energy for a charged particle. The energy loss is approximately proportional to V^{-2}, where V is the speed of the particle; thus, in the nonrelativistic region B to C, −dE/dx is proportional to E^{-1}, and in the relativistic region above C, −dE/dx is roughly independent of E. At low energies in the region A to B, the theory is complicated because the charge of the particle varies due to capture and loss of electrons.*

valid if the collision time is longer than the period of the electron in its orbit. The requirement that $2b/V$ be less than this time sets an upper limit on b. The lower limit on b can be obtained from the requirement that the maximum velocity the electron can obtain from a collision is $2V$ (from the classical mechanics of collisions of a heavy particle with a light particle). In any case, L is a slowly varying function, and the main dependence of the energy loss per unit length is given by the other factors in Eq. (10–41). We see that $-dE/dx$ varies inversely with the square of the velocity of the particle and is proportional to the square of the charge of the particle. Since $Z/A \approx \frac{1}{2}$ for all matter, the energy loss is proportional to the density of the material. It is convenient to define a thickness parameter:

$$\ell = \rho x \qquad \text{in g/cm}^2 \tag{10–43}$$

The energy loss $-dE/d\ell$ does not vary much from one material to another. A sketch of $-dE/dx$ versus energy is shown in Figure 10–38. From points B to C on this curve, the energy loss is proportional to $1/V^2$. For relativistic particles, the speed does not vary much with energy and the curve varies only because of the term L. The low-energy portion of the curve from A to B is not given by this theory. At very low energies, the charged particle may pick up an electron. Thus the charge varies, and the energy-loss function is not simple. Particles with kinetic energy greater than their rest energy are called *minimum ionizing particles.* The energy loss per unit path length is approximately constant for these particles, and the maximum path length or range is just proportional to the energy. In general, the range can be defined by

$$R = \int_0^R dx = \int_E^0 \frac{dE}{dE/dx} \qquad (10\text{-}44)$$

A sketch of the range versus energy is given in Figure 10–39. The range of a 4-MeV α particle is about 2.5 cm in air. Since the range is inversely proportional to the density of the stopping material, the range is much smaller in dense material.

The range-energy relation for electrons is more complicated because of the statistical fluctuations due to the small mass of the electron.

If the energy of the charged particle is large compared with its rest energy, the energy loss due to radiation as the particle slows down is important. This radiation is called *Bremsstrahlung*. The ratio of the energy loss by radiation and that lost through ionization is proportional to the energy of the particle and to the atomic number Z of the stopping material. This ratio equals 1 for electrons of about 10 MeV in lead.

NEUTRONS Since neutrons are uncharged, they do not interact with electrons in matter. Neutrons lose energy by nuclear scattering, or they are captured. For energies large compared with kT, the most important processes are elastic scattering and inelastic scattering. If we have a collimated beam of intensity I, any scattering or absorption will remove neutrons from the beam. If the sum of the cross sections for all such processes is σ, the number removed from the beam

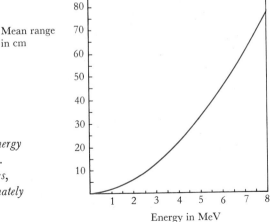

figure 10–39

Mean range versus energy for protons in dry air. Except at low energies, the range is approximately linear with energy.

Mean range in cm

Energy in MeV

is σI per nucleus. If n is the number of nuclei per cubic centimeter, the number of neutrons removed in a distance dx is

$$-dN = \sigma In A \, dx \tag{10-45}$$

where A is the area of the neutron beam and $N = IA$ is the number of neutrons. Thus

$$-dN = \sigma n N \, dx$$

and

$$N = N_0 e^{-\sigma n x} \tag{10-46}$$

or

$$I = I_0 e^{-\sigma n x} \tag{10-47}$$

Thus the number of neutrons in the beam decreases exponentially with distance, and there is no range.

The main source of energy loss for a neutron is usually elastic scattering. (In materials of intermediate weight, such as iron and silicon, the inelastic-scattering cross section is quite large, and this process is also of importance. We shall neglect inelastic scattering here.) The maximum energy that can be lost in one elastic collision occurs when the collision is head-on. This can be easily calculated.

Consider a neutron of mass m with speed v_L making a head-on collision with a nucleus of mass M at rest in the lab frame (see Figure 10-40). In the center-of-momentum reference frame, moving with speed V relative to the lab frame, the speed of the nucleus is V and the speed of the neutron is v, where $mv = MV$. The speeds of the neutron in the two reference frames are related by

$$v_L = v + V = \frac{M + m}{m} V$$

The energy lost by the neutron is most easily found by calculating the energy gained by the nucleus. Since the collision merely reverses the directions of the particles without changing their speeds in the center-of-momentum frame, the final speed of the nucleus is V in this frame and $2V$ in the lab frame. The energy gained by the nucleus in the lab frame is thus

$$\tfrac{1}{2}M(2V)^2 = 2M \left(\frac{m}{M + m}\right)^2 v_L{}^2 = \frac{4mM}{(M + m)^2} \tfrac{1}{2}mv_L{}^2 \tag{10-48}$$

The fractional energy lost by a neutron in one collision is thus

$$-\frac{\Delta E}{E} = \frac{4mM}{(M+m)^2} = \frac{4(m/M)}{[1+(m/M)]^2} \qquad (10\text{-}49)$$

This fraction has a maximum value of 1 when $M = m$ and approaches $4(m/M)$ for $M \gg m$.

PHOTONS   The intensity of a photon beam, like that of a neutron beam, decreases exponentially with distance through an absorbing material; the intensity is given by Eq. (10-47), where σ is the cross section for absorption per atom. The important processes which remove photons from a beam are the photoelectric effect at low energies, Compton scattering at intermediate energies, and pair production at high energies. The photonuclear cross sections, such as $\sigma(\gamma,n)$, are very small compared with these atomic cross sections

figure 10-40   *Collision of neutron with nucleus in laboratory system and center-of-mass system. The speed of the nucleus after the collision in the laboratory system is 2V, where V is related to the initial speed of the neutron in the laboratory system by $V = mv_L/(m+M)$. The energy lost by the neutron equals that gained by the nucleus.*

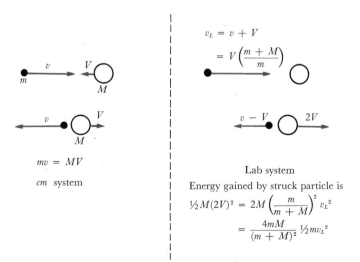

$v_L = v + V$

$= V\left(\dfrac{m+M}{m}\right)$

Lab system

Energy gained by struck particle is

$$\tfrac{1}{2}M(2V)^2 = 2M\left(\frac{m}{m+M}\right)^2 v_L{}^2$$

$$= \frac{4mM}{(m+M)^2}\,\tfrac{1}{2}mv_L{}^2$$

$mv = MV$

cm system

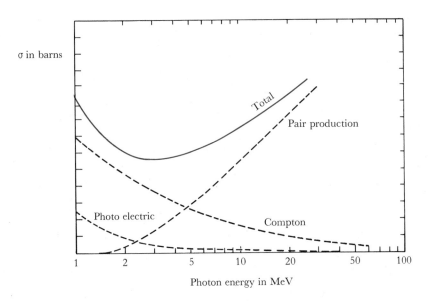

σ in barns

Photon energy in MeV

figure 10–41   *Photon attenuation cross section versus energy for lead. The cross sections for the photoelectric effect, Compton scattering, and pair production are shown by the dashed curves. The total cross section (solid curve) is the sum of these.* [*From C. Davisson and R. Evans,* Reviews of Modern Physics, **24,** *79 (1952).*]

and can usually be neglected. We can write the total absorption cross section as

$$\sigma_a = \sigma_{pe} + \sigma_{cs} + \sigma_{pp} \tag{10-50}$$

(In detailed calculations, some care is necessary in defining what is meant by absorption. For example, if the beam is well collimated, small-angle scattering will remove photons from it, whereas such scattering will not affect a broad, uncollimated beam. We shall neglect such details here.)

The cross section for the photoelectric effect decreases rapidly with energy for those energies above that of the ionization of K-shell electrons. At lower energies, there are sharp increases in the photoelectric cross section at energies corresponding to those of the ionization of the K, L, M, etc., shell electrons because at these energies more electrons are available to be ejected. The photoelectric effect cannot occur unless the electron is bound in an atom which can recoil to conserve momentum (see Problem 3–18).

If the energy of the photon is large compared with the binding energy of the electrons, the electrons can be considered to be free, and Compton scattering is the principal mechanism for the removal of photons from the beam. If the photon energy is greater than $2m_ec^2 = 1.02 \text{ MeV}$, the photon can disappear with the creation of an electron-positron pair. This process is called *pair production* (refer to Figure 10–32). The cross section for pair production increases rapidly with the photon energy and is the dominant factor in σ_a at high energies. Like the photoelectric effect, pair production cannot occur in free space. If we consider the reaction $\gamma \rightarrow e^+ + e^-$, there is some reference frame in which the total momentum of the electron-positron pair is zero, but there is no reference frame in which the photon's momentum is zero. Thus a nucleus is needed nearby to absorb the momentum by recoil. The cross section for pair production is proportional to Z^2 of the absorbing matter. The three partial cross sections, σ_{pe}, σ_{cs}, and σ_{pp}, are shown as a function of energy with the total cross section in Figure 10–41.

SUMMARY All nuclei are made up of N neutrons and Z protons. The nuclear radius is proportional to $A^{1/3}$; thus the volume is proportional to the number of particles A, and the density is independent of A. The radius varies from about 1 fermi for the proton to about 10 fermis for the heaviest nuclei.

The binding energy of a nucleus is given by

$$BE = [Nm_n + Zm_p - M_a]c^2$$

The binding energy per nucleon is about 8.3 MeV for most nuclei. The general variation of the binding energy from nucleus to nucleus can be understood by analogy with a liquid drop, which also has a constant density. There are important deviations from the average behavior due to shell structure. The nuclear shell model, assuming a strong spin-orbit force, gives the observed closed-shell magic numbers of 2, 8, 20, 28, 50, 82, and 126.

Information concerning the excited states of nuclei can be obtained from radioactive decay and nuclear reactions. Many low-energy reactions can be described as proceeding through an intermediate compound nucleus whose decay depends on the energy and angular momentum of the state but not on the manner of formation.

Elementary particles other than the photon and the undetected graviton can be classified as baryons (nucleons and heavier particles), mesons (pions and kaons), or leptons (electrons, positrons, muons, and neutrinos). The mesons and baryons interact with each other through strong nuclear interactions, whereas the leptons interact through weak interactions.

Charged particles lose energy almost continuously in matter by ionization (and radiation at high energies) and have a well-defined range. Neutrons and photons do not have a range; the intensity of a neutron or photon beam decreases exponentially with distance through matter. Neutrons lose energy in a discrete way by elastic or inelastic collisions with nuclei, and they are absorbed at low energies. Photons lose energy by Compton scattering or are absorbed at low energies by the photoelectric effect or at high energies by pair production.

REFERENCES

1. R. Beyer (ed.), *Foundations of Nuclear Physics*, Dover Publications, Inc., New York, 1949.
   This paperback book contains 13 original papers, eight in English by Anderson, Chadwick, Cockroft and Walton, Fermi, Lawrence and Livingston, Rutherford (two papers), and Yukawa. The others are in German or French.
2. R. Evans, *The Atomic Nucleus*, McGraw-Hill Book Company, New York, 1955.
3. M. Mayer and J. H. D. Jensen, *Elementary Theory of Nuclear Shell Structure*, John Wiley & Sons, Inc., New York, 1955.
4. American Association of Physics Teachers, *Mössbauer Effect*, selected reprints published by the American Institute of Physics, New York.
5. H. Frauenfelder, *The Mössbauer Effect*, W. A. Benjamin, Inc., New York, 1962.
6. B. Harvey, *Introduction to Nuclear Physics and Chemistry*, Prentice-Hall, Inc., Englewood Cliffs, N. J., 1962.
7. I. Kaplan, *Nuclear Physics*, Addison-Wesley Publishing Company, Inc., Reading, Mass., 1962.
8. Enrico Fermi, *Nuclear Physics*, notes compiled by J. Orear, A. Rosenfeld, and R. Schluter, The University of Chicago Press, Chicago, 1956.
9. W. Price, *Nuclear Radiation Detection*, McGraw-Hill Book Company, New York, 1958.
10. C. Swartz, *The Fundamental Particles*, Addison-Wesley Publishing Company, Inc., Reading, Mass., 1965.
11. *Scientific American Reprints*, published by W. H. Freeman and Company, San Francisco.
    M. Gell-Mann and E. Rosenbaum, "Elementary Particles," July, 1957, reprint 213.
    Chew, M. Gell-Mann, and A. Rosenfeld, "Strongly Interacting Particles," February, 1964, reprint 296.
    R. D. Hill, "Resonance Particles," January, 1963, reprint 290.

PROBLEMS

10-1. Use the atomic masses given in the table on page 493 and the mass of the electron, $m_e = 5.49 \times 10^{-4}$ u, to calculate:
(a) The energy required to remove $1n$ from He^4
(b) The energy required to remove $1p$ from He^4
(c) The binding energy per nucleon of He^4
(d) The Q value for the reaction $H^3 + H^1 \rightarrow He^3 + n + Q$

10-2. Calculate the binding energy of the last neutron in Pb^{208} and in Pb^{207}.

10-3. Radium Ra^{226} decays by α decay to Rn^{222} with a half-life of 1,620 years.
(a) Calculate the approximate energy of the α particle, neglecting recoil of the Rn nucleus.
(b) How many disintegrations per second are there in 1 gram of radium? (This number used to be defined as 1 curie. The curie is now defined as 3.70×10^{10} disintegrations per second.)

10-4. Cu^{62} is produced at a constant rate and decays by e^+ decay with a half-life of about 10 minutes. How long does it take to produce 90 percent of the equilibrium value of Cu^{62}?

10-5. The nuclei listed below have filled j shells plus or minus one nucleon. (For example, Si^{29} has the $1d_{5/2}$ shell filled for both neutrons and protons plus one neutron in the $2s_{1/2}$ shell.) Use the shell model to predict the orbital and total angular momentum of these nuclei: $_{14}Si^{29}$, $_{17}Cl^{37}$, $_{31}Ga^{71}$, $_{27}Co^{59}$, $_{32}Ge^{73}$, $_{16}S^{33}$, and $_{38}Sr^{87}$.

10-6. What is the compound nucleus for the reaction of α particles on $_8O^{16}$? What are some of the possible product nuclei and particles for this reaction?

10-7. If the width of a resonance for the formation of a compound nucleus is 10 eV, what is the lifetime of this state?

10-8. The total absorption cross section for γ rays in lead is about 20 barns at 15 MeV. What thickness of lead will reduce the intensity of 15-MeV rays by $1/e$?

10-9. Indicate which of the reactions listed below violate one or more conservation laws, and name the law or laws in each case.
(a) $p^+ \rightarrow \pi^+ + e^+ + e^-$
(b) $p^+ + \bar{p}^- \rightarrow \gamma + \gamma$
(c) $n \rightarrow p^+ + \pi^-$
(d) $\mu^- \rightarrow e^- + \nu + \bar{\nu}$
(e) $e^+ + e^- \rightarrow \gamma$
(f) $\nu + p^+ \rightarrow n + e^+$

SET B

10-10. (a) Using the Compton-scattering result that the maximum change in wavelength is $\Delta\lambda = 2hc/Mc^2$ and the approximation $\Delta E \approx -hc\Delta\lambda/\lambda^2$, show that for a photon to lose an amount of energy E_p to a proton, the energy of the photon must be at least

$$E = (\tfrac{1}{2}Mc^2E_p)^{1/2}$$

(b) Calculate the photon energy needed to produce a 5.7-MeV proton by Compton scattering.

(c) Calculate the energy given an N^{14} nucleus in a head-on collision with a 5.7-MeV neutron.

(d) Calculate the photon energy needed to give an N^{14} nucleus this energy by Compton scattering.

10-11. A photon of energy E is incident on a deuteron at rest. In the center-of-momentum reference frame, both the photon and deuteron have momentum P. Prove that the approximation $P = E/c$ is good by showing that the deuteron with this momentum has energy much less than E. If the binding energy of the deuteron is 2.22 MeV, what is the threshold energy in the lab for photodisintegration?

10-12. For constant odd A, the semiempirical mass formula as a function of Z is a parabola. The integer nearest the minimum of $M(Z)$ should be the Z value for the beta stable isobar for that A. Using the constants given in Section 10·2, find the Z for which $dM/dZ = 0$ for the A values $A = 27$, $A = 65$, and $A = 139$. Does this calculation give the correct stable isobars, Al^{27}, Cu^{65}, and La^{139}?

10-13. Ac^{228} decays into Th^{228} with a half-life of 6.13 hours. Th^{228} decays into Ra^{224} with a half-life of 1.9 years. Sketch the number of Th^{228} nuclei present as a function of time, assuming that, at $t = 0$, there are N_0 nuclei of Ac^{228} and no nuclei of Th^{228}.

10-14. An empirical expression for the range of α particles in air is $R(\text{cm}) = 0.31E^{3/2}$ for E in MeV and $4 < E < 7$ MeV:

(a) What is the range in air of a 5-MeV α particle?

(b) Express this range in g/cm^2 using $\rho \approx 10^{-3}\ g/cm^3$ for air.

(c) Assuming the range in g/cm^2 is the same in Aluminum, find the range in Aluminum in cm for a 5-MeV α particle.

10-15. The cross section for the reaction $Cu^{63}(p,n)Zn^{63}$ is about 0.5 barn for 11-MeV protons. Copper has a density of 8.9 g/cm^3 and is about 69 percent Cu^{63}.

(a) What is the rate of production of Zn^{63} nuclei, using a 10^{-6}-amp proton beam on a copper target of thickness 0.1 mm?

(b) The half-life for Zn^{63} is 38 minutes. How much Zn^{63} is there after 38 minutes of activation?

(c) How much is there after 10 days of activation? What is the decay rate of Zn^{63} at this time?

10–16. (a) Show that after N head-on collisions of a neutron with a carbon nucleus at rest, the energy of a neutron is approximately $(0.72)^N E_0$, where E_0 is the original energy.

(b) How many head-on collisions are required to reduce the energy of a neutron from 2 MeV to 0.02 eV, assuming stationary carbon nuclei?

APPENDIX A
PROPERTIES
OF NUCLEI

(1) *Atomic Number*   (2) *Name of Element*   (3) *Symbol*   (4) *Chemical Atomic Weight*   (5) *Mass Number, * indicates radioactive*   (6) *Mass*   (7) *Spin and Parity*   (8) *Percent Abundance*   (9) *Half-life (if radioactive) in years (y), days (d), minutes (m), or seconds (s). Nuclei with half-lives of less than one year are not included unless they are part of a naturally occurring radioactive chain. The masses are from J. H. E. Mattauch, W. Thiele, and A. H. Wapstra,* "1964, Atomic Mass Table," Nuclear Physics **67,** 1 (1965). *Other data are from* The Chart of The Nuclides, *9th ed., revised to July, 1966, by D. T. Goldman and J. R. Roesser; distributed by Educational Relations, General Electric Company, Schenectady, N.Y.*

(1)	(2)	(3)	(4)	(5)	(6)	(7)	(8)	(9)
Z	*element*	*symbol*	*chemical atomic weight*	*mass number (* indicates radioactive) A*	*mass*	*spin & parity*	*percent abundance*	*half-life (if radioactive) $t_{1/2}$*
0	(Neutron)	n		1*	1.008665	$\frac{1}{2}+$		12 m
1	Hydrogen	H	1.0079	1	1.007825	$\frac{1}{2}+$	99.985	
	Deuterium	D		2	2.014102	$1+$	0.015	
	Tritium	T		3*	3.016050	$\frac{1}{2}+$		12.26 y

(1)	(2)	(3)	(4) chemical atomic weight	(5) mass number (* indicates radioactive) A	(6) mass	(7) spin & parity	(8) percent abundance	(9) half-life (if radioactive) $t_{1/2}$
2	Helium	He	4.0026	3	3.016030	$\frac{1}{2}$ +	0.00013	
				4	4.002603	0 +	≈100	
3	Lithium	Li	6.939	6	6.015125	1 +	7.42	
				7	7.016004	$\frac{3}{2}$ −	92.58	
4	Beryllium	Be	9.0122	9	9.012186	$\frac{3}{2}$ −	100	
				10*	10.013534	0 +		2.7×10^6 y
5	Boron	B	10.811	10	10.012939	3 +	19.78	
				11	11.009305	$\frac{3}{2}$ −	80.22	
6	Carbon	C	12.01115	12	12.000000	0 +	98.89	
				13	13.003354	$\frac{1}{2}$ −	1.11	
				14*	14.003242	0 +		5,730 y
7	Nitrogen	N	14.0067	14	14.003074	1 +	99.63	
				15	15.000108	$\frac{1}{2}$ −	0.37	
8	Oxygen	O	15.9994	16	15.994915	0 +	99.759	
				17	16.999133	$\frac{5}{2}$ +	0.037	
				18	17.999160	0 +	0.204	
9	Fluorine	F	18.9984	19	18.998405	$\frac{1}{2}$ +	100	
10	Neon	Ne	20.183	20	19.992440	0 +	90.92	
				21	20.993849	$\frac{3}{2}$ +	0.257	
				22	21.991385	0 +	8.82	
11	Sodium	Na	22.9898	22*	21.994437	3 +		2.60 y
				23	22.989771	$\frac{3}{2}$ +	100	
12	Magnesium	Mg	24.312	24	23.985042	0 +	78.70	
				25	24.986809	$\frac{5}{2}$ +	10.13	
				26	25.982593	0 +	11.17	
13	Aluminum	Al	26.9815	26*	25.986892	5 +		7.4×10^5 y
				27	26.981539	$\frac{5}{2}$ +	100	
14	Silicon	Si	28.086	28	27.976929	0 +	92.21	
				29	28.976496	$\frac{1}{2}$ +	4.70	
				30	29.973763	0 +	3.09	
				32*	31.974020	0 +		≈700 y
15	Phosphorus	P	30.9738	31	30.973765	$\frac{1}{2}$ +	100	
16	Sulfur	S	32.064	32	31.972074	0 +	95.0	
				33	32.971462	$\frac{3}{2}$ +	0.76	
				34	33.967865	0 +	4.22	
				36	35.967089	0 +	0.014	
17	Chlorine	Cl	35.453	35	34.968851	$\frac{3}{2}$ +	75.53	
				36*	35.968309	2 +		3×10^5 y
				37	36.965898	$\frac{3}{2}$ +	24.47	

(1) Z	(2) element	(3) symbol	(4) chemical atomic weight	(5) mass number (* indicates radioactive) A	(6) mass	(7) spin & parity	(8) percent abundance	(9) half-life (if radioactive) $t_{1/2}$
18	Argon	A	39.948	36	35.967544	$0\ +$	0.337	
				38	37.962728	$0\ +$	0.063	
				39*	38.964317	$\frac{7}{2}\ -$		270 y
				40	39.962384	$0\ +$	99.60	
				42*	41.963048	$0\ +$		33 y
19	Potassium	K	39.102	39	38.963710	$\frac{3}{2}\ +$	93.10	
				40*	39.964000	$4\ -$	0.0118	1.3×10^9 y
				41	40.961832	$\frac{3}{2}\ +$	6.88	
20	Calcium	Ca	40.08	40	39.962589	$0\ +$	96.97	
				41*	40.962275	$\frac{7}{2}\ -$		7.7×10^4 y
				42	41.958625	$0\ +$	0.64	
				43	42.958780	$\frac{7}{2}\ -$	0.145	
				44	43.955492	$0\ +$	2.06	
				46	45.953689	$0\ +$	0.0033	
				48	47.952531	$0\ +$	0.18	
21	Scandium	Sc	44.956	45	44.955920	$\frac{7}{2}\ -$	100	
22	Titanium	Ti	47.90	44*	43.959572	$0\ +$		47 y
				46	45.952632	$0\ +$	7.93	
				47	46.951768	$\frac{5}{2}\ -$	7.28	
				48	47.947950	$0\ +$	73.94	
				49	48.947870	$\frac{7}{2}\ -$	5.51	
				50	49.944786	$0\ +$	5.34	
23	Vanadium	V	50.942	50*	49.947164	$6\ +$	0.24	$\approx 6 \times 10^{15}$ y
				51	50.943961	$\frac{7}{2}\ -$	99.76	
24	Chromium	Cr	51.996	50	49.946054	$0\ +$	4.31	
				52	51.940513	$0\ +$	83.76	
				53	52.940653	$\frac{3}{2}\ -$	9.55	
				54	53.938882	$0\ +$	2.38	
25	Manganese	Mn	54.9380	55	54.938050	$\frac{5}{2}\ -$	100	
26	Iron	Fe	55.847	54	53.939616	$0\ +$	5.82	
				55*	54.938299	$\frac{3}{2}\ -$		2.4 y
				56	55.939395	$0\ +$	91.66	
				57	56.935398	$\frac{1}{2}\ -$	2.19	
				58	57.933282	$0\ +$	0.33	
				60*	59.933964	$0\ +$		$\approx 10^5$ y
27	Cobalt	Co	58.9332	59	58.933189	$\frac{7}{2}\ -$	100	
				60*	59.933813	$5\ +$		5.24 y
28	Nickel	Ni	58.71	58	57.935342	$0\ +$	67.88	
				59*	58.934342	$\frac{3}{2}\ -$		8×10^4 y

(1) Z	(2) element	(3) symbol	(4) chemical atomic weight	(5) mass number (* indicates radioactive) A	(6) mass	(7) spin & parity	(8) percent abundance	(9) half-life (if radioactive) $t_{1/2}$
(28)	(Nickel)			60	59.930787	0 +	26.23	
				61	60.931056	$\frac{3}{2}$ −	1.19	
				62	61.928342	0 +	3.66	
				63*	62.929664			92 y
				64	61.927958	0 +	1.08	
29	Copper	Cu	63.54	63	62.929592	$\frac{3}{2}$ −	69.09	
				65	64.927786	$\frac{3}{2}$ −	30.91	
30	Zinc	Zn	65.37	64	63.929145	0 +	48.89	
				66	65.926052	0 +	27.81	
				67	66.927145	$\frac{5}{2}$ −	4.11	
				68	67.924857	0 +	18.57	
				70	69.925334	0 +	0.62	
31	Gallium	Ga	69.72	69	68.925574	$\frac{3}{2}$ −	60.4	
				71	70.924706	$\frac{3}{2}$ −	39.6	
32	Germanium	Ge	72.59	70	69.924252	0 +	20.52	
				72	71.922082	0 +	27.43	
				73	72.923462	$\frac{9}{2}$ +	7.76	
				74	73.921181	0 +	36.54	
				76	75.921405	0 +	7.76	
33	Arsenic	As	74.9216	75	74.921596	$\frac{3}{2}$ −	100	
34	Selenium	Se	78.96	74	73.922476	0 +	0.87	
				76	75.919207	0 +	9.02	
				77	76.919911	$\frac{1}{2}$ −	7.58	
				78	77.917314	0 +	23.52	
				79*	78.918494	$\frac{7}{2}$ +		7×10^4 y
				80	79.916527	0 +	49.82	
				82	81.916707	0 +	9.19	
35	Bromine	Br	79.909	79	78.918329	$\frac{3}{2}$ −	50.54	
				81	80.916292	$\frac{3}{2}$ −	49.46	
36	Krypton	Kr	83.80	78	77.920403	0 +	0.35	
				80	79.916380	0 +	2.27	
				81*	80.916610	$\frac{7}{2}$ +		2.1×10^5 y
				82	81.913482	0 +	11.56	
				83	82.914131	$\frac{9}{2}$ +	11.55	
				84	83.911503	0 +	56.90	
				85*	84.912523	$\frac{9}{2}$ +		10.76 y
				86	85.910616	0 +	17.37	
37	Rubidium	Rb	85.47	85	84.911800	$\frac{5}{2}$ −	72.15	
				87*	86.909186	$\frac{3}{2}$ −	27.85	5.2×10^{10} y

(1)	(2)	(3)	(4)	(5)	(6)	(7)	(8)	(9)
Z	element	symbol	chemical atomic weight	mass number (* indicates radioactive) A	mass	spin & parity	percent abundance	half-life (if radioactive) $t_{1/2}$
38	Strontium	Sr	87.62	84	83.913430	0 +	0.56	
				86	85.909285	0 +	9.86	
				87	86.908892	$\frac{9}{2}$ +	7.02	
				88	87.905641	0 +	82.56	
				90*	89.907747	0 +		28.8 y
39	Yttrium	Y	88.905	89	88.905872	$\frac{1}{2}$ −	100	
40	Zirconium	Zr	91.22	90	89.904700	0 +	51.46	
				91	90.905642	$\frac{5}{2}$ +	11.23	
				92	91.905031	0 +	17.11	
				93*	92.906450	$\frac{5}{2}$ +		9.5×10^5 y
				94	93.906313	0 +	17.40	
				96	95.908286	0 +	2.80	
41	Niobium	Nb	92.906	91*	90.906860			(long)
				92*	91.907211			$\approx 10^7$ y
				93	92.906382	$\frac{9}{2}$ +	100	
				94*	93.907303	6 +		2×10^4 y
42	Molybdenum	Mo	95.94	92	91.906810	0 +	15.84	
				93*	92.906830			$\approx 10^4$ y
				94	93.905090	0 +	9.04	
				95	94.905839	$\frac{5}{2}\ldots$	15.72	
				96	95.904674	0 +	16.53	
				97	96.906021	$\frac{5}{2}\ldots$	9.46	
				98	97.905409	0 +	23.78	
				100	99.907475	0 +	9.63	
43	Technetium	Tc		97*	96.906340			2.6×10^6 y
				98*	97.907110			1.5×10^6 y
				99*	98.906249	$\frac{9}{2}$ +		2.1×10^5 y
44	Ruthenium	Ru	101.07	96	95.907598	0 +	5.51	
				98	97.905289	0 +	1.87	
				99	98.905936	$\frac{5}{2}$ +	12.72	
				100	99.904218	0 +	12.62	
				101	100.905577	$\frac{5}{2}$ +	17.07	
				102	101.904348	0 +	31.61	
				104	103.905430	0 +	18.58	
45	Rhodium	Rh	102.905	103	102.905511	$\frac{1}{2}$ −	100	
46	Palladium	Pd	106.4	102	101.905609	0 +	0.96	
				104	103.904011	0 +	10.97	
				105	104.905064	$\frac{5}{2}$ +	22.23	
				106	105.903479	0 +	27.33	

(1)	(2)	(3)	(4)	(5)	(6)	(7)	(8)	(9)
Z	element	symbol	chemical atomic weight	mass number (* indicates radioactive) A	mass	spin & parity	percent abundance	half-life (if radioactive t_{1/2}
(46)	(Palladium)			107*	106.905132			7×10^6 y
				108	107.903891	0 +	26.71	
				110	109.905164	0 +	11.81	
47	Silver	Ag	107.870	107	106.905094	$\frac{1}{2}$ −	51.82	
				109	108.904756	$\frac{1}{2}$ −	48.18	
48	Cadmium	Cd	112.40	106	105.906463	0 +	1.22	
				108	107.904187	0 +	0.88	
				109*	108.904928	$\frac{5}{2}$ +		453 d
				110	109.903012	0 +	12.39	
				111	110.904188	$\frac{1}{2}$ +	12.75	
				112	111.902762	0 +	24.07	
				113	112.904408	$\frac{1}{2}$ +	12.26	
				114	113.903360	0 +	28.86	
				116	115.904762	0 +	7.58	
49	Indium	In	114.82	113	112.904089	$\frac{9}{2}$ +	4.28	
				115*	114.903871	$\frac{9}{2}$ +	95.72	
50	Tin	Sn	118.69	112	111.904835	0 +	0.96	
				114	113.902773	0 +	0.66	
				115	114.903346	$\frac{1}{2}$ +	0.35	
				116	115.901745	0 +	14.30	
				117	116.902958	$\frac{1}{2}$ +	7.61	
				118	117.901606	0 +	24.03	
				119	118.903313	$\frac{1}{2}$ +	8.58	
				120	119.902198	0 +	32.85	
				121*	120.904227			25 y
				122	121.903441	0 +	4.72	
				124	123.905272	0 +	5.94	
51	Antimony	Sb	121.75	121	120.903816	$\frac{5}{2}$ +	57.25	
				123	122.904213	$\frac{7}{2}$ +	42.75	
				125	124.905232	$\frac{7}{2}$ +		2.7 y
52	Tellurium	Te	127.60	120	119.904023	0 +	0.089	
				122	121.903064	0 +	2.46	
				123*	122.904277	$\frac{1}{2}$ +	0.87	1.2×10^{13} y
				124	123.902842	0 +	4.61	
				125	124.904418	$\frac{1}{2}$ +	6.99	
				126	125.903322	0 +	18.71	
				128	127.904476	0 +	31.79	
				130	129.906238	0 +	34.48	
53	Iodine	I	126.9044	127	126.904070	$\frac{5}{2}$ +	100	

(1)	(2)	(3)	(4)	(5)	(6)	(7)	(8)	(9)
Z	element	symbol	chemical atomic weight	mass number (* indicates radioactive) A	mass	spin & parity	percent abundance	half-life (if radioactive) $t_{1/2}$
(53)	(Iodine)			129*	128.904987	$\frac{7}{2}$ +		1.6×10^7 y
54	Xenon	Xe	131.30	124	123.906120	0 +	0.096	
				126	125.904288	0 +	0.090	
				128	127.903540	0 +	1.92	
				129	128.904784	$\frac{1}{2}$ +	26.44	
				130	129.903509	0 +	4.08	
				131	130.905085	$\frac{3}{2}$ +	21.18	
				132	131.904161	0 +	26.89	
				134	133.905815	0 +	10.44	
				136	135.907221	0 +	8.87	
55	Cesium	Cs	132.905	133	132.905355	$\frac{7}{2}$ +	100	
				134*	133.906823	4 +		2.1 y
				135*	134.905770	7 +		2×10^6 y
				137*	136.906770	$\frac{7}{2}$ +		30 y
56	Barium	Ba	137.34	130	129.906245	0 +	0.101	
				132	131.905120	0 +	0.097	
				133*	132.905879			7.2 y
				134	133.904612	0 +	2.42	
				135	134.905550	$\frac{3}{2}$ +	6.59	
				136	135.904300	0 +	7.81	
				137	136.905500	$\frac{3}{2}$ +	11.32	
				138	137.905000	0 +	71.66	
57	Lanthanum	La	138.91	137*	136.906040			6×10^4 y
				138*	137.906910	5 −	0.089	
				139	138.906140	$\frac{7}{2}$ +	99.911	
58	Cerium	Ce	140.12	136	135.907100	0 +	0.193	
				138	137.905830	0 +	0.250	
				140	139.905392	0 +	88.48	
				142*	141.909140	0 +	11.07	5×10^{15} y
59	Praseodymium	Pr	140.907	141	140.907596	$\frac{5}{2}$ +	100	
60	Neodymium	Nd	144.24	142	141.907663	0 +	27.11	
				143	142.909779	$\frac{7}{2}$ −	12.17	
				144*	143.910039	0 +	23.85	2.1×10^{15} y
				145	144.912538	$\frac{7}{2}$ −	8.30	
				146	145.913086	0 +	17.22	
				148	147.916869	0 +	5.73	
				150	149.920960	0 +	5.62	
61	Promethium	Pm		145*	144.912691			18 y
				146*	145.914632			1600 d

(1) Z	(2) element	(3) symbol	(4) chemical atomic weight	(5) mass number (* indicates radioactive) A	(6) mass	(7) spin & parity	(8) percent abundance	(9) half-life (if radioactive) $t_{1/2}$
(61)	(Promethium)			147*	146.915108	$\frac{7}{2}$ +		2.6 y
62	Samarium	Sm	150.35	144	143.911989	0 +	3.09	
				146*	145.912992	0 +		1.2×10^8 y
				147*	146.914867	$\frac{7}{2}$ −	14.97	1.08×10^{11} y
				148*	147.914791	0 +	11.24	1.2×10^{13} y
				149*	148.917180	$\frac{7}{2}$ −	13.83	4×10^{14} y
				150	149.917276	0 +	7.44	
				151*	150.919919	$\frac{7}{2}$ −		90 y
				152	151.919756	0 +	26.72	
				154	153.922282	0 +	22.71	
63	Europium	Eu	151.96	151	150.919838	$\frac{5}{2}$ +	47.82	
				152*	151.921749	3 −		12.4 y
				153	152.921242	$\frac{5}{2}$ +	52.18	
				154*	153.923053	3 −		16 y
				155*	154.922930	$\frac{5}{2}$ +		1.8 y
64	Gadolinium	Gd	157.25	148*	147.918101	0 +		85 y
				150*	149.918605	0 +		1.8×10^6 y
				152*	151.919794	0 +	0.20	1.1×10^{14} y
				154	153.920929	0 +	2.15	
				155	154.922664	$\frac{3}{2}$ −	14.73	
				156	155.922175	0 +	20.47	
				157	156.924025	$\frac{3}{2}$ −	15.68	
				158	157.924178	0 +	24.87	
				160	159.927115	0 +	21.90	
65	Terbium	Tb	158.925	159	158.925351	$\frac{3}{2}$ +	100	
66	Dysprosium	Dy	162.50	156*	155.923930	0 +	0.052	2×10^{14} y
				158	157.924449	0 +	0.090	
				160	159.925202	0 +	2.29	
				161	160.926945	$\frac{5}{2}$ +	18.88	
				162	161.926803	0 +	25.53	
				163	162.928755	$\frac{5}{2}$ −	24.97	
				164	163.929200	0 +	28.18	
67	Holmium	Ho	164.930	165	164.930421	$\frac{7}{2}$ −	100	
				166*	165.932289	0 −		1.2×10^3 y
68	Erbium	Er	167.26	162	161.928740	0 +	0.136	
				164	163.929287	0 +	1.56	
				166	165.930307	0 +	33.41	
				167	166.932060	$\frac{7}{2}$ +	22.94	
				168	167.932383	0 +	27.07	

(1) Z	(2) element	(3) symbol	(4) chemical atomic weight	(5) mass number (* indicates radioactive) A	(6) mass	(7) spin & parity	(8) percent abundance	(9) half-life (if radioactive) $t_{1/2}$
(68)	(Erbium)			170	169.935560	0 +	14.88	
69	Thulium	Tm	168.934	169	168.934245	$\frac{1}{2}$ +	100	
				171*	170.936530	$\frac{1}{2}$ +		1.9 y
70	Ytterbium	Yb	173.04	168	167.934160	0 +	0.135	
				170	169.935020	0 +	3.03	
				171	170.936430	$\frac{1}{2}$ −	14.31	
				172	171.936360	0 +	21.82	
				173	172.938060	$\frac{5}{2}$ −	16.13	
				174	173.938740	0 +	31.84	
				176	175.942680	0 +	12.73	
71	Lutecium	Lu	174.97	173*	172.938800	$\frac{7}{2}$ +		1.4 y
				175	174.940640	$\frac{7}{2}$ +	97.41	
				176*	175.942660		2.59	2.2×10^{10} y
72	Hafnium	Hf	178.49	174*	173.940360	0 +	0.18	2.0×10^{15} y
				176	175.941570	0 +	5.20	
				177	176.943400	$\frac{7}{2}$ −	18.50	
				178	177.943880	0 +	27.14	
				179	178.946030	$\frac{9}{2}$ +	13.75	
				180	179.946820	0 +	35.24	
73	Tantalum	Ta	180.948	180	179.947544		0.0123	
				181	180.948007	$\frac{7}{2}$ +	99.988	
74	Wolfram (Tungsten)	W	183.85	180	179.947000	0 +	0.14	
				182	181.948301	0 +	26.41	
				183	182.950324	$\frac{1}{2}$ −	14.40	
				184	183.951025	0 +	30.64	
				186	185.954440	0 +	28.41	
75	Rhenium	Re	186.2	185	184.953059	$\frac{5}{2}$ +	37.07	
				187*	186.955833	$\frac{5}{2}$ +	62.93	5×10^{10} y
76	Osmium	Os	190.2	184	183.952750	0 +	0.018	
				186	185.953870	0 +	1.59	
				187	186.955832	$\frac{1}{2}$ −	1.64	
				188	187.956081	0 +	13.3	
				189	188.958300	$\frac{3}{2}$ −	16.1	
				190	189.958630	0 +	26.4	
				192	191.961450	0 +	41.0	
				194*	193.965229	0 +		6.0 y
77	Iridium	Ir	192.2	191	190.960640	$\frac{3}{2}$ +	37.3	
				193	192.963012	$\frac{3}{2}$ +	62.7	
78	Platinum	Pt	195.09	190*	189.959950	0 +	0.0127	7×10^{11} y

(1) Z	(2) element	(3) symbol	(4) chemical atomic weight	(5) mass number (* indicates radioactive) A	(6) mass	(7) spin & parity	(8) percent abundance	(9) half-life (if radioactive) $t_{1/2}$
(78)	(Platinum)			192	191.961150	0 +	0.78	
				194	193.962725	0 +	32.9	
				195	194.964813	$\frac{1}{2}$ −	33.8	
				196	195.964967	0 +	25.3	
				198	197.967895	0 +	7.21	
79	Gold	Au	196.967	197	196.966541	$\frac{3}{2}$ +	100	
80	Mercury	Hg	200.59	196	195.965820	0 +	0.146	
				198	197.966756	0 +	10.02	
				199	198.968279	$\frac{1}{2}$ −	16.84	
				200	199.968327	0 +	23.13	
				201	200.970308	$\frac{3}{2}$ −	13.22	
				202	201.970642	0 +	29.80	
				204	203.973495	0 +	6.85	
81	Thallium	Tl	204.19	203	202.972353	$\frac{1}{2}$ +	29.50	
				204*	203.973865	2 −		3.75 y
				205	204.974442	$\frac{1}{2}$ +	70.50	
		Ra E″		206*	205.976104			4.3 m
		Ac C″		207*	206.977450			4.78 m
		Th C″		208*	207.982013	5 +		3.1 m
		Ra C″		210*	209.990054			1.3 m
82	Lead	Pb	207.19	202*	201.927997	0 +		3×10^5 y
				204*	203.973044	0 +	1.48	1.4×10^{17} y
				205*	204.974480			3×10^7 y
				206	205.974468	0 +	23.6	
				207	206.975903	$\frac{1}{2}$ −	22.6	
				208	207.976650	0 +	52.3	
		Ra D		210*	209.984187	0 +		22 y
		Ac B		211*	210.988742			36.1 m
		Th B		212*	211.991905	0 +		10.64 h
		Ra B		214*	213.999764	0 +		26.8 m
83	Bismuth	Bi	209.980	207*	206.978438			30 y
				208*	207.979731			3.7×10^5 y
				209	208.980394	$\frac{9}{2}$ −	100	
		Ra E		210*	209.984121	1 −		5.1 d
		Th C		211*	210.987300			2.15 m
				212*	211.991876	1 −		60.6 m
		Ra C		214*	213.998686			19.7 m
				215*	215.001830			8 m
84	Polonium	Po		209*	208.982426	$\frac{1}{2}$ −		103 y

(1)	(2)	(3)	(4)	(5)	(6)	(7)	(8)	(9)
Z	element	symbol	chemical atomic weight	mass number (* indicates radioactive) A	mass	spin & parity	percent abundance	half-life (if radioactive) $t_{1/2}$
(84)	(Polonium)	Ra F		210*	209.982876	0 +		138.4 d
		Ac C'		211*	210.986657			0.52 s
		Th C'		212*	211.989629	0 +		0.30 μs
		Ra C'		214*	213.995201	0 +		164 μs
		Ac A		215*	214.999423			0.0018 s
		Th A		216*	216.001790	0 +		0.15 s
		Ra A		218*	218.008930	0 +		3.05 m
85	Astatine	At		215*	214.998663			$\approx$ 100 μs
				218*	218.008607			1.3 s
				219*	219.011290			0.9 m
86	Radon	Rn						
		An		219*	219.009481			4.0 s
		Tn		220*	220.011401	0 +		56 s
		Rn		222*	222.017531	0 +		3.823 d
87	Francium	Fr						
		Ac K		223*	223.019736			22 m
88	Radium	Ra	226.05					
		Ac X		223*	223.018501	$\frac{1}{2}$ +		11.4 d
		Th X		224*	224.020218	0 +		3.64 d
		Ra		226*	226.025360	0 +		1620 y
		Ms Th$_1$		228*	228.031139	0 +		5.7 y
89	Actinium	Ac		227*	227.027753	$\frac{3}{2}$ +		21.2 y
		Ms Th$_2$		228*	228.031080			6.13 h
90	Thorium	Th	232.038					
		Rd Ac		227*	227.027706			18.17 d
		Rd Th		228*	228.028750	0 +		1.91 y
				229*	229.031652	$\frac{5}{2}$ +		7300 y
		Io		230*	230.033087	0 +		76000 y
		UY		231*	231.036291			25.6 h
		Th		232*	232.038124	0 +		1.39 $\times$ 10^{10} y
		UX$_1$		234*	234.043583	0 +		24.1 d
91	Protoactinium	Pa	231.0359	231*	231.035877	$\frac{3}{2}$ $-$		32480 y
		UZ		234*	234.043298			6.66 h
92	Uranium	U	238.03	232*	232.037168	0 +		72 y
				233*	233.039522	$\frac{5}{2}$ +		1.62 $\times$ 10^5 y
				234*	234.040904	0 +	0.0057	2.48 $\times$ 10^5 y
		Ac U		235*	235.043915	$\frac{7}{2}$ $-$	0.72	7.13 $\times$ 10^8 y
				236*	236.045637	0 +		2.39 $\times$ 10^7 y
		UI		238*	238.048608	0 +	99.27	4.51 $\times$ 10^9 y

(1)	(2)	(3)	(4)	(5)	(6)	(7)	(8)	(9)
Z	element	symbol	chemical atomic weight	mass number (* indicates radioactivity) A	mass	spin & parity	percent abundance	half-life (if radioactive) $t_{1/2}$
93	Neptunium	Np	237.0480	235*	235.044049			410 d
				236*	236.046624			5000 y
				237*	237.048056	$\frac{5}{2}$ +		2.14×10^6 y
94	Plutonium	Pu	239.0522	236*	236.046071	0 +		2.85 y
				238*	238.049511	0 +		89 y
				239*	239.052146	$\frac{1}{2}$ +		24360 y
				240*	240.053882	0 +		6700 y
				241*	241.056737	$\frac{5}{2}$ +		13 y
				242*	242.058725	0 +		3.79×10^5 y
				244*	244.064100	0 +		7.6×10^7 y

APPENDIX B
PROBABILITY
INTEGRALS

When calculating various average values using the Maxwell-Boltzmann distribution, integrals of the following type occur:

$$I_n = \int_0^\infty x^n e^{-\lambda x^2}\, dx$$

where n is an integer. These can be obtained from I_0 and I_1 by differentiation. Consider I_n to be a function of λ, and take the derivative with respect to λ:

$$\frac{dI_n}{d\lambda} = \int_0^\infty -x^2 x^n e^{-\lambda x^2}\, dx = -I_{n+2} \qquad \text{(B-1)}$$

Thus, if I_0 is known, all the I_n for n even can be obtained, and if I_1 is known, all the I_n for n odd can be obtained from Eq. (B-1). I_1 can easily be evaluated using the substitution $u = \lambda x^2$, $du = 2\lambda x\, dx$:

$$I_1 = \int_0^\infty x e^{-\lambda x^2}\, dx = \tfrac{1}{2}\lambda^{-1} \int_0^\infty e^{-u}\, du = \tfrac{1}{2}\lambda^{-1}$$

Thus

$$I_3 = -\frac{d(\frac{1}{2}\lambda^{-1})}{d\lambda} = \frac{1}{2}\lambda^{-2}$$

and

$$I_5 = -\frac{d(\frac{1}{2}\lambda^{-2})}{d\lambda} = \lambda^{-3}$$

The evaluation of I_0 is more difficult, but it can be done using a trick. We evaluate I_0^2:

$$I_0^2 = \int_0^\infty e^{-\lambda x^2}\, dx \int_0^\infty e^{-\lambda y^2}\, dy = \int_0^\infty \int_0^\infty e^{-\lambda(x^2+y^2)}\, dx\, dy$$

where we have used y as the dummy variable of integration in the second integral. If we now consider this to be an integration over the xy plane, we can change to polar coordinates $r^2 = x^2 + y^2$ and $\tan\theta = y/x$. The element of area $dx\, dy$ becomes $r\, dr\, d\theta$, and the integration over positive x and y becomes integration from $r = 0$ to $r = \infty$ and from θ to 0 to $\theta = \pi/2$. Thus

$$I_0^2 = \int_0^\infty \int_0^{\pi/2} e^{-\lambda r^2} r\, dr\, d\theta = \frac{\pi}{2} I_1 = \frac{\pi}{4\lambda}$$

and

$$I_0 = \frac{\sqrt{\pi}}{2}\lambda^{-1/2}$$

Thus

$$I_2 = \frac{\sqrt{\pi}}{4}\lambda^{-3/2}$$

and

$$I_4 = \frac{3\sqrt{\pi}}{8}\lambda^{-5/2}$$

APPENDIX C
STATISTICAL DERIVATION OF THE MAXWELL-BOLTZMANN DISTRIBUTION

We divide the six-dimensional space x, y, z, p_x, p_y, p_z into r cells of equal size and compute the probability of a particular arrangement — N_1 particles in cell 1, N_2 in cell 2, N_i in cell i, etc. This probability is proportional to the number of different ways the distribution can be realized. Consider the r cells to be arranged in a line. The number of ways of placing N particles in a line is $N!$ because there are N ways of choosing the first particle, $N - 1$ ways of choosing the second, etc. Some of these permutations result in the same number in a particular cell. If there are N_i particles in a cell, $N_i!$ of the $N!$ permutations merely rearrange the N_i particles in the cell. We do not wish to distinguish the order of the particles in a particular cell. Thus the number of ways of realizing a particular distribution is

$$W = \frac{N!}{N_1!N_2! \cdots N_r!} \tag{C-1}$$

We find the most probable distribution by finding the distribution N_i for which W is a maximum. We can vary the numbers N_i in any way consistent with the conservation of the number of particles

$$\sum N_i = N \tag{C-2}$$

and the conservation of energy

$$\sum N_i E_i = U \tag{C-3}$$

If there are no restrictions at all, W is a maximum for $N_i = 1$ for all i. If we have only the restriction that N is constant, W is a maximum for $N_i = N/r$, that is, the particles are equally divided among the cells. This is the distribution that results if we flip N coins and put them into a heads box or a tails box. The most probable distribution is with an equal number in each box. However, each cell in our six-dimensional space has an energy associated with it:

$$E = V(x,y,z) + \frac{1}{2m} (p_x{}^2 + p_y{}^2 + p_z{}^2)$$

We thus wish to maximize W with the conditions (C–2) and (C–3). It is easier to maximize the function

$$y = \ln W = \ln N! - \sum_i \ln N_i!$$

A change of δN_i produces a change in y of

$$\delta y = -\sum_i \frac{\partial \ln N_i!}{\partial N_i} \delta N_i \tag{C-4}$$

For large N_i, we can use the approximation

$$\frac{\partial \ln N_i!}{\partial N_i} \approx \ln N_i$$

Consider $P(N) = \ln N!$:

$$P(N + \Delta N) - P(N) = \ln(N + \Delta N)! - \ln(N!)$$
$$= \ln(N + \Delta N) + \ln(N + \Delta N - 1)$$
$$+ \cdots + \ln(N + 1)$$

There are ΔN terms in $P(N + \Delta N) - P(N)$. For large N, each term is approximately equal to $\ln N$. Thus $P(N + \Delta N) - P(N) \approx \Delta N \ln N$ and $dP(N)/dN \approx \ln N$; thus

$$\delta y \approx -\sum \ln N_i \delta N_i = 0 \tag{C-5}$$

If all N_i were independent, we could set the coefficient of each equal to zero; however, we have two conditions

$$\sum \delta N_i = 0 \tag{C-6}$$

and

$$\sum E_i \, \delta N_i = 0 \tag{C-7}$$

If we multiply Eq. (C–6) by an arbitrary constant α and Eq. (C–7) by another arbitrary constant β and add to Eq. (C–5), we obtain

$$\sum (\ln N_i + \alpha + \beta E_i) \, \delta N_i = 0$$

We can vary all but two of the N_i independently and choose those two to satisfy the conservation of particles and energy conditions. Let us choose δN_1 and δN_2 to be the two that are not independent. Then

$$(\ln N_1 + \alpha + \beta E_1) \, \delta N_1 + (\ln N_2 + \alpha + \beta E_2) \, \delta N_2$$
$$+ \sum_{j=3}^{r} (\ln N_j + \alpha + \beta E_j) \, \delta N_j = 0$$

We now choose the constants α and β to make the coefficients of δN_1 and δN_2 zero. Since the other N_j are independent, the coefficients of δN_j, in the sum, must also be zero. Thus we have

$$\ln N_i + \alpha + \beta E_i = 0 \qquad \text{for all } i$$
$$N_i = Ae^{-\beta E_i}$$

where $A = e^{-\alpha}$ is the normalization constant. The constant β can be shown to equal $1/kT$ by computing the average kinetic energy of molecules in an ideal gas.

APPENDIX D
ADJUSTED VALUES
OF CONSTANTS
AND CONVERSION
FACTORS

Except for the proton and neutron masses, these values are from *Physics Today*, February 1964; recommended by the National Academy of Sciences-National Research Council. The number in ( ) is the uncertainty based on three standard deviations applied to the last digits in the preceeding number. The values for the mass of the proton and the neutron are taken from J. H. E. Mattauch et. al., 1964 Atomic Mass Table, Nuclear Physics **67**, 1, 1965. The abbreviations for the units are A—ampere; Å—angstrom; C—coulomb; eV—electron-volt; F—fermi; G—gauss; g—gram; J—joule; m—meter; N—newton; T—tesla; u—unified mass unit.

constant	symbol	value ( ) gives uncertainty in last digits	unit
Speed of light	c	$2.997925(3) \times 10^8$	m/sec
Elementary charge	e	$1.60210(7) \times 10^{-19}$	C
Avogadro constant	N_A	$6.02252(28) \times 10^{23}$	mole^{-1}
Faraday constant	F	$9.64870(16) \times 10^4$	C/mole
Planck constant	h	$6.6256(5) \times 10^{-34}$	J-sec
		$4.13556(12) \times 10^{-15}$	eV-sec
$h/2\pi$	$\hbar$	$1.05450(7) \times 10^{-34}$	J-sec

constant	symbol	value ( ) gives uncertainty in last digits	unit
$(h/2\pi)$	$(\hbar)$	$6.5819(2) \times 10^{-16}$	eV-sec
Gas constant	R	$8.3143(12) \times 10^{0}$	J/°K-mole
		$1.9872(3) \times 10^{0}$	cal/°K-mole
Boltzmann constant	k	$1.38054(18) \times 10^{-23}$	J/°K
		$8.6170(12) \times 10^{-5}$	eV/°K
Gravitational constant	G	$6.670(15) \times 10^{-11}$	Nm^2/kg^2
Rydberg constant	R_∞	$1.0973731(3) \times 10^{7}$	m^{-1}
Permeability of free space	μ_0	$4\pi \times 10^{-7}$	N/A^2
Coulomb constant	K $(= 1/4\pi\epsilon_0) = 10^{-7}c^2)$	$8.987689(18) \times 10^{9}$	Nm^2/C^2
Fine-structure constant	α	$7.29720(10) \times 10^{-3}$	
	α^{-1}	$1.370388(19) \times 10^{2}$	
Bohr radius	a_0	$5.29167(7) \times 10^{-11}$	m
Electron rest mass	m_e	$9.1091(4) \times 10^{-31}$	kg
		$5.48597(9) \times 10^{-4}$	u
		$5.11006(5) \times 10^{5}$	eV/c^2
Proton rest mass	m_p	$1.67252(8) \times 10^{-27}$	kg
		$1.00727659(8) \times 10^{0}$	u
		$9.38256(15) \times 10^{8}$	eV/c^2
Neutron rest mass	m_n	$1.67482(8) \times 10^{-27}$	kg
		$1.0086652(1) \times 10^{0}$	u
		$9.39550(15) \times 10^{8}$	eV/c^2
Bohr magneton	μ_B	$9.2732(6) \times 10^{-24}$	J/T
		$5.7882(6) \times 10^{-9}$	eV/G
Nuclear magneton	μ_N	$5.0505(4) \times 10^{-27}$	J/T
		$3.1524(4) \times 10^{-12}$	eV/G
Compton wavelength of electron	$h/m_e c$	$2.42621(6) \times 10^{-12}$	m
Compton wavelength of proton	$h/m_p c$	$1.32140(4) \times 10^{-15}$	m

CONVERSION FACTORS

$1 \text{ Å} = 10^{-10}$ m
$1 \text{ F} = 10^{-15}$ m
$1 \text{ T} = 1 \text{ weber/m}^2 = 10^4 \text{ G}$
$1 \text{ eV} = 1.60210(7) \times 10^{-19}$ J
$1 \text{ u} = 9.31478(15) \times 10^{8}$ eV/c^2
$1 \text{ g} = 6.02252(28) \times 10^{23}$ u
$\phantom{1 \text{ g}} = 5.60984(34) \times 10^{32}$ eV/c^2
$1 \text{ cal}_{th} = 4.1840$ J
$1 \text{ kcal/mole} = 4.33634(7) \times 10^{-2}$ eV/molecule

ANSWERS TO SELECTED PROBLEMS

CHAPTER 1
1-1. $(2L/c)(1 - V^2/c^2)^{-1}$; $(2L/c)(1 - V^2/c^2)^{-1/2}$, difference is approximately LV^2/c^3.

1-2. 0.6 meter; 2.5×10^{-9} sec

1-3. (a) $0.994c$ (b) 6×10^4 m/sec (c) 1×10^{-6} percent

1-4. $0.8c$

1-7. (a) 30.5 MeV/c (b) 239 MeV/c

1-8. 0.58 percent

1-9. 3.4×10^2 gauss

1-10. 5.51 MeV

1-11. (a) 114 MeV (b) $0.84c$ (c) 209 MeV/c

1-12. 2.14×10^8 kg

1-13. 3.8×10^{-3} sec

1-15. 3.4 min

1-23. (a) About 17 keV for electron; 31 MeV for proton

    (b) About 1.6 MeV for electron; 2.97 GeV for proton

CHAPTER 2
2-1. Set (A) $\bar{x} = 340$; $\sigma = 6$; set (B) $\bar{x} = 340$; $\sigma = 13$

2-2. $\bar{s} = 6$; $\sigma = 1.89$

2–3. $A = 2/X_0^2$; $\bar{x} = 2X_0/3$; $x_{rms} = X_0/\sqrt{2}$; $\sigma = X_0/\sqrt{18}$

2–4. 1.78×10^3 m/sec; $11,900°$K

2–6. $(2m/\pi kT)^{1/2}$

2–7. $\frac{1}{2}kT$

2–8. 7.8×10^3 °K

2–9. 2.57

2–13. $(2kT/\pi m)^{1/2}$

2–21. (a) $mR(V_0 - 2V)$ (b) $\frac{1}{2}V_0$ (c) $V_0 z/z_0$

CHAPTER 3

3–1. 0.254×10^{-19}; 25 percent

3–2. 152 sec

3–3. (a) 3.1 eV (b) 1.03 eV

3–4. 6,830 Å; 1.82 eV

3–5. 1.55 eV to 3.1 eV

3–6. 1.5×10^{13}

3–7. $V = 27.0$ cm^3; $d = 2.82$ Å; $E = 4.4$ keV

3–8. 0.31 Å

3–10. $2.76R$

3–11. 1.75×10^{11} C/kg

3–13. 1.31×10^{14}

3–15. (a) $I \approx 5 \times 10^{13}$ eV/cm^2-sec

(b) 5×10^{-3} eV/sec, taking area of atom to be 1 Å^2

(c) 400 sec

3–19. (a) 14.99 MeV (b) 14.98 MeV

3–25. (a) $(1 + e^{-\epsilon/kT})^{-1}$ (b) $\epsilon(1 + e^{\epsilon/kT})^{-1}$

CHAPTER 4

4–1. 10^6; 10^4 layers

4–2. (a) 45.5 F (b) 260 F (c) 0.013

4–3. 4.68 F

4–6. (a) 1,215 Å; 1,026 Å; 972.5 Å $\cdots$ 911.8 Å (b) Balmer series limit, 3,647 Å

4–7. Paschen: 18,756 Å; 12,821 Å; 10,941 Å $\cdots$ 8,206 Å
Bracket: 40,523 Å; 26,259 Å; 21,661 Å $\cdots$ 14,588 Å

4–8. (a) 2.56×10^{-3} Å (b) 2.82 keV (c) 4.4 Å

4–9. Zirconium, $Z = 40$

4–10. Calcium, $Z = 20$

4–11. (a) -108.8 eV (b) $+27.2$ eV (c) $+27.2$ eV

4–12. 1.26

4–16. 1.19×10^{-5}

4–21. 0.8 MeV

CHAPTER 5

5–1. 5.08 F

5–2. 2.02 Å

5–3. $6.28 = 2\pi$

5-4. (a) 12.4 F   (b) 12.4 F; since $E \gg mc^2$ for electron, $E \approx pc$ for it as well as for photon.

5-5. 2.06×10^{-2} eV

5-6. 5.3×10^{-18} cm

5-7. 3.3×10^{-16} sec

5-8. $\Delta\phi = \infty$

5-9. (a) 2.07×10^{-3} eV   (b) 0.83 MeV

5-10. 39.4 MeV

5-21. (a) 0.96×10^{-11} eV   (b) 9.6 eV

CHAPTER 6

6-2. $0; 0.13a^2; 0; h^2/16a^2; 0.09h$

6-3. (a) 0.01   (b) 0.005   (c) 0.0025

6-4. For $n = 2$:   (a) 0   (b) 0.01   (c) 0.0075

For $n = 3$:   (a) 0.01   (b) 0.005   (c) 0.01

6-6. $R = 1.53$ Å, taking minimum in curve to be at 1 eV

6-7. 3×10^{19}

6-13. Calculation gives 0.15

CHAPTER 7

7-1. (a) $l(l+1)\hbar^2/2I$ (c) 1.51×10^{-2} eV   (d) 8.21×10^5 Å

7-2. (a) 8.4×10^{30} (b) 4×10^{-30} rev/min

7-5. (b) $g = \frac{5}{2}$

7-6. (a) $\frac{1}{2}\sqrt{35}\,\hbar$ or $\frac{1}{2}\sqrt{15}\,\hbar$ (b) $\pm\frac{5}{2}$, $\pm\frac{3}{2}$, $\pm\frac{1}{2}$, for $j = \frac{5}{2}$; $\pm\frac{3}{2}$, $\pm\frac{1}{2}$, for $j = \frac{3}{2}$

7-7. (a) $\sqrt{2}\,\hbar$ (b) 71°   (c) 45°

7-9. (a) 2, 1, 0   (b) 1, 0   (c) 3, 2, 1, for $l = 2$ and $s = 1$; 2 for $l = 2$ and $s = 0$; 2, 1, 0, for $l = 1$ and $s = 1$; 1 for $l = 1$ and $s = 0$ and for $l = 0$ and $s = 1$; 0 for $l = 0$ and $s = 0$
(d) $j_1 = \frac{3}{2}$ or $\frac{1}{2}$; $j_2 = \frac{3}{2}$ or $\frac{1}{2}$ (e) 3, 2, 1, 0, for $j_1 = j_2 = \frac{3}{2}$; 2, 1, for $j_1 = \frac{3}{2}$ and $j_2 = \frac{1}{2}$ or for $j_2 = \frac{3}{2}$ and $j_1 = \frac{1}{2}$; 1, 0, for $j_1 = j_2 = \frac{1}{2}$
The results in (c) and (e) are the same; 3 occurs once, 2 three times, 1 four times, and 0 two times.

7-11. 3.15×10^{-12} eV/gauss

7-15. $\frac{4}{3}(R_0/a_0)^3 \approx 9 \times 10^{-15}$

7-16. (a) $-\frac{5}{3}$ (b) $a_2 = -10$; $a_4 = +\frac{35}{3}$

7-17. $C_0 = C_1 = 1$; $C_2 = -\frac{1}{2}$; $C_3 = -\frac{3}{2}$; $C_4 = +\frac{3}{8}$

7-19. (a) 1, 0   (b) $\mu_N \ll \mu_B$

CHAPTER 8

8-1. 0.48 Å

8-2. (a) $12.5\hbar\omega$ (b) $6.5\hbar\omega$

8-3. Li, Rb, Ag, Cs, and Fr are similar to Na, the others to Hg.

8-4. $\frac{1}{2}$; no

8-6. He and Mg

8-7. (a) 2.14×10^{-3} eV   (b) 3.7×10^5 gauss

8–9. (a) 1.82 eV   (b) 51.2 MeV
8–11. 2.32×10^{-5} eV; 6.27×10^{-2} Å

CHAPTER 9

9–1. (a) -5.16 eV   (b) 4.63 eV   (c) $+0.21$ eV
9–4. (a) 3.1 eV   (b) 1.0×10^8 cm/sec   (c) 3.6×10^4 °K
(d) 0.96
9–5. (a) 5.5 eV   (b) 1.39×10^8 cm/sec   (c) 6.4×10^4 °K
(d) 1.0
9–6. 5.39 eV in atom; 2.82 eV in metal
9–7. 4.920 °K
9–9. (a) -6 eV   (b) 0.5 eV
(c) $n \simeq 5.6$; $C = (1.4)^{n-1}$ $14.4 \simeq 67.7$
9–11. (a) 0.179 eV   (b) 2.8×10^{-47} Kg-m^2 $= 1.68 m_p$-Å^2
(c) 1.33 Å
9–12. $f_1/f_0 = 1.67$; $f_2/f_0 = 0.86$

CHAPTER 10

10–1. (a) 20.6 MeV   (b) 19.8 MeV   (c) 7.07 MeV
(d) -0.76 MeV
10–2. 7.38 MeV for Pb^{208}; 6.37 MeV for Pb^{207}
10–3. (a) 4.87 MeV   (b) 3.62×10^{10} radiations/sec
10–4. 33.3 min
10–7. 6.6×10^{-17} sec, using $\tau \approx \hbar/\Gamma$
10–8. 1.54 cm
10–10. (b) 51.7 MeV   (c) 1.42 MeV   (d) 96 MeV
10–15. (a) 1.8×10^9 per sec   (b) 3×10^{12} nuclei
(c) 6×10^{12} nuclei; 1.8×10^9 per sec

INDEX